750

Shear + 2,125
      − 2935

Moment   9030
          5700
          8380
          3270
          6600

As. 3 — 4-4 ⎫
4-5 ⎪ Solve each
4-6 ⎬ of these
4-13 ⎭ graphically as
            well!

VACUUM COLUMN. NOTE THE MANY STRUCTURAL SUPPORTS, CATWALKS, AND STAIRWAYS. A WORK REQUIRING THE COMBINED ATTENTION OF CHEMICAL, MECHANICAL, ELECTRICAL, METALLURGICAL, AND STRUCTURAL ENGINEERS.

ELEMENTS OF STRUCTURAL ENGINEERING

By

ERNEST C. HARRIS

PROFESSOR AND CHAIRMAN

DEPARTMENT OF CIVIL ENGINEERING AND ENGINEERING MECHANICS

FENN COLLEGE

THE RONALD PRESS COMPANY ∽ NEW YORK

PREFACE

This is a text in Structural Engineering for the non-civil engineering student. The material is presented, wherever possible, from his point of view. The principles are presented, then their application is shown by examples and problems that are largely of the type commonly met by mechanical, electrical, and other non-civil engineers. Thus, examples of bridges are omitted, while examples of structural theory applied to such things as cranes and conveyor supports are included. The complete original design of buildings is omitted, but the same principles are used in examples in which the effect of new electrical or mechanical equipment on the safety of existing structures is analyzed.

Some of the illustrative examples and problems are given in basic form, stripped of all details. Others are presented as they are encountered in practice, so that the student is given a chance to determine the loads and to reduce the problem to its basic form before solving. The problems are of two kinds: shorter ones suitable for homework assignments and for classroom use, and longer ones suitable for supervised problem sessions. This book includes tables of section properties, load data, and other standards. For his study of Chapters 7 and 8, the student should obtain a copy of *Specification for the Design, Fabrication and Erection of Structural Steel for Buildings*, published by the American Institute of Steel Construction. For his study of Chapter 9 he will need a copy of *Building Code Requirements for Reinforced Concrete*, published by the American Concrete Institute. The use of separate specifications is a definite advantage, since the text and the specifications can be open simultaneously. The examples used in this text are based on the 1946 AISC *Specification* and the 1951 ACI *Code*.

If it is used for a two-term course, the book may be divided into two general sections. Chapters 2 through 6 deal with analysis; Chapters 7, 8, 9, and 10 with design.

An attempt has been made to satisfy in one text the needs of the non-civil engineering student. It is hoped that this concentration on the analysis and design problems in fields other than civil engineering will serve to impress the student with the value of a thorough structural engineering knowledge in his own chosen technical field.

The author is grateful to Mr. Clifford D. Williams for consenting

iii

to the reproduction in this book of drawings and other material from the textbook *Structural Design in Metals*, written by Mr. Williams and myself.

Acknowledged also is the assistance of Dr. A. A. Toprac, who provided many helpful suggestions; and that of Professor J. Arendt, Professor F. J. Gallo, and Mr. M. Shuga, in whose classes many of the problems and examples in this book have been developed and tested.

ERNEST C. HARRIS

Cleveland

January, 1954

CONTENTS

APPENDIX TABLES

APPENDIX A

APPENDIX B

APPENDIX C

ELEMENTS OF
STRUCTURAL ENGINEERING

CHAPTER 1

INTRODUCTION

1-1. Structural Engineering. Early engineering work was classified as either "military" or "civil." The classification "civil" included all engineering works that were not for military purposes. As technical knowledge increased, new classifications emerged from civil engineering. Thus mechanical and electrical engineering became distinct branches of engineering. Civil engineering still contained all the other works. Further division led to chemical, metallurgical, aeronautical, and other specific categories of engineering.

Structural engineering has always been a part of civil engineering. However, it too may in time emerge from civil and become a distinct branch of engineering.

The work of the structural engineer includes the planning, analysis, design, and construction of structures such as buildings, bridges, aircraft, and ships. His knowledge and skill are also applied in the design of structural parts of machines, process equipment, etc.

1-2. Relationship to Other Engineering Branches. While engineering work may usually be classified as mechanical, electrical, metallurgical, etc., it is rarely that an engineer can confine his thinking to subjects entirely within a single field. The dividing lines between the work of the various types of engineer are not distinct. Overlaps often occur, so that each type of engineer finds it valuable to know something about the work of the other types. Engineers of the various branches must often work together. In such cases knowledge of the other fields can aid in producing harmonious cooperation.

An example of an engineering project requiring the cooperation of many types of engineers is the design of an oil refinery. Chemical engineers are needed to determine the process to be used. Problems of flow and machinery are properly those of the mechanical engineer. The selection of the proper alloys to resist the heat and corrosive influences requires the knowledge of the metallurgical engineer, and the design of the structure to support the apparatus calls for the skill of the structural engineer.

It may be easy to make these classifications on paper, but in practice it is not so. Flow problems may be solved by the chemical engineer or

3

by the civil as often as by the mechanical. The design of pressure vessels may be done by either mechanical or structural engineers. In the design of piping, structural problems exist which are as important as the flow problems. Thus it is seen that these engineers will find knowledge of fields other than their major field quite helpful.

As another example, consider the engineer employed by a manufacturer of materials-handling equipment. The design of a conveyor system requires structural, electrical, and mechanical knowledge. In such work, especially where the size of the engineering force is small, an engineer must often solve problems which properly belong to another classification than that in which he has received his major training.

The overlap of the branches of engineering will be illustrated further by many example problems in the other chapters of this book. Where practical, it will be the policy to make those examples cases like those that a *non-structural* engineer might encounter and be required to solve. The need for structural knowledge by other types of engineers will be illustrated also through problems for solution by the student.

1–3. Analysis and Design. Structural theory may be divided into "analysis" and "design." In practice the two types of theory are often used simultaneously, without obvious separation. In studying the theory, however, it is convenient to make the division.

Analysis is the application of mechanics (statics and dynamics) to the determination of loads, forces, shears, and bending moments on the structure. Analysis is usually accomplished by mathematical means alone, although graphical means are sometimes employed. More rarely, analysis is made by the use of models.

Design is the process of determining the type of structure and the proportions of the various members of the structure. The process of determining the general layout of the structure so that it will serve its purpose is called "functional design" or "planning." Examples of *functional design* would be the determination of the location of a bridge and the number of lanes that would be required, or of the best layout for a building. *Detail design*, the type that is more likely to affect the average engineer, is the process of applying the science of strength of materials to the selection of size, shape, and material for the various members of the structure. The selection to insure strength is the most important purpose of detail design, although stiffness, appearance, economy, and other factors are also considered. Detail design is usually made by mathematical means. Occasionally a model study or a full-sized test is made to assist in the final design.

Chapters 2, 3, 4, 5, and 6 of this book cover analysis and Chapters 7, 8, 9, and 10 cover detail design.

1-4. Specifications. Specifications are sets of rules governing the quality of a material or a product, the nature and extent of a project, or the procedure to be used in either design or construction. Specifications are often written by the engineer for a particular project only. Other specifications are written as standards, and are used whenever their content is applicable to the work being done. A few of these standard specifications will be described in the paragraphs which follow.

The specifications of the American Society for Testing Materials are probably the best example of materials specifications. Reference to a material as "conforming to the ASTM Designation number—" insures that the material used meets specified standards of quality, strength, durability, etc. A specification written for a particular project would need to contain only a reference to the number of the ASTM Designation; the exact requirements would not need to be rewritten. Other examples of materials specifications are the *Federal Specifications*, published by the United States Government.

The type of specification most frequently used in structural work is that giving rules for design procedure. Such specifications are usually compiled by committees of experienced engineers. They represent the collective opinion, often the compromise, of those persons on the subject of sound engineering practice. The use of these specifications helps to insure consistent and reasonable standards of safety and economy. These specifications are based on the previous experience of other engineers. Their use saves much time, and saves repetition of previous experiments and of costly errors. An example of the design specification is the *Specification for the Design, Fabrication and Erection of Structural Steel for Buildings* by the American Institute of Steel Construction. This specification will be referred to as the "AISC *Specification*." A copy of this *Specification* should be obtained for use with this book. It is probably the most widely used design specification. The student should glance through the *Specification* at this point, so as to become familiar with the types of subject matter covered by a design specification.

Other design specifications include the AREA (American Railway Engineering Association) Specification, covering the design of railway bridges; AASHO (American Association of State Highway Officials), for the design of highway bridges; ACI (American Concrete Institute), covering the design of reinforced concrete for buildings; ANC (Army-Navy-Civil) specifications for various phases of aircraft design; and the specifications by the Aluminum Company of America, covering the design of structures using aluminum alloys.

Students may notice unexplained differences between specifications covering similar subjects. Sometimes the differences are thought to be indications of disagreement or of inconsistency among engineers. More often, the differences are explainable and are intentional. As an example, consider the AISC and the AREA specifications. Although the type of steel used is the same, the AREA Specification requires lower allowable values of unit stress and has a larger "minimum allowable thickness of material" than the AISC Specification. These differences are justified when the type of service for each structure is considered. The railway bridge is repeatedly loaded and unloaded, with much vibration. The building, on the other hand, is loaded mainly by permanent loads or by loads which vary in amount more slowly and less frequently than those on the railway bridge. The seriousness of the failure of a railway bridge is usually greater than that of the failure of a member of a building. The expected useful life for the railway bridge is often more than for the building. The possibility of future increases in the load to be carried is greater for the bridge than for the building. The corrosive influences for the railway bridge are usually severe. These reasons and others justify the use of a stricter standard for bridge design than is common for use in building design.

1–5. Loads.   The forces applied to a structure or to a structural member are referred to as "loads." For example, the structural I-beam shown by Fig. 1–1 has the following loads acting on it:

1. The force of gravity on the beam itself; i.e., the weight of the beam itself
2. The weight of the floor planks
3. The weight of the stored materials

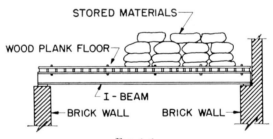

Fig. 1–1.

The downward forces from the three sources listed are resisted by upward forces which are applied to the ends of the beam by the brick walls. These resisting forces are called "reactions."

Loads are classified as either "dead" loads or "live" loads. *Dead loads* are those which are always on the structure. They are due to the weights of the parts of the structure itself and of any items that are permanently located on the structure. Examples of dead loads in buildings include the weights of floor slabs, structural steel, finish floor material, partitions, walls, plumbing, light fixtures, ventilating equipment, etc. Table 4 of Appendix B, giving weights of common building materials, will aid in the determination of the amount of dead loads.

Any load that is not permanently applied is called *live load*. Live loads that are static while they are on the structure, but which may be removed or reapplied are called "moveable live loads." Live loads which are in motion during their application are called "moving live loads." Examples of moveable live loads are the weights of stored materials, furniture, human occupants, and most machinery. Examples of moving live loads are the weights of trains, truck and automobile traffic, and travelling cranes, and the weights of things carried by such equipment.

Loads are also classified as concentrated, uniform, or varying, according to the nature of their application. A concentrated load is one which is applied entirely at one location on the member, or is distributed over so short a length as to make it impractical to consider that distribution. For example, the reactions on the beam of Fig. 1–1, or the forces applied to a runway rail by crane wheels should be considered as concentrated.

Uniform loads are those which are distributed along the member so as to cause equal forces on successive unit lengths of the member. For example, the wood plank floor and the I-beam itself cause uniform load on the entire length of the beam of Fig. 1–1. The stored materials cause uniform load on the portion of the length of beam beneath them.

Varying loads are considered less frequently than uniform loads. A varying load is distributed along the length of the member, but is of constantly varying intensity from one point to another. An example of varying load is the horizontal force of the water on the side wall of the tank shown by Fig. 1–2. That load varies from an intensity of

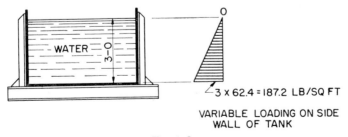

3 x 62.4 = 187.2 LB/SQ FT

VARIABLE LOADING ON SIDE
WALL OF TANK

Fig. 1–2.

zero at the top surface to an intensity of 187.2 lb per sq ft at the bottom edge of the side wall. Another example of varying load is the weight of loose materials which are stored in a pile, such as the weight of a conical pile of sand.

1–6. Design Loads. The actual live loads which occur in structures are often so complex and so many variations of load are possible, that the use of actual loads in design is not practical. For such cases, well-tested and proven equivalent loadings are used. The floor and roof designs for most buildings are based on the assumption that a uniform load is a suitable equivalent load to use as a substitute for the actual loading. The uniform load is considered to occur over the entire floor area, or over only selected portions if a partial loading gives more severe stress conditions. Known amounts of concentrated load, such as the weights of large machinery, are considered along with a suitable uniform load. The intensity of uniform load to use depends on the intended use of the structure. Table 5 (Appendix B) gives values of floor live loads that are in common use. (The values given by the applicable building codes or specifications should be used where they differ from the suggested values given by this table.)

Standard sets of concentrated loads are used in railway bridge design to simulate the worst conditions that are caused by the many types of locomotive used. One such standard load is the Cooper E–72 load shown by Fig. 1–3. The Cooper loading probably does not closely

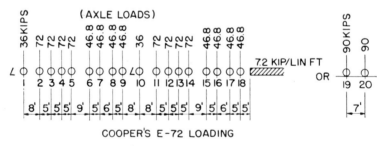

COOPER'S E-72 LOADING

Fig. 1–3.

resemble any actual locomotive. The stress values that are computed using it, however, are much like the maximum stress values to be expected under actual loads. The name "E–72" is given because the load on one axle of the drive wheels (No. 2, for example) is 72 kips. (A kip is a kilo-pound, or 1,000 pounds.) Other standard Cooper loadings have axles in the same position as those shown, and have the same relative sizes of axle loads. The Cooper E–60 loads, for example, are each 60/72 times those shown for the E–72 loading. The Cooper E–72 loading is specified by the 1949 AREA *Specification*. Individual railroads often have other standard loadings which simulate more closely the loads caused by the locomotives used by that road.

Highway structures are subject to a very complex type of loading and to countless variations of loading. Rather than attempt to use the actual loads, which consist of mixtures of heavy trucks and mis-

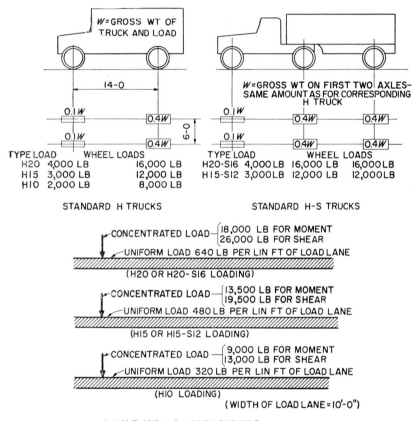

F IG. 1–4.

cellaneous other vehicles, highway engineers use design loads similar to those shown by Fig. 1–4. The loads shown are those of the *Standard Specifications for Highway Bridges*, by the American Association of State Highway Officials. Generally, truck-wheel loads are used whenever their use gives higher stresses than lane loadings. To avoid the need for trying both kinds of load, the AASHO Specification gives definite instructions as to which type of loading to use. *The fact that design loads need not necessarily closely resemble the actual loads is clearly shown by the lane loadings of Fig. 1–4.*

The live loads caused by cranes and certain machinery are usually easy to determine. In such cases the actual loads are computed and are used in design.

The principal live loads on the roofs of buildings are those due to snow and to wind. Ice is occasionally considered. (A roof used for a promenade would, of course, be subject to live load by human occupancy.) The weight of snow to be considered varies with the location of the structure and the slope of the roof. The snow load recommended by the American Standards Association is a minimum of 20 lb per sq ft of horizontal projection of the roof area, with larger loads up to 40 lb per sq ft depending on the geographical location. Local building codes usually specify the amount of snow load to be used. It would require an unusually heavy snowfall to cause snow loads of the magnitude of some of the values given. However, partial melting of the snow, followed by freezing and more precipitation may cause a heavy mass to develop, varying in nature from solid ice to wet snow.

In the design of exposed electric power substations, towers, etc., it is often assumed that a $\frac{1}{2}$-inch coating of ice is present on the wires, equipment, and structure. A large part of the total stress may be due to the ice load. The ice is assumed to weigh 57 lb per cu ft, or 0.033 lb per cu in.

1–7. Wind Loads. Wind load must be considered in the design of many structures. In some structures, such as tall chimneys, towers, and supports for electrical substation apparatus, etc., the wind load is one of the most important ones. The amount of wind load is quite difficult to predict. Wind is variable, occurring in gusts rather than in a steady flow. The wind velocity is not uniform at all parts of the structure. The wind is affected by elevation and by the presence of nearby buildings, cliffs, valleys, etc. Its direction is usually horizontal, but it may receive a vertical component of motion as it approaches or passes over an obstruction. Its course may be curved rather than straight.

The force of wind on a structure is composed of both positive and negative pressures, i.e., pressure and suction. The windward surface of a structure is subject to positive pressure. The leeward surface and most roofs are subject to suction. The windward surface of sloping roofs may have either suction or positive pressure, depending on the degree of slope and many other factors. Fig. 1–5 shows a typical mill-type building and the external wind forces on the building. In addition to the external forces shown, because of openings in the building there may also be changes of internal pressures. Since the wind direction is not necessarily normal to the side of the building, wind forces may tend to twist the building in a horizontal plane.

Because the exact wind loads are so complex and variable, it is essential that safe simplifications of the actual loads be used for design purposes. A simple method that has found much use since the early nineteenth century is that of assuming a positive pressure to exist on

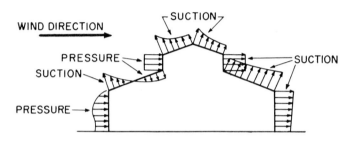

WIND EFFECT ON OUTSIDE SURFACE OF MILL−TYPE BUILDING

FIG. 1–5.

the windward vertical surfaces and a reduced positive pressure on the windward slope of sloping roofs. No pressure or suction was considered on the leeward side or roof. The Duchemin formula, used to determine the reduced load, is

$$p_n = p\left(\frac{2 \sin \alpha}{1 + \sin^2 \alpha}\right)$$

in which p_n is the pressure intensity normal to the sloping surface, p is the pressure intensity normal to the vertical surface, and α is the slope of the roof. The value of the pressure p is determined from the formula

$$p = 0.0033\,V^2$$

in which V is the wind velocity in miles per hour. This value of p is about 1.3 times as great as the dynamic pressure or velocity pressure of the air against the vertical surface. The velocity pressure is equal to

$$q = 0.002558\,V^2$$

The value of p differs from the value of q because of the suction that exists on the leeward side. The term p, while it is treated as a pressure on the windward side, is intentionally made large enough to cover the effect of both the pressure and the suction in computations relative to stability of the entire structure.

Much effort has been made to develop standards of wind loading which simulate the actual more closely. A method that has been received favorably is the ASCE method.[1] The ASCE method is the result of ten years of activity by a subcommittee of the American Society of Civil Engineers. It will be briefly summarized below.

1. For design of bracing and stability computations for tall buildings, use a uniformly distributed force of 20 lb per sq ft of vertical windward surface for the first 300 ft above the ground. Above 300 ft, the force is to increase at the rate of 2.5 lb per sq ft for each 100 ft of additional height. The wind force need not be separated into pressure and suction, except for computations involving the attachment of wall and roof materials to the main structure.

2. For buildings such as mill buildings, armories, hangars, structures with rounded roofs, or structures with large open interiors, or walls in which large openings may occur, the pressure and suction effects should be considered, according to the following rules:

   a) On the outside of vertical plane surfaces, normal to the wind direction, a pressure equal to $0.8q$ for the windward wall, and a suction of $0.5q$ on the leeward wall. The value of q is given by the formula

   $$q = 0.002558\,V^2$$

   in which V is the wind speed in miles per hour. [The total force is seen to be 1.3 times the value of q. The value of p, equal to 20 lb per sq ft (given in Item 1 above) corresponds to a wind velocity of 77.8 miles per hour. For this velocity, q is 15.5 lb per sq ft.]

   b) On the outside of sloping surfaces, the values of pressure or suction given by Fig. 1–6 for the windward side, and a suction of 9 lb per sq ft for the leeward side.

   c) For inside surfaces of buildings nominally airtight, but having leakage through small openings, 4.5 lb per sq ft, either pressure or suction.

   d) For inside surfaces of buildings having 30 per cent or more of the wall surfaces open, or subject to being opened or broken open, a pressure of 12 lb per sq ft, or a suction of 9 lb per sq ft. (Interpolate for openings less than 30 per cent.)

[1] "Wind Bracing in Steel Buildings," Final Report of Sub-Committee No. 31, Committee on Steel of the Structural Division, *Trans. ASCE*, **105** (1940), p. 1713.

e) On external walls parallel to the wind, a suction of 9 lb per sq ft.

(In each of the rules for interior surfaces, the pressure is used when the openings are on the windward side, and the suction when the openings are on the leeward. The pressures and suctions given in Item 2 are for heights below 300 ft. For heights above 300 ft, the values given should be increased in the same proportion that the force specified in Item 1 bears to 20 lb per sq ft.)

The complete report gives loads for curved roofs, and other information on wind loads and bracing.

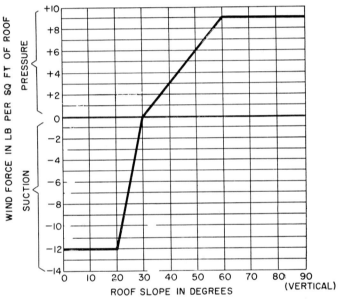

WIND PRESSURES ON WINDWARD SIDE OF ROOF; ASCE RECOMMENDATION

Fig. 1–6.

While the ASCE method is a little more difficult to apply than the older Duchemin method, it does simulate the actual wind forces more closely. Once the wind-load combinations have been determined for the various surfaces, the analysis is as simple as with the older method. The use of the ASCE method will be illustrated by an example later in this chapter.

A non-structural engineer might need to consider wind forces on objects other than buildings, such as cylindrical or spherical tanks, chimneys, and open steel frameworks such as are used to support electrical apparatus. A specification covering pressures for tanks, towers, and chimneys is given by the American Standards Association.[2] The Association gives pressures for use with buildings by the following table:

Height Zone (ft)	Wind Pressure (lb per sq ft)
Less than 50	20
50 to 99	24
100 to 199	28
200 to 299	30
300 to 399	32
400 to 499	33
500 to 599	34
600 to 799	35

Etc., for heights up to 1,600 ft

The wind loads for tanks, towers, and chimneys are those given in the above table for buildings, times the following factors:

Shape	Factor
Square or rectangular	1.00
Hexagonal or octagonal . . .	0.80
Round or elliptical	0.60

Wind forces on exposed structural steel are usually taken as the basic pressure for vertical surfaces acting on one and one-half times the area exposed to the wind.

It should be understood that in all of the standards here mentioned, the winds are not assumed to be of hurricane intensity. When structures are constructed to resist hurricanes, the wind loads used must be larger than those given here as examples. The local code requirements in areas subject to hurricanes should be consulted.

1–8. Impact. A moving object may cause dynamic loads, which are due to its motion, as well as live loads, which are due to the force of gravity on its mass. This dynamic load is called "impact." Impact is an energy load. It results when kinetic energy of the moving object is changed into strain energy within the structure.

Impact usually occurs with the sudden application of load to a member, such as the loading of a crane runway girder by a rapidly moving crane. The sudden stopping of a downward moving elevator, or of a load being lowered by a hoist, causes impact. Impact results when wheels cross irregularities such as track joints. Impact forces are caused by reciprocating parts of machinery.

[2]*Minimum Design Loads In Buildings and Other Structures*, American Standards Association, A58.1-1945.

The nature of impact is complicated, and the computation of exact forces is often not practical. However, safe standards for the amounts of certain impact forces have been established. Some specifications recognize that the impact effect is usually less for long flexible structures than for short or very rigid ones. For example, the AASHO Specification for highway bridges requires that impact be considered as a percentage of the live load, and that the percentage to be used is given by the formula

$$I = \frac{50}{L + 125}$$

in which I is the impact percentage, and L is the length of span loaded to produce the maximum live-load stresses. Similar expressions are given by the AREA and other specifications.

The AISC Specification for buildings of structural steel gives the following percentages:

For supports of elevators.	100 per cent of the live load
For traveling crane support girders and their connections	25 per cent
For supports of light machinery, shaft or motor driven, not less than	20 per cent
For supports of reciprocating machinery or power-driven units, not less than	50 per cent
For threaded hanger rods supporting floors and balconies	$33\frac{1}{3}$ per cent

Obviously a single specification cannot cover adequately the impact forces for all types of equipment and machinery. The above values are stated as minimums. The manufacturers of machinery are often able to furnish information and recommend proper impact values.

1–9. Earthquake Forces. In some areas the effects of possible earthquakes must be considered in structural design. The nature of the structure is sometimes controlled by this factor.

The force produced on a structure by an earthquake is a dynamic force. It results from the acceleration of the structure in the direction of the quake movement. The movement is usually mainly horizontal. The inertia of the structure causes it to resist such movement. The resulting forces on each part of the structure are proportional to the mass of the part and to the rate of acceleration of the quake movement. If the horizontal acceleration were as great as that of gravity, the horizontal force on each part would be equal to the weight of that part. Normally the intensity of horizontal acceleration is a small fraction of the acceleration g due to gravity. If the horizontal acceleration is only $0.1g$, the horizontal loads used are equal to 0.1 times the weight of the part. The value of horizontal acceleration to be used is controlled by local conditions and is usually specified by local codes. The amount of vertical acceleration is usually found to be negligible as compared to the horizontal.

1–10. Load Combinations. At first thought it might seem wise to consider all possible combinations of load in design. There are, however, combinations of load that may be possible, but are so highly improbable that it is consistent with good engineering practice to neglect them. For example, it is *possible* that snow load of full intensity could exist in the form of solidified material, and that the full design value of wind could occur without blowing off any of the snow. But it is so *improbable* that such a load combination would ever occur, that it would be better to design for the more probable types of loading. In the event that the improbable type of loading were ever to occur, the material of the structure would be overstressed. Because of the factor of safety used (see Art. 1–11), collapse would not occur, although some permanent deformation might. Since such overload would be very rare, neither fatigue failure nor very large permanent deformations would occur.

The combinations of load to be considered are sometimes defined by specification.

Combinations of roof loads often considered include the following:

1. Dead load alone
2. Snow load over the entire roof, plus dead load
3. Full wind, plus dead load
4. Full snow with one-half wind, plus dead load

If ice loads are to be considered, they would be considered in each of the above combinations. If live loads other than wind, snow, and ice are expected, they also should be included, provided the combination is not highly improbable. For example, it would be well to consider the weight of a man in addition to the snow loads. For small elements such as a precast roof plank, that load combination would probably control. The effect of such a small additional weight would be negligible in the design of larger members such as roof trusses, however.

For structures such as outdoor supports for electrical apparatus, the combination of dead load with ice and full wind is often controlling. The possibility of the breaking of a wire on one side only of the structure is often considered. When this happens, the structure may have a horizontal force which was previously counterbalanced by the tension of the wire that is broken. Since such breakage usually occurs when the wind is blowing and the wires are covered with ice, it is logical to assume the broken wire in combination with maximum wind and ice loads.

Occasionally, however, economic considerations make it advisable to ignore this worst possible combination. In such cases it might be more expensive in the long run to design the structure to resist the worst possible combination than it would be to risk the possible failure.

Because the combination of maximum wind with the other loads is rare, and because the wind force is "spotty," not occurring over the entire structure, stresses caused by combinations of load which include wind are often permitted to be higher than those caused by other combinations. For example, the AISC Specification permits unit stresses caused by load combinations which include wind to be 1/3 higher than those permitted for dead load, live load, and impact alone. Since higher stresses are permitted when the loads include wind, the design of most members is controlled by load combinations which do not include wind.

Another example of the improbability of complete loading is found in floor loads for buildings such as office buildings. It is not probable that the uniform live load used in the design of the members of such a building will occur over all of the floor area at the same time. Members which receive the maximum values of stress when large areas are loaded could logically be designed for a uniform load of less than the stipulated value. Some specifications contain instructions as to the percentage of full live load to be assumed in such cases. For example, the American Standards Association provides for reduction of uniform live loads as follows:

3–6. Reduction of Live Load
    (a) No reduction shall be applied to the roof load.
    (b) For live loads of 100 lb or less per square foot, the design live load for any member supporting 150 square feet or more may be reduced at the rate of 0.08 per cent per square foot of area supported by the member, except that no reduction shall be made for areas to be occupied as places of public assembly. The reduction shall exceed neither R as determined by the following formula, nor 60 per cent:

$$R = 100 \times \left(\frac{D + L}{4.33L} \right)$$

in which

R = reduction in per cent
D = dead load per square foot of area supported by the member
L = design live load per square foot of area supported by the member.

For live loads exceeding 100 pounds per square foot, no reduction shall be made, except that the design live loads on columns may be reduced 20 per cent.

Through reference to it in the AISC Specification, the above quotation from the requirements suggested by the American Standards Association is made a part of the AISC Specification.

In bridges the probability of complete live loading of all tracks or lanes becomes less as the number of tracks or lanes becomes larger. Bridge specifications allow a reduction in the design live load for members receiving the maximum stresses from the loading of more than two tracks or lanes. The overstress that might occur should the bridge ever be completely loaded is rare enough that fatigue failure will not result. The reductions of live load specified are kept low enough so that the stress under full live load would still not exceed the elastic limit.

It may be necessary to apply similar reasoning to the choosing of design load combinations for structures not covered by a specification. If certain load combinations are considered too improbable to use as design conditions, it is a good idea to be certain that even the highly improbable, nevertheless possible, combination of loads will not cause ultimate collapse of the structure. The seriousness of such a collapse and its effect on persons and property will, of course, influence the selection of design conditions.

1-11. Factor of Safety. The names "factor of uncertainty" and "factor of ignorance" are sometimes used as synonyms for "factor of safety." The factor of safety is sometimes taken as the ratio of ultimate stress to the actual unit stress under design loads. For example, the stress permitted for tension members under the 1949 AISC Specification is 20,000 pounds per square inch (psi), while the ultimate tensile strength of the steel used must be not less than 60,000 psi. Thus the factor of safety with respect to ultimate for tension is 60,000 ÷ 20,000, or a minimum of 3. Does such a factor indicate that up to 3 times the design load could be applied without causing damage to the structure? No, it does not. It means that up to about 3 times the design load *might* be applied without causing complete collapse. However, yielding and permanent deformation of the material will occur when the stress exceeds the yield strength of the material. The value of a structure is usually impaired by permanent deformation, so the limit of usefulness is measured by the yield stress. For structural steel, the yield strength may be as low as 33,000 psi, or 1.65 times the working stress. The loads could be increased to only 1.65 times the design loads without danger of damage to the structure. The factor of safety with respect to yielding is maintained to cover uncertainty and ignorance as to the exact loading, the behavior of the materials, etc.

Factors of safety vary between specifications. The writers of the specifications, in choosing the factors, are influenced by many con-

Courtesy of Chicago Bridge and Iron Co.

OIL REFINERY TOWERS. AN EXAMPLE OF THE RESULT OF COOPERATIVE EFFORTS
BY ENGINEERS OF MANY BRANCHES.

siderations, including the seriousness of failure, the possibility of fatigue, the expected life of the structure, and the degree of certainty with which the loads can be predicted.

1-12. Structural Materials. The most commonly used structural materials are steel, timber, brick, tile, and concrete. Lightweight alloys, particularly those of aluminum, are being used for many structural applications. A brief description of some of these materials will be given here. For more detailed information, the reader should refer to any textbook on engineering materials.

The steel most widely used for structural plates and shapes is referred to as "structural steel." The AISC and many other specifications require that this material conform to that described by the ASTM Designation A 7. It is low-carbon steel (0.20 to 0.35 per cent carbon) made by either the open-hearth or the electric-furnace process. The ultimate strength is 60,000 to 72,000 psi, and the yield strength not less than 33,000 psi. It can be welded easily by either gas or electric-arc methods.

Structural rivets are made of steel conforming to ASTM Designation A 141. The nominal diameters of the rivets vary (by intervals of $\frac{1}{8}$ inch) from $\frac{1}{2}$ in. to $1\frac{1}{4}$ in., with the $\frac{3}{4}$-in. and $\frac{7}{8}$-in. as the most common sizes.

Other steels used for structural work include nickel steel and silicon steel. Both of these are used where steel with higher tensile strength than ordinary structural steel is required. Structural steel having about 0.20 per cent of copper added is used where ordinary structural steel may be subject to rusting.

Several grades of steel are used as concrete reinforcing material. The code of the American Concrete Institute describes the acceptable types by reference to the applicable ASTM designation number. These steels are broadly classified, for design purposes, either as "structural" grade, or as "intermediate" or "hard" grade.

Many types of aluminum alloy are used for structural purposes. They include those designated as 17S-T4, 24S-T4, 24S-T36, and 61S-T6. In the designations for these alloys, the numbers before the letter "S" indicate the composition of the alloy, the letter "S" is used to identify it as an aluminum alloy, and the letter and numbers following the letter "S" indicate the temper of the material. For example, the designation "24S-T4" indicates aluminum alloy 24S (the percentage composition of which is covered by the Army-Navy specification number AN-A-12), solution heat treated.

A large variety of aluminum alloys exist, some being especially suited to resist extreme corrosive conditions, others having strength equal to that of structural steel, some suitable for gas welding, others

Courtesy of Chicago Bridge and Iron Co.

HORTONSPHERES AND HORTONSPHEROIDS FOR STORAGE OF GASES UNDER PRESSURE.

to spot welding, and so on. Up-to-date data on the properties and the uses of the aluminum alloys are available from the manufacturers of aluminum.

The most widely used species of timber for structural purposes are Douglas fir, yellow pine, and white pine. The availability of suitable local species affects the choice of timber.

Concrete is made by mixing cement, fine aggregate, coarse aggregate, and water in the correct proportions. Often the solid materials are

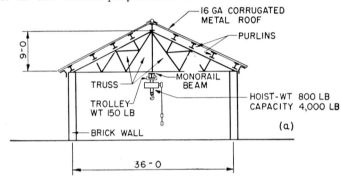

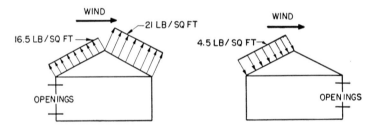

(b)   TWO CASES OF WIND LOADING ON ROOF (TOTALS OF INSIDE AND OUTSIDE EFFECTS)

FIG. 1-7.

used in some arbitrary proportions and water is added to produce the desired consistency. Such a procedure may result in a concrete that is not satisfactory in strength, appearance, or durability. More scientific methods of proportioning are now in common use. Adequate strength, workability, durability, and other properties can be assured when the mix is scientifically designed and controlled. The properties of concrete will be discussed further in Chapter 9.

EXAMPLE 1-1. Fig. 1-7(a) shows the cross section of an existing factory building. A monorail and hoist are to be added by the owner.

If you, as the owner's plant engineer, were required to check the strength of the roof truss, so as to be sure that the new equipment could be safely added, what loads and what load combinations would you consider? Assume that the code requirements for live loads include snow at 25 lb per sq ft of horizontal projection of roof, that the ASCE wind loads are to be used, and that the impact is as specified by AISC.

The dead loads are those caused by the corrugated metal roof, the purlins, the truss itself, and the monorail beam. These loads must be considered in all load combinations. The dead loads from the purlins and roof are applied to the truss as concentrated loads at each panel point along the top chord of the truss. The weight of the monorail beam is applied to the truss at the center bottom-chord panel point. The dead load of the truss itself should be distributed and applied at all joints of the truss. For light trusses such as this, however, little error is caused if the truss weight is assumed to act as concentrations of load at the top-chord panel points only.

The live loads are those caused by snow, wind, and the monorail. The amounts are:

Snow—25 lb per sq ft of horizontal projection of roof area.

Wind—a suction of 4.5 lb per sq ft on the outside of one side of the roof (see Fig. 1–6) and a suction of 9 lb per sq ft on the outside surface of the other half of the roof. Assuming that 30 per cent or more of the wall surfaces are capable of being opened, the inside surface of the roof could have either a pressure of 12 lb per sq ft or a suction of 9 lb per sq ft. The inside and outside effects are combined, and the two cases of wind loading are shown by Fig. 1–7(b). The wind loads are applied to the truss itself as concentrations of load at the panel points of the upper chord.

Monorail—4,000 lb of lifted load, plus 800 lb weight of hoist, plus 150 lb weight of trolley, or a total of 4,950 lb. This total load would cause a concentration of load to reach the truss at the middle panel point of the bottom chord. The exact amount of the force on the truss would depend on the length of the trolley, i.e., on the manner in which the 4,950 lb is spread along the monorail beam.

The impact is specified by AISC as 25 per cent for traveling cranes. A monorail is subject to practically the same sort of shock and vibrations that would be expected for a traveling crane, therefore the same percentage will be used. The impact force on the truss would be 25 per cent of the live load force caused on the truss by the total moving load, which includes the load lifted, the weight of the hoist, and the weight of the trolley.

$$I = 0.25 \times 4{,}950 = 1{,}238 \text{ lb}$$

The design load combinations would be:

1. Dead load, monorail live load, impact, and snow
2. Dead load, monorail live load, impact, and wind

Because of the rareness and improbability of obtaining the full values of monorail live load, impact, and wind simultaneously, the allowable unit stress would be increased by 33 1/3 per cent for the second combination. (See AISC Specification.) The wind loading which resulted in the higher stress for the truss members would be used. Since the bars of the truss might not all have the maximum stress under the same loads, it might be necessary to make analyses using each type of wind loading. The combination of dead load, monorail live load, impact, snow load, and half wind load might be considered. Examination of local codes would assist in deciding which combinations to use.

1–13. Accuracy of Computations. The loads on structures are gener- ally not known to a high degree of accuracy. The results of computations can be no more accurate than the data on which they are based. Thus, slide rule accuracy is acceptable, and answers may in general be given to three significant figures.

PROBLEMS

1–1. The cross section of a small industrial building is shown by Fig. 1–8.
    a) What is the amount of the dead load per square foot of roof?
    b) What is the approximate weight of the truss? (Symbols on the drawing show the size of steel angles used. For example, the bottom chord con- sists of two angles, each $3\frac{1}{2}$ in. $\times$ 3 in. $\times \frac{3}{8}$ in. The weight per foot for angles may be found in Appendix A. Scale lengths from the drawing. Add 10 per cent to cover the weight of gusset plates, rivet heads, and other details.)

1–2. Assume that your building is to have a new crane runway installed. It will be supported, if possible, by new brackets riveted to the existing columns. These brackets are shown dotted by Fig. 1–8. The column strength must be checked to determine whether the crane load can be added. Design compu- tations for the building are not available, so in checking the column strength you must "start from scratch." List by name all the types and sources of load that would be considered. Give the intensity of such loads where possible.

1–3. A section through a small building is shown by Fig. 1–9. The second floor was used as office space, but is to be used in the future, if possible, for light manufacturing.

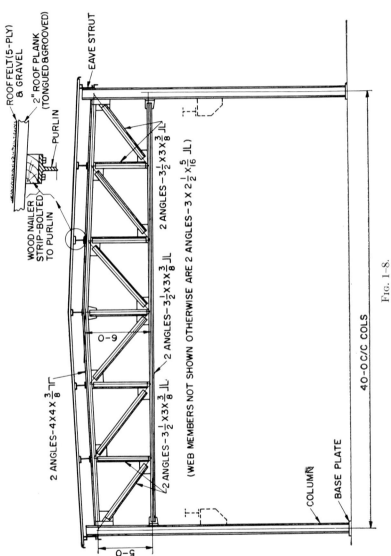

FIG. 1-8.

What is the total load per square foot to be used in checking the strength of the floor slab?

What is the total load per square foot of floor and ceiling to be used when checking the strength of the floor beams?

1.-4. Compute the wind loads for the building of Fig. 1–8, using the ASCE method. Assume that over 30 per cent of the wall is window space. Show both combinations of wind load, that with inside pressure and that with inside suction.

1–5. The roof planks will naturally be nailed down to the building of Fig. 1–8. Are the nails needed in order to prevent uplift of the roof material by internal and external wind forces?

1–6. What are the wind loads for the building of Fig. 1–8 according to the Duchemin method? In order to compare with the results by the ASCE method, use a wind velocity of 77.8 miles per hour.

1–7. A cylindrical tank 10 ft high and 6 ft in diameter is to be mounted on a short tower on the roof of an existing building. The center of the tank will be 70 ft above the ground. Bracing for the tower will be designed to resist horizontal loads on the tank and the tower. Use the ASCE method to determine the total wind force on the tank.

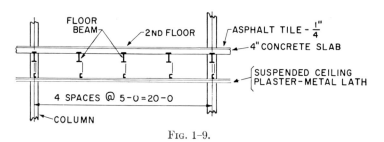

FIG. 1–9.

CHAPTER 2

EQUILIBRIUM AND REACTIONS

2–1. Resolution and Composition of Forces. Knowledge of how to determine the resultant of any group of forces, including the amount, direction, and line of action of that resultant, and of the methods of resolving a force into components is essential before proceeding with the subject matter of this and subsequent chapters. The resolution and composition of forces are illustrated by the examples below. These examples are intended not as a means for *learning* resolution and composition, but rather as a means by which the student may *check* his present ability. If the student does not clearly understand the examples below, or if he cannot himself solve similar problems, he should carefully review the subjects of resolution and composition of forces in a textbook on mechanics or statics.

EXAMPLE 2–1. A vertical force of 100 lb and a horizontal force of 200 lb are applied to a body as shown in Fig. 2–1(a). Find the resultant.

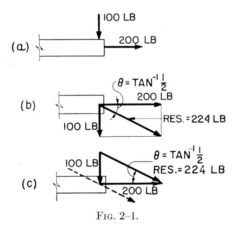

FIG. 2–1.

Fig. 2–1(b) shows the graphical solution. The resultant is completely defined by this solution; amount, direction, and location are given. Notice that the resultant acts on a line through the intersection of the two forces.

An alternate graphical solution is given by Fig. 2–1(c). The resultant shown has the correct amount and direction, but is not shown in the correct location. The correct location is shown dotted.

The resultant can be determined mathematically by visualizing the diagrams of Fig. 2–1 and computing the length and direction of the vector representing the resultant, rather than by scaling from the diagram.

EXAMPLE 2–2. Find the horizontal and vertical components of the force shown in Fig. 2–2(a).

The solution is by the reverse procedure to that of Example 2–1. Fig. 2–2(b) shows a graphical solution for the amount and direction of each component, but does not show the correct location for the components. Components of a given force *must* intersect each other at a point on the line of action of the given force. The solution of Fig. 2–2(c) is correct as to amount, direction, and line of action of the components. The pairs of dotted arrows indicate other possible locations for the components of the given force.

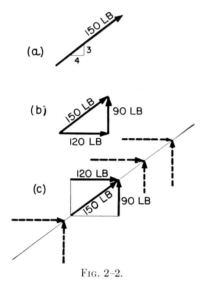

FIG. 2–2.

EXAMPLE 2–3. Fig. 2–3 shows the graphical solution for the resultant of a pair of forces which are not at right angles to each other. A

FIG. 2–3.

mathematical solution can also be made by visualizing the diagram and then computing the length and direction of the resultant vector.

EXAMPLE 2–4. Find the resultant of the three forces shown by Fig. 2–4(a).

The graphical solution of Fig. 2–4(b) gives the amount and direction of the resultant, but it does not give the line of action. The solution shown by Fig. 2–4(c), which is merely the repeated use of the operation shown in Example 2–3, gives correctly the amount, direction, and line of action of the resultant.

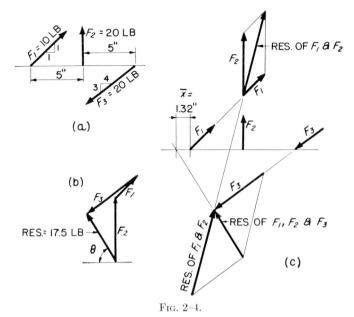

Fig. 2–4.

The resultant is easily determined mathematically by substituting vertical and horizontal components for each of the original forces, as shown below:

Force	Vertical Component	Horizontal Component
1	7.1↑	7.1→
2	20.0↑	0.0
3	12.0↓	16.0←
Resultant	15.1↑	8.9←

$$\text{Resultant} = \sqrt{(15.1)^2 + (8.9)^2} = 17.5 \text{ lb}$$

$$\theta = \tan^{-1}\left(\frac{15.1}{8.9}\right) = 59.4°$$

The dimension $\bar{x}$ is computed by taking moments about the intersection of the base line and force number 1. If the horizontal and vertical components are used, rather than the original forces, the horizontal components will all have zero moment about the intersection point.

$$15.1\bar{x} = (20 \times 5) - (12 \times 10)$$
$$\bar{x} = -1.32 \text{ in.}$$

The resultant is completely defined as a force of 17.5 lb, acting upward and to the left, at an angle of 59.4° to the horizontal, and passing

Courtesy of American MonoRail Co.

GRAB FOR LIFTING BOXES. THIS TYPE OF DEVICE WOULD USUALLY BE DESIGNED BY A MECHANICAL ENGINEER, ALTHOUGH A STRUCTURAL ENGINEER MIGHT BE REQUIRED TO DO SO. THE JOB IS A "CROSS" BETWEEN MACHINE DESIGN AND STRUCTURAL DESIGN.

through a point 1.32 in. to the left of the intersection of force number 1 and the base line.

EXAMPLE 2–5. Find the resultant of the forces shown by Fig. 2–5. The amount of the resultant is 13 lb upward. The location of the resultant is determined by taking moments about point A.

$$13\bar{x} = (10 \times 4) + (6 \times 8)$$
$$\bar{x} = 6.7 \text{ ft}$$

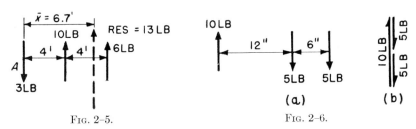

FIG. 2–5.   FIG. 2–6.

EXAMPLE 2–6. Find the resultant of the forces shown by Fig. 2–6(a).

If a force polygon is constructed, as in Fig. 2–6(b), it will be seen that the resultant of the given forces is a zero force. This can be shown by merely adding the given forces algebraically. If moments of the given forces are taken about some point, however, the sum of these moments is not zero. For example, taking moments about a point on the line of action of the left force,

$$(5 \times 12) + (5 \times 18) = 150 \text{ in.-lb}$$

The resultant of the forces given is a moment of 150 in.-lb.

2–2. Equilibrium. Equilibrium is defined as the state in which there is no change in the motion of a body. A body at rest is in equilibrium if it remains at rest, neither moving nor rotating. A moving body is in equilibrium if it continues to move without changing direction or velocity.

A body having forces applied in one plane only could change its state of rest or uniform motion in three ways. It could accelerate vertically, accelerate horizontally, or have rotational acceleration. To prevent these three types of change, it is necessary that the forces acting satisfy the following three conditions:

1. The sum of the horizontal components must equal zero. ($\Sigma H = 0$)
2. The sum of the vertical components must equal zero. ($\Sigma V = 0$)
3. The sum of the moments of all the forces applied to the body, taken about any point, must equal zero. ($\Sigma M = 0$)

   If there is any point about which the sum of the moments is not zero, the system is *not* in equilibrium.

The above three statements are called the "laws of equilibrium" for a system of forces in one plane. The application of the laws will be illustrated by the two examples which follow.

EXAMPLE 2–7. A structural member and the applied forces are shown by Fig. 2–7. Is the member in equilibrium?

The question will be answered by checking each of the equations of equilibrium to determine whether they are satisfied by the given force system.

$$\Sigma V = -12 - 8 + \left(\frac{4}{5} \times 25\right) = 0 \quad \text{Satisfied}$$

$$\Sigma H = -15 + \left(\frac{3}{5} \times 25\right) = 0 \quad \text{Satisfied}$$

$$\Sigma M \text{ (about point } A) = -\left(\frac{4}{5} \times 25 \times 6\right) + (8 \times 14)$$

$$= -8 \text{ ft-lb} \quad \text{Not satisfied}$$

The force system is, therefore, not in equilibrium. The body would rotate counterclockwise. The resultant is not truly zero, but is a couple.

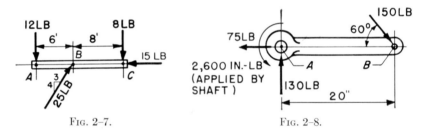

FIG. 2–7.   FIG. 2–8.

EXAMPLE 2–8. Is the machine element shown by Fig. 2–8 in equilibrium?

$$\Sigma V = 130 - 150 \sin 60° = 0 \quad \text{Satisfied}$$
$$\Sigma H = -75 + 150 \cos 60° = 0 \quad \text{Satisfied}$$
$$\Sigma M \text{ (about point } B) = (130 \times 20) - 2,600 = 0 \quad \text{Satisfied}$$

The system is, therefore, in equilibrium. Note that the applied moment at the left end is treated the same in the third equation regardless of which point is selected as the moment center for the equation.

2–3. Types of Support and Conventional Symbols. The nature of the support given to a structural member must be determined before an analysis of the forces on the member can be made. For systems of forces in a single plane, three basic types of support can occur. These are represented symbolically in Fig. 2–9. Note that in each symbol, the member is indicated as a single line, or as an "ideal" structure.

The support indicated by the symbol (a) can provide only one degree of restraint. It can prevent motion toward or away from the plane indicated by the short line. Thus only one force can be applied to the

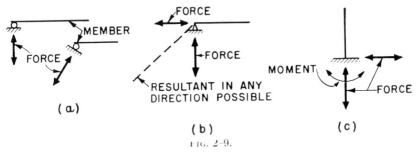

FIG. 2–9.

member by this type of support; that force will be normal to the indicated plane. Examples of this type of support are:

1. The wheel of a crane, which can prevent only vertical movement of the crane, the force between it and the rail being normal to the rail.
2. A brick wall, supporting the end of a beam which merely rests on the wall without being anchored to it.
3. A column, supporting a beam and having a large resistance to vertical forces, but being too flexible to resist horizontal forces without much deformation.
4. A hanger rod, used to support a pipe from a roof beam. The rod can apply only vertical force to the pipe.

Symbol (a) is intended to indicate that a force is possible in either direction normal to the plane; i.e., either upward or downward.

The support of type (b) provides two degrees of restraint. It prevents both vertical and horizontal movement. The support is commonly referred to as a "pinned support." The force possible at such a support could be indicated as a single force in a particular direction, or as a vertical force and a horizontal force acting together. Examples of this type of support are:

1. A wall, well braced, and supporting the end of a beam that is anchored to the wall.
2. The bearing of a shaft, preventing motion of the shaft either vertically or horizontally, but permitting rotation.
3. A crane wheel having the brakes applied so as to prevent horizontal motion of the crane. The wheel can transmit both vertical and horizontal reactions to the crane.

The support indicated by Fig. 2–9(c) provides three degrees of restraint. It prevents vertical movement, horizontal movement, and rotation. This type of support is commonly referred to as the "fixed end." It can transmit to the member a horizontal force, a vertical force, and a moment. Examples are:

1. The shaft supporting the machine element of Example 2–8.
2. A large concrete block having the end of a beam imbedded in it.

In practice it is often difficult to provide complete resistance to end rotation of a member, so that support conditions may occur that are intermediate between types (b) and (c). Similarly, support conditions between types (a) and (b) may occur.

Two other symbols should be explained at this point. The connection of members to each other so that free rotation of one may occur with respect to the other is represented by the symbol of Fig. 2–10(a). Such a joint is called a "pinned" or a "pin-connected" joint.

If the connection of the members is made so that rotation of one relative to the other is not possible, the symbol of Fig. 2–10(b) may be used. This connection is called a "rigid" connection; the members so connected are said to be "continuous."

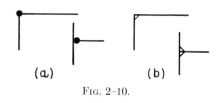

(a)   (b)

Fig. 2–10.

The symbols of Figs. 2–10(a) and (b) are used only when their omission might lead to confusion. In beams and frames, the members are continuous unless shown otherwise by use of the symbol of Fig. 2–10(a). The members of trusses are assumed to be pinned, even though the symbol may be omitted.

It is important in analysis to know which support or connection conditions exist. The nature of the support provided affects the stability and other action of structural members. Carefully planned details are often used so as to insure the desired type of support.

2–4. Reactions. Forces or moments applied to a structural member by its supports are called reactions. If the loads on a member are known, the amounts of the three reactions required to maintain equilibrium can be computed using the equations of equilibrium. The computation of reactions is illustrated by the examples which follow.

EXAMPLE 2–9.   Find the reactions for the beam shown by Fig. 2–11.

Reactions V_a and V_b will be assumed to be upward forces; H_a will be assumed to act toward the right. If an assumed direction is wrong, the algebraic sign of the answer obtained will be negative. The applied

Courtesy of Cleveland Electric Illuminating Co.

STEEL TOWERS SUPPORTING POWER LINES. TOWERS MUST RESIST HORIZONTAL
LOADS FROM WIND AND WIRE PULL.

load is substituted by a downward component of 800 lb and a horizontal component to the left of 600 lb. The solution follows.

$$\Sigma H = 0; \quad H_a - 600 = 0; \quad H_a = 600 \text{ lb} \rightarrow$$

$$\Sigma M_a = 0; \quad -10V_b + (800 \times 5) = 0; \quad V_b = 400 \text{ lb} \uparrow$$

$$\Sigma M_b = 0; \quad 10V_a - (800 \times 5) = 0; \quad V_a = 400 \text{ lb} \uparrow$$

The value of the third unknown solved could have been determined using the equation $\Sigma V = 0$, instead of by the moment equation. It is often an advantage, however, to solve for two of the reactions by moments, and then check the solution using the previously unused equation. Substituting the answers obtained above into the equation for vertical forces,

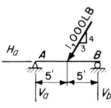

$$-800 + 400 + 400 = 0$$

FIG. 2–11.   The values obtained satisfy the equation. (Similarly, if the equation for vertical forces had been used to obtain the value of V_a, the answers could have been checked by substituting in the equation $\Sigma M_b = 0$.)

EXAMPLE 2–10. A small jib crane is attached to the column of a factory building as shown by Fig. 2–12. The loads on the crane are its own weight, an electric hoist weighing 800 lb, a trolley weighing 80 lb, a lifted load of 2,000 lb, and an impact equal to 25 per cent of the lifted load. Compute the reactions for the crane boom. (The boom is the horizontal member AB.)

The solution to this example is given in the form of a computation sheet in Fig. 2–12. It is good engineering practice to make all computations in a neat and orderly fashion. The operations made and the quantities used should be adequately labeled. A computation sheet in actual practice often becomes part of the permanent record of an engineering project. It may be used again by the engineer who made it. The checker will often refer to the original computation sheet. It may in the future be helpful to another engineer who plans either a similar structure or revisions to the one for which the computation sheet was made. The time required to make an orderly computation sheet exceeds that for a sloppy, disorderly one by only a negligible amount. The future time and trouble that is saved make the time of its preparation well spent. The computation sheet should represent the original work where possible. Time is wasted when disorderly original work must be recopied. Any computation worth making at all is worth making correctly and neatly.

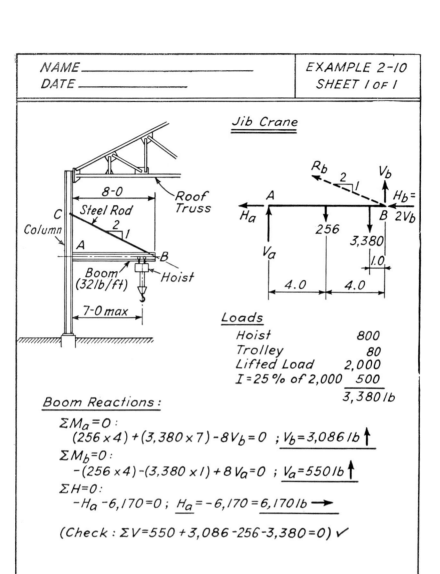

Jib Crane

Loads

Hoist	800
Trolley	80
Lifted Load	2,000
$I = 25\%$ of 2,000	500
	3,380 lb

Boom Reactions:

$\Sigma M_a = 0$:

$(256 \times 4) + (3,380 \times 7) - 8 V_b = 0$; $V_b = 3,086\,lb\,\uparrow$

$\Sigma M_b = 0$:

$-(256 \times 4) - (3,380 \times 1) + 8 V_a = 0$; $V_a = 550\,lb\,\uparrow$

$\Sigma H = 0$:

$-H_a - 6,170 = 0$; $H_a = -6,170 = 6,170\,lb \longrightarrow$

(Check : $\Sigma V = 550 + 3,086 - 256 - 3,380 = 0$) ✓

Tie-Rod Tension:

$R_b = \sqrt{(3,086)^2 + (6,170)^2} = 6,910\,lb$

Fig. 2-12.

37

An occasional example in this text will be shown in the computation-sheet form. The student should thus be reminded constantly to strive toward neat, orderly, and well-labeled computations. The heading shown is only one of many types. Most engineering offices have a standard form with spaces for the job number and title, the checker's signature, etc. Many engineering colleges have forms to be used as standards by their students.

While the original problem may appear complicated, it can be easily reduced to the simple problem shown by the free-body diagram of Fig. 2–12. End A is attached to the column by a rather shallow connection which permits the boom to rotate in a horizontal plane. The connection is assumed to be a pinned one, capable of providing vertical and horizontal reactive forces only. Thus, two unknown forces, V_a and H_a, exist at end A. At end B the reaction is parallel to the rod BC. (The rod is slender and, like a rope, can have only tensile forces applied to it.) Reaction R_b is assumed to act upward and to the left. The components H_b and V_b are substituted for it. Note that the components intersect on the line of action of reaction R_b, and that their directions are consistent with the assumed direction of R_b. The relationship of V_b and H_b is known from the slope of R_b. Component H_b is replaced by $2V_b$, reducing the unknowns to three.

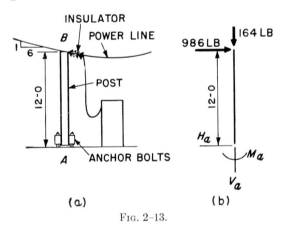

Fig. 2–13.

The negative sign in the solution of H_a indicates that the direction was assumed incorrectly. The final answer is given as a positive number with the direction shown by an arrow so as to eliminate all ambiguity.

The answers as given in Fig. 2–12 show the forces applied *to the boom* by the other members of the structure. If the problem were to determine the loads applied to the column by the crane, the following answers would result. The forces applied *by* the boom to the other members are equal and opposite to the reactions just computed. While the column pushes the boom toward the right at A with a force of 6,170 lb, the boom pushes the column toward the left with an equal force. Similarly, a downward force of 550 lb acts on the column at A, and at point C the column receives a downward load of 3,086 lb and a horizontal one of 6,170 to the right.

EXAMPLE 2–11.   Fig. 2–13(a) shows a post used to support an electric power line. The tensile force in the wire is 1,000 lb. The base of the post is attached rigidly to a concrete mat. Compute the reactions for the post.

The problem is resolved into the simple free-body diagram of Fig. 2–13(b). The reactions are a horizontal force, a vertical force, and an end moment.

Assume M_a clockwise.

$$\Sigma M_a = +M_a + (986 \times 12) = 0$$
$$M_a = -11,830$$
$$= 11,830 \text{ ft-lb, counterclockwise}$$

By the equations $\Sigma V = 0$ and $\Sigma H = 0$,

$$V_a = \underline{164 \text{ lb} \uparrow}$$
$$H_a = \underline{986 \text{ lb} \leftarrow}$$

2–5. Condition Equations.   The structure shown by Fig. 2–14(a) has four reactions. The three equations of equilibrium are not sufficient to provide a solution for more than three unknowns. An additional equation may be written, however, because the structure is pin-connected at point B. The structure may be cut at point B and either half treated as a free body. In Fig. 2–14(b) the left half is shown. The equation $\Sigma M_b = 0$ may be written for that half alone. This equation and the three equilibrium equations for the entire structure may be used to solve for the four reactions, V_a, H_a, V_c, and H_c. The additional equation, based on a condition existing within the structure, is called a "condition" equation.

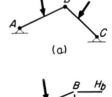

(a)

(b)

FIG. 2–14.

It is possible to solve for the reactions by treating each half of the structure separately, although it is sometimes easier to solve using the condition equation along with the equilibrium equations for the entire structure. Both procedures will be illustrated by the next example.

EXAMPLE 2–12.   The bracket shown by Fig. 2–15(a) is subject to two loads, one applied to the horizontal member and one to the inclined member. The possible reactions are two at A and two at C. The members are so joined at B that rotation of member AB with respect to member BC is not prevented by the connection. The three equilibrium equations for the entire structure can be supplemented by an equation

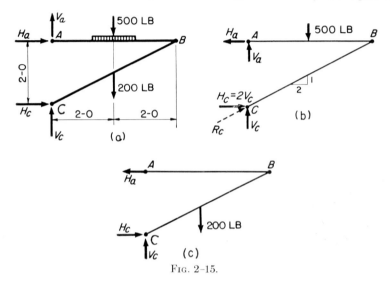

FIG. 2–15.

based on this internal condition. The assumed directions for the reactions are indicated by the arrows on Fig. 2–15(a).

$$\Sigma M_c = 2H_a + (2 \times 500) + (2 \times 200) = 0; \quad H_a = -700 = \underline{700\ \text{lb}\leftarrow}$$

$$\Sigma M_a = -2H_c + (2 \times 500) + (2 \times 200) = 0; \quad H_c = 700\ \text{lb}\rightarrow$$

$$(\Sigma H = -700 + 700 = 0; \quad \text{checks})$$

Condition equation: $\Sigma M_b = 0$ for member AB only.

$$\Sigma M_b = 4V_a - (2 \times 500) = 0; \quad V_a = \underline{250\ \text{lb}\uparrow}$$

$$\Sigma V = V_c + 250 - 500 - 200 = 0; \quad V_c = \underline{450\ \text{lb}\uparrow}$$

As an alternate method of solution, consider the structure first as loaded by the 500-lb load alone, and then by the 200-lb load alone. The reactions due to the simultaneous application of the two loads will be equal to the sums of the reactions due to the 500-lb load alone plus those due to the 200-lb load alone. The two separate load conditions are shown by Figs. 2–15(b) and (c).

In order that BC should not rotate about B, any force applied at C

must go through point B. Therefore the reaction at point C of Fig. 2–15(b) can only be parallel to member BC. The reaction R_c is divided into components H_c and V_c. Component H_c is known to be equal to $2V_c$. By use of the three equilibrium equations the reactions are found to be as follows:

$$H_a = 500 \text{ lb}\leftarrow; \quad V_a = 250 \text{ lb}\uparrow; \quad H_c = 500 \text{ lb}\rightarrow; \quad V_c = 250 \text{ lb}\uparrow$$

Similarly, for Fig. 2–15(c), the reaction at A is parallel to AB, and the reactions are:

$$H_a = 200 \text{ lb}\leftarrow; \quad V_a = 0; \quad H_c = 200 \text{ lb}\rightarrow; \quad V_c = 200 \text{ lb}\uparrow$$

For the combined loading;

$$H_a = 500 + 200 = \underline{700 \text{ lb}\leftarrow}$$
$$V_a = 250 + 0 = \underline{250 \text{ lb}\uparrow}$$
$$H_c = 500 + 200 = \underline{700 \text{ lb}\rightarrow}$$
$$V_c = 250 + 200 = \underline{450 \text{ lb}\uparrow}$$

These answers are identical with those obtained in the first solution.

Still another method of analysis is indicated by Figs. 2–16(a) and (b). The four reactions for member AB as a free body are shown with

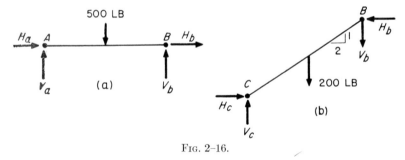

FIG. 2–16.

assumed directions in Fig. 2–16(a). Since the reactions at end B of member AB are provided by end B of member BC, the reactions V_b and H_c of member BC are the same as those for member AB but of opposite direction. Thus the directions of V_b and H_b are assumed in a consistent manner for each free body. If equilibrium equations are written for each of the two free bodies, there will be enough equations to permit simultaneous solution for the six unknowns shown.

2–6. Stability and Statical Determinateness. It is usual to determine whether a structure is stable or unstable, and whether statically determinate or statically indeterminate *before* computing the reactions.

Discussion of the subject is held till this point, however, since this topic is so much easier to understand after having studied and practiced the solving of reactions.

A stable structure is one that will remain in its original position, except for slight changes due to the elastic stretching or shortening of its material, regardless of the position or direction of loading. For example, the simple beam of Fig. 2–17(a) is stable for any position or

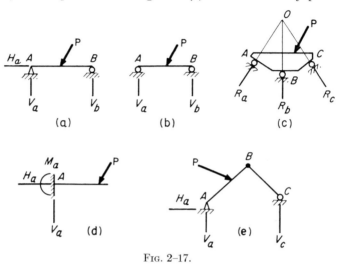

Fig. 2–17.

direction of the load P; for any loading, the reactions shown can satisfy the equations of equilibrium. For the beam of Fig. 2–17(b), however, it is impossible to satisfy the equation $\Sigma H = 0$ except for vertical loads. With the load shown, the beam would move to the left. The body of Fig. 2–17(c) is unstable except for loads whose line of action passes through point O, since satisfaction of the equation $\Sigma M = 0$ is impossible. If loaded as shown, the body would start to rotate clockwise. The three reactions shown for the cantilever beam of Fig. 2–17(d) are sufficient to satisfy the equilibrium equations, and the beam is stable. The hinged member of Fig. 2–17(e) is unstable. The load would cause member AB to rotate clockwise about point A, and C of member BC would move to the right; and the structure would collapse. If the support at C were changed to a pinned support, providing a total of four reactions, the structure would become stable. [See Fig. 2–14(a).]

With the aid of the examples just shown, the following general requirements for external stability of plane structures can be established:

1. *The number of reactions must be equal to or more than the number of equilibrium equations plus condition equations.*

    2. *The reactions must include at least two non-parallel forces.*

    3. *If all the reactions are forces, they must not all be concurrent.*

If any of these conditions is not met, the structure is unstable.

A structure is statically determinate (externally) if the unknown reactions can all be solved using only static equations. Thus, if a stable structure has unknown reactions equal in number to the equilibrium equations plus condition equations, the structure is statically determinate. If there are more reactions than static equations (equilibrium plus condition), the structure is statically indeterminate. To solve for the reactions of such structures, additional equations are required; the additional equations are elastic equations involving the elastic deformations of the structure.

The beam of Fig. 2–18(a) has three reactions. Three equations can be written, therefore the beam is statically determinate. The beam of Fig. 2–18(b) has five reactions, but only three static equations can be

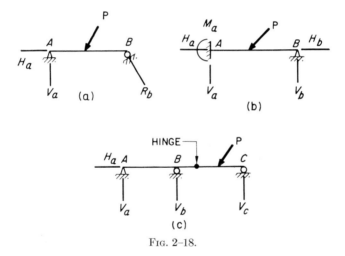

Fig. 2–18.

written. Two elastic equations would be required, therefore the beam is said to be statically indeterminate to the second degree. The structure of Fig. 2–18(c) has four reactions. Three equilibrium equations and one condition equation can be written, making a total of four equations. The structure is statically determinate.

It is advisable to check for stability and statical determinateness before attempting to solve for the reactions. If the check shows the structure to be unstable, the support conditions can be corrected before proceeding with the analysis. The correct procedure for analysis is indicated when it is known whether the structure is statically determinate or statically indeterminate. Time may often be saved, particularly on more complex problems, when this knowledge is obtained in advance.

The determination of stability and statical determinateness, as just discussed, applies only to external conditions and to structures and forces in one plane. In a later chapter, the effect of the internal framework will be considered.

2-7. Graphical Solution of Reactions. The fact that the resultant of the reactions is equal and opposite to the resultant of the applied forces makes the graphical solution of reactions possible. The graphical solution is not difficult. However, the cases in which the graphical solution is more convenient than a mathematical solution are rare. For this reason, the graphical solution for reactions is not explained in this text. (Later in the text, however, both the mathematical and graphical solutions are considered for trusses, since truss problems are often solved more easily by graphical means than by mathematical.) For information about the graphical solution of reactions, the student is referred to other texts on structural theory, or on graphic statics.

PROBLEMS

2-1. Solve for the reactions of the beam shown by Fig. 2–19. Distributed loads so shown are toward the member unless otherwise noted.

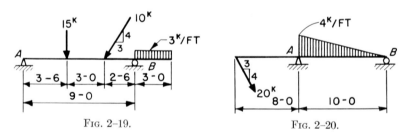

FIG. 2–19.   FIG. 2–20.

2-2. Solve for the reactions of the beam shown by Fig. 2–20.

2-3. The owner of the building shown by Fig. 2–21 plans to add a penthouse and air-conditioning equipment as shown. The strength of the structure should be checked before this new load is added. In checking the strength of the connections the maximum reactions must be determined. What is the maximum total reaction on (a) a purlin, and (b) a truss? (c) What is the maximum column load?

Data not shown on the drawing are: snow load, 25 lb per sq ft of horizontal projection; weight of air-conditioning equipment, 3,000 lb; weight of penthouse framing and cover, 1,000 lb; truss weight about 3,000 lb per truss.

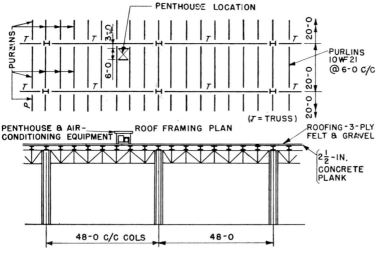

Fig. 2–21.

2–4. Compute the reactions for the structure shown in Fig. 2–22.

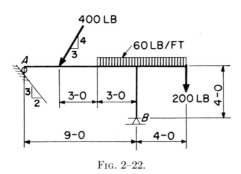

Fig. 2–22.

2–5. Fig. 2–23 shows the proposed installation of a jib crane to the column of an existing building. Such a crane can have a very serious effect on the column. Compute the forces applied to the column by the crane when the hoist and load are in the position shown. Use the AISC recommended allowance for impact. The lifted load is one ton, hoist and trolley weight 500 lb, and boom weight 350 lb. The column is 12 in. wide.

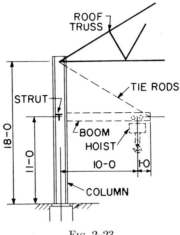

FIG. 2–23.

2-6. A hoisting arrangement is made as shown in Fig. 2–24. The derrick is

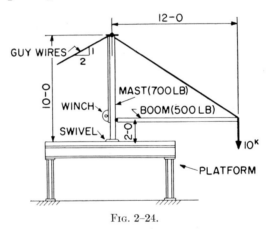

FIG. 2–24.

mounted on an existing platform and is guyed to buried "dead men" of concrete.

a) Compute the reactions of the derrick.
b) What forces are applied to the platform?
c) What is the obvious structural defect of the arrangement shown?

2–7. Compute the reactions for the structure of Fig. 2–25.

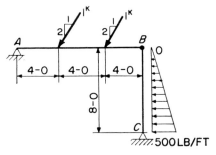

Fig. 2–25.

2–8. For each of the structures shown by Fig. 2–26, determine whether stable or unstable. If the structure is stable, determine whether statically determinate or statically indeterminate. If it is statically indeterminate, to what degree?

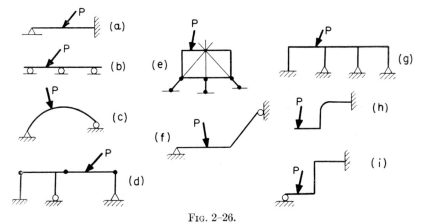

Fig. 2–26.

CHAPTER 3

SHEAR, THRUST, AND BENDING MOMENT

3–1. Analysis of Internal Stress Conditions. A loaded structural member is shown by Fig. 3–1(a). Assume that a knowledge of the internal stress conditions at section A–A is desired. To permit determination of these conditions, the member is imagined to be cut at section

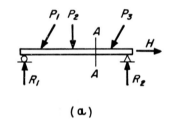

(a)

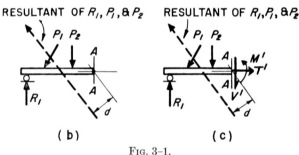

RESULTANT OF R_1, P_1, & P_2 RESULTANT OF R_1, P_1, & P_2

(b)   (c)

Fig. 3–1.

A–A. One portion (either one) is then considered to be isolated from the other and is analyzed as a free body. The portion to the left of the cut is shown by Fig. 3–1(b). Obviously the external forces acting on that portion are not in equilibrium. If the left portion were acted upon only by the forces shown, it would rotate clockwise about the center of section A–A, and would move upward and to the left.

Yet when the left portion is attached to the right one, no such movement occurs. Therefore, the right portion actually exerts on the left such force and moment as are required to keep the left portion in equilibrium. These internal forces T' and V' and the moment M' are illustrated in Fig. 3–1(c). The amounts of each can be determined using the equations of equilibrium for the portion shown.

The resultant of the external forces R_1, P_1, and P_2 is shown dotted. The vertical component of this resultant is called the *shear* at the section. It would cause the isolated portion to move parallel to the cut or transverse to the axis of the member. The *shear* V is balanced by the *resisting shear* V'.

The horizontal component of the dotted resultant is called the *thrust* at the section. The effect of the *thrust* T is balanced by the effect of the *resisting thrust* T'.

The dotted resultant tends to rotate the left portion about the center of section A–A with a moment equal to the product of the resultant and the distance d. This moment is called the *bending moment* M at the section. Its effect is balanced by that of the *resisting moment* M'.

When the shear, thrust, and bending moment at a section are known, the unit stresses in the material can be computed and the safety of the structure determined. It is important that an engineer have an accurate understanding of shear, thrust, and bending moment, and that he be familiar with their computation. Nothing is so crippling to one who must solve structural problems as an inadequate knowledge of this phase of structural theory. The student should give special attention to this chapter. He should solve as many of the problems as practical, since it is only through practice that his skill is developed.

3–2. Definitions. An understanding of shear, thrust, and bending moment is made easier by reference to accurate definitions. Actual memorization of the following definitions may be helpful to most students.

Shear: Shear at a section is the algebraic sum of all the force components parallel to the section and acting on the member to one side only of the section.

Thrust: Thrust at a section is the algebraic sum of all the force components perpendicular to the section and acting on the member to one side only of the section.

Bending Moment: Bending moment at a section is the algebraic sum of any applied moments and of the moments of all forces acting on the member on one side only of the section, taken about the center of gravity of the section.

These definitions should be carefully studied until they are completely understood. It is important to notice the word "all" in each of the definitions. The most frequent error made in computing bending moment is the failure to consider one of the forces. Also, it should be noted that forces and moments applied to *one side only* are considered. *Either* side may be used, provided the forces and moments considered are all on the same side of the cut and provided *all* forces and moments on that side are considered.

3–3. Algebraic Signs. It is often convenient to use algebraic signs to indicate the sense of the shear, thrust, and moment. While other sign conventions are possible, the following is most commonly used:

1. Shear is positive when the resultant V of the transverse forces and the resisting shear force V' form a clockwise couple. (Thus, the shear at section $A–A$ of Fig. 3–1 is positive.)
2. Thrust is positive when it causes an internal tensile force T' to be developed in the member. (Thus, the thrust is positive at section $A–A$ of Fig. 3–1.)
3. Bending moment is positive when, acting without thrust, it would cause compression to exist on the top side of the member. [In Fig. 3–1(c), the resisting moment M' is caused by couples consisting of compressive stresses pushing against the face of the upper part of the section and tensile stresses pulling against the lower part of the section. Thus, the bending moment at section $A–A$ is positive.]

The student should realize that the sign for shear is a matter of viewpoint. For example, a person viewing the member of Fig. 3–1 from the other side (from the back of the sheet) would describe the shear at section $A–A$ as negative. Also, the sign for bending moment is rather meaningless as defined above when the member is vertical or curved. The important thing is to know which side of the member is stressed in compression by the bending moment. This fact will become clear when the articles about shear and bending moment diagrams are studied.

3–4. Shear and Bending Moment Values for Common Loadings. A simple beam having a concentrated load P is shown by Fig. 3–2(a). The reactions are given in terms of the load P and the dimensions a,

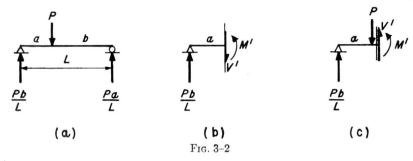

(a)   (b)   (c)

Fig. 3–2

b, and L. The portion to the left of the load is shown as a free body in
Fig. 3–2(b). A downward resisting shear V' and a counterclockwise
resisting moment M' are required to maintain equilibrium. The definitions given are used to obtain the following values at a section just
to the left of the load:

$$\text{Shear: } V = \frac{Pb}{L}$$

$$\text{Bending Moment: } M = \frac{Pab}{L}$$

At a section just to the right of the load, as shown by Fig. 3–2(c),

$$V = -\frac{Pa}{L}$$

and

$$M = \frac{Pab}{L}$$

The student should confirm these values. For the special case of a
concentrated load at the center of the span L, dimensions a and b are
each equal to $L/2$, so that

$$V = \frac{P}{2} \text{ left of the load}$$

or

$$-\frac{P}{2} \text{ right of the load}$$

and

$$M = \frac{PL}{4} \text{ at the load}$$

Fig. 3–3(a) shows a simple beam having a uniform load of amount
w per unit of length. The entire load on the beam is wL and the vertical
reactions are each $wL/2$. The beam is imagined to be cut at a distance

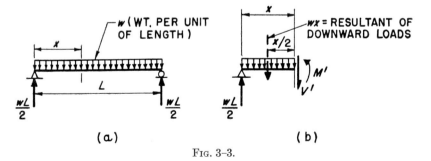

(a)   (b)

Fig. 3–3.

x from the left end. One portion is shown isolated in Fig. 3–3(b). Using the definitions, the shear and bending moment at distance x from the end are

$$V = \frac{wL}{2} - wx$$

and

$$M = \frac{wLx}{2} - \frac{wx^2}{2}$$

Note that the effects of both the reaction and the downward load between the end and the section are included.

At the center of the span, the distance x is $L/2$, so that

$$V = \frac{wL}{2} - \frac{wL}{2} = 0$$

and

$$M = \frac{wL^2}{4} - \frac{wL^2}{8} = \frac{wL^2}{8}$$

It will be very helpful to remember the values for centerline bending moment as developed for the two simple cases above. Values for many other common loadings are given by handbooks such as *Steel Construction*, published by the American Institute of Steel Construction. An experienced engineer can often save time by using these formulas. The beginner is cautioned, however, against the indiscriminate use of formulas. One who does not thoroughly understand the derivation and meaning of a formula can easily make serious errors by using it. Also, many complex loadings are not covered by handbook formulas. A good engineer is able to compute bending moments and shears for *any* type of loading. Such skill is not obtained by using the handbook formulas as "crutches." It is advisable for the student to avoid the use of the handbook formulas, except for those of the two simple cases given above. Thus he can develop the skill which makes possible his solution of the more difficult problems. After he has obtained that skill, his use of handbook formulas as time savers becomes sound engineering practice.

3–5. Superposition.   The principle of superposition is as follows:

> If a member is subjected to a number of loads, the sum of the stresses (or displacements) at any point due to these loads applied separately is equal to the stress (or displacement) that would occur at that point if all the loads were applied simultaneously, provided the material is not stressed beyond its elastic limit.

This principle can often be used to simplify the determination of shears, thrusts, and bending moments due to combinations of simple loadings. Its use will be illustrated by Example 3–2.

EXAMPLE 3-1.   A beam with both concentrated and uniform loads is shown by Fig. 3-4(a). Compute the bending moment and shear on a section just to the left of the 7-kip load.

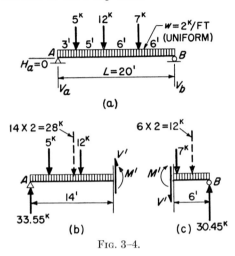

FIG. 3-4.

The reactions are determined first.

$$M_a = -20V_b + (3 \times 5) + (8 \times 12) + (14 \times 7) + (10 \times 20 \times 2)$$
$$= 0 \qquad\qquad V_b = 30.45 \text{ kips} \uparrow$$
$$M_b = +20V_a - (17 \times 5) - (12 \times 12) - (6 \times 7) - (10 \times 20 \times 2)$$
$$= 0 \qquad\qquad V_a = \underline{33.55} \text{ kips} \uparrow$$
$$64.00 \uparrow$$

$$5 + 12 + 7 + 40 = 64 \downarrow \quad \text{(Checks by } \Sigma V = 0)$$

The portion to the left of the cut is shown by Fig. 3-4(b). The sum of the external transverse loads on this portion is

$$33.55 - 5 - 28 - 12 = -11.45 \text{ kips}, \quad \text{or} \quad 11.45 \text{ kips downward}$$

Thus V' is upward and the shear $V = -11.45$ kips. (Using the other portion of the beam, shown by Fig. 3-4(c), the sum of the external loads is $30.45 - 7 - 12 = 11.45$ kips upward, and the internal force V' is downward. Thus the shear V is -11.45 kips.)

Using the left portion, the bending moment

$$M = +(33.55 \times 14) - (5 \times 11) - (12 \times 6) - (28 \times 7) = 146.7 \text{ ft-k}$$

(Using the right portion, $M = +(30.45 \times 6) - (12 \times 3) = 146.7$ ft-k)

The above computations for shear and moment were made twice, using first the portion to the left of the section, and then the portion to the right. Ordinarily the computations are made using one portion only.

preferably that portion which gives the easier solution. The repetition is made in this example to illustrate the fact that the same results are obtained regardless of which portion is used, and to suggest an easy method of checking the answers obtained.

EXAMPLE 3–2. In installing a new heating system for a small factory, a plant engineer finds it necessary to suspend a unit heater from the existing roof members. The details are shown by Fig. 3–5. Assuming

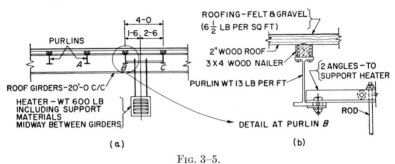

FIG. 3–5.

that the roof live load (from snow) is 25 lb per sq ft, compute the shear next to the end of the purlin and the bending moment at the center of the purlin span. The purlin is a simple beam, supported at its ends by the roof girders.

The solution is shown in computation-sheet form by Fig. 3–6. The first part of the problem is to determine the loads on the purlin. The heater load of 600 lb is distributed to purlins B and C by the action of the support angles $\overline{BC}$ as a simple beam. The reactions of those angles become the loads on the purlins. The larger load occurs on purlin B and equals $600 \times 2.5/4 = 375$ lb. (The support angles themselves comprise so small a part of the 600-lb weight that no appreciable error is caused by assuming the entire 600 lb to act at the centerline of the heater.) The 375-lb load is concentrated at the mid-span of the purlin.

The other loads are uniform, and are tabulated in pounds per foot of purlin. Each foot of purlin receives roof and snow loads from a one-foot strip of roof extending from the center of space AB to the center of space BC.

The problem is thus reduced to an analysis of the simple loading condition shown on the free-body diagram of Fig. 3–6. The loading is a combination of two simpler loadings—a uniform load, and a concentrated load at the center of the span. The principle of superposition is used on the computation sheet for this problem.

EXAMPLE 3–3. A gate covering the inlet to a tank is shown by Fig. 3–7(a). The gate consists of a light steel plate, stiffened by vertical

Effect of Heater on Purlins

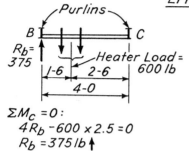

$\Sigma M_C = 0$:

$4R_b - 600 \times 2.5 = 0$

$R_b = 375\,lb\uparrow$

Purlin B Loads:

Conc. -375 lb from heater

Uniform-

Snow, 4×25	=	100.0
Roofing, 4×6.5	=	26.0
Roof Planks,		
$(40\,lb/cf;\ 1\frac{1}{2}\,in.)$		
$4 \times 0.13 \times 40$	=	20.8
Nailer $(2\frac{5}{8} \times 3\frac{5}{8})$		
$\frac{9.5}{144} \times 40$	=	2.6
Purlin	=	13.0
Total	=	162.4

Use 162 lb/ft

Purlin B

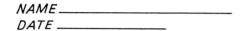

End Shear

Unif. $10 \times 162 = 1,620$

Conc. $\frac{1}{2} \times 375 = \underline{188}$

$V = 1,808\,lb$

℄ Bending Moment

Unif. $\dfrac{162 \times \overline{20}^2}{8} = 8,100$

Conc. $\dfrac{375 \times 20}{4} = 1,875$

$M = 9,975\,ft\text{-}lb$

FIG. 3-6.

bars at 10-in. centers and by horizontal bars at the top and bottom edges. The parts are welded together. The gate is acted upon by the pressure of water in the tank. The inlet tube is assumed to be empty. Compute the shear and bending moment at the center of one of the vertical ribs.

The gate is much longer in one direction than in the other, and is reinforced vertically only. Thus it receives no appreciable support from the vertical edges. The reactions to the water pressure are provided by

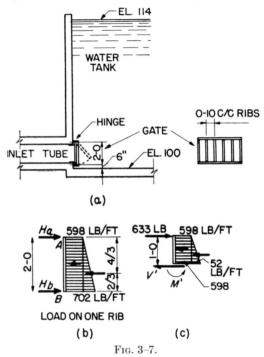

Fig. 3–7.

contact with the tank at the upper and lower edges. Each interior rib is a simple beam, and carries the load from a 10-in. width of gate.

A free-body diagram of one rib is shown by Fig. 3–7(b). The water pressure varies from that of an 11.5-ft head at the top edge to that of a 13.5-ft head at the bottom. The load on one rib varies in intensity from

$$11.5 \times 62.5 \times 10/12 = 598 \text{ lb per lin ft at the top}$$

to

$$13.5 \times 62.5 \times 10/12 = 702 \text{ lb per lin ft at the bottom}$$

For convenience in computation, the load is divided into a uniform load of 598 lb per lin ft, and a load varying from zero to 104 lb per lin ft.

These loads are represented by the rectangle and triangle of Fig. 3–7(b).

$$\Sigma M_a = (598 \times 2 \times 1) + \left(\frac{104 \times 2}{2} \times \frac{4}{3}\right) - 2H_b = 0; \; H_b = \quad 667 \text{ lb}$$

$$\Sigma M_b = -(598 \times 2 \times 1) - \left(\frac{104 \times 2}{2} \times \frac{2}{3}\right) + 2H_a = 0; \; H_a = \quad \underline{633} \text{ lb}$$

$$1{,}196 + 104 = 1{,}300 \text{ lb}$$

$$(\text{Checks by } \Sigma H = 0)$$

The upper half of the beam is shown by Fig. 3–7(c).

$$V = 633 - (598 \times 1) - \left(\frac{52 \times 1}{2}\right) = 9 \text{ lb}$$

$$M = (633 \times 1) - (598 \times 1 \times \tfrac{1}{2}) - \left(\frac{52 \times 1}{2} \times \frac{1}{3}\right)$$

$$= 325 \text{ ft-lb, compression on the right side}$$

3–6. Shear and Moment Diagrams.   Graphs can be constructed showing the amounts of shear and bending moment at all sections along a member. These graphs are called "shear diagrams" and "moment diagrams." Samples of the diagrams are shown by Fig. 3–8(a) and (b).

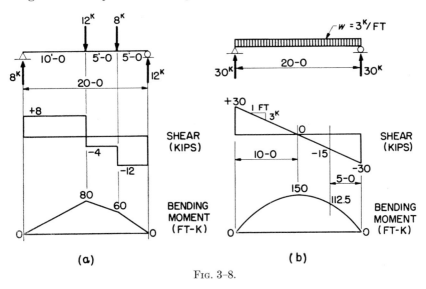

Fig. 3–8.

An ordinate gives the amount of shear or bending moment existing in the member at the location of that ordinate. For example, at a section 5 ft from the right end of the uniformly loaded beam the shear is −15 kips and the bending moment is 112.5 ft-kips. The student should check the diagrams by comparing the ordinates with computed values at a few points on each beam.

At first, it may seem that shear and moment diagrams are of academic interest only. Such is not the case. They are very valuable tools of structural engineering. Among their uses are the following:

1. To aid in locating the points of maximum bending moment
2. To aid in determining the size and spacing of welds or rivets in built-up members
3. To aid in locating stiffeners for beam webs
4. To aid in determining the length and location of cover plates or reinforcing plates for built-up beams
5. To aid in determining the location and amount of steel bars in reinforced concrete members
6. To aid in computing deflections and rotations of members under load

Many of these uses will be illustrated in the ensuing chapters.

For some purposes the diagrams should be drawn to scale, while for others a sketch is sufficient. Their intelligent use should permit time to be saved in actual engineering work.

3–7. Relationships of Load, Shear, and Moment. The shear and moment diagrams can be drawn by plotting enough points to show clearly the nature of the curves. The work involved, however, can be lessened by a knowledge of the relationships of load, shear, and bending moment. The following relationships are illustrated by the curves of Figs. 3–8(a) and (b):

1. Where only concentrated loads occur
   a) The shear diagram is horizontal between loads
   b) The change of shear at a section is equal to the load at the section, and
   c) The moment diagram is straight between loads
2. Where distributed loads occur, the shear diagram is sloped and the moment diagram is curved.
3. The *intensity* of load (force per unit length) is equal to the slope of the shear diagram at that section. (Where there is no load, the shear diagram is horizontal. At a concentrated load, the load intensity is infinity and the shear diagram is vertical. Where the load intensity is 3 kips per ft, the slope of the shear diagram is 3 kips per ft.)
4. The shear is equal to the slope of the moment diagram. (Refer to Fig. 3–9. The bending moment at section 1 is $M = R(a + x) - Fx = aR + Vx$. At a distance dx to the right

of section 1, $M' = R(a + x + dx) - F(x + dx) - dF\,dx/2$.
The last term is practically zero, so that $M' = aR + Vx + V\,dx$.
The change of moment, $M' - M$ is $dM = V\,dx$. The rate of
change of moment is $dM/dx = V$.)

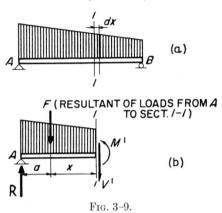

FIG. 3–9.

5. The difference of bending moment between two sections equals
   the area of the shear diagram between those sections. (This
   is obtained by integration of the equation $dM = V\,dx$. The
   relationship is illustrated by the curves of Fig. 3–8. For example,
   the difference between the end and centerline bending moments
   in Fig. 3–8(b) is $\frac{1}{2} \times 30 \times 10 = 150$ ft-k.)
6. The maximum (or minimum) bending moment occurs where
   the shear is zero. (At maximum and minimum points the slope
   of the moment diagram is zero, or the slope changes from positive
   to negative.)

An exception exists to items 4, 5, and 6 above. If one of the loads
on the member is an applied moment, the moment diagram will have
an abrupt offset equal to the applied moment load. Thus in item 5, the
difference in bending moment will equal the area of the shear diagram
plus any moment load applied between the two sections. This type of
loading will be illustrated by Example 3–6.

EXAMPLE 3–4.   Draw shear and moment diagrams for the beam of
Fig. 3–10(a).

The reactions at A and E are computed and are found to be 12.5
kips and 9.5 kips, respectively. The shear is determined starting at the
left end. For all sections from A to B, the sum of the transverse loads
to the left is 12.5 kips. At those sections the shear is 12.5 kips. Moving
toward the right, a change of shear equal to 10 kips occurs as point B
is passed; at that point the shear changes to 2.5 kips. No further change

occurs until point C, where the shear drops by 8 kips to a value of
-5.5 kips. At point D, a further drop of 4 kips changes the shear to
-9.5 kips. Continuing to the right, as point E is passed, the 9.5 kip
reaction changes the shear to zero.

The point of maximum bending moment is C, a point at which the
shear is zero. If the maximum were the only bending moment required,
a moment diagram would not need to be drawn. The shear diagram

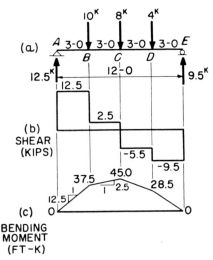

F<small>IG</small>. 3–10.

would have served its purpose in merely locating the point of maximum
bending moment.

The moment diagram is straight between loads. Ordinates will be
computed for the load points only.

At A, $M_a = 0$

At B, $M_b = 12.5 \times 3 = 37.5$ ft-k

At C, $M_c = (12.5 \times 6) - (10 \times 3) = 45.0$ ft-k

At D, $M_d = 9.5 \times 3 = 28.5$ ft-k

At E, $M_e = 0$

The above computation of bending moments is merely an exact
application of the definition for bending moment given in Art. 3–2.
The relationships between shear and bending moment could have been
applied to obtain the same values. For example, M_a is zero, therefore
the bending moment at C is the area of the shear diagram between A
and C, or

$$M_c = (12.5 \times 3) + (2.5 \times 3) = 45.0 \text{ ft-k}$$

Similarly,

$$M_d = M_c - (5.5 \times 3) = 28.5 \text{ ft-k}$$

The slope of each segment of the moment diagram is equal to the shear at that location.

EXAMPLE 3–5. A transformer weighing 15,000 lb is to be placed on a concrete floor slab. To avoid cracking the slab, a series of steel beams is used to distribute the 15,000-lb weight over a larger floor area. The transformer and beams are shown by Fig. 3–11(a). Draw the shear and moment diagrams for one beam.

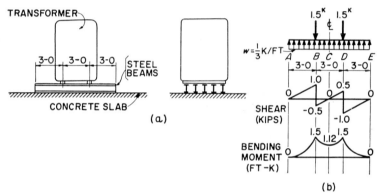

FIG. 3–11.

If the beams are properly designed, their bending deformation will be so slight that the upward pressure of the concrete slab on the beams can be considered uniform. The upward force per linear foot of one beam will be

$$w = \frac{15}{5 \times 9} = \frac{1}{3} \text{ kip per ft}$$

The weight of the beam itself increases this force. However, it does not affect either the shear or the bending moment of the beam. Hence, the weight of the beam is not considered in this problem. The loads for one beam are shown by Fig. 3–11(b).

The shear diagram is drawn starting at the left end. The shear there is zero, increasing toward the right at the rate of 1/3 kip per foot. An abrupt change of 1.5 kips occurs at the concentrated load. Between B and C the change of shear is again equal to the load per foot. Proceeding similarly, the diagram is completed giving zero shear at point E.

The shear is zero at points A, B, D, and E. These are points of either maximum or minimum M. The bending moments at the end points A

and E are known to be zero. Bending moment M_b is equal to M_a plus the area of the shear diagram between A and B.

$$M_b = 0 + (\tfrac{1}{2} \times 1.0 \times 3) = 1.5 \text{ ft-k, compression on top}$$
$$M_c = 1.5 - (\tfrac{1}{2} \times 0.5 \times 1.5) = 1.12 \text{ ft-k, compression on top}$$
$$M_d = 1.12 + (\tfrac{1}{2} \times 0.5 \times 1.5) = 1.5 \text{ ft-k, compression on top}$$

The direction of curvature of the moment diagram can be determined from the shear values. At A the shear is zero; therefore, the moment diagram has zero slope, or is horizontal. Moving to the right, the shear and the slope of the moment diagram increase. The curve is concave upward as shown. If the distance from end A to some section is called x,

$$M_x = wx \cdot \frac{x}{2} = \frac{wx^2}{2}, \quad \text{between } A \text{ and } B$$

and

$$M_x = \frac{wx^2}{2} - 1.5(x - 3), \quad \text{between } B \text{ and } D$$

Both of these expressions are equations of parabolas. Wherever the load is uniform, the moment diagram is parabolic.

EXAMPLE 3–6. A bracket is added to a building column to provide support for a pipe. The combined weight of the pipe and its contents is

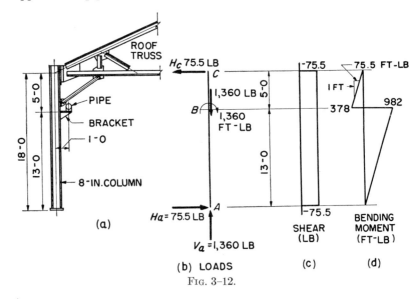

Fig. 3–12.

68 lb per ft. The columns are spaced 20 ft apart, so that each bracket supports 20×68 or 1,360 lb. The column and bracket are shown by

Fig. 3–12(a). The column can be assumed to be pin-connected at the base and at the truss level. Shear and moment diagrams are to be drawn.

The load on the column consists of a downward force of 1,360 lb and a moment of $1,360 \times 1.0 = 1,360$ ft-lb at the bracket location. The free-body diagram is shown by Fig. 3–12(b).

$$\Sigma M_a = -18H_c + 1,360 = 0; \quad H_c = 75.5 \text{ lb} \leftarrow$$
$$H_a = 75.5 \text{ lb} \rightarrow$$
$$V_a = 1,360 \text{ lb} \uparrow$$

No transverse loads other than H_a and H_c occur, so the shear is constant along the entire column. Since the shear is constant, the slope of the moment diagram is also constant, except at the location of the applied moment load.

$$M_a \text{ and } M_c = 0$$

The rate of change of M is $V = 75.5$ ft-lb per foot of length. Thus M at 5 ft 0 in. from C, but slightly above B is

$$75.5 \times 5 = 378 \text{ ft-lb, compression on left}$$

Similarly the bending moment just below B is

$$75.5 \times 13 = 982 \text{ ft-lb, compression on right}$$

The moment diagram of Fig. 3–12(d) shows these values. The abrupt change in bending moment is $378 + 982$, or 1,360 ft-lb, which is the amount of the applied moment load at B.

3–8. Which Method to Use. It is neither necessary nor wise to confine one's self to using one single method in drawing shear and moment diagrams. If an ordinate can be most easily computed by cutting a section and taking moments of the loads on the isolated portion, that method should be used. But, if for another ordinate the use of the relationships of load, shear, and bending moment provides an easier solution, the relationships should be used. The two methods may be used in a single problem if their use makes the solution quicker.

3–9. Points of Contraflexure. The point at which the bending moment changes from positive to negative is called the "point of contraflexure." Fig. 3–13 shows a beam having such a point. To one side of the point, the compression due to bending is on the top of the beam; to the other side of the point, it is on the bottom. The bending moment becomes zero at the point of contraflexure.

It is sometimes desirable to locate the points of contraflexure. (For example, the point of contraflexure is often a suitable location for the splicing of materials. It is the point at which changes in the pattern of concrete reinforcement may occur. A knowledge of its location is sometimes useful in computing deflections, and it is necessary when calculating the resistance of a steel beam to certain types of failure.) The next example will illustrate the determination of its location.

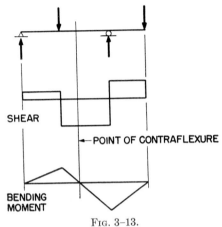

FIG. 3–13.

EXAMPLE 3–7. Draw shear and moment diagrams and locate the point of contraflexure for the beam of Fig. 3–14(a). The live load on the platform is 60 lb per sq ft. A chain hoist is to be attached to the outer end of the beam.

The load per ft of beam consists of the following:

Floor slab weight $10 \times \frac{1}{3} \times 150 = \quad$ 500 lb/ft

Beam weight $\qquad\qquad\qquad\qquad = \quad$ 30 lb/ft

Floor live load $10 \times 60 \qquad\qquad = \quad$ 600 lb/ft

$$w = \overline{1{,}130} \text{ lb/ft}$$

Fig. 3–14(b) shows a free-body diagram. The small portion of load between the extreme left end of the beam and the center of the left support is ignored.

$$\Sigma M_a = (15 \times 1.13 \times 7.5) + (2.2 \times 14.5) - 11 V_b = 0;$$
$$V_b = 14.46 \text{ k} \uparrow$$
$$\Sigma M_b = -(15 \times 1.13 \times 3.5) + (2.2 \times 3.5) + 11 V_a = 0;$$
$$V_a = 4.69 \text{ k} \uparrow$$
$$\text{Check by } \Sigma V: \quad (1.13 \times 15) + 2.2 = \overline{19.15} \text{ k}$$

The shear diagram is constructed in the usual manner. The location of the point of zero shear is determined using the relationship between unit load and slope of the shear diagram. The computation is shown in Fig. 3–14(c).

The bending moments are now determined at a few points, using either sections or the relationships between shear and moment, whichever is more convenient.

At A, $M_a = 0$

At 4.15 ft right of A, $M = \frac{1}{2} \times 4.69 \times 4.15$

$$= 9.75 \text{ ft-k, compression-top}$$

At B, $M_b = (2.2 \times 3.5) + (4 \times 1.13 \times 2)$

$$= 16.75 \text{ ft-k, compression-bottom}$$

At C, $M_c = (0.5 \times 1.13 \times 0.25) = 0.14 \text{ ft-k, compression-bottom}$

Wherever the load is uniform and downward, the moment diagram is parabolic and concave downward (if drawn on the compression side). Plotting the computed ordinates and sketching such a curve between

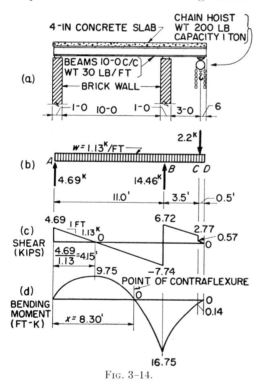

Fig. 3-14.

them, the diagram of Fig. 3–14(d) is obtained. The curve is broken at each concentrated load; i.e., one parabola extends from A to B, one from B to C, and one from C to D. The beam has one point of contraflexure.

There are two ways in which the location of the point of contraflexure could be determined. The curve from A to the contraflexure point is symmetrical about the point of maximum moment. Therefore, the distance x to the point of contraflexure is $2 \times 4.15 = 8.30$ ft. If the curve were not symmetrical, or if the location of the maximum point were not known, a method like that which follows would be used.

At distance x from point A,

$$M_x = 4.69x - \frac{1.13x^2}{2}$$

At the point of contraflexure $M_x = 0$. Setting the above expression for M_x equal to zero, and solving for x gives

$$x = 0, \quad \text{or} \quad 8.30 \text{ ft}$$

Since this value of x places the contraflexure point within the range for which the M_x equation used is correct, the answer of 8.30 ft is

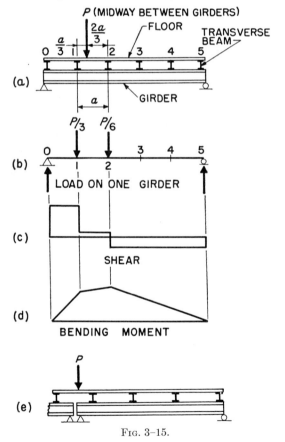

FIG. 3–15.

accepted. (Occasionally a problem will arise for which the value of x obtained is beyond the range of the curve for the equation used. In such cases, a repetition is necessary, using an equation that is correct for the next part of the diagram.)

3–10. Girders Loaded by Transverse Beams. The type of framing shown by Fig. 3–15(a) is quite common. The loads applied to the floor are transferred by the flooring material to the transverse beams. The transverse beams in turn carry the load to the girder. Roofs, building floors, and bridge floors are commonly constructed in this manner.

In analyzing such a girder for the shear and bending moment due to loads applied to the floor, it must be remembered that the load reaches the girder at panel points only. (Panel points are the sections at which transverse members occur.) For example, in Fig. 3–15(a) a load P is applied to the floor between panel points 1 and 2, and midway between two girders. Half of the load P reaches each girder. The load $P/2$ on one girder is applied to the girder as shown in Fig. 3–15(b). The floor material has been assumed to act as a simple beam in distributing the load P between the transverse beams. The shear and bending moment diagrams are as shown by parts (c) and (d) of Fig. 3–15. Note that in the example shown, it is not necessary to consider the actual division of the loads when computing the reactions of the girder. This is true except for loads in the end panel of a girder having no transverse beam at its end. [Fig. 3–15(e).]

The same system is shown with uniform floor load in Fig. 3–16(a). The actual loading of the girder is shown by Fig. 3–16(b). (The term w

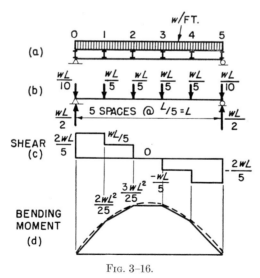

Fɪɢ. 3–16.

Courtesy of Shaw-Box Crane & Hoist Division, Manning, Maxwell & Moore, Inc.

10-Ton Overhead Cranes Serving Materials Storage Yard. Crane Girders Are Supported by A-Frames, Designed to Resist Lateral Loading Caused by Sudden Starting or Stopping of Trolley Motion and by Wind. Bracing Trusses Between A-Frames Prevent Damage by Longitudinal Loadings.

is the load per unit length of girder. For example, if there were only two girders, and if they were 20 ft apart, a uniform load of 100 lb per sq ft of floor would cause w for one girder to be 1,000 lb per lin ft.)

Parts (c) and (d) of Fig. 3–16 show the shear and moment diagrams for the girder. Superimposed on the solid moment curve is a dotted parabola, which represents the moment diagram for a beam receiving the uniform load directly instead of through transverse beams. The bending moment of the girder is the same at panel points as it is for the uniformly loaded beam. This will be true only if there are transverse beams at each end of the girder. If only the bending moment values are required, time may be saved by using the ordinates of the parabola. (Ordinates of a parabola are easily computed by offsets from a tangent to the curve at its maximum ordinate. The offset from this tangent is proportional to the square of the distance from the maximum ordinate.)

3–11. Shear and Moment Diagrams for Frames. A simple frame and its shear and moment diagrams are shown in Fig. 3–17. Members AB and BC are rigidly joined to each other so that no rotation of one

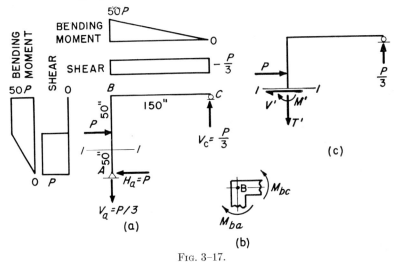

Fig. 3–17.

member with respect to the other can occur at point B. Such members are called "continuous."

No new principles are involved in the shear and moment diagrams for such a structure. The bending moment values at the rigid connection must balance so that the corner material is in equilibrium. For example, if the material at joint B is isolated, as in Fig. 3–17(b), the two moments shown must be equal and opposite. The moment labeled M_{ba} is that applied to the corner material by end B of Beam AB; M_{bc}

is applied by end B of beam BC. Both are shown in such directions as would cause compression on the outside of the frame. Where only two members are joined, the moment diagram has the same ordinate and is on the same side for both members. There is no relationship, however, between the shears in the vertical and horizontal parts of the frame. Loads transverse to the horizontal leg are parallel to the vertical leg. They enter the computations for shear and bending moment at any section of the horizontal leg, and for thrust and bending moment at sections of the vertical leg.

EXAMPLE 3–8. Draw shear and moment diagrams for the frame of Fig. 3–17(a). Determine the thrust for all parts of the frame.

The first step is the determination of the reactions.

$$\Sigma M_a = +50P - 150V_c = 0; \quad V_c = P/3 \uparrow$$
$$\Sigma H = 0; \quad H_a = P \leftarrow$$
$$\Sigma V = 0; \quad V_a = P/3 \downarrow$$

The shear for all sections on the horizontal leg BC is the reaction V_c. The sign is negative, since a portion cut from the horizontal leg would show V_c upward on the right and a resisting shear V' downward on the cut section. The forces V_c and V' are a counterclockwise couple.

A uniform shear indicates a straight line for the moment curve. The ordinate above B is $150 \times V_c = 50P$, compression on top.

For the vertical leg, shear equal to H_a or $+ P$ exists from the bottom to the mid-point. Between the mid-point and the top, the shear is zero, therefore the value of M is constant in that length. M at mid-height

Courtesy of Chicago Bridge and Iron Co.

HORTONSPHERES OF 3,000 BBL CAPACITY, DESIGNED FOR 45-PSI PRESSURE.

is $50 \times H_a$ or $50P$, compression on the left. These values are shown on the diagrams of Fig. 3–17(a).

If the structure is cut anywhere between B and C, and either half treated as a free body, it is seen that the thrust T for sections between B and C is zero. If the cut is between A and B, however, the thrust T' required to keep either portion in equilibrium is a tensile force (pull) of $P/3$. This is illustrated by Fig. 3–17(c). The thrust in the vertical leg is $+ P/3$.

EXAMPLE 3–9. The frame of a heavy trailer is shown by Fig. 3–18(a). The trailer is pulled by a truck and is carrying a machine weighing 12,000 lb. Draw the diagrams for shear and moment due to the live load.

A free-body diagram of the trailer frame is shown in Fig. 3–18(b). The loads are 6 kips at point C and 6 kips at point D. The reactions at B and G are computed below.

$$\Sigma M_b = +(12 \times 7.5) - 19V_g = 0; \quad V_g = 4.73 \text{ kips} \uparrow$$
$$\Sigma M_g = -(12 \times 11.5) + 19V_b = 0; \quad V_b = 7.27 \text{ kips} \uparrow$$
$$12.00 = \overline{12.00} \text{ (Checks by } \Sigma V = 0)$$

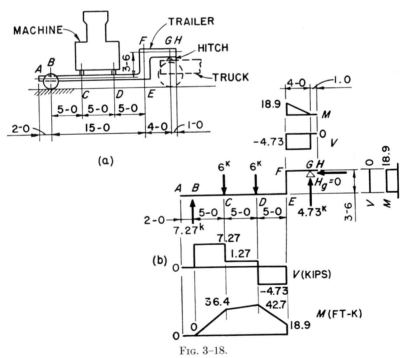

FIG. 3–18.

The shear diagrams are constructed first, starting at end A and proceeding right to point E for member AE, etc. The shear is zero for all sections on the vertical member *EF*. The moment diagrams are easily drawn by starting at points of known zero bending moment and by using the relationships between shear and bending moment to obtain ordinates for the other sections.

PROBLEMS

3–1. For the structure in Fig. 3–19, compute the shear:

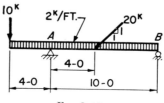

FIG. 3–19.

a) Just to the right of support *A*
b) Just to the left of the point of application of the inclined load

3–2. For the structure of Fig. 3–19, compute the bending moment at:
a) Support *A*
b) The point of application of the inclined load

3–3. For the structure of Fig. 3–19, what is the maximum thrust (axial load), and in what portion of the beam length does it occur?

3–4. Assuming the purlins to weigh 21 lb per lin ft, and snow load of 20 lb per sq ft of horizontal projection, what is the maximum bending moment for a purlin of the building in Fig. 1–8 (Problem 1–1)?

3–5. A new stairway is to be built for access to a mezzanine office and locker room. The stairway is shown by Fig. 3–20. The width is 3 ft 6 in. The sup- port for the treads is provided by one beam along each side of the stairway. What is the maximum bending moment for one of these beams? Use the

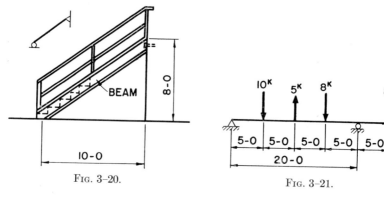

FIG. 3–20.

FIG. 3–21.

recommended live load for first-floor corridors, and assume the total dead load to be 70 lb per lin ft of horizontal projection.

3–6. Draw shear and moment diagrams for the beam of Fig. 3–21.

3–7. Draw shear and moment diagrams for one purlin at the location of the new air-conditioning equipment in Fig. 2–21 (Problem 2–3). Assume the weight of the equipment and penthouse to be supported by the short added beams shown on the roof framing plan. These in turn transmit the load to the purlins.

3–8. Fig. 3–22 shows the plan view of a beam placed over a space between two buildings for the support of a power line. Assume the tension in each wire to be 400 lb. Draw diagrams for the shear and bending moment due to the wire pulls.

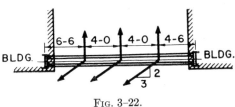

FIG. 3–22.

3–9. Fig. 3–23 shows a plan for supporting three transformers in an existing factory building. The transformers weigh about 5 kips each. Their load

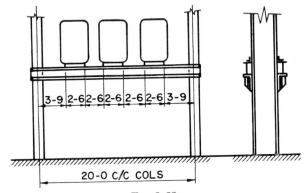

FIG. 3–23.

reaches the supporting beams as uniform load over a length of 2 ft 6 in. for each transformer. Draw shear and moment diagrams for one of the two supporting beams.

3–10. For the maximum bending moment in the beam of Problem 3–9, what percentage of error is caused by assuming each transformer load to be concentrated at the center of the transformer?

3-11. Fig. 3–24 shows a beam with its shear diagram and moment diagram. Solve for the missing dimensions, shears, loads and reactions. (While this "back-

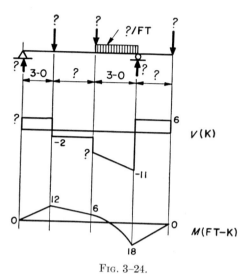

Fig. 3–24.

ward" type of problem is seldom encountered in practice; it serves as a good test of one's knowledge regarding the relationships of load, shear, and bending moment.)

3-12. An air cylinder is used for rapid raising and lowering of baskets of parts into a cleaning tank. The cylinder is to be supported by a horizontal beam. The beam is supported by the building trusses. The arrangement is shown in Fig. 3–25. As a first step in selecting the beam, draw the shear and mo-

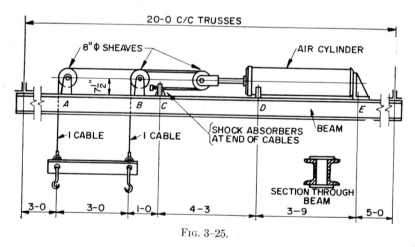

Fig. 3–25.

ment diagrams. The cylinder weight is 500 lb. The lifted load is 500 lb and impact is 100 per cent. Neglect the weight of the beam itself. The brackets at A, B, C, and E can resist both horizontal and vertical components of force. The support for the air cylinder at D provides vertical support only. The beam is 12 in. deep.

3–13. Draw shear and moment diagrams for the beam of Fig. 2–19 (Problem 2–1). Locate the point of contraflexure.

3–14. Draw shear and moment diagrams for the girder of Fig. 3–26.

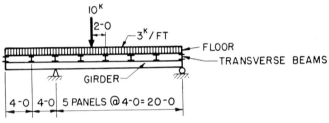

Fɪɢ. 3–26.

3–15. The cross section of a building is shown in Fig. 3–27. The roof is designed for a snow load of 20 lb per sq ft of horizontal projection. Revisions in the manufacturing process require that four 10-in. pipes be carried along the building just below the rafter. The pipes will weigh about 57 lb per lin ft each. The liquid to be carried has a specific gravity of about 1.2. As plant engineer, you are required to check the strength of the rafter and its connections. Draw the shear and moment diagrams for the rafter under full loading.

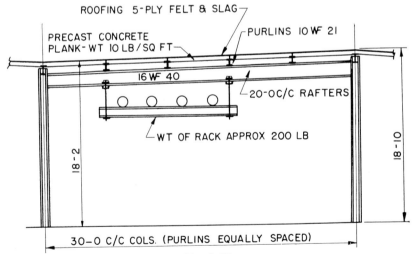

Fɪɢ. 3–27.

3–16. Draw shear and moment diagrams for the frame of Fig. 3–28.

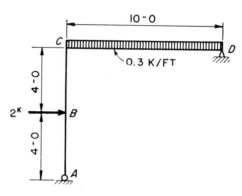

Fig. 3–28.

3–17. Fig. 3–29 shows the framework for a cupola charger designed to travel suspended from an overhead rail. The weight of the bottom-dump bucket and its contents is about 1,000 lb. The cab and operator will weigh about 800 lb and can be assumed as concentrated at point A. Neglecting the weight of the frame itself, draw shear and moment diagrams for the frame.

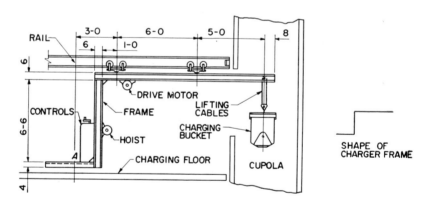

Fig. 3–29.

3–18. A new tank is to be built above an existing pit. The method of supporting the tank is shown in Fig. 3–30. Frames consisting of two vertical members

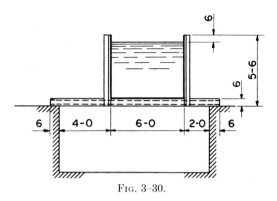

Fig. 3–30.

welded to a horizontal beam span the existing pit. The frames are placed at 3-ft centers along the tank. The tank will contain water. Draw the live-load shear and moment diagrams for one frame.

CHAPTER 4

ANALYSIS OF TRUSSES AND BRACING[1]

4–1. Nature and Purpose of Trusses. The structural framework shown by Fig. 4–1(a) is called a truss. A truss is merely an assembly of short members, connected to each other so that the spaces between

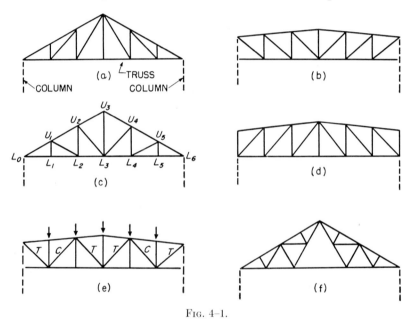

Fig. 4–1.

them are triangular. The members are usually subject to direct axial (thrust) tensile or compressive stresses only. Shear and bending stresses are either negligible or absent.

Individual members of a truss are called "bars." They are usually made from angles, channels, or tubes. In larger trusses the members are often built-up members, consisting of angles, plates, and other sections connected together. Typical cross sections for truss members are shown by Fig. 4–2(a).

[1] The work in this chapter will be made easier if the student obtains an engineer's scale, although an architect's scale can be used, if necessary.

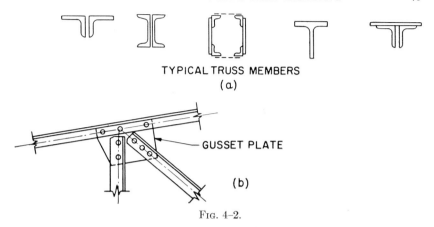

TYPICAL TRUSS MEMBERS
(a)

GUSSET PLATE

(b)

FIG. 4-2.

The points where the truss bars intersect are called "joints." The joints are often labeled according to their position on the truss. The upper joints are labeled with a letter U and the lower ones with a letter L. The number of spaces from the left end is given by a number. The joints of the truss in Fig. 4–1(c) are labeled in this manner.

The bars entering a joint are usually connected to a "gusset plate." A detail of this type is shown in Fig. 4–2(b).

Loads are usually applied to trusses at the joints only. When this is the case, the points of load application are called "panel points." The space between successive panel points is a "panel"; the distance between them is a "panel length."

The bars along the top of a truss form the "top chord"; the individual members are called "top chord members." Those along the bottom of the truss form the "bottom chord" and are referred to as "bottom chord members." The members between the top and bottom chords are called "web members." They can usually be further described as "web verticals" or "web diagonals."

It was stated earlier that the stresses in the bars of a truss are primarily tension or compression. Yet the function of the truss as a whole is the same as that of a beam. Its function is to resist transverse loads. The truss is used in place of the beam whenever it is more practical for reasons of lightness, economy, or rigidity. For example, imagine a roof truss of the type shown in Fig. 4–1(a) having a span of 60 ft. If the trusses are 20 ft apart, each truss would be subject to the dead loads and live loads from a 20-ft by 60-ft roof area. It would require a very heavy beam to support these roof loads on a 60-ft span. A truss for the same span and loads would be lighter than the beam, more rigid, and probably less expensive. The truss would be used, provided special architectural or detail requirements did not prevent its use.

Structures are sometimes subject to appreciable horizontal loads. Trusses may be used in such cases to replace horizontal beams, since their depth gives the trusses rigidity which helps them to brace the structure effectively.

The use of trusses extends to an amazing variety of structures. Their use in bridges and in the roofs of industrial buildings are, of course, most obvious ones. In buildings, trusses may also replace beams in any part of the structure. They may be used in the support of floors, tanks, furnaces, or heavy machines. The framework of heavy machines often includes trusses. Other examples are found in airplane fuselages, aircraft engine mounts, electrical substations, transmission towers, heavy gates, farm machinery, conveyor supports, derrick booms, truck frames, and cranes. The reader could likely extend this list himself by careful observation in any industrial plant.

4–2. Common Types of Truss. There is no limit to the number of possible arrangements of truss bars. A few of the simpler arrangements function so well, however, that they find frequent use. The types shown by Fig. 4–1 are commonly used as roof trusses. Those of parts (a) and (b) are called "Pratt" trusses. The Pratt truss, when uniformly loaded, has tensile stress in the web diagonals. Those of parts (c) and (d) are "Howe" trusses. The Howe truss under uniform load has its web diagonals in compression. The Warren truss of Fig. 4–1(e) has the diagonals in alternating positions. When uniform load is applied the

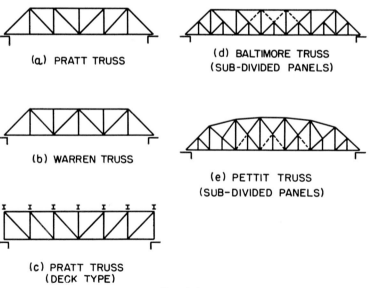

(a) PRATT TRUSS

(b) WARREN TRUSS

(c) PRATT TRUSS
(DECK TYPE)

(d) BALTIMORE TRUSS
(SUB-DIVIDED PANELS)

(e) PETTIT TRUSS
(SUB-DIVIDED PANELS)

Fig. 4–3.

diagonals between the center and the end have alternate types of stress—one tension, the next compression, and so on. The truss of part (*f*) is the Fink truss. The flat-topped Pratt (b), the Howe (c), the flat-topped Warren (e), and the Fink (*f*) are used more than any other types of roof truss.

Fig. 4–3 shows a few common types of bridge truss. Those of Figs. 4–3(a), (b), and (c) are suitable for shorter spans. For longer spans, however, it is sometimes necessary to subdivide the panels. In this way excessively long floor members can be avoided. One possible arrangement with subdivided panels is the Baltimore truss shown by Fig. 4–3(d). For appearance and economy reasons, larger trusses may be of variable depth. One such truss is the Pettit truss of Fig. 4–3(e).

Trusses are classified also as single-plane or double-plane trusses. The difference can be seen by the cross sections of Fig. 4–4. In the single-plane truss, one gusset plate is used at each joint. The members are usually placed symmetrically as shown by Fig. 4–4(a). Most building

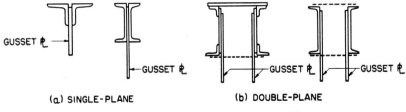

(a) SINGLE-PLANE   (b) DOUBLE-PLANE

SECTIONS THROUGH TOP CHORD AT JOINTS

FIG. 4–4.

trusses are of this type. When the top chord members are very heavy, the double-plane arrangement is used. In it, two gusset plates are used at a joint. Bridge trusses are usually double-plane trusses. An occasional heavy building truss may also be double-plane.

4–3. Mathematical Analysis of Trusses. In the usual methods of truss analysis, two assumptions are made, as follows:

1. The bars are pin connected at each joint.
2. The deformations of the truss are negligible.

It is best to discuss these assumptions briefly before proceeding. The reason for assuming pin connections at each end of each bar is, frankly, that it makes the mathematical analysis easy. Part (a) of Fig. 4–5 shows a pin-connected truss. The dotted lines indicate the original position; the solid lines indicate the position after loading. The bars have been either shortened or lengthened, but they are still straight. If the bars were so connected, then only axial tension or compression could exist in the bar. Shear and bending moment could not occur.

Courtesy of Link-Belt Co.

COAL-HANDLING SYSTEM. AT LEFT, COAL IS RAISED FROM PIT BY BUCKET ELEVATOR AND MOVED BY SCREW CONVEYOR TO HOPPER. AT RIGHT, SKIP HOIST RAISES COAL FROM STORAGE PILE TO HOPPER. NOTE TRUSS USED TO SUPPORT SCREW CONVEYOR AND CATWALK.

Courtesy of Link-Belt Co.

STRUCTURAL SUPPORTS FOR MOTOR-DRIVEN BELT CONVEYOR AT IRON ORE CONCENTRATING PLANT. VERTICAL-PLANE TRUSSES RESIST VERTICAL LOADS. A HORIZONTAL TRUSS AT THE BOTTOM-CHORD LEVEL RESISTS WIND AND ACCIDENTAL LATERAL LOADS. THE CATWALK IS SUPPORTED BY OUTRIGGED BRACKETS.

Consider now that the truss members are riveted to gusset plates. Such a truss is shown by part (b) of Fig. 4–5. To move to the loaded position (shown solid) the bars must bend, as well as either shortening or lengthening. In other words, the bars must actually have axial load, bending moment, and shear. The average truss has its bars rigidly connected to the gusset plates by riveting or welding. For simplicity of fabrication, long members are made which are continuous over several panel lengths. For example, the bottom chord from L_0 to L_4 in Fig.

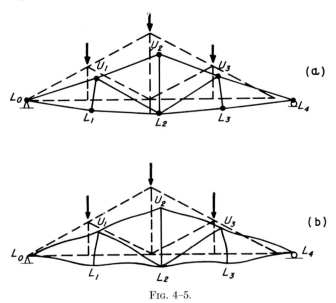

Fig. 4–5.

4–5(b) would be made in one piece. These trusses will deform in the manner shown by Fig. 4–5(b). How, then, can the assumption of pin connections be justified?

The answer is that the usual truss member is long and "limber," so that it is easier to deform by bending than by axial load. Conversely, as it is deformed laterally when the truss is loaded, the bending moments and shears caused are small. For the usual truss, the moment and shear in the members are negligible as compared to the axial load in the members. Thus, if we compute the axial loads, assuming the shears and bending moments in the bars to be zero, we are introducing little error. (In those cases where the members are quite stiff, having a ratio of length to depth of 10 or less, the bending moment and shear can be computed.[2] The method of computation is fairly complicated. The additional

[2] C. D. Williams, *Analysis of Statically Indeterminate Structures* (Scranton, Pa.; International Textbook Co., 1946), Chap. 8.

stresses thus computed are called "secondary stresses.") Computations of actual truss deformations justify the second assumption. The movements of points on the truss may be appreciable in themselves, but they are very small compared to the original truss dimensions. The geometry of the truss, for stress computation purposes, may be assumed unchanged.

The only tools needed to solve for the bar stresses in a pin-connected statically determinate truss are the three laws of equilibrium.

The method of applying these laws is the same as was used in finding the values of thrust, shear, and bending moment at a section of a beam. (See Art. 3–1.) Reworded to suit the case of trusses, the procedure is:

1. Imagine the truss to be cut through completely at a section which includes the bar whose stress is desired. The section must generally be chosen so that not more than three bars are cut. Isolate the portion of the truss on *one* side of this cut. Include with this isolated portion all loads and reactions actually applied to its panel points.

2. Place on the isolated portion symbols for the forces that could occur at the cut ends of the members. Since we are assuming that the members have pinned ends, only axial forces will be shown. These axial forces must balance the applied loads and reactions so as to keep the isolated portion in equilibrium. These axial forces are the unknowns which must be solved. If three bars have been cut, there will be three such unknowns.

3. Use the three equilibrium equations to solve for the unknowns. This is exactly like solving for reactions as in Chapter 2.

This basic method, called the *Method of Sections*, is best learned by observing examples. The three examples which follow should be studied carefully.

EXAMPLE 4–1. The line diagram of a truss from an electrical substation is shown by Fig. 4–6(a). A new piece of equipment weighing 600 lb is to be added as shown. What stresses would the new load cause in the bars marked a, b, c, and d? The reactions are computed and their amounts indicated on Fig. 4–6(a).

Imagine the truss to be cut along section 1–1 as shown on Fig. 4–6(a). The portion to the left of this cut is shown isolated in part (b) of Fig. 4–6. The forces acting on the isolated portion are the vertical reaction and a possible axial load in each bar cut. The axial loads in those bars are of whatever amount is required to maintain the equilibrium of the isolated portion. It is not known in advance whether these bar stresses are tension or compression. Assume that they are all tensile stresses. If they were tensile, the forces exerted on the isolated portion by the remainder of the truss would be "pulls" at the cut ends, as shown in Fig. 4–6(b). The portion of truss isolated is shaded to emphasize the fact that the bar arrangement within that portion is of no importance. All that must be solved are three unknowns S_a, S_b, and S_c. The values of these would be the same regardless of the bar arrangement in the

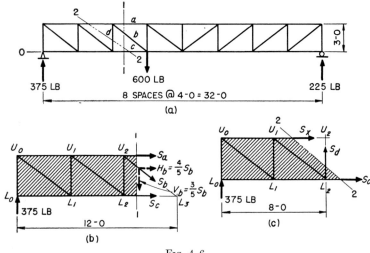

Fig. 4–6.

area $U_0U_2L_2L_0$. Their values would be the same even if the shaded area were filled with solid material rather than being trussed.

To solve for S_a, balance moments about the point at which S_b and S_c intersect. That point is L_3.

$$\Sigma M_{L3} = (12 \times 375) + 3S_a = 0; \quad S_a = -1,500 \text{ lb}$$

The force S_a was assumed tensile. The negative solution indicates an incorrect assumption. Therefore, S_a is compressive. It is usual practice to use a minus sign to indicate compression, so the value shown above is readily understood to mean 1,500 lb compression.

To obtain S_c, moments about U_2 are computed.

$$\Sigma M_{U2} = (375 \times 8) - 3S_c = 0; \quad S_c = 1,000 \text{ lb, tension}$$

To obtain S_b, resolve S_b into its vertical and horizontal components. Call these V_b and H_b, respectively. The components are shown dotted on Fig. 4–6(b).

$$\Sigma V = +375 - V_b = 0; \quad V_b = 375 \text{ lb } \downarrow$$
$$S_b = \tfrac{5}{3} \times 375 = 625 \text{ lb, tension}$$

The value of S_b could have been obtained by use of the equation for horizontal forces. That equation will be used here to check the solution.

$$\Sigma H = S_a + H_b + S_c = -1,500 + (\tfrac{4}{5} \times 625) + 1,000 = 0$$

The equation is satisfied by the values obtained for S_a, S_b, and S_c.

To solve for the axial load in bar d, the truss is assumed to be cut on section 2–2. The portion to the left of the cut is shown isolated in Fig. 4–6(c). For that portion, the equation for vertical forces is written.

$$\Sigma V = 375 + S_d = 0; \quad S_d = -375 \text{ lb}$$

Again, the minus sign indicates that the assumption of a tensile stress was incorrect. The minus sign is understood to indicate compression, so that the answer as written above requires no further interpretation. The stress in bar d is 375 lb compression.

EXAMPLE 4–2. A line diagram for an existing roof truss in a small pumping station is shown by Fig. 4–7(a). It is desired to pick up one

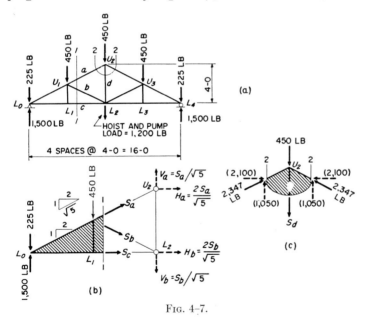

FIG. 4–7.

of the pumps, using a chain hoist attached to the bottom chord of the truss at joint L_2. The pump weighs 900 lb and the hoist 300 lb. The dead loads from the roof are of the amounts shown on the diagram. (These include a small amount to cover the weight of the truss itself.) Compute the stress in members a, b, c, and d, due to the combination of dead loads, hoist, and pump.

The end reactions are determined to be 1,500 lb each. Imagine the truss to be cut on section 1–1. The portion to the left of the section is shown isolated in Fig. 4–7(b). The stresses in bars a, b, and c are assumed to be tensile. Arrows to conform with this assumption are shown on the isolated portion.

To solve for S_a, moments are computed about the point at which S_b and S_c intersect (point L_2). For convenience, S_a should be replaced by its vertical and horizontal components. These components, V_a and H_a, may be placed anywhere that is convenient, *provided their intersection is on the line of action of the force S_a.* The most convenient points at which to place the components would be vertically above the moment center L_2 (point U_2), or horizontally to the left of it (point L_0). In this example S_a is resolved at point U_2.

$$\Sigma M_{L2} = (1275 \times 8) - (450 \times 4) + 4H_a = 0; \quad H_a = -2,100 \text{ lb}$$
$$S_a = \sqrt{5} \, H_a/2 = \underline{-2,347 \text{ lb}} \quad \text{or} \quad 2,347 \text{ lb, compression}$$

Similarly, to obtain S_b, resolve S_b into components V_b and H_b. Compute moments about the point at which the other two unknowns intersect.

$$\Sigma M_{L0} = (450 \times 4) + 8V_b = 0; \quad V_b = -225 \text{ lb}$$
$$S_b = \sqrt{5} \, V_b = \underline{-503 \text{ lb}} \quad \text{or} \quad 503 \text{ lb, compression}$$

To obtain S_c, moments about U_1 are computed.

$$\Sigma M_{U1} = (1275 \times 4) - 2S_c = 0; \quad \underline{S_c = 2,550 \text{ lb, tension}}$$

Now imagine the original truss to be cut along section 2–2. The portion above the cut is shown isolated in Fig. 4–7(c). The stress in member a is already known to be 2,347 lb compression. Arrows and amounts representing the forces applied to the isolated portion by member a and the top chord member to the right of U_2 are shown. By use of the equation $\Sigma H = 0$, it is known that the stress in the top chord member U_2U_3 is the same as S_a. The only other unknown force on the removed portion is S_d. The 2,347-lb forces may be divided into components as shown.

$$\Sigma V = 1,050 + 1,050 - 450 - S_d = 0; \quad \underline{S_d = 1,650 \text{ lb, tension}}$$

4–4. Analytical Method of Joints. Notice that the portion of truss isolated in Fig. 4–7(c) is merely one joint of the truss, and that all the forces on the portion are concurrent at that joint. Whenever all the forces on an isolated portion are concurrent, it is possible to solve for only two unknowns. The equation $\Sigma M = 0$ cannot be used. Only the equations $\Sigma V = 0$ and $\Sigma H = 0$ are effective. Thus, whenever a joint is isolated in truss analysis, the section must cut a maximum of two bars having unknown stress.

Many trusses can be completely analyzed by the use of such sections.

The analysis is started by isolating some joint having only two bars. Solution is made for the stress in these two bars. The values obtained are then re-used at some adjacent joint so as to reduce the number of unknowns there to two. Similarly, joint after joint is analyzed until the values of all the bar stresses have been found. This method is called the "Method of Joints." Actually, it is merely a special case of the method of sections.

EXAMPLE 4–3. In this example the truss and loading of Example 4–2 will be used again. Values for all the bar stresses will be obtained using the method of joints. The truss is shown again in Fig. 4–8(a), having letter symbols for all the bars.

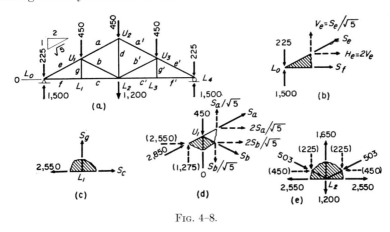

FIG. 4–8.

Joint L_0 has only two bars entering. It is isolated in Fig. 4–8(b). Force S_e is resolved into its components, V_e and H_e.

$$\Sigma V = 1{,}500 - 225 + V_e = 0; \quad V_e = -1{,}275$$
$$S_e = \sqrt{5}\, V_e = -2{,}850 \text{ lb}$$

$$\Sigma H = S_f + H_e = S_f - (2 \times 1{,}275) = 0; \quad S_f = 2{,}550 \text{ lb}$$

Joint U_1 still has bars a, b, and g with unknown stress. That joint cannot yet be analyzed. Joint L_1, however, has only two unknown stresses, S_c and S_g. That joint is considered next. Fig. 4–8(c) shows joint L_1 isolated. The force applied to the joint by bar f is a pull of

2,550 lb toward the left. By observation and mental application of the equation $\Sigma V = 0$, it is seen that $S_g = 0$.

$$\Sigma H = -2,550 + S_c = 0; \quad S_c = 2,550 \text{ lb}$$

Now joint U_1 can be considered. It is shown by Fig. 4–8(d). Bar e was determined to be in compression, therefore it pushes against the isolated portion with a force of 2,850 lb. This force and the unknowns S_a and S_b are shown on the figure resolved into their vertical and horizontal components. Two equations will be written and solved simultaneously.

$$\Sigma V = -450 + 1,275 + S_a/\sqrt{5} - S_b/\sqrt{5} = 0$$
$$1,844 + S_a - S_b = 0$$
$$\Sigma H = 2,550 + 2S_a/\sqrt{5} + 2S_b/\sqrt{5} = 0$$
$$2,850 + S_a + S_b = 0$$

When solved these equations give $S_a = -2,347$ lb, and $S_b = -503$ lb.

The truss and its loading are symmetrical about the center, so it is known that the stress in bar a' is the same as that in bar a, that in b' is equal to that in b, etc. The only remaining unsolved bar is d. The solution of S_d was performed in the previous example using joint U_2. S_d was found to be 1,650 lb.

Joint L_2 will be analyzed as a check on the solutions. The joint is shown in Fig. 4–8(e). The equation $\Sigma H = 0$ is obviously satisfied.

$$\Sigma V = 1,650 - 225 - 225 - 1,200 = 0$$

Both equations are satisfied using the bar stress values obtained.

The method of sections and the method of joints each have their advantages. The method of joints is often more easily understood by students than is the method of sections. The method of joints gives a partial check of the solutions when the final joint is reached. It is often cumbersome, however, and errors made in the early stage of the analysis can carry through and affect most or all of the later work. The author believes that it is best to mix the two methods. In other words, use whichever method works more easily for the bars being solved. If sections cutting three non-intersecting bars (as in Examples 4–1 and 4–2) permit easy solution, use the method of sections. If a particular bar is more readily solved by isolation of a single joint, then use the method of joints at that joint.

4–5. Graphical Solution of Bar Stresses. Students often shy away from graphical methods. Sometimes this is because of the inconvenience of locating suitable equipment for graphical work. More often though, it is because of an incorrect notion that graphical work is less accurate than analytical work. Carefully prepared graphical solutions are at least as accurate as slide-rule solutions. The graphical solutions are usually much more accurate than the load data given. Further, graphical solutions are often time savers; they can be made in less time than purely analytical ones. In such cases, it is certainly good engineering practice to use graphical methods. A problem in which the graphical method is nearly always used in engineering practice is the complete analysis of roof trusses. The graphical method is so widely used and understood, that the diagrams made in the graphical solution are often included as basic data on the design drawings for the structure.

Fig. 4–9(a) shows a roof truss and the panel loads which are transferred to it by the roof purlins. The end reactions are shown as merely R_L and R_R.

In making an analytical solution by joints, joint L_0 would be isolated first, since only two bars enter that joint. Joint L_0 is considered first in the graphical solution also. The forces acting on the joint material at L_0 are the reaction R_L, the load $P/2$, the bar stress S_a and the bar stress S_b. Joint L_0 and these forces are shown by Fig. 4–9(b). These forces are in equilibrium, therefore their vectors will form a closed force polygon. Fig. 4–9(c) shows this polygon. In making it, a line is first drawn upward from the starting point O, having a length scaled to represent the reaction R_L. From the arrow end of R_L a downward vector for load $P/2$ is added. The lines of action of the two remaining forces, S_a and S_b, are known but their amounts are not. The polygon is closed with two lines having these known directions. Their intersection at point x is located. The amounts of the forces S_a and S_b are represented by the length of their vectors. Since the polygon is traversed continuously *in the direction of the forces that are in equilibrium*, we may conclude that force S_a pulls the joint L_0 toward the right, and that force S_b pushes joint L_0 downward and toward the left. Fig. 4–9(b) shows this interpretation. Thus, if bar a *pulls* on the joint, its bar stress S_a is tension. Bar b *pushes* against the joint; its bar stress S_b is compression.

Now that the bar stress S_a is known, there are only two unknown forces, S_c and S_d, entering joint L_1. That joint is shown isolated in Fig. 4–9(d). Since bar a is in tension, force S_a must *pull* on the material at L_1. A polygon for the three forces turns out to be a straight line as shown by Fig. 4–9(e). Thus, S_c is zero, and S_d is a tensile force of the same magnitude as S_a.

Joint U_1 can be solved next. The two unknowns at U_1 are the bar stresses S_e and S_f. Bar stress S_b is known to be compressive from the analysis at joint L_0. Therefore, force S_b *pushes* against the joint material,

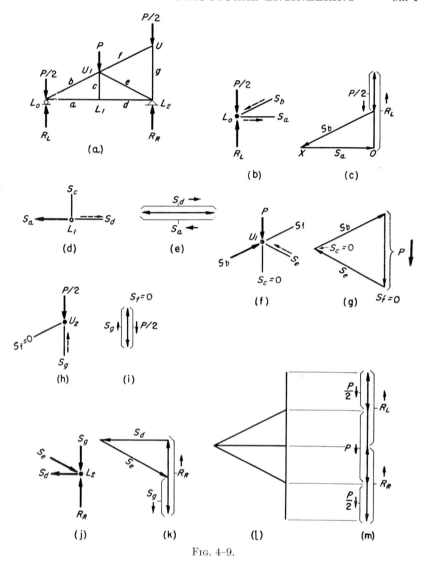

FIG. 4–9.

as shown by Fig. 4–9(f). Force S_c is already known to be zero. The lines of action for the unknown forces, S_e and S_f, are parallel to members e and f, respectively. The direction along the lines of action is not yet known, however. Fig. 4–9(g) shows a force polygon for the forces at joint U_1. The first vector drawn is that for S_c; next for S_b; and so on, taking the forces in clockwise order around the joint. The polygon shows S_f to be zero, and S_e to be upward toward the left, as shown on Fig 4–9(f). Bar e is in compression.

In Figs. 4–9(h) and (i) similar operations are shown for joint U_2. Figs. 4–9(j) and (k) show them for joint L_2.

It should now be noticed that each polygon was drawn with the forces arranged in order of their occurrence circulating clockwise around the joint. When the polygons are all drawn in this manner, they can be superimposed on each other. They are shown superimposed in Fig. 4–9(l). This combination of polygons is called the "Maxwell diagram." It would be a good idea to study the Maxwell diagram carefully before proceeding beyond this paragraph. Notice how the individual polygons fit, one above the other. Try to trace the individual polygons through the combined diagram. Notice that no duplication of vectors occurs. For example, vector S_e occurs in the individual polygons for joints U_1 and L_2. Yet a single line serves for both polygons in the Maxwell diagram. Finally, notice that the combined diagram also contains a polygon showing the equilibrium of the external forces and reactions. This polygon is removed and drawn separately in Fig. 4–9(m). Notice that the forces it contains are taken in clockwise order of their occurrence, circulating around the outside of the entire structure. The polygon for external forces and reactions is called the "load line."

The Maxwell diagram can be drawn directly, without first drawing individual polygons in isolated positions. To do this, the work is started with the load line. Then polygons for each joint are added, until the diagram is completed. The procedure will be illustrated by the next two examples.

4–6. Bow's Notation.   The labeling of the Maxwell diagram is made easier by use of a system of notation called *Bow's notation*. Fig 4–10 shows Bow's notation applied to the truss of Fig. 4–9. The interior spaces are numbered. The spaces between external loads are lettered. A force is named according to the spaces it lies between, reading clockwise about the joint in each case. Thus at joint L_0, the reaction is ea, the applied load ab, the top-chord stress is b–1, and the bottom-chord stress is 1–e. At joint U_1, the top-chord stress to the left is called 1–b, and so on. The simplicity and value of this notation should be made apparent by the examples which follow.

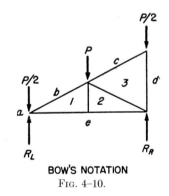

BOW'S NOTATION
Fig. 4–10.

The scale used for the Maxwell diagram should not be too small. The diagrams in the figures of this text are too small. They were, of course, reduced for printing from larger-scale drawings. A suitable scale would be one that spread the diagram over most of an $8\frac{1}{2}$ in. by 11 in. sheet. For more complicated diagrams, two such sheets joined together will allow a larger scale. In engineering offices tracing paper is used, and the diagrams often occupy a width of two feet or more on the sheet. Making the diagrams is easier when an engineer's scale, rather than an

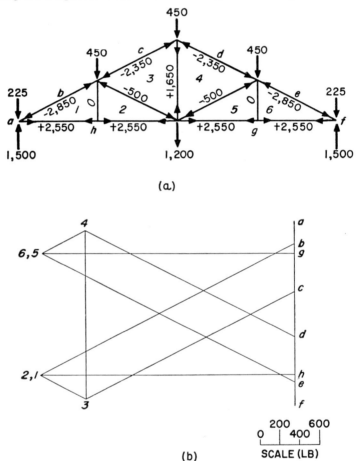

Fig. 4–11.

architect's scale, is used. The engineer's scale is calibrated decimally. It usually has inches divided into 10, 20, 30, 40, 50, and 60 units. Thus, on the diagram, scales such as 1 in. = 400 lb, 1 in. = 3 kips, or 1 in. = 600 lb are easy to handle.

EXAMPLE 4–4. Solve graphically the bar stresses for the truss of Example 4–2. The truss and its loads are shown again in Fig. 4–11(a).

The slopes of bars are usually traced from the truss picture to the Maxwell diagram. *Therefore, the truss must be drawn accurately to scale and not too small.* Bow's notation is applied to the truss picture.

The load line is drawn first. Arrows are not needed to show the direction of the forces. For example, the 1,200-lb load acting downward at the center of the bottom chord is called gh, not hg. (Read clockwise around truss.) Reading from g to h on the load line shows the direction of gh to be downward also. Similarly, the force called bc is downward on the truss picture, and the vector bc is downward on the load line.

A polygon for the forces at L_0 is added next. The forces at that joint are ha, ab, b–1, and 1–h. The polygon for these forces is started at h on the load line, then drawn to a, b, and 1, and finally back to h to close the polygon.

Similar polygons are added for each joint to complete the diagram. The student should study the completed diagram carefully, and follow through it the path of each polygon.

Interpretation of the diagram to determine the kind of bar stress, i.e., whether tensile or compressive, is carried on as each polygon is drawn. The polygon for joint L_0 follows the path h–a–b–1–h. The direction of line b–1 is downward and toward the left. The bar b–1 pushes in this same direction against joint L_0 as indicated by the small arrowhead shown on the member near L_0. Also, vector 1–h is toward the right, and bar 1–h pulls toward the right. An arrowhead is shown on the truss near L_0 to indicate that fact. The polygon h–1–2–h for joint L_1 shows force h–1 as pulling joint L_1 to the left. The arrowhead on bar h–1 near joint L_1 records the fact. All the polygons are interpreted in this way to obtain the complete set of direction arrows shown on the picture of the truss. Arrows pointing *away* from the joint indicate *tension* in the bar. Arrows pointing *toward* the joint indicate *compression* in the bar. As a check on the interpretation, note that the arrows at opposite ends of a bar should be in opposite directions.

The amounts of the bar stress are scaled from the Maxwell diagram. It is usual to record the answers, either on the truss picture or in a table of bar stresses. The first method of recording is used in this example.

EXAMPLE 4–5. Revisions in a plant layout have made it necessary to maintain a clear space adjacent to a truck dock. Provision must be made to carry sacks a distance of 24 ft out from the dock to the back end of the trucks. One possible solution to the problem is shown in Fig. 4–12(a). A 24-ft length of roller conveyor is available. It could be supported between two light trusses, cantilevered from the dock. The plant engineer is asked to figure the bar stresses and design the truss.

The first step is to interpret the conditions and to make a line diagram

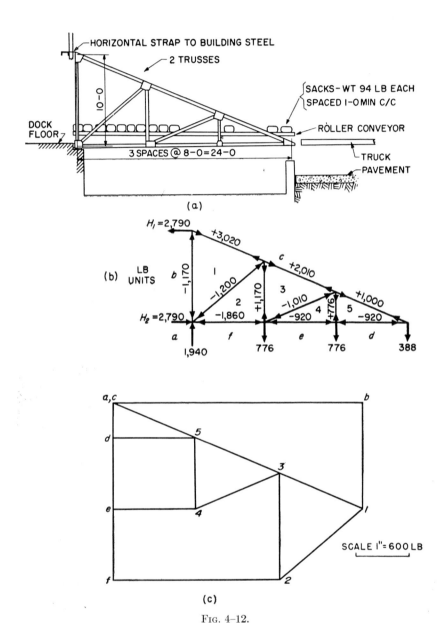

FIG. 4-12.

of the truss showing its loads and reactions. It is necessary to estimate the truss weight. Assume this to be 15 lb per ft of span for each truss. (In the complete design, corrections would be made later if this estimate were greatly in error.) It will not cause appreciable error if the truss weight is considered to be applied entirely at the bottom chord. The load on one interior panel point of one truss would then be:

$$\text{Sacks } \tfrac{1}{2} \times 8 \times 94 = 376 \text{ lb}$$
$$\text{Conveyor } \tfrac{1}{2} \times 8 \times 70 = 280$$
$$\text{Truss } 8 \times 15 \qquad = 120$$
$$\text{Panel load} = \overline{776} \text{ lb}$$

The end panel points each support only a 4-ft length of conveyor, so the end loads are approximately $\tfrac{1}{2} \times 776$ or 388 lb each.

The type of supports shown in Fig. 4–12(a) control the reaction directions. The reaction at the top can be only horizontal, parallel to the strap. That at the bottom can be in any direction; it can have a vertical component and a horizontal component.

$$\Sigma M = -10H_1 + 776(8 + 16) + (388 \times 24) = 0; H_1 = 2{,}790 \text{ lb}\leftarrow$$
By $\Sigma H = 0$, $H_2 = 2{,}790$ lb$\rightarrow$
By $\Sigma V = 0$, $V_2 = 2{,}328$ lb $\uparrow$

The net external force at L_0 is the algebraic sum of the reaction and the panel-point load, or $2{,}328 - 388 = 1{,}940$ lb upward.

The original data has now been "boiled down" to give the simple problem shown by Fig. 4–12(b). Bow's notation can now be added and the Maxwell diagram drawn. The load line, polygon a–b–c–d–e–f–a, is not a straight line this time. After the load line, polygon b–c–1–b for joint U_0 is drawn. Joint L_0 is then solved by drawing polygon f–a–b–1–2–f. The work proceeds until polygons have been drawn for all the joints. In each polygon, the clockwise sequence of members and forces about the joint is followed. The results are interpreted and recorded on Fig. 4–12(b). The student should follow through the Maxwell diagram carefully. Check particularly the determination of whether the bar stress is tension or compression.

4–7. Accuracy and Error of Closure. In the graphical method of joints, just as in the analytical method, error can be accumulated as the work proceeds. The accumulation of error is apparent near the end of the solution when one of the polygons fails to close. If the error of closure is large, it may indicate a serious mistake in some part of the problem. Incorrect values of reactions cause much trouble of this type. If the error of closure is small, it is probably just the accumulation of very small errors. Closure can often be accomplished by working backwards, starting with the last joint and proceeding back through the problem. Sometimes the presence of a slight error of closure can be ignored, particularly if correcting it does not appreciably change any answers.

The amount of accumulated error can often be minimized by working from both ends of the truss toward the middle. Most trusses have more than one joint at which the Maxwell diagram can be started, so this procedure can usually be used. The diagram for Example 4–5 (Fig. 4–12) could be started at either joint U_0 or the extreme right end (joint L_3).

4–8. Substitute Members. In analyzing a truss by the method of joints (analytical or graphical), a stage is sometimes reached where it is impossible to find another joint having only two unknowns. A truss which presents this difficulty is the Fink truss, shown by Fig. 4–13.

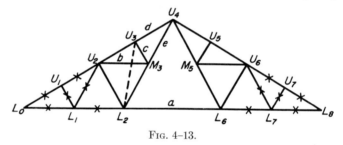

Fig. 4–13.

The Maxwell diagram can be started at either end. For example, a polygon for joint L_0 can be drawn first. Next a polygon for joint U_1 can be added, and then one for joint L_1. Similarly, polygons could be drawn for joints L_8, U_7, and L_7. After those polygons have been drawn, bar stresses will be known for all bars marked with an $\times$ on Fig. 4–13.

There are no joints remaining at which there are only two unknowns. Joint U_2 has three unknowns and joint L_2 has three also. Thus, further progress by the method of joints alone is not possible.

To proceed with the analysis, one of the two following methods must be employed:

1. Solve analytically, by the method of sections, for the stress in some bar not yet solved. Bar a of Fig. 4–13 would be a suitable one. With the stress in bar a known, the method of joints could be used to complete the solution.

2. Temporarily substitute the bar shown dotted in Fig. 4–13 for bars b and c. This substitution would not affect the stress in bars a, d, or e. (The student should verify this fact.) When the

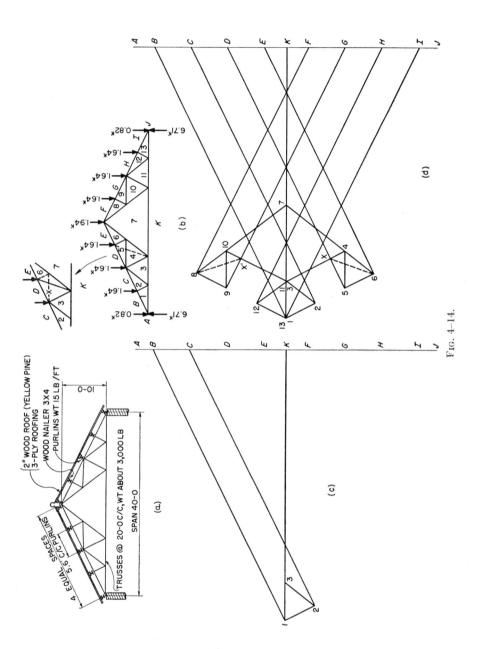

Fig. 4-14.

stress in bar d has been solved, the substitute bar can be considered removed, the original ones replaced, and the solution carried backwards to determine the stress in bars b and c.

EXAMPLE 4–6. A Fink roof truss is shown by Fig. 4–14(a). Determine graphically the bar stresses due to dead load.

The panel load for each panel point must be determined first. The top-chord panel points receive vertical dead load from the roof, roofing, purlins, and nailers. The weight of the truss itself is small as compared to the other loads, so the truss weight will be considered applied entirely at the top-chord panel points. The panel load for each interior panel point is as follows:

$$\text{Roof} \quad 44 \times \frac{1.625}{12} \times 5.6 \times 20 \quad = \quad 667$$

$$\text{Roofing} \quad 1 \times 5.6 \times 20 \qquad\qquad = \quad 112$$

$$\text{Purlin} \quad 15 \times 20 \qquad\qquad\quad = \quad 300$$

$$\text{Nailer} \quad 44 \times \frac{2.625 \times 3.625}{144} \times 20 = \quad 58$$

$$\text{Truss} \quad \text{Assumed } \tfrac{1}{6} \text{ of 3,000 lb} \quad = \quad 500$$

$$\text{Panel load} = \overline{1,637} = 1,640 \text{ lb}$$

This panel load will be used for all interior panels except the top one. Two purlins are supported at that point, so the load there is 1,940 lb. The load at the end panel points will be taken as 1/2 of 1,640, or 820 lb.

Fig. 4–14(b) shows a line diagram of the truss and Fig. 4–14(c) a part of the Maxwell diagram. The load line was constructed first. Polygons for the three joints nearest the left were then constructed, thus locating points 1, 2, and 3 on the Maxwell diagram. Further progress is prevented by the existence of too many unknowns at all other joints. To draw a polygon for joint U_2, it is necessary to locate points 4 and 5 on the Maxwell diagram. To draw the polygon for joint L_2 requires locating points 4 and 7.

To get past this "bottleneck" substitute members are used. Bars 4–5 and 5–6 are temporarily replaced by bar x–6. Joint U_2 is then analyzed by drawing polygon 3–2–c–d–x–3, shown on Fig., 4–14(d). Joint U_3 is analyzed by drawing polygon x–d–e–6–x. Bar stress e–6 is not affected by the substitution; therefore, the stress obtained for e–6 is the stress for the actual truss. Now that the stress in e–6 is known, it is possible to solve for the remaining unknown stresses, 6–5 and 5–d, at joint U_3. This is now done by using the actual bars and drawing polygon d–e–6–5–d for joint U_3. Then polygon 3–2–c–d–5–4–3 is constructed for joint U_2. The balance of the stresses can now be solved without difficulty. To minimize error, the solution is brought from both ends toward the center. A similar substitution is needed on the right half of the truss. The stress values can be scaled from the diagram.

Study the construction carefully. Observe how the substitution eliminates the difficulty and facilitates determining the actual bar stress in member e–6.

4–9. Maximum Bar Stresses. Many different combinations of loading on a truss are possible. Four such combinations were shown by Art. 1–10. Seldom does a single combination of loads give the maximum stress values for all bars of a truss. Usually one combination causes the maximum bar stresses for the top and bottom chords, and others cause the maximum bar stresses for the web members. A member may have a "reversal of stress." In other words, it may have tensile stress under one load combination and compressive stress under another.

It is often important to know the maximum bar stresses, both tensile and compressive, for all members of the truss. An easy way to obtain these maximum values is illustrated by Example 4–7. Maxwell diagrams are drawn for each type of loading. The results for each type are tabulated. Combinations are selected giving the maximum tensile and compressive stresses for each bar of the truss. This is an application of the principle of superposition (Art. 3–5).

EXAMPLE 4–7. Assume that the truss of Fig. 4–14 and Example 4–6 is to be analyzed by a plant engineer to determine whether a conveyor can be supported safely from the bottom chord at panel point L_2. If prints of the truss design drawings were available, the stresses due to the conveyor could be added to those shown on the drawing. However, no such prints are available, so it is necessary to make a complete analysis of the truss. The load at point L_2 will be 500 lb due to the empty conveyor, plus 1,000 lb live load. The dead load will be active at all times. The live load can be included or omitted, whichever causes the larger stress. The local code specifies a snow load of 20 lb per sq ft of horizontal projection, and wind loads as recommended by the American Society of Civil Engineers (Art. 1–7). Load combinations are not specified by the local code.

First, what combinations are the logical ones to include? This may be the subject of argument. Most engineers, however, would agree on the following:

1. Dead load
2. Dead load and snow load
3. Dead load and wind
4. Dead load, snow load, and one-half of wind load

To each of the above, conveyor live load would be added if it caused a larger stress. Wind would be considered acting in either direction.

As the solution of the problem progresses, it may become obvious that some of the load combinations listed above are not needed. Until shown to be otherwise, however, they will be considered as possible critical load combinations.

The stresses for each type of load will be solved separately and tabulated. Selected stress values in the tabulation will then be added to obtain stresses due to the various load combinations.

The Maxwell diagram for the original dead loads was constructed in Fig. 4–14. The values obtained are tabulated in column 2 of Fig. 4–17.

The panel load due to snow is $20 \times 5 \times 20 = 2,000$ lb. Except for a slight variation at panel point U_4, the dead-load panel loads are each 1,640 lb. Ignoring this slight variation, the snow load stresses are 2,000/1,640, or 1.22 times the dead-load stresses. No Maxwell diagram is drawn for the snow loads. The snow-load stresses in column 3 of Fig. 4–17 are obtained by multiplying the values in column 2 by 1.22.

Fig. 4–15(a) shows the ASCE wind loads for a wind blowing from the left. (See Art. 1–7.) The roof slope is 1 to 2, or 26.6 degrees. It is assumed that the building is nominally airtight, having only leakage through small openings. The outside forces on the roof are 4.1 lb per sq ft suction on the windward half, (See Fig. 1–6.) and 9 lb per sq ft suction on the leeward half. The forces on the inside surface are 4.5 lb per sq ft, either pressure or suction. The worst combination includes the inside pressure. The panel wind loads are shown by Fig. 4–15(b). The horizontal components of the end reactions are assumed to be equal. The vertical components are solved by use of the equations of equilibrium.

$$\Sigma M_{L0} = -(3.84 \times 11.2) - (6.05 \times 24.6) + 40V_R = 0; \quad \underline{V_R = 4.80 \text{ k} \downarrow}$$

$$\Sigma M_{L6} = +(3.84 \times 24.6) + (6.05 \times 11.2) - 40V_L = 0; \quad \underline{V_L = 4.05 \text{ k} \downarrow}$$

The Maxwell diagram for wind from the left is shown in Fig. 4–15(c). The bar stresses obtained from this diagram are tabulated in column 4 of Fig. 4–17.

Since the truss is symmetrical, the stresses caused by a wind from the right can be taken from the same diagram. For example, the stress in member 2–3 caused by wind from the right is the same as the stress in member 11–12 under wind from the left. The stresses caused by wind from the right are tabulated in column 5 of Fig. 4–17.

Fig. 4–16(a) shows the truss with one kip of conveyor live load at panel point L_2. The Maxwell diagram for this load is shown in Fig. 4–16(b). The conveyor dead load at L_2 is only 500 lb. Thus the bar

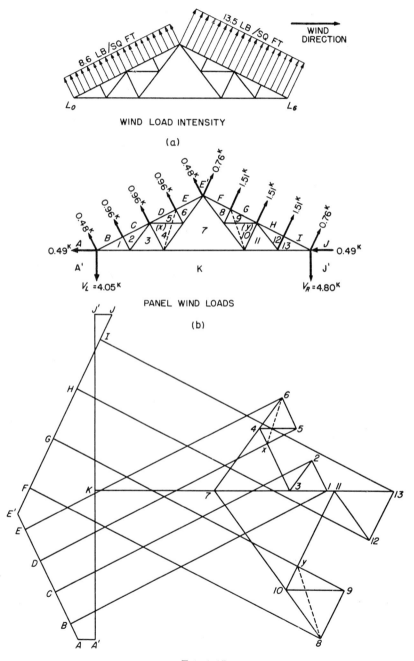

FIG. 4–15.

stresses caused by conveyor dead load are one-half of the stresses caused by conveyor live load. The bar stresses caused by conveyor dead and live loads are tabulated in columns 6 and 7.

Columns 8 to 11 show the bar stresses for various load combinations. By now it is apparent that some of the load cases set up at the beginning of this example are not critical. In the case of each member, the stresses

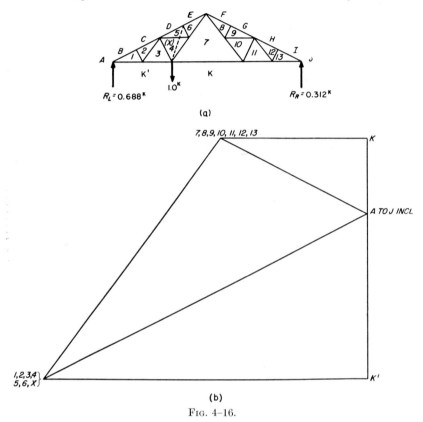

Fig. 4–16.

caused by original dead load, conveyor dead load, snow, and conveyor live load all have the same algebraic sign. Obviously, then, the total stresses of column 10 should be greater than those of either column 8 or 9. For most purposes columns 8 and 9 might be omitted, since column 10 gives the critical values. (In checking a timber truss, however, columns 8 and 9 would both be needed. This is because of varying allowable unit stresses for loads of different duration.) Column 11 shows stress values only where including wind causes a total stress of opposite sign to those of column 10. (If any total stresses including wind were larger than those of column 10 and of the same sign, those stresses also

MEMBER	BAR STRESSES FROM MAXWELL DIAGRAMS						COMBINED STRESSES			
	ORIGINAL DEAD LOAD	SNOW	WIND FROM LEFT	WIND FROM RIGHT	CONVEYOR DEAD LOAD	CONVEYOR LIVE LOAD	DL ONLY (COLS. 2 & 6)	DL+SNOW (COLS. 3 & 8)	DL+SNOW+CONVEYOR LL (COLS. 7 & 9)	DL+WIND (COLS. 8 & 4 OR 5)
COL. I	2	3	4	5	6	7	8	9	10	11
B – 1	-13.1	-16.0	8.1	9.2	-0.8	-1.5	-13.9	-29.9	-31.4	
C – 2	-12.4	-15.1	8.1	9.2	-0.8	-1.5	-13.2	-28.3	-29.8	
D – 5	-11.7	-14.3	8.1	9.2	-0.8	-1.5	-12.5	-26.8	-28.3	
E – 6	-11.0	-13.4	8.1	9.2	-0.8	-1.5	-11.8	-25.2	-26.7	
F – 8	-11.0	-13.4	9.2	8.1	-0.4	-0.7	-11.4	-24.8	-25.5	
G – 9	-11.7	-14.3	9.2	8.1	-0.4	-0.7	-12.1	-26.4	-27.1	
H – 12	-12.4	-15.1	9.2	8.1	-0.4	-0.7	-12.8	-27.9	-28.6	
I – 13	-13.1	-16.0	9.2	8.1	-0.4	-0.7	-13.5	-29.5	-30.2	
K – 1	11.8	14.4	-6.5	-8.4	0.7	1.4	12.5	26.9	28.3	
K – 3	10.2	12.4	-5.5	-6.7	0.7	1.4	10.9	23.3	24.7	
K – 7	6.9	8.4	-3.3	-3.3	0.3	0.6	7.2	15.6	16.2	
K – 11	10.2	12.4	-6.7	-5.5	0.3	0.6	10.5	22.9	23.5	
K – 13	11.8	14.4	-8.4	-6.5	0.3	0.6	12.1	26.5	27.1	
1 – 2	-1.5	-1.8	1.0	1.5	0	0	-1.5	-3.3	-3.3	
2 – 3	1.6	2.0	-1.0	-1.7	0	0	1.6	3.6	3.6	-0.1
3 – 4	-3.0	-3.7	1.9	3.0	0	0	-3.0	-6.7	-6.7	
4 – 5	1.6	2.0	-1.1	-1.7	0	0	1.6	3.6	3.6	-0.1
5 – 6	-1.5	-1.8	1.0	1.5	0	0	-1.5	-3.3	-3.3	
4 – 7	3.3	4.0	-2.2	-3.4	0.7	1.3	4.0	8.0	9.3	-0.1
6 – 7	4.9	6.0	-3.2	-5.0	0.7	1.3	5.6	11.6	12.9	-0.1
7 – 8	4.9	6.0	-5.0	-3.2	0	0	4.9	10.9	10.9	-0.1
7 – 10	3.3	4.0	-3.4	-2.2	0	0	3.3	7.3	7.3	-0.1
8 – 9	-1.5	-1.8	1.5	1.0	0	0	-1.5	-3.3	-3.3	
9 – 10	1.6	2.0	-1.7	-1.1	0	0	1.6	3.6	3.6	-0.1
10 – 11	-3.0	-3.7	3.0	1.9	0	0	-3.0	-6.7	-6.7	
11 – 12	1.6	2.0	-1.7	-1.0	0	0	1.6	3.6	3.6	-0.1
12 – 13	-1.5	-1.8	1.5	1.0	0	0	-1.5	-3.3	-3.3	

Fig. 4–17.

would be included.) The stresses for a combination of dead load, snow load, conveyor load, and one-half of wind load would obviously be smaller than those of column 10, since the wind stresses are all of opposite sign. Thus, the values of column 10 will be the controlling ones.

The tabular method can be extended to cover any desired combination of load conditions. Many short cuts will become apparent as one becomes familiar with the procedure. No attempt was made here to shorten the tabulation. The student's first exposure to the procedure should be more effective if the example shows all of the tabulated data.

Bracing

4–10. Bracing Types and Purposes. Bracing members are sometimes classified as "secondary members" by the specifications. Secondary members are those which do not participate in resisting the main dead and live loads for which the structure is designed.

Secondary or not, bracing members are still very important members. Their main function is to keep the structure in its original intended shape, except for small elastic deformations. Without bracing, a steel framework made up of vertical columns and horizontal beams or trusses might fold and collapse sidewise, in the manner of a deck of cards which is placed on edge and then released. Such lateral movement and collapse would be initiated by some lateral force. The force might be one whose effect can be computed, such as wind force, horizontal impact forces from cranes or machinery, or the tension of electric power lines. When forces such as these occur, the required bracing can be designed to resist the computed loads.

But lateral forces can result also from accidental side loads, or from the presence of a column that is not exactly plumb. Lateral forces occur on the compression side of members in bending when the member is not perfectly straight. Such forces as these cannot be computed accurately. Experience has shown that they are usually small forces when the workmanship requirements of the codes are observed. Thus, bracing which resists such forces alone is usually of a nominal size, conforming to code requirements for minimum size but not designed to carry computed loads.

Summarizing, bracing is used to "plumb up" the structure during construction, and to keep it in place after construction, resisting computed lateral loads, and resisting forces which defy computation but which might cause lateral movement or buckling of the members.

Bracing that is needed during the erection of buildings may sometimes be removed after construction is completed; but the indiscriminate removal of bracing may be dangerous! One should make certain before removal of any member that the member is not needed to resist load, either computed load or that which cannot be computed. Some building bracing systems are quite complex, especially those of large mill buildings.[3] Very careful study of the entire structure and its types of loading may be needed in order to determine the purpose of a particular member.

Bracing can be divided into two main types, as shown by the two parts of Fig. 4–18. In (a) the diagonal braces extend to the ends or

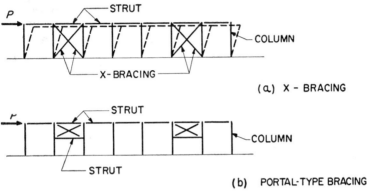

FIG. 4–18.

intersections of the members being braced. This is commonly called X-bracing. The sketch in (a) could represent a series of columns and beams at the side of a building, or a series of crane girders with supporting columns or vertical A-frames. Without the diagonal braces, the entire structure would "lay down" as shown dotted. The action of X-bracing framed in this manner causes axial load in the bracing members and in the braced members. No changes of bending moment are caused. The structure with bracing may be either simple or statically indeterminate, depending on the nature of the braces used. When it is statically indeterminate, a reliable simplifying assumption can be made, so that the analysis can be completed by statics. The general method of sections and the method of joints are used. The analysis of this type of bracing will be shown by Example 4–8.

The second main type of bracing is shown by Fig. 4–18(b). This is usually called "portal-type" bracing. The diagonals in this case do not go to the end of the vertical members. The result is that bending moment and shear, as well as axial load, are caused in the vertical members. Another example of this type of bracing action is shown by Fig. 4–20 (discussed in the next article). Structures with portal-type bracing are statically indeterminate. To use statics for their analysis,

[3] C. W. Dunham, *Planning Industrial Structures* (New York: McGraw-Hill Book Co., Inc., 1948). For bracing, see pp. 210–63.

simplifying assumptions must be made or elastic equations must be added.

EXAMPLE 4–8. An existing crane runway in a building is to be extended outside into a storage yard. The runway will be extended for four bays (spans) of 20 ft 0 in. each. Support for the crane runway girders will be provided by columns as shown in Fig. 4–19(a). What type of

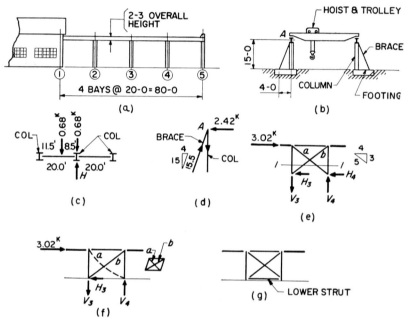

FIG. 4–19.

bracing is required and for what force should each brace member be designed? Data on the crane are as follows: capacity 5 tons; weight of hoist and trolley, 3,600 lb; maximum wheel load, 15,100 lb; number of wheels, 2 per end truck, spaced 8 ft 6 in. apart.

Bracing must be provided in each plane. Bracing to resist the lateral force from the crane and wind force on the girders can be provided by diagonal members at each column, as shown in Fig. 4–19(b). The lateral forces are computed first.

Weight of trolley plus lifted load = 13,600 lb

Horizontal load at one end truck = 10% of 13,600 = 1,360 lb

(See Section 10(d) of the AISC Specification.)

This load reaches the runway as 2 equal forces spaced 8 ft 6 in. apart; a force of 0.68 kip at each wheel. The largest horizontal force on one column occurs when one of the wheels is at the column line. This position is shown in the free-body diagram of Fig. 4–19(c). The reaction to these horizontal loads becomes a lateral load applied to the top of the column.

$$H \text{ (from crane)} = 0.68(11.5 + 20)/20 = 1.07 \text{ kips}$$

Assuming a wind pressure of 20 lb per sq ft on an area of 1 1/2 times the projected area of the exposed steel, the wind force on one span of runway is

$$20 \times 1.5 \times 2.25 \times 20 = 1,350 \text{ lb} = 1.35 \text{ kips}$$

The sum of the horizontal loads from the crane and wind is 2.42 kips. This is shown as a force acting toward the left in Fig. 4–19(d), but it can obviously act in either direction. The horizontal component of the force in the brace is 2.42 kips. The stress in the brace is

$$\frac{15.5}{4} \times 2.42 = 9.35 \text{ kips, either tension or compression}$$

The change of vertical load in the column is equal to the vertical component of the brace load, or $15/4 \times 2.42 = 9.05$ kips, either increase or decrease.

There are many methods of bracing the runway in a longitudinal direction. In this example, X-bracing systems like that shown by Fig. 4–18(a) will be considered. The force to be resisted is given by the AISC Specification as 10 per cent of the maximum wheel loads. For one runway, the longitudinal force is

$$2 \times 15.1 \times 0.10 = 3.02 \text{ kips}$$

Diagonal bracing need not be used in each bay. If one bay is braced so as to remain rectangular, the adjacent bays must also remain rectangular by virtue of their attachment to the braced bay. By this reasoning it might seem that one braced bay could be depended upon to support the entire length of a long building. It is usual, however, to rely upon this extension of bracing action for a limited distance only. The bracing of one bay in every four is usually acceptable. Assume here that bay 3–4 will be braced. Longitudinal load in other bays will be transferred to bay 3–4 by the runway girders. The girders will act as either tension members or compression "struts" in making the transfer.

With the choice of bracing limited to X-bracing, there is still much variety as to its arrangement. Fig. 4–19(e) shows one possible arrangement in which rigid bracing members are used. By "rigid" it is meant in this case that the braces are stiff enough to serve as compression members if necessary. In the portion isolated there are four unknown reactions; the structure is statically indeterminate to the first degree. One simplifying assumption or one elastic equation must be added in order to solve by statics. The assumption, verified by more nearly exact analysis, is that the horizontal components of stress in the two diagonals are equal. That is, the shear on section 1–1 is equally divided between the two diagonals. Thus,

$$H_3 = H_4 = 1.51 \text{ kips}$$

$$\Sigma M_3 = -20V_4 + (15 \times 3.02) = 0$$

$$V_4 = 2.26 \text{ kips, up}$$

$$\Sigma V = 0; \quad V_3 = 2.26 \text{ kips, down}$$

The stress in diagonal a is compressive and that in diagonal b tensile, for the direction of load shown. The load is reversible so that the stress in one diagonal is

$$1.51 \times \frac{5}{4} = 1.89 \text{ kips, either tension or compression}$$

Long compression members tend to be heavier and more expensive than tension members for the same or even greater loads. This is particularly true when the loads are light. For this reason two slender, non-rigid tension members are often used in place of the two rigid diagonals just considered. Such bracing is indicated by Fig. 4–19(f). With the load toward the right, the rectangular panel tends to deform as shown, shortening member a and stretching member b. Member a, being too slender to resist appreciable compression, buckles slightly and leaves the entire bracing job to member b which is in tension. There are three unknown reactions and the structure is statically determinate.

$$H_3 = 3.02 \text{ kips}$$

$$V_4 = \tfrac{3}{4} \times 3.02 = 2.26 \text{ kips, up}$$

$$V_3 = 2.26 \text{ kips, down}$$

$$S_b = \tfrac{5}{4}H_3 = 3.78 \text{ kips, tension}$$

With the direction of the longitudinal force reversed, member b becomes inactive and member a is stressed in tension.

The force in the diagonal is small enough so that the braces can be made of round steel rods, threaded at each end. Rod bracing has the advantages of low cost and of adjustability. The nuts can be tightened or loosened as necessary to keep the rods under a slight initial tension.

In Fig. 4–19(g) a lower strut is shown. The lower strut serves to keep the bottom of the columns the correct distance apart. It causes the longitudinal load to be shared by the footings at column 3 and column 4, regardless of which type of X-bracing is used. The bottom strut is advisable when there is any doubt as to the stability of the footings under horizontal load.

The crane runway girder in this example served as a strut to carry the longitudinal load to the braced bay. In larger cranes the girders may have slotted holes at their connection to certain columns, so that the strut action may not be possible. In that case, a more elaborate bracing system would be necessary.

4–11. Portal Bracing. The presence of X-bracing interferes with passageway between the columns of the braced bay. Portal bracing is useful if such passage is desirable. It is also more attractive in appearance than X-bracing, and it may be chosen in some cases for that reason.

Single bays with portal bracing are shown by Fig. 4–20. The columns in (a) have pinned bottom ends; i.e., they have little or no resistance to rotation of the end of the column in the plane of the paper. There are four unknown reactions and no condition equations; therefore, the structure is statically indeterminate to the first degree. A solution by statics is possible after one simplifying assumption is made. The assumption made is that reactions H_a and H_b are equal. This assumption is fairly accurate for loads between points C and D, provided both columns have the same length and cross section. With H_a and H_b assumed equal, the values of all the reactions can be solved. The columns have a change of axial load equal to V_a or V_b. They also have shear and bending moment caused by the horizontal reactions. The right column is shown isolated in Fig. 4–20(b). In Fig. 4–20(c) the shear and moment diagrams for the column are given. The stresses in the trusswork of diagonals and struts can be computed by the method of sections or by the method of joints.

The portal-braced bay of Fig. 4–20(d) is similar except that its columns have the lower end fixed. The unknown reactions are six in number. This exceeds the number of static equations by three, and the structure is statically indeterminate to the third degree. Three elastic equations must be added or three simplifying assumptions made.

The force P moves the frame slightly, and changes its shape as shown exaggerated in Fig. 4–20(d). Unless the depth of the truss, d, is small, the truss will be quite stiff, so that the major part of the deformation occurs in the columns. Thus, the columns may be assumed to remain vertical at their lower ends and at the bottom of the truss. The deformed column shape (elastic curve) is like that of a column fixed against rotation at each end. In such columns only two unknowns, shear and

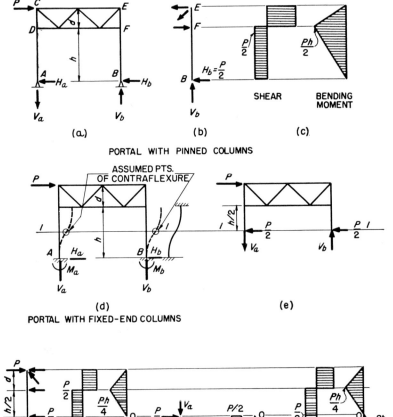

FIG. 4-20.

thrust, exist in each column at the point of contraflexure. The portal-braced bay with fixed columns is then analyzed as follows:

1. A point of contraflexure is assumed for the right column, at mid-height between the bottom of the column and the bottom of the bracing.

2. A similar point of contraflexure is assumed for the left-hand column.

3. A section (1–1) is passed through the assumed points of contraflexure.

4. The portion above the section is assumed isolated, as in Fig. 4–20(e). Four unknowns exist on the isolated portion. One more assumption, that the column shears are equal at the points of contraflexure, is made. The remaining three unknowns for the isolated portion are solved by statics.

5. The portion of each column below the section (1–1) is now analyzed. The reactions for the upper portion are reversed and applied as loads to the lower portions. This is shown by Fig. 4–20(g) for one column. In that picture, the forces $P/2$ and V_a at the upper end are now known. The three reactions at the lower end are solved by statics.

6. Bending moments and shears for the columns are now computed. In Fig. 4–20(f) the upper portion of the column is isolated and its shear and moment diagrams drawn. In (g) diagrams are drawn for the lower half. The diagrams are combined in Fig. 4–20(h) to show the variation of shear and bending moment for the complete height of column.

7. The bar stresses for the diagonal braces and the struts are computed by the method of sections or by the method of joints.

The column bending moments for a frame with pin-ended columns are twice as large as those for a frame of the same size having fixed-end columns. Fixed ends are not easy to produce. The average column is probably nearer to the pinned condition than to the fixed-end condition. With both upper and lower ends perfectly fixed, the point of contraflexure is at the mid-height. As rotation of either end occurs, the point of contraflexure shifts toward that end. Rotation of the lower end is more probable; thus, conditions intermediate between that of Fig. 4–20(a) and that of (d) are common.

4–12. Mill Building Bents. The cross section of the steel framework for a simple "mill-type" building is shown by Fig. 4–21(a). The assembly of trusses, columns, and braces in the plane of one such cross section is called a "bent." The type of braces shown here are called "knee braces." Without the knee braces, the bent would be stable only for vertical loads. With horizontal loads, such as wind loads, the columns would rotate and the bent would collapse.

In the bent of Fig. 4–21(b) no knee brace is needed. The members marked x and y serve the same purpose as the knee braces. They prevent the column from rotating with respect to the truss, and thus permit the bent to receive horizontal load without collapsing.

Both of the bents shown are statically indeterminate. They are merely more elaborate examples like the portal-braced bay shown in the preceding article. The difference is in the location of the loads. The mill building bent may receive horizontal load at each purlin location along the top chord, and at the location of each horizontal member (girt) connecting the siding to the building columns. These loads are shown in Fig. 4–21(a).

In the analysis of bents, points of contraflexure for the columns are assumed, just as for the portal. Loads acting above the points of contraflexure are assumed to be resisted equally by the two columns, causing equal shears at their points of contraflexure. The portion above

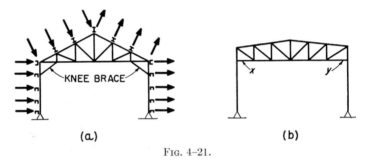

KNEE BRACE

(a)   (b)

FIG. 4–21.

a section cutting the bent at the assumed points of contraflexure is removed and analyzed just as for the portal. Horizontal and vertical reactions are computed for that portion. The horizontal reaction is the column shear; the vertical reaction, the axial load. The columns below the section each receive as loads the values computed for shear and axial load at the point of contraflexure, plus any horizontal loads applied to the column below that point. The next example will show the analysis of such a bent.

With respect to dead loads, snow loads, and other vertical loads, the truss of the bent is analyzed as if the knee brace (or member x or y) were not present. In other words, the truss is treated as if simply supported at the points of its connection to the columns. The presence of the bracing member and the action of the entire bent is considered only when horizontal loads are present. The stresses due to various loadings are then combined, as in Example 4–7, to determine the maximum stress for each member.

EXAMPLE 4–9. In Examples 4–6 and 4–7 a Fink roof truss was completely analyzed as a step in determining whether a new conveyor system can be suspended from the truss. The truss is shown in Fig. 4-14. The ends of the truss are shown supported on brick walls.

Assume now that the plant supervision has decided to extend the conveyor for the full length of the plant, and that in the newer portion of the building the trusses are supported by columns with knee braces as shown in Fig. 4-22(a). An analysis must be made for that portion

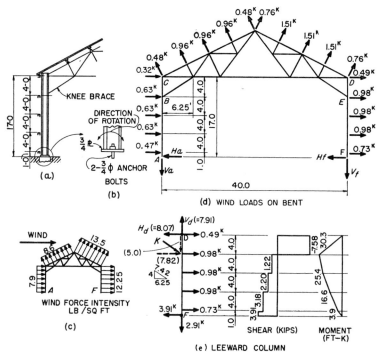

(d) WIND LOADS ON BENT

(c)

(e) LEEWARD COLUMN

FIG. 4-22.

of the building also. The truss layout and roof details are the same as for the older section. The sides of the new portion are of light-weight material supported by girts. How would the analysis of this section differ from that of Examples 4-6 and 4-7?

The bent is analyzed for dead load, snow load, and the conveyor loads, just as it was in the previous examples. The presence of the knee brace is ignored. The analysis of the wind stresses, however, is different from the previous analysis.

The columns have end details as shown by Fig. 4-22(b). The anchor bolts are not in the best position to resist rotation of the column end, and they are not large bolts. It would be best to assume the columns to be pinned. The assumed points of contraflexure are at the bottom.

Fig. 4–22(c) shows the intensity of the wind loads. Those for the roof are taken from Fig. 4–15. Those for the sides consist of an external pressure of $0.8q$ for the windward column and an external suction of $0.5q$ for the leeward column (see Art. 1–7), each combined with an internal pressure of 4.5 lb per sq ft. The wind forces reach the bent as concentrations of load at the purlins and girts. The concentrated loads for one bent are shown by Fig. 4–22(d). Each concentration is the product of the load intensity and the surface area supported by the one purlin or girt.

Horizontal loads (and components of load) above the points of contraflexure are assumed to be resisted equally by the two columns. Thus, since the assumed points of contraflexure are at the bottom, reactions H_a and H_f are equal. By $\Sigma H = 0$,

$$H_a = H_f = 3.91 \text{ kips}$$

The vertical reaction at F is solved next. Note that in computing the moments of the inclined loads, their horizontal and vertical components are used. (For the windward side, the horizontal component is 8.6 times the vertical projection of the sloping surface; the vertical component is 8.6 times the horizontal projection.)

$$\Sigma M_a = 0$$

Load	Arm	Moment (+ clockwise)
7.9 × 17 × 20 = 2,680	8.5	+ 22,900
12.25 × 17 × 20 = 4,160	8.5	+ 35,500
8.6 × 10 × 20 = 1,720	22	− 37,800
8.6 × 20 × 20 = 3,440	10	− 34,400
13.5 × 10 × 20 = 2,700	22	+ 59,400
13.5 × 20 × 20 = 5,400	30	− 162,000
		− 116,400 ft-lb

$$-116{,}400 + 40V_f = 0; \quad V_f = 2{,}910 \text{ lb, down}$$
$$\Sigma V = 0$$
$$-V_a + 3{,}440 + 5{,}400 - 2{,}910 = 0; \quad V_a = 5{,}930 \text{ lb, down}$$

The leeward column is isolated as a free body in Fig. 4–22(e). The girt loads and bottom reactions are shown as known loads. Three unknown forces exist where the column is connected to the truss and knee brace. Those three forces hold the column in equilibrium against the known loads shown. The direction of the knee-brace stress K is parallel to the brace. The connection of the truss at D can provide any direction of reaction necessary, so two unknown components, H_d and V_d, are shown.

ΣM (about the intersection of force K with the column) $= 0$

$(4 \times 0.49) - (0.98 \times 2 \times 6) - (0.73 \times 12) + (3.91 \times 13) - 4H_d = 0$

$$H_d = 8.07 \text{ kips, to left}$$

By $\Sigma H = 0$,

$$H_k = 7.82 \text{ kips, to right}$$

$$K = 7.82 \times \frac{7.42}{6.25} = 9.30 \text{ kips, compression}$$

By $\Sigma V = 0$,

$$V_d = 7.91 \text{ kips, up}$$

The shear and moment diagrams for the leeward column are drawn in Fig. 4–22(e).

Normally, a similar analysis would be made for the windward column also. The forces K, H_d, and V_d shown in Fig. 4–22(e), along with similar forces computed for the windward column, would be reversed in direction for use as reactions for the truss. The truss analysis would then be completed and the results tabulated as was done in Examples 4–6 and 4–7.

EXAMPLE 4–10. A platform formerly used for the support of a bin is shown in Fig. 4–23. With the installing of a new power line, it is found

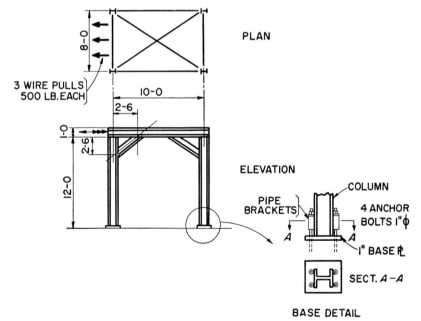

FIG. 4–23.

Check on Use of Existing Platform as Dead-End Tower
Effect of Wire Pulls:

Total Pull = $3 \times 500 = 1,500$ lb
Pull per Side = 750 lb
Assume Fixed-end Columns

Assumed Pt. of Contraflexure

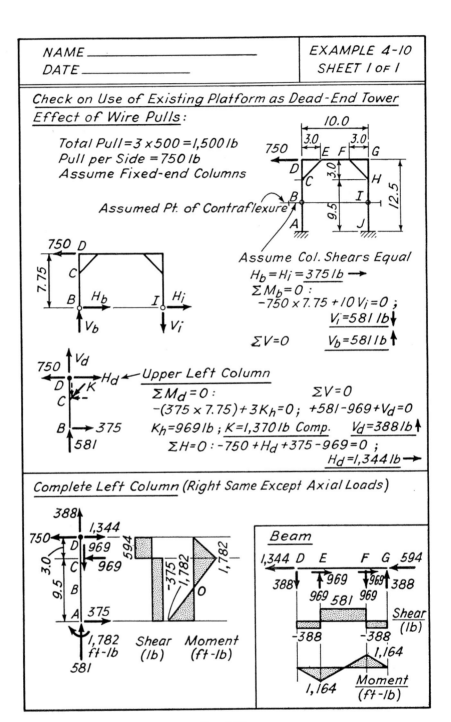

Assume Col. Shears Equal
$H_b = H_i = 375$ lb $\rightarrow$
$\Sigma M_b = 0$:
$-750 \times 7.75 + 10 V_i = 0$;
$V_i = 581$ lb $\downarrow$
$\Sigma V = 0$ $V_b = 581$ lb $\uparrow$

Upper Left Column
$\Sigma M_d = 0$: $\Sigma V = 0$
$-(375 \times 7.75) + 3K_h = 0$; $+581 - 969 + V_d = 0$
$K_h = 969$ lb ; $K = 1,370$ lb Comp. $V_d = 388$ lb $\uparrow$
$\Sigma H = 0 : -750 + H_d + 375 - 969 = 0$;
$H_d = 1,344$ lb $\rightarrow$

Complete Left Column (Right Same Except Axial Loads)

Beam

Shear (lb)   Moment (ft-lb)

Shear (lb)

Moment (ft-lb)

FIG. 4-24.

118

desirable to use this platform as a dead-end tower, the entire pull being transmitted to the tower as shown. The strength of the structure must be checked first, however. As one step in the check, the structure is

Courtesy of Cleveland Electric Illuminating Co.

Trusses Are Used Much in Electric Substations. Horizontal-Plane Trusses Resist Horizontal Loads from Wind and Wire Pull; Vertical-Plane Trusses Resist Gravity Loads.

analyzed to determine the thrusts, moments, and shears caused by the new loading.

This example is solved completely on the typical computation sheet of Fig. 4–24.

PROBLEMS

4–1. Solve, using the method of sections, for the stress in bars a, b, c, and d of the truss in Fig. 4–25.

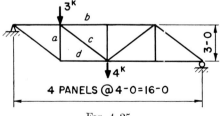

Fig. 4–25.

4–2. Use the method of sections to compute the stress in bars e, f, g, and h of the truss in Fig. 4–26.

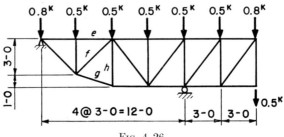

Fig. 4–26.

4–3. Use the analytical method of joints to solve for all the bar stresses in the truss of Fig. 4–27.

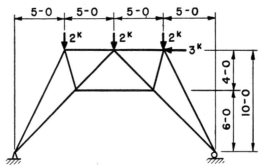

Fig. 4–27.

4–4. Compute analytically the stresses in all members of one truss of the tower shown in Fig. 4–28. Assume the wires to be symmetrically located between two trusses.

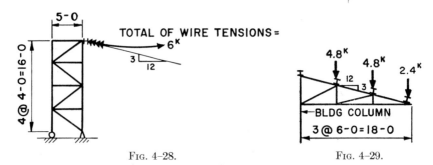

Fig. 4–28.   Fig. 4–29.

4-5. Compute analytically the stress in all members of the canopy truss of Fig. 4–29. The loads shown include snow load and dead load, and are transferred to the truss by the purlins shown.

4-6. A catwalk is required to be placed over a large tank. No overhead support is available, so a footbridge, as shown in Fig. 4–30, is constructed. The

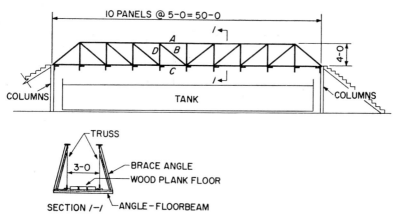

Fig. 4–30.

dead load on the bridge is estimated at 60 lb per ft. Assume a live load of 100 lb per ft of bridge. Compute analytically the stress due to combined full live load and dead load in the members marked *A*, *B*, *C*, and *D*.

4-7. A basket for carrying wet cotton scraps is shown in Fig. 4–31. It consists of a canvas lining attached to a light framework of welded tubing. Each of the long sides is trussed as shown. The basket is lifted by hoist hooks placed over the end trunnions. Find the stresses in all members of the truss. Assume the weight of the container itself to be negligible.

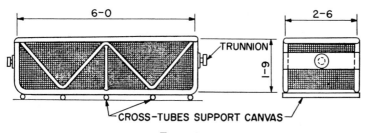

Fig. 4–31.

4–8. A light rack for lifting long bins of partially finished work and relocating them in the plant is fabricated as shown in Fig. 4–32. Compute the stresses

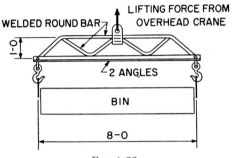

FIG. 4–32.

in each bar of the truss. Assume the truss weight to be negligible. The bin and its contents weighs 1,500 lb.

4–9. A traveling jib crane is used to carry sand in a foundry building. The crane bridge is supported by 2 cantilevered trusses, as shown in Fig. 4–33.

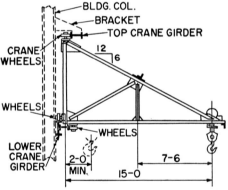

FIG. 4–33.

The hoist and trolley operate on rails between the trusses. The entire assembly moves lengthwise along the building. Crane girders are located at the top and bottom of the left end of the trusses. Note that the upper girder is able to resist horizontal forces only, while the lower girder can resist both horizontal and vertical forces.

Solve analytically for the maximum bar stresses caused by live load on the truss. The trolley and hoist weigh 1,200 lb. The weight of the sand bin and its contents is 2 tons. The load may be moved to any position within the range shown. The rails between the trusses transmit load to the trusses at panel points only.

4–10. Solve graphically for the bar stresses in the truss of Problem 4–5 (Fig. 4–29).

4–11. Compute graphically the stress in all members of the truss of Problem 4–6 (Fig. 4–30), when subject to full live and dead loads.

4–12. Compute graphically the stress in the bars of the 6-panel Fink truss of Fig. 4–34. (The 6-panel Fink truss is sometimes used in timber construction.)

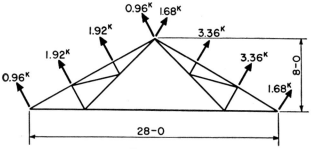

FIG. 4–34.

4–13. A solid advertising sign measuring 10 ft high by 26 ft long is supported by 2 steel trusses, as shown by Fig. 4–35. A truss is located at 5 ft from each end of the sign. The trusses are connected through the roof material to the

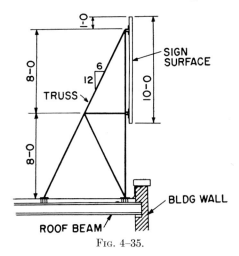

FIG. 4–35.

existing roof beams. Determine graphically the bar stresses due to a wind pressure of 25 lb per sq ft.

4–14. An existing building roof is shown in Fig. 4–36. It is desired to lift a machine weighing 10,000 lb by use of two chain hoists attached to the bottom chord of the roof truss as shown. What will the total bar stresses be when no snow is present? What will they be if the roof has a snow load of 10 lb per sq ft when the machine is lifted? Assume the truss weight to

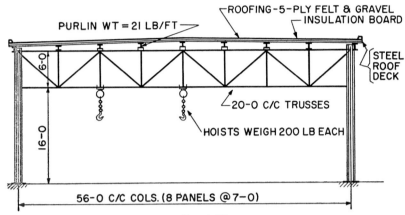

FIG. 4–36.

be 5,400 lb, divided equally among the panels and applied at the upper panel points. The steel deck weighs 4 lb per sq ft and the insulation 2 lb per sq ft.

4–15. Complete the analysis for the windward column of Example 4–9 and Fig. 4–22.

4–16. Complete the analysis of the truss of Example 4–9 and Fig. 4–22 to find the wind-load stresses.

4–17. Analyze the bent of Example 4–9 and Fig. 4–22, but having heavy base plates and heavy anchor bolts located on the flange faces of the columns. Assume fixed-end conditions.

4–18. The support for a machine is made using a portal as shown in Fig. 4–37. Assume that the machine exerts a horizontal impact force of 5 kips on each

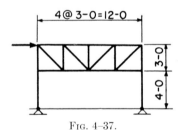

FIG. 4–37.

portal of the supporting structure. Solve for the reactions. Find the maximum column bending moments. Solve for the bar stresses in the truss.

4–19. Repeat the analysis of Example 4–10 assuming pinned ends for the columns.

4–20. The footbridge of Problem 4–6 is over an outdoor tank. Wind will damage the structure unless it is laterally braced. Outrigged braces (see Fig. 4–30) transfer wind loads from the top chord to the plane of the bottom chord. A lateral bracing system must be placed in a horizontal plane at the bottom-chord level, as shown in Fig. 4–38. The lateral system is merely a

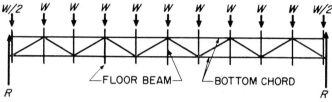

FIG. 4–38.

horizontal truss for the resistance of horizontal loads. The truss receives concentrated loads at each floorbeam, the amount of load being the total wind force for the half panel on either side of the floorbeam. Use a wind pressure of 20 lb per sq ft, acting on 1.5 times the exposed vertical area for one truss. Assume the vertical projection to average 1.2 sq ft per ft of truss. Compute the stresses for the members of the lateral system.

CHAPTER 5

ANALYSIS WITH MOVING LOADS

The methods of analysis given in Chapters 2, 3, and 4 are valid for static loads, movable loads, or moving loads. When movable or moving loads occur, however, the analysis must be preceded by determining the location for such loads. Sometimes this is done by inspection. For example, in the simple beam of Fig. 5–1(a), it should be obvious that the bending moment at the center will be greatest when the wheel load is at the center. For the beam of Fig. 5–1(b), however, it is not obvious where the maximum bending moment will occur, nor where the loads must be placed to cause the maximum bending moment. The position of the loads to give the greatest stress in bar A of the truss in Fig. 5–1(c) is not obvious.

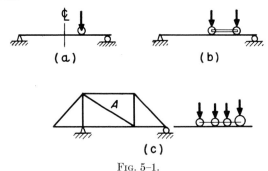

Fig. 5–1.

Special techniques are available to determine the loads to be applied and the position of the loads on the structure. Those techniques include the use of *influence lines* and of criteria which are derived from the influence lines.

5–1. Influence Lines. An influence line is a graph showing the effect of a unit load as it moves across the structure. The influence line is drawn for a single function, such as the vertical reaction, or the bending moment at a particular point of the span. The ordinate at any point on the line gives the value of the function caused by a unit load at the point of the ordinate.

As an example, consider the simple beam of Fig. 5–2. When the one-lb load is at point A, reaction V_a is one lb. When the load moves to the center of the span, V_a is $\frac{1}{2}$ lb. When the load is at point B, V_a is zero. These values of V_a are plotted as ordinates at point A, the center, and point B, respectively. The line joining the plotted points is called the influence line for reaction V_a. Its ordinates each represent the value of V_a that would be caused by a one-lb load at the location of the ordinate. The units of the ordinate are pounds per pound.

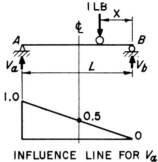

INFLUENCE LINE FOR V_a

Fig. 5–2.

If the equation $\Sigma M = 0$ is written with point B as the moment center, and with the distance of the load from point B called x,

$$V_a = 1 \cdot x/L$$

The influence line of Fig. 5–2 is merely the graph of the above equation, with V_a as ordinate and x as abscissa.

Fig. 5–3 shows the influence line for bending moment at the center of the span. It can be obtained by the same procedure as was used to

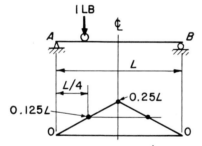

INFLUENCE LINE FOR ℄ BENDING MOMENT

Fig. 5–3.

obtain the influence line for V_a. With the load at A, or at B, the bending moment at the center is zero. With the load at the center, the bending moment at the center is $1 \cdot L/4$ or $0.25L$. With the load at the one-quarter point of the span, the opposite end reaction is 0.25 lb, and the center bending moment is $0.25L/2$, or $0.125L$. Thus the influence line for bending moment at the center is the triangle shown in Fig. 5–3.

It is an unfortunate coincidence that an influence line for bending moment is often the same shape as a moment diagram. Do not try to use or justify this similarity. Try instead to ignore it. The influence line has nothing at all to do with the moment diagram. The two are different, have different meanings, have different uses, and are constructed by different methods.

As a third sample, consider an influence line for shear at the one-quarter point of the span. The beam is shown in Fig. 5–4. Obviously,

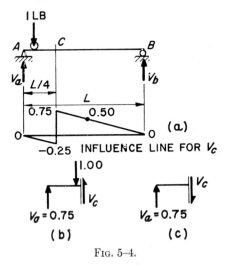

FIG. 5–4.

the shear is zero when the load is at either end, A or B. When the load is a very small distance to the left of point C, the reaction V_a is 0.75, and the portion to the left of C is loaded as shown in Fig. 5–4(b). The sum of the loads on this portion is 0.25 lb downward, so the shear at C is -0.25 lb. When the load is just to the right of C, the isolated portion in Fig. 5–4(c) is loaded by the reaction V_a only, and the shear V_c is $+0.75$ lb. Thus, as the load moves toward the right across point C, the shear at C suddenly changes from -0.25 lb to $+0.75$ lb. When the load is at the center of the span, V_a is 0.50 lb upward and the shear at C is $+0.50$ lb. These values of shear at point C are plotted in Fig. 5–4(a) to give the influence line for shear V_c.

Influence lines can be drawn for other functions also, such as the stress in a particular bar of a truss, or the deflection of a point on a structure.

5–2. The Use of Influence Lines.   It might appear from the preceding article that influence lines have academic interest only, but that is not the case. They are useful in three practical ways, as follows:

1. In determining the load locations for maximum or minimum values of a function
2. In determining the amount of the function after the load locations have been selected

3. In the derivation of rules and criteria for the placing of loads to give the maximum or minimum value of a function

All of these uses will be illustrated in the balance of this chapter. The second one will be explained at this point. Consider the simple beam of Fig. 5–5(a) to be loaded with two concentrated loads and a

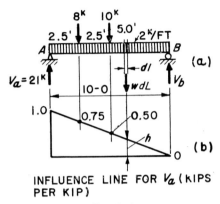

INFLUENCE LINE FOR V_a (KIPS PER KIP)

Fig. 5–5.

uniform load, as shown. The total reaction V_a, obtained by the methods of Chapter 2, is 21 kips. This value can be obtained also by use of the influence line for V_a and the principle of superposition. If a one-kip load at the center causes $V_a = 0.50$ kip, then 10 kips of load at the center cause V_a to be 10 times as much, or 5 kips. Similarly, the 8-kip load causes V_a of 8 times 0.75, or 6 kips.

Imagine now that the uniform load is a series of concentrated loads, closely spaced at a distance dL apart, and each equal to $w\,dL$. The effect of one of these loads on the reaction is $wh\,dL$, h being the influence ordinate directly beneath the small load $w\,dL$ in question. The reaction V_a caused by all of these increments is $\int_0^L wh\,dL$ or $w\int_0^L h\,dL$. The term $\int_0^L h\,dL$ is the area under the influence line. The reaction caused by the uniform load is then $2\left(\dfrac{1.0 \times 10}{2}\right) = 10.0$ kips. The total reaction is $5 + 6 + 10 = 21$ kips.

In summary, two rules can be stated.

1. The amount of a function due to a concentrated load equals the product of the load and the influence ordinate beneath the load.
2. The amount of a function due to a uniform load equals the load per unit length times the area under the influence line. (If the uniform load does not extend over the full length of the member, use the area under the loaded portions only.)

The example shown above could be solved quite easily without using an influence line. It is necessary to use a very simple case as a first illustration. The real advantage of influence lines occurs in the more complicated cases.

EXAMPLE 5–1. The beam of Fig. 5–6 is subject to a movable uniform load of one kip per ft and a moving concentrated load of 4 kips. Influence

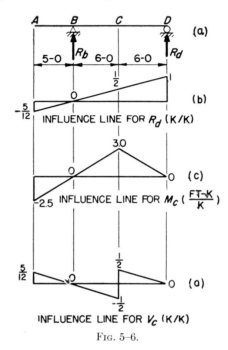

FIG. 5–6.

lines will be used to asist in solving for (a) maximum downward reaction at point D; (b) maximum bending moment at point C; and (c) maximum shear at point C.

To obtain the influence line for R_d, values of R_d must be computed for various positions of a one-kip downward load. For example, if one kip is placed at D, the reaction R_d will be one kip upward, or $+1$. If the one-kip load is at point C, the reaction at D is one-half kip upward, or $+\frac{1}{2}$. If the one-kip load is at A, the reaction at D will be $\frac{5}{12}$ kip downward, or $-\frac{5}{12}$. A load at B will cause zero reaction at D. These values of the reaction at D are plotted *beneath the position of the unit load* which would cause them. The resulting influence line for the reaction at D is shown in Fig. 5–6(b).

The influence line for R_d shows that downward (negative) values of R_d are caused by loads placed anywhere between points A and B.

(Loads between B and D would cause upward reactions at D.) Therefore, to obtain the maximum downward reaction, the 4-kip concentrated load will be placed at A, and uniform load will be placed from A to B only. Applying the two rules developed in Art. 5–2,

$$R_d = \left(4 \times \frac{-5}{12}\right) + \left(1 \times \frac{1}{2} \times \frac{-5}{12} \times 5\right)$$
$$= -2.71 \text{ kips, or } 2.71 \text{ kips downward}$$

The influence line for bending moment at point C is computed next. If a unit load is at C, the reaction R_d is $\frac{1}{2}$ kip upward, and M_c is $\frac{1}{2} \times 6$, or 3 ft-kips. If a unit load is at A, R_d is $\frac{5}{12}$ kip downward, and M_c is $-\frac{5}{12} \times 6$, or -2.5 ft-kips. Loads at B or D will cause zero bending moment at C. Plotting these points gives the influence line of Fig. 5–6(c). From experience, the author knew the general form of the line and felt that the four points computed were sufficient; a beginner would

Courtesy of Link-Belt Co.

A PORTABLE STACKER PLACES COAL FROM A SELF-UNLOADING SHIP ON RESERVE STORAGE PILES. NOTICE THE MANY STRUCTURAL MEMBERS REQUIRED, INCLUDING TRUSSES ON THE STACKER BOOM.

probably benefit by plotting more. When in doubt, plot a few extra points.

There are two possible answers for the maximum bending moment at C. If the maximum positive value is desired, uniform load will be placed between B and D with the concentrated load at C. Thus,

$$M_c = (4 \times 3.0) + (1 \times \tfrac{1}{2} \times 3.0 \times 12) = 30.0 \text{ ft-kips}$$

For maximum negative bending moment, the concentrated load is placed at A with uniform load from A to B.

$$M_c = 4(-2.5) + 1(-2.5 \times \tfrac{1}{2} \times 5) = -16.25 \text{ ft-kips}$$

Fig. 5–6(d) shows the influence line for shear at point C. With the unit load at point C, reaction R_d is $\tfrac{1}{2}$ kip upward. If the load is a very small distance to the left of C, the sum of the transverse loads to the right of C is $\tfrac{1}{2}$ kip upward, and the shear at C is $-\tfrac{1}{2}$ kip. With the unit load just to the right of C, the sum of the transverse loads to the right of C is $\tfrac{1}{2}$ kip downward, and the shear at C is $+\tfrac{1}{2}$ kip. The shear at C is computed similarly for other positions of the unit load. The influence line is obtained by plotting the various shear values.

To obtain the maximum positive value of shear V_c, the concentrated load is placed at the point of maximum positive ordinate (just right of C), and uniform load is placed wherever it will cause a positive shear V_c (from A to B and from C to D).

$$V_c = \left(4 \times \frac{1}{2}\right) + \left(1 \times \frac{1}{2} \times \frac{5}{12} \times 5\right) + \left(1 \times \frac{1}{2} \times \frac{1}{2} \times 6\right) = 4.54 \text{ kips}$$

Similarly, for maximum negative shear,

$$V_c = 4(-\tfrac{1}{2}) + 1(-\tfrac{1}{2} \times \tfrac{1}{2} \times 6) = -3.50 \text{ kips}$$

EXAMPLE 5–2. A belt-conveyor support is shown by Fig. 5–7(a). The boom supports the conveyor by closely spaced idler pulleys, so that the conveyor loads on the boom can be assumed as uniformly distributed. The boom consists of two beams, one on each side of the belt. Two adjustable cables support the outer end of the boom. The beams, pulleys, and belt weigh about 60 lb per ft of boom. The damp sand to be carried will weigh about 40 lb per ft length of belt.

Some proposed revisions to the boom require cutting holes in it at point B. These will undoubtedly affect the structural strength. As one step in checking the strength, the maximum bending moment and maximum shear at point B must be determined. This will be done using influence lines.

Fig. 5–7(b) shows the influence line for bending moment at point B. A unit load at either A or C causes zero bending moment at B. A one-lb load at B causes the vertical reaction at A to be $\frac{4}{11}$ lb upward.

$$M_b = 7V_a = 28/11 = 2.55 \text{ ft-lb, compression on top}$$

The influence ordinate at B is $+2.55$ ft-lb per lb. A one-lb load at D causes V_a to be $\frac{9}{11}$ lb downward. The bending moment M_b causes compression on the bottom.

$$M_b = 7V_a = -63/11 = -5.73 \text{ ft-lb}$$

The influence ordinate at D is -5.73 ft-lb per lb.

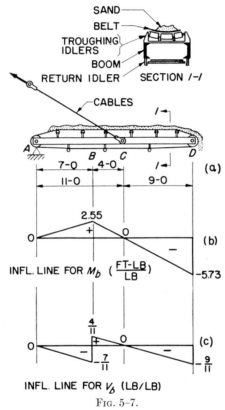

INFL. LINE FOR V_b (LB/LB)

Fig. 5-7.

Dead load occurs over the entire length. The bending moment M_b due to dead load is the load per foot times the area under the influence line.

$$\text{Positive area} = 2.55 \times 11/2 = 14.0$$
$$\text{Negative area} = -5.73 \times 9/2 = -25.8$$
$$\text{Total area} = -11.8$$

M_b due to dead load $= -11.8 \times 30 = -354$ ft-lb on one beam

The live load can occur on any part or all of the length. For the numerically largest bending moment, live load should occur over the negative influence area only (point C to point D).

M_b due to live load $= -25.8 \times 20 = -516$ ft-lb on one beam

The maximum moment M_b is $-354 - 516 = -870$ ft-lb for each beam.

The influence line for shear at point B is shown in Fig. 5–7(c). The student should compute the shear at B **due** to a one-lb load at various locations, so as to verify the influence ordinates shown.

$$\text{Positive area} = \frac{1}{2} \times \frac{4}{11} \times 4 \qquad = \quad 0.73$$

Negative areas:

$$A \text{ to } B: -\frac{1}{2} \times \frac{7}{11} \times 7 = -2.23$$

$$C \text{ to } D: -\frac{1}{2} \times \frac{9}{11} \times 9 = \underline{-3.68}$$

$$\text{Total negative area} \qquad = -5.91$$

$$\text{Total area} = \overline{-5.18}$$

Dead load will occur over the entire length. For the numerically largest shear V_b, live load should be placed over the negative areas only, from A to B and from C to D.

Courtesy of American MonoRail Co.

MONORAIL CARRIER USED IN TEXTILE PLANT. NOTE OVERHEAD SUPPORTING BEAMS, TRUSSES, AND FRAMES.

$$V_b \text{ due to dead load} = -5.18 \times 30 = -155$$
$$V_b \text{ due to live load} = -5.91 \times 20 = -118$$
$$\text{Maximum shear at } B = -273 \text{ lb for each beam}$$

5–3. Influence Lines for Girders Supporting Transverse Beams.
Beams often receive loads indirectly as illustrated in Fig. 5–8. The live

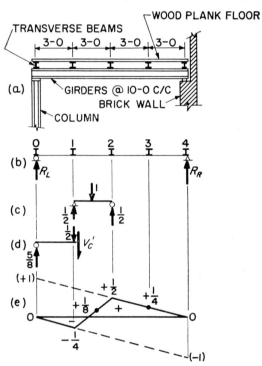

INFL. LINE FOR SHEAR IN PANEL I–2
(K/K)

Fig. 5–8.

and dead loads on the floor are carried directly by the beams which
show in end view. The end reactions of these beams become the loads
on the larger beam. The larger beam which supports transverse beams
is often called a girder. Some influence lines, especially those for shear,
are more complex for such a girder than for a beam which may receive
load directly at any point.

This type of construction is very common. Examples are building
roof framing, building floor framing, and bridge floors.

EXAMPLE 5–3. Use influence lines to find the maximum live-load
shear in panel 1–2 of the girder shown in Fig. 5–8(a). The structure is a

balcony such as might be added to an existing factory building for the storage of materials, etc. The live load is movable, 300 lb per sq ft.

Part (b) of Fig. 5–8 shows the idealized structure. Load can reach the girder at the location of the transverse beams only. These points are called "panel points"; the space between two panel points is called a "panel." Since loads occur at panel points only, the shear due to floor loads is constant throughout a particular panel. (The weight of the girder itself, however, is distributed along the length of the girder. This will cause slight variations of *total* shear within panels.)

A unit load at panel point number 1 (ppl) causes a reaction R_L of $\frac{3}{4}$. The shear in panel 1–2 is

$$V_{1-2} = +\tfrac{3}{4} - 1 = -\tfrac{1}{4}$$

For a unit load at pp2, R_L is $\frac{1}{2}$, and $V_{1-2} = +\frac{1}{2}$. Similarily, a unit load at pp3 causes $V_{1-2} = +\frac{1}{4}$.

When the unit load is between panel points, the flooring, through its own action as a beam, transmits the load to the girder at the two adjacent panel points. For example, with the load midway between ppl and pp2, the flooring acts as shown in Fig. 5–8(c). The girder receives $\frac{1}{2}$ kip of load at each panel point, 1 and 2. The reaction R_L is $\frac{5}{8}$. If the girder is cut at any section between ppl and pp2, the portion to the left of the section will appear as in Fig. 5–8(d). From this figure,

$$V_{1-2} = +\tfrac{5}{8} - \tfrac{1}{2} = +\tfrac{1}{8}$$

Thus, the influence ordinate at the mid-point of panel 1–2 is $+\frac{1}{8}$ kip per kip.

The values of V_{1-2} computed for the various load positions are plotted to obtain the influence line in Fig. 5–8(e). Actually, it is not necessary to compute the ordinate for the mid-point of the panel. That was done here only to illustrate that the influence line is straight between panel points.

There is obviously more positive area than negative, so the positive shear will be the maximum. Live load should be placed between the right end and the point of zero influence ordinate. This point, by simple geometry, is 2 ft from pp2. The live load per foot of girder is $300 \times 10 = 3,000$ lb.

$$\text{Maximum } V_{1-2} = 3,000 \times \tfrac{1}{2} \times \tfrac{1}{2} \times 8 = 6,000 \text{ lb}$$

Note that if the influence line from pp4 to pp2 is extended as a straight line to the left end, it reaches an ordinate of $+1$. Also, the line from pp0 to ppl is "aimed" toward an ordinate of -1 at the right end. This fact helps in the construction of influence lines for shear.

5–4. Criteria for Load Positions. Art. 5–2 gave three uses for influence lines. The last of these is in the derivation of criteria for determining load locations. In this chapter they will be used to develop two very useful criteria for the load positions causing maximum bending moment, and to develop a method and a criterion for finding the load positions for maximum shear. The criteria for moment and the method and criterion for shear are particularly helpful when a series of loads occurs, such as those caused by the wheels of a monorail conveyor or by cranes on a runway.

5–5. Maximum Bending Moment at a Particular Section. Fig. 5–9 shows a beam and a series of moving loads. What position of the loads

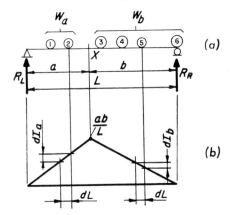

INFL. LINE FOR BENDING MOMENT AT X

Fɪɢ. 5–9.

will cause the largest bending moment at point X? (The spacing between loads is fixed.)

The influence line for bending moment at point X is shown in Fig. 5–9(b). With a unit load at X, R_L is $1 \times b/L$, and the bending moment at X is aR_L or ab/L.

The sum of the loads in length a is called W_a; the sum in length b is called W_b. If all loads move a distance dL to the left, a change in bending moment M_x occurs. Wheels 1 and 2 move to points of lower influence ordinate. Their movement causes a decrease in M_x. Wheels 3 to 6 all move to points of higher influence ordinate and cause an increase in M_x.

The increase of influence ordinate dI equals dL times the slope of the influence line. Thus for length a, the slope of the line is b/L, and

$$dI_a = \frac{b}{L}\,dL$$

For length b, the slope is a/L, and

$$dI_b = \frac{a}{L} dL$$

The decrease in M_x due to movement of the wheels in length a is $W_a \, dI_a$. The increase due to movement of the wheels in length b is $W_b \, dI_b$. Substituting for dI_a and dI_b, the total change in M_x is

$$dM_x = \frac{a \, dL}{L} W_b - \frac{b \, dL}{L} W_a$$

When M_x is maximum, the rate of change dM_x/dL will be zero.

$$\frac{dM_x}{dL} = \frac{aW_b}{L} = \frac{bW_a}{L} = 0$$

Cancelling and rearranging gives

$$\frac{W_a}{a} = \frac{W_b}{b}$$

The above is the mathematical statement of the criterion. It can be stated in words as follows:

The bending moment at a particular section is greatest when the average load (per unit of length) to the left of the section is equal to the average load to the right.

Since the algebraic sign of dM_x remains the same until a particular load passes point X, the zero value of dM_x occurs *as* a load passes X. Thus the maximum bending moment M_x occurs when a load is directly over point X.

EXAMPLE 5–4. A new monorail is added to the bottom chord of roof trusses, as shown in Fig. 5–10. The monorail tractor and carriers have wheel loads as shown in (b). What is the maximum live-load bending moment at the center of a monorail beam?

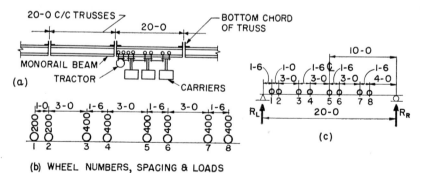

(b) WHEEL NUMBERS, SPACING & LOADS

FIG. 5–10.

Wheel positions are tried until those which satisfy the criterion have been determined. This is easiest if the solution is tabulated. A selected wheel is assumed first to be just to the right of the center. A comparison of the quantities W_a/a and W_b/b is made. The load is then allowed to pass just to the left of the center, and another comparison made. If W_a/a is smaller than W_b/b before the wheel crosses the center point, but is larger than W_b/b afterward, then at the instant of passing W_a/a is equal to W_b/b. The criterion is then satisfied.

Wheel at Center Point	Wheel Position	Average on Left	Average on Right	Criterion
1	Right of center point	0	< 1,600/10	Not Satisfied
	Left " " "	200/10	< 1,400/10	
2	Right " " "	200/10	< 1,800/10	Not Satisfied
	Left " " "	400/10	< 1,600/10	
3	Right " " "	400/10	< 2,000/10	Not Satisfied
	Left " " "	800/10	< 1,600/10	
4	Right " " "	800/10	< 2,000/10	Not Satisfied
	Left " " "	1,200/10	< 1,600/10	
5	Right " " "	1,200/10	< 1,600/10	*Satisfied*
	Left " " "	1,600/10	> 1,200/10	
6	Right " " "	1,400/10	> 1,200/10	Not Satisfied
	Left " " "	1,800/10	> 800/10	

The maximum bending moment at the center of the span will occur when wheel number 5 is at the centerline. (Once the procedure is understood, it is easy to visualize that positions with wheels 1 or 2 at the center could not possibly be the controlling ones. The tabulations for those positions could have been left out, as it was for wheels 7 or 8 at the center.)

The critical position is shown by Fig. 5–10(c).

$$R_L = \frac{1}{20} [400(4.0 + 5.5 + 8.5 + 10.0 + 13.0 + 14.5)$$

$$+ 200(17.5 + 18.5)] = 1,470 \text{ lb}$$

$$M_{ctr} = (10 \times 1,470) - 200(7.5 + 8.5) - 400(3.0 + 4.5) = 8,500 \text{ ft-lb}$$

When wheels enter or leave the span as various positions are tried, more than one position may be found to satisfy the criterion. The bending moments for each such position must be compared to find the maximum.

5–6. Other Applications of the Moment Criterion. The criterion developed in Art. 5–5 is derived from the influence line for bending moment. The criterion depends entirely on the shape of that line. Therefore, if the influence line for some other function is the same shape as the one for moment (Fig. 5–9), the position of the loads for the maximum value of that function can be found by using the moment criterion. The next example will illustrate this.

EXAMPLE 5–5. What is the maximum live load caused on one truss by the monorail system of Fig. 5–10?

The influence line for the load on the center truss is shown in Fig. 5–11. It is similar in shape to that of Fig. 5–9, and the criterion for

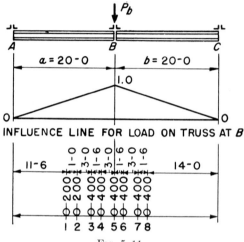

FIG. 5–11.

moment can be used. The dimensions a and b are the lengths of the limbs of the influence line; in this case each is 20 ft.

Load at Truss	Wheel Position	Average on Left		Average on Right	Criterion
3	Right of B	$400/20$	$<$	$2,000/20$	Not Satisfied
	Left of B	$800/20$	$<$	$1,600/20$	
4	Right of B	$800/20$	$<$	$2,000/20$	Not Satisfied
	Left of B	$1,200/20$	$<$	$1,600/20$	
5	Right of B	$1,200/20$	$<$	$1,600/20$	*Satisfied*
	Left of B	$1,600/20$	$>$	$1,200/20$	

The critical position is the one with wheel 5 at the support B. Fig. 5–11 shows the wheels in this position. The live load transferred to the truss at B is the sum of the right reaction of beam AB and the left reaction of beam BC. The maximum live load transferred to the truss is

$$P_b = \frac{1}{20} [200(11.5 + 12.5)$$

$$+ 400(14.0 + 15.5 + 18.5 + 20 + 17 + 15.5)]$$

$$= 2,250 \text{ lb}$$

5–7. Absolute Maximum Bending Moment.   The criterion derived in Art. 5–5 gives the position of loads for the maximum bending moment at a particular point on the beam. But *which* point on the beam will have the highest bending moment? One might suspect the mid-point of the span, but usually (when a series of concentrated loads are involved) points either side of the center will have higher bending moments. To find the absolute maximum bending moment a new criterion is needed.

Fig. 5–12(a) shows a series of loads. The resultant of all wheel loads on the beam is W. The line of action of the resultant is a distance b from

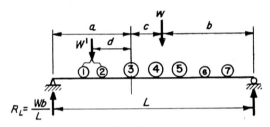

FIG. 5–12.

the right end. The left reaction is obtained by equating the sum of the moments about the right end to zero.

$$R_L = Wb/L$$

The bending moment under wheel number 3 is

$$M_3 = \frac{Wb}{L}(a) - W'd$$

in which W' is the resultant of loads 1 and 2, and $W'd$ is their moment about load 3.

Substituting $(L - b - c)$ for a,

$$M_3 = Wb - Wb^2/L - Wbc/L - W'd$$

If all loads move a short distance db, a change of bending moment occurs. The rate of change is dM_3/db. When M_3 is maximum, the rate of change is zero.

$$\frac{dM_3}{db} = W - 2Wb/L - Wc/L = 0$$

$$L - 2b - c = 0$$

Substituting $(a + b + c)$ for L, and solving,

$$a + b + c - 2b - c = 0$$

$$a = b$$

This last equation is the mathematical statement of the criterion. It says, in effect, that the largest bending moment to occur under wheel number 3 occurs when dimensions a and b are equal. The criterion is stated as follows:

The maximum bending moment under a particular load on a simple beam occurs when that load is as far from one end of the beam as the center of gravity of all loads on the beam is from the other end.

An alternate statement, preferred by many engineers is

The maximum bending moment under a particular load on a simple beam occurs when that load is as far to one side of the center of the span as the center of gravity of all the loads is to the other side.

This criterion should be applied to find the maximum bending moment under wheel 3; then to find the maximum under wheel 4; and then to other wheels as required. Comparisons of the maximum bending moment under various wheels are made to determine which is the absolute maximum bending moment.

EXAMPLE 5–6. What is the maximum live load bending moment on one of the monorail beams of Example 5–4? The beam and loads are shown again in Fig. 5–13. It would be obvious after a little practice with this type of problem that the absolute maximum will not occur under wheels 1, 2, 7, or 8. The maximum bending moments under wheels 3, 4, 5, and 6 will be found and compared.

First, moments are taken about wheel 8 to find the center of gravity of the loads.

$$\bar{x} = \frac{400(1.5 + 4.5 + 6.0 + 9.0 + 10.5) + 200(13.5 + 14.5)}{2,800}$$

$$= 6.50 \text{ ft}$$

In Fig. 5–13(a) the loads are placed for the maximum bending moment under wheel 3.

$$a = b = \tfrac{1}{2}(L - c) = \tfrac{1}{2}(20.00 - 4.00) = 8.00 \text{ ft}$$

(This position is checked to make certain that all loads assumed on the beam still lie on the beam. If these values of a and b caused certain loads to leave the beam, a and b would be recomputed omitting those loads.)

$$R_L = \frac{2,800 \times 8.00}{20} = 1,120 \text{ lb}$$

$$M_3 = 1,120 \times 8.00 - 200(3.0 + 4.0) = 7,560 \text{ ft-lb}$$

For the maximum bending moment under wheel 4, the wheels are placed as shown in Fig. 5–13(b).

$$a = b = \tfrac{1}{2}(20.00 - 2.50) = 8.75 \text{ ft}$$

With the wheel group in this position, all the loads are still on the beam.

$$R_L = \frac{2,800 \times 8.75}{20} = 1,230 \text{ lb}$$

$$M_4 = 1,230 \times 8.75 - (400 \times 1.5) - 200(4.5 + 5.5) = 8,160 \text{ ft-lb}$$

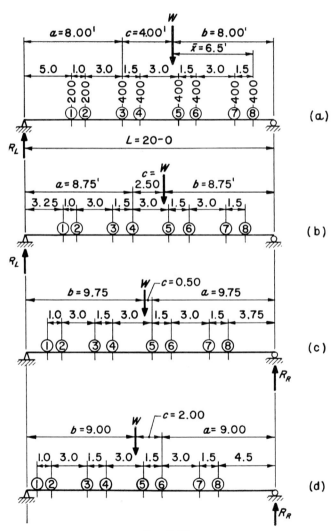

Fig. 5–13.

Fig. 5–13(c) shows the wheels located for the maximum bending moment under wheel 5. Notice that dimension a is now at the right end, and b at the left.

$$a = b = \tfrac{1}{2}(20.00 - 0.50) = 9.75 \text{ ft}$$

All the loads are still on the beam.

$$R_R = \frac{2{,}800 \times 9.75}{20} = 1{,}360 \text{ lb}$$

$$M_5 = (1{,}360 \times 9.75) - 400(1.5 + 4.5 + 6.0) = 8{,}460 \text{ ft-lb}$$

In Fig. 5–13(d) the complete set of eight wheels is placed to give the maximum bending moment that can exist under wheel 6.

$$a = b = \tfrac{1}{2}(20.00 - 2.00) = 9.00 \text{ ft}$$

With the wheels so placed, all wheels are still on the beam.

$$R_R = \frac{2{,}800 \times 9.00}{20} = 1{,}260 \text{ lb}$$

$$M_6 = (1{,}260 \times 9.00) - 400(3.0 + 4.5) = 8{,}340 \text{ ft-lb}$$

The largest live load bending moment is, therefore, 8,460 ft-lb, and occurs under wheel 5 at a section 0.25 ft from the center of the span.

The maximum total bending moment would consist of the above 8,460 for live load, plus a percentage of 8,460 for impact, plus the dead load bending moment at the same point.

EXAMPLE 5–7. Assume that you are an engineer in a manufacturing plant. A crane breakdown of serious nature has occurred. It is estimated that the crane will be out of service for three weeks. Bins of partially completed parts are normally carried by crane from one operation to another over a depressed ramp. The bins must now be pushed by hand. To avoid a very long trip, it is decided to bridge the depressed area. Fig. 5–14(a) shows the temporary arrangement to be used. For what bending moment should the timber beams be designed?

The bending moment due to live load will be much larger than that due to dead load. It will be assumed, therefore, that the absolute maximum total occurs at the point of maximum live-load bending moment. The maximum moment will occur under wheel number 1 when the bin wheels are located as shown in Fig. 5–14(b). Each wheel load is one-fourth of 2,200 lb, or 0.55 kips.

For the bin load,

$$R_L = \frac{1}{7.67}(1.1 \times 2.83) = 0.406 \text{ kips}$$

$$M = 0.406 \times 2.83 = 1.15 \text{ ft-kips}$$

The uniform load per beam due to the weight of the bridge is estimated as follows:

Floor planks (Assume 40 lb/cu ft) 8.1
Channel guide 4.1
Guard rail (2 × 4) 1.7
Posts (about 1 ft of post per ft of span) . . 1.7
Beam (estimate 4 × 6) 5.6

Total = 21.2 lb/ft

For dead load, the moment at the location of wheel number 1 is

$$\frac{0.022 \times 2.83 \times 4.83}{2} = 0.15 \text{ ft-kips}$$

Some allowance should be made for the weight of men pushing the bin. If they actually pushed the bin all the way, their weight would very

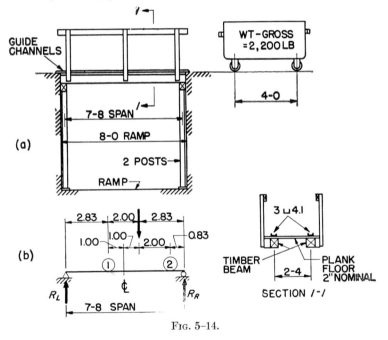

Fig. 5–14.

likely not be on the span at the same time as the bin. It is probably better to assume that the pushers will ride the bin. Their effect could be covered by a percentage increase in the live-load bending moment. Assuming two 200-lb men, an increase of 400/2,200 or 18.2 per cent would be required.

The design bending moment would be

$$(1.15 \times 1.182) + 0.15 = 1.51 \text{ ft-kips}$$

5–8. Maximum Shear at a Section.   A method for placing a series of loads so as to give maximum shear at a section can be found by using the influence line. Fig. 5–15(a) shows an influence line for shear at point C of a beam. In (b) is shown a series of loads. If the entire series of loads moves to the left, all move to algebraically larger influence ordinates. The movement causes an increase of shear. The increase of shear, as loads whose total is W move a distance a to the left, is Wa/L.

With continued movement toward the left, the shear increases until a wheel reaches point C. As point C is passed, the wheel moves from a region of positive influence ordinate to one of negative. The change of influence ordinate is -1.0. This causes a decrease of shear equal to W_1, the load which passes point C.

Now, assume that some wheels rolled off the span while all the wheels were moving a distance a to the left. Call these wheels which left the span W_2; and the distance they moved while still on the span, call b. The increase of shear due to their movement is not W_2a/L, but only W_2b/L.

Similarly, if a wheel weighing W_3 entered the span and moved only a distance c while on the span, the increase of shear caused by W_3 would be W_3c/L.

The total change of shear at C during movement of all wheels a distance a is

$$\Delta V = \frac{Wa}{L} - W_1 + \frac{W_2b}{L} + \frac{W_3c}{L}$$

The symbols used in this expression are defined as follows:

W The total of loads which move the entire distance a while on the span

W_1 The load passing the section in question

W_2 The load which leaves the span during the movement

b The distance moved through by W_2 while still on the span

W_3 The load which enters the span during the movement

c The distance moved through by W_3 while on the span

The largest shear occurs when a load is just to the right of point C. But *which* load should be there? A simple method of determining this uses the expression just developed for the change in shear. The first wheel is placed at the right of C, then all wheels are moved to the left until wheel 2 is at the right of C. The change ΔV is computed. If ΔV is positive, obviously the shear is algebraically greater for the second position than for the first. The wheels are moved again, wheel 3 being brought to point C. The change ΔV due to this movement is computed.

This process is continued until ΔV is negative. The shear for the position previous is then known to be a maximum. Sometimes it is necessary to

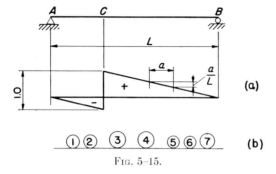

(a)

(b)

Fig. 5–15.

proceed further, since more than one maximum may be observed. (Minimums should also be considered since they may be numerically greater than the maximums.)

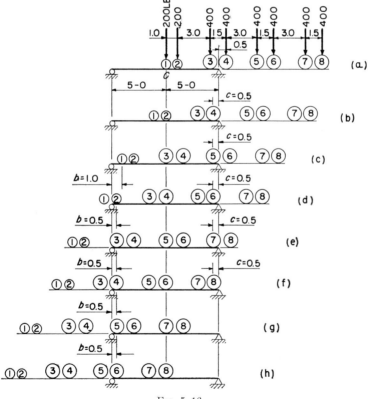

Fig. 5–16.

The method here described is called the "Moving-Up-of-Loads Method." When the position for maximum shear has been determined, the shear at the section is computed in the usual way.

EXAMPLE 5–8. In the alterations to the monorail system of Example 5–4, one 10-ft span of monorail beam is required. It may be necessary to use an existing 10-ft length of beam for this purpose. The piece has a large hole in its web at the middle of the length. The hole will reduce the shear strength. What is the maximum shear at the center of this 10-ft span?

The span and loads are shown in Fig. 5–16. The loads are started in position (a) and are moved 1.0 ft to the position shown in (b). For that movement,

$$\Delta V = \frac{800 \times 1}{10} - 200 + \frac{400 \times 0.5}{10} = -100 \text{ lb}$$

The changes for all movements through the positions from (a) to (h) of Fig. 5–16 are tabulated.

Movement	Wa/L	$-W_1$	$+ W_2b/L$	$+ W_3c/L$	$= \Delta V$	$\Sigma(\Delta V)$
No. 1 at C to No. 2 at C	80	-200	0	20	-100	-100
No. 2 at C to No. 3 at C	360	-200	0	20	180	$+ 80$
No. 3 at C to No. 4 at C	210	-400	20	20	-150	$- 70$
No. 4 at C to No. 5 at C	480	-400	10	20	110	$+ 40$
No. 5 at C to No. 6 at C	240	-400	20	20	-120	$- 80$
No. 6 at C to No. 7 at C	480	-400	20	0	100	$+ 20$
No. 7 at C to No. 8 at C	180	-400	20	0	-200	-180
No. 8 passing to left of C	—	-400	—	—	-400	-580

The right-hand column above gives the summation of the changes of shear. By these summations, it can be seen that the third position gives the largest positive shear. The final position gives the largest negative shear. Which of these two positions gives the *numerically* largest shear is not known, so the shear for both positions will be computed.

For the position of Fig. 5–16(c),

$$R_L = \frac{1}{10} [200(9 + 8) + 400(5 + 3.5 + 0.5)] = 700 \text{ lb}$$

The centerline shear $V_c = 300$ lb.

For the position of Fig. 5–16(h), with wheel 8 just to the left of C, the shear V_c is 660 lb less, or

$$V_c = 300 - 660 = -360 \text{ lb}$$

The maximum amount of live-load shear at the center of the span is -360 lb.

EXAMPLE 5–9. At its ends, the beam of Example 5–8 is attached to existing building steel by clamps such as shown in Fig. 5–17(a). What is the maximum live-load reaction on one such clamp?

The heavier loads are at the right end of the series. The largest clamp reaction results when the heavy loads are near the clamp. So, for the largest reaction on the clamp shown, the loads are turned around to the position shown in Fig. 5–17(b).

The end reaction is the same as the end shear in this case. The end reaction change will equal ΔV. In the expression derived for ΔV, the terms W_2 and b will not appear, since loads leave the span the instant they pass the point of the shear in question. The movements and changes of end reaction are tabulated below.

Movement	Wa/L	$-W_1$	$+ W_3c/L$	$= \Delta V$
No. 8 at end to No. 7 at end	240	−400	40	−120
No. 7 at end to No. 6 at end	480	−400	20	100
No. 6 at end to No. 5 at end	210	−400	30	−160
No. 5 at end to No. 4 at end	360	−400	0	− 40

For all positions except the starting one, the sum of the ΔV values is negative. Therefore, the largest clamp reaction results from having wheel 8 at the clamp and wheels 4 to 7 in the span. This position is shown in Fig. 5–17(b).

$$R_L = \frac{400}{10} (1 + 4 + 5.5 + 8.5 + 10) = 1,160 \text{ lb}$$

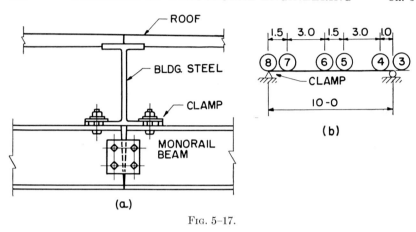

FIG. 5–17.

5–9. Maximum Shear in a Panel.   When a member is divided into panels and receives load from transverse members at the panel points only, a shear criterion can be used. Fig. 5–18 shows a girder and the influence line for shear in panel 1–2. (See Fig. 5–8(e); Example 5–3.) In Example 5–3, the influence line alone was used to decide the location of

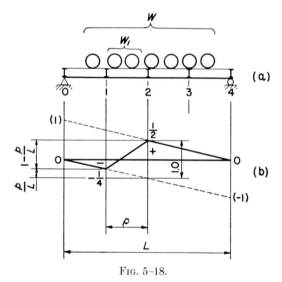

FIG. 5–18.

uniform load to cause the greatest shear in the panel. The influence line could be used also if a single concentrated load were present with uniform load. If more than one concentrated load were present, however, it would be necessary to try several positions. The trials can be made easily using the criterion that will be developed.

Assume the loads to be moving toward the left, with one wheel just approaching panel point 2. For a slight movement dL, all wheels except those in panel 1–2 shift to a point of algebraically larger influence ordinate. The increase of shear due to their movement is $(W - W_1)dL/L$. The wheels in panel 1–2 move to points of algebraically smaller ordinate. The decrease due to their movement is $W_1 \, dL \left(\dfrac{1.0 - p/L}{p} \right)$. The term in parentheses is the slope of the influence line in panel 1–2. The total change of shear in panel 1–2 is

$$dV = \frac{(W - W_1) \, dL}{L} - W_1 \, dL \left(\frac{1.0 - p/L}{p} \right)$$

For the maximum shear V in the panel, dV/dL is zero.

$$\frac{dV}{dL} = \frac{W}{L} - \frac{W_1}{L} - \frac{W_1}{p} + \frac{W_1}{L} = 0$$

Solving the above expression gives the criterion,

$$\frac{W}{L} = \frac{W_1}{p}$$

In words, this criterion may be stated as follows:

The shear in a panel is maximum (for a particular set of loads) when the average load per unit of length on the span is equal to the average in the panel.

As the loads are moved from one position to the next, some loads may pass off of the span and others may enter. Thus, with different groups of wheels present, more than one position may satisfy the criterion. When this happens, the shear for each position which satisfies should be computed. Those shears should be compared and the highest one selected.

While the non-civil engineer may seldom encounter a problem with a girder having panels, he may often become involved with trusses. The criterion just derived is of great value in truss work. Its application will be shown in one of the examples which follow Art. 5–10.

5–10. Maximum Bar Stresses in Trusses. Influence lines for bar stresses in a truss can be drawn and used just as they are for bending moments and shears in a beam. The positions of loads for maximum bar stresses can be obtained by the direct use of the influence lines, or by the use of criteria derived from the influence lines.

All truss stresses can be found using values of shear in various panels, or of moment at certain points. For example, consider the truss of Fig. 5–19(a). The stress U_1U_2 is obtained by cutting through the panel on section 1–1, isolating the portion to the left, and writing the equilibrium equation for moments about L_2. The moment about L_2 of the forces to the left of the cut is equal to the bending moment at panel point 2. The stress U_1U_2 is equal to the bending moment at L_2, divided by h. Thus, the influence line for the stress U_1U_2 is the same as that for the bending moment at panel point 2, but with all ordinates divided by h. This line is shown in Fig. 5–19(b).

Similarly, the stress in the diagonal U_1L_2 is equal to the shear in panel 1–2, multiplied by the length-to-height ratio b/h. The influence line for the stress U_1L_2 is that for the shear in panel 1–2, but with all ordinates multiplied by b/h. The line is shown in Fig. 5–19(c).

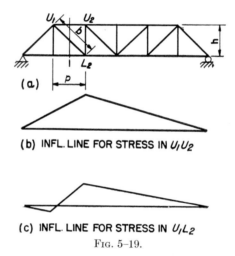

(b) INFL. LINE FOR STRESS IN U_1U_2

(c) INFL. LINE FOR STRESS IN U_1L_2

Fig. 5–19.

Both of these influence lines could be used directly to determine the location for a uniform load or a single concentrated load. They could also be used to compute the amount of the bar stress. But if more than one concentrated load were present, it would seldom be possible to decide by inspection where the loads should be placed. The criteria developed for maximum bending moment at a particular section (Art. 5–5) and for maximum shear in a panel (Art. 5–9) must be used. Their use will be shown by Example 5–10.

Another type of truss is shown in Fig. 5–20(a). In this truss the top chord is sloping. To solve for the stress in U_1U_2 the portion to the left of section 1–1 is isolated. The equation $\Sigma M = 0$ is written about L_2. The stress in U_1U_2 is equal to the bending moment at L_2 divided by a lever arm. Thus, the influence line for the stress U_1U_2 is of the same shape as that for bending moment at L_2. The criterion for maximum moment at L_2 can also be used to find the load position for the maximum stress in U_1U_2.

To obtain the stress U_1L_2, moments must be computed about the intersection of the other two unknowns. This is at point a of Fig. 5–20(b). None of the criteria developed in this chapter are applicable. If the influence line for U_1L_2 were drawn, it would appear as shown in Fig.

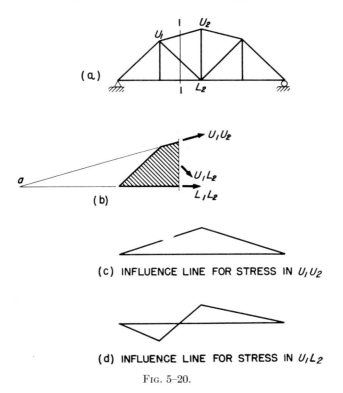

(a)

(b)

(c) INFLUENCE LINE FOR STRESS IN U_1U_2

(d) INFLUENCE LINE FOR STRESS IN U_1L_2

Fig. 5–20.

5–20(d). The end portions of the line are not parallel, as is the case for shear in a panel. A special criterion can be developed giving the load position. It is a complex criterion, however, and its study is believed to be beyond the practical requirements for a non-civil engineering student.

EXAMPLE 5–10. The belt conveyor of Fig. 5–21(a) is used to carry materials from one building over a 30-ft space to another building. Two trusses are used to support the conveyor. The dead load of the belt, idlers, and truss amounts to 40 lb per ft on one truss. The live load is 150 lb per ft of conveyor, or 75 lb per ft on each truss. The live load can occur anywhere along the length. Find the maximum total stress in members U_1U_2 and U_1L_2.

First, consider member U_1U_2. Its stress is equal to the bending moment at L_2 divided by 4 ft. A load of one lb at L_2 causes a bending moment of 7.5 ft-lb at panel point 2, or a stress U_1U_2 of $7.5/4 = 1.88$ lb compression. The influence line for the stress in U_1U_2 is shown in Fig. 5–21(b).

From the influence line it is obvious that live load placed anywhere

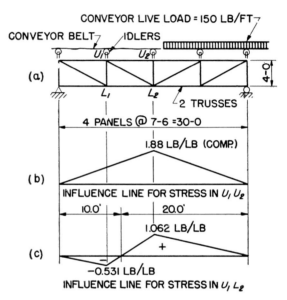

FIG. 5–21.

will add to the stress in member U_1U_2. So, live load is assumed over the entire length. The sum of dead and live loads is $40 + 75 = 115$ lb per ft on each truss. Using the influence line area,

$$U_1U_2 = 115 \times \tfrac{1}{2} \times 1.88 \times 30 = 3,240 \text{ lb, compression}$$

Member U_1L_2 is considered next. The length of the member is $\sqrt{(4)^2 + (7.5)^2} = 8.5$ ft. Stress U_1L_2 is equal to the shear in panel 1–2 times the ratio $8.5/4$. The shear influence ordinates at panel points 1 and 2 are $-\tfrac{1}{4}$ and $+\tfrac{1}{2}$, respectively. (See Example 5–3 and Fig. 5–8.) These ordinates are multiplied by $8.5/4$ to obtain the influence line shown in Fig. 5–21(c). Notice that loads near the left end cause compression, while those elsewhere cause tension. For cases like this a *reversal of stress* may be possible. A reversal of stress, or stress reversal, is a change of the total stress from tension to compression as the loading is changed. For member U_1L_2, both the maximum tension and the maximum possible compression should be computed.

For live load only,

Maximum compression $= 75 \times \frac{1}{2} \times 0.531 \times 10.0 = 199$ lb

Maximum tension $= 75 \times \frac{1}{2} \times 1.062 \times 20.0 = 796$ lb

Dead load is present over the entire span length. The stress U_1L_2 due to dead load is

$40 \times \frac{1}{2}[(1.062 \times 20.0) - (0.531 \times 10.0)] = 319$ lb, tension

Since the dead-load tension (319 lb) exceeds the largest live-load compression (199 lb), a stress reversal cannot occur. The member U_1L_2 will always be in tension.

Maximum $U_1L_2 = 796 + 319 = 1,115$ lb, tension

EXAMPLE 5–11. Consider once more the monorail revision that has been used in previous examples in this chapter. When monorails cross

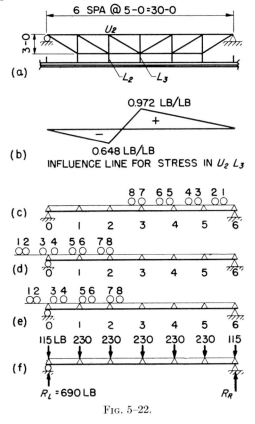

FIG. 5–22.

over long spans without intermediate supports, a truss is often used. Assume that the monorail supports in this case must have a clear span of 30 ft across a driveway. The truss to be used is shown in Fig. 5–22. The weight of the monorail track and fittings is 6 lb per ft. The weight of the truss is about 40 lb per ft, giving a total dead load of 46 lb per ft. One part of a complete analysis of the truss would be to determine which members have reversal of stress. Does member U_2L_3 have a reversal of stress? What are the stresses?

The stress U_2L_3 is equal to the shear in panel 2–3 multiplied by the length/height ratio of the member. The length of U_2L_3 is

$$\sqrt{(5)^2 + (3)^2} = 5.83 \text{ ft}$$

$$U_2L_3 = \left(\frac{5.83}{3}\right)V_{2-3}$$

The influence line for the stress in U_2L_3 is shown in Fig. 5–22(b). This line is the same shape as the influence line for shear in a panel, so the criterion developed in Art. 5–9 will be used to determine the load location.

The maximum tension should occur when a load is at panel point L_3 with most of the other loads to the right of L_3 (i.e., over the positive area of the influence line). The loads will be backed on from the right, so that the heavier loads are closest to L_3. The loads are shown in Fig. 5–22(c). The load at L_3 is considered to be first just to the right of L_3, and then just to the left of L_3, in order to determine when the average load per unit length in panel 2–3 becomes equal to the average for the entire span. In the tabulation below, the *panel* length, rather than one ft, will be used as the unit of length. Note that there are 6 panel lengths.

Load at L_3	Wheel Position	Average in Panel 2–3	Average on Span	Criterion
8	Right of L_3	0	< 2,800/6	
	Left of L_3	400	< 2,800/6	Not Satisfied
7	Right of L_3	400	< 2,800/6	
	Left of L_3	800	> 2,800/6	*Satisfied*

Since further movement brings no additional loads onto the span, the position with wheel number 7 at L_3 is the only one that will satisfy the criterion. This position is shown in Fig. 5–22(c).

The shear in panel 2–3 is the reaction R_L of the entire truss at U_0, minus the load coming to the truss at panel point L_2. (Wheel 8 causes load on the truss at L_2 and L_3.)

$$R_L = \frac{1}{30} [400(16.5 + 15 + 12 + 10.5 + 7.5 + 6) + 200(3 + 2)]$$

$$= 933 \text{ lb}$$

The largest positive live load shear is

$$V_{2-3} = 933 - \frac{400 \times 1.5}{5} = 813 \text{ lb}$$

For the maximum compression in U_2L_3 the loads will be placed so that a wheel is at panel point 2 (location of the largest negative influence ordinate). The loads will be allowed to approach from the left, the heaviest loads first.

Load at L_2	Wheel Position	Average in Panel 2-3		Average on Span	Criterion
8	Left of L_2	0	$<$	2,000/6	
	Right of L_2	400	$>$	2,000/6	Satisfied
7	Left of L_2	400	$=$	2,400/6	
	Right of L_2	800	$>$	2,400/6	Satisfied
6	Left of L_2	800	$>$	2,600/6	
	Right of L_2	1,200	$>$	2,600/6	Not Satisfied
5	Left of L_2	800	$>$	2,800/6	
	Right of L_2	1,200	$>$	2,800/6	Not Satisfied

The criterion is satisfied by two load positions; each gives the maximum shear in panel 2-3 for the particular group of loads then on the span. The panel shear for each of the two positions will be computed.

The position with wheel 8 at L_2 is shown in Fig. 5-22(d).

$$R_R = \frac{400}{30} (1 + 4 + 5.5 + 8.5 + 10) = 387 \text{ lb}$$

$$V_{2-3} = 0 - 387 = -387 \text{ lb}$$

The position with wheel 7 at L_2 is shown in Fig. 5-22(e).

$$R_R = \frac{400}{30} (1 + 2.5 + 5.5 + 7 + 10 + 11.5) = 500 \text{ lb}$$

$$V_{2-3} = \frac{400 \times 1.5}{5} - 500 = -380 \text{ lb}$$

The largest negative live load shear in the panel is -387 lb.

The dead load of 46 lb per ft is always present over the full span. The panel loads due to dead load are shown in Fig. 5-22(f).

$$R_L = 46 \times 15 = 690 \text{ lb}$$

$$V_{2-3} = 690 - 115 - 230 - 230 = 115 \text{ lb}$$

The panel shear V_{2-3} due to combined live load and dead load will range from

$$-387 + 115 = -272 \text{ lb (loads approaching panel from left)}$$

to

$$813 + 115 = \quad 928 \text{ lb (loads approaching panel from right)}$$

A reversal of stress does occur in member U_2L_3.

The bar stress will range from

$$U_2L_3 = -272 \times 5.83/3 = -529 = 529 \text{ lb, compression}$$

to

$$U_2L_3 = \quad 928 \times 5.83/3 = 1,800 \text{ lb, tension}$$

The example thus far illustrates the finding of the bar stress for only one member. A complete analysis would include similar work for all the members. The volume of work may be reduced somewhat by two facts. The first of these is that data obtained for one member may sometimes be used again for another. For example, the stress in U_2L_2 of this truss is equal to the shear in panel 2–3. Thus, from data already obtained, the stress range for U_2L_2 is 272 lb tension to 928 lb compression. The second is that in designing a truss it is usually not practical to use a different cross section for each panel of the top and bottom chords. Computation for only the most highly stressed panels is then sufficient. In this example, the panels nearest the center would have the highest chord stresses.

PROBLEMS

5–1. Draw influence lines for the beam of Fig. 5–23, as follows:

    a) Vertical reaction at B
    b) Shear at C
    c) Shear just to the right of B
    d) Bending moment at B
    e) Bending moment at C

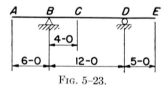

Label all important ordinates.

FIG. 5–23.

5–2. The beam of Fig. 5–23 is subject to a uniform dead load of 300 lb per ft and a movable live load of 800 lb per ft. The live load can be discontinuous. Use the influence lines to solve for the maximum (numerical) values of the functions in parts a to e of Problem 5–1.

5–3. A portable roller conveyor is to be made, with supports as shown in Fig. 5–24. The live load is 100 lb per lin ft, not necessarily continuous. The

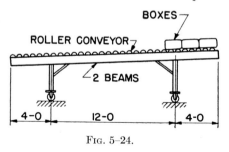

FIG. 5–24.

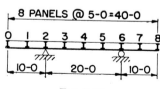

FIG. 5–25.

weight of the rollers and beams is 44 lb per lin ft. Draw influence lines and use them to determine the following for one beam:

a) Maximum load on one support
b) Maximum shear next to a support
c) Maximum bending moment at a support
d) Maximum bending moment at mid-span

5-4. Fig. 5–25 shows a girder with each end overhanging the support. Draw the influence line for shear in panel 2–3. The dead load is 400 lb per ft of girder, and the movable live load 900 lb per ft. What is the maximum shear for panel 2–3?

Draw the influence line for shear in panel 3–4. What is the maximum shear for this panel?

5-5. Draw the influence line for bending moment at panel point 4 of the girder shown in Fig. 5–25. Use the loads of Problem 5–4. What is the maximum bending moment at panel point 4?

Draw the influence line for bending moment at panel point 2. What is the maximum bending moment at that point?

5-6. A series of loads is shown by Fig. 5–26. What is the maximum bending moment caused at the center of a 20-ft simple span as the series of loads crosses? Under what wheel does it occur?

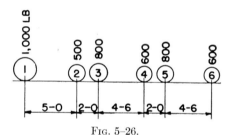

Fig. 5–26.

5-7. An existing crane runway has one crane only. To speed up the service it is desired to add another crane to the runway. The cranes, runway beams, and loads are shown by Fig. 5–27. The loads include the crane dead load,

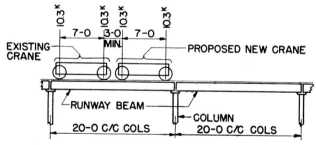

Fig. 5–27.

live load, and impact according to the AISC Specification. The runway weighs 85 lb per ft.

With the new crane added, what will be the maximum load on one column? What is the percentage of increase over the maximum column load with the existing crane only?

5-8. Assume that the space between the two equal loads of Fig. 5-1(b) is a, and that the span is L. When the space a is small, the bending moment with both loads on the beam is larger than could be caused by one load alone. When a is larger, one load alone can cause a greater bending moment than the two loads together. In terms of L, what is the spacing a beyond which one load alone causes the greater bending moment?

5-9. For the runway beam of Problem 5-7, what is the maximum bending moment? By what percentage is this larger than the moment with the existing crane only?

5-10. As an emergency measure, trucks are required to enter your plant by way of a temporary bridge over a railway loading dock. The truck and its wheel live loads are shown in Fig. 5-28. What is the maximum live load

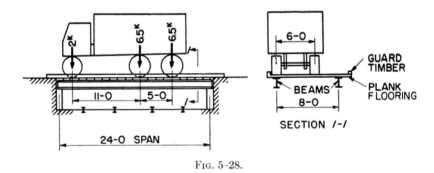

FIG. 5-28.

bending moment for one beam? Note that the truck can be off center to the degree shown by section 1-1.

5-11. What would be the maximum total bending moment on one beam of the temporary crossover of Example 5-7 (Fig. 5-14) if a series of bins were pushed by an electric truck? The electric truck in question has its axles 3 ft 6 in. apart. The truck load, including the operator and impact, is 500 lb per wheel. The truck wheel would be 2 ft 6 in. from the bin wheel. Bins are connected together with a space of 1 ft 0 in. between wheels of adjacent bins.

5-12. What would be the maximum total end shear for one beam of Problem 5-11?

5-13. Parts are carried on a series of four-wheeled trolleys, pulled by a tractor, as shown in Fig. 5-29. The loads are 170 lb at each pair of trolley wheels, and 200 lb at each pair of tractor wheels. The I-beam serving as a mono-rail has a span of 15 ft.

a) What is the maximum live load end reaction?
b) What is the maximum live-load applied by the system to the supporting truss, assuming a 15-ft monorail span on each side?
c) What is the maximum live-load bending moment?

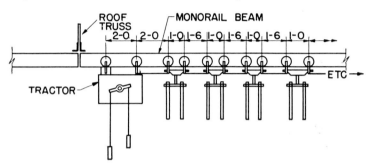

Fig. 5–29.

5–14. A 24-ft simple span is divided into six panels of 4 ft each. What is the maximum shear in panel 1–2 due to passage of the series of loads in Fig. 5–26?

5–15. Continue the analysis of the truss of Example 5–11 to determine the maximum stresses in: (a) the top chord; (b) the bottom chord; (c) member U_1L_2; (d) member U_1L_1. Check the possibility of stress reversal in (c) and (d).

5–16. Fig. 5–30 shows the plan view (looking down) of a truss connected between two frames to support electrical cables coming into transformers below. Wires 1 and 2 will be installed immediately. The others will be

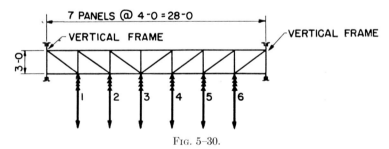

Fig. 5–30.

installed later as required. The pull on each wire will be 900 lb. Find the maximum stress in: (a) the compression chord; (b) the tension chord; and (c) each web member, including reversals, if any.

CHAPTER 6

DEFLECTIONS IN BEAMS

6-1. Importance of Deflections. A beam bends and moves as it is loaded. The amount and direction of the movement at a particular point on the beam is called the *deflection* of the point. Deflections are of much more than mere academic interest. There are many cases in which knowledge of the amount and direction of the deflection is useful. A few common cases are listed below:

1. The maximum deflection must often be limited for functional reasons. For example, a beam supporting a machine must not bend so far as to cause the moving parts to bind. A crane runway girder must have a very small deflection; if the deflection were large, the runway would be too "hilly."

2. The maximum deflection must sometimes be limited so as to prevent a weak or sloppy appearance. This is particularly important where a weak-looking structure might have a bad psychological effect on customers or workers.

3. The maximum deflection must often be limited so as to avoid damage to adjoining materials. For example, the beam deflection that is permitted after a plastered ceiling has been hung from the beam is limited to about 1/360 of the span of the beam. More deflection would probably crack the plaster.

4. Vibrations can often be controlled by using a very rigid structure. The deflection of a beam is an inverse measure of its rigidity.

5. The computation of deflections is the starting point in solving statically indeterminate structures. Sometimes the deflection amounts are used directly in the solution. More often the deflection computations enter into the derivation of methods which are used to solve statically indeterminate structures.

There are many methods of solving for deflections. The two that will be shown in this chapter are quite basic, and the easiest to understand. They are completely adaptable to any beam which is not stressed to more than the elastic limit.

162

6-2. The Moment-Area Method.   Fig. 6–1(a) shows a short piece of a beam. Imagine the beam to have a bending moment M on a short length ds only. The bending moment will cause tension on one side of the beam and compression on the other. The material will be stretched on the tension side and shortened on the compression side. According

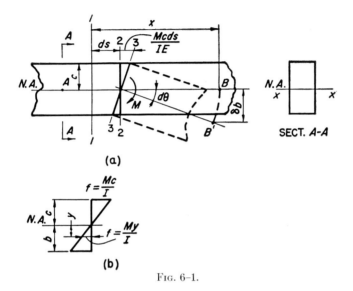

Fɪɢ. 6–1.

to the flexure formula (see any text on Strength of Materials) the bending stress at any distance y from the neutral axis is

$$f = \frac{My}{I}$$

The term I is the moment of inertia of the cross section of the beam about a transverse line (x–x) through the neutral axis. The stress on the extreme upper fibers of the beam in Fig. 6–1(a) is Mc/I (extreme fiber stress). The top fiber will be stretched by this stress. The amount of the stretch is computed by Hooke's Law as

$$\frac{f\,ds}{E} = \frac{Mc\,ds}{IE}$$

The bottom fibers will shorten. If the distance from the neutral axis to the bottom is b, the amount of shortening is $Mb\,ds/IE$. The result is that the cross section at 2–2, originally parallel to section 1–1, has moved to position 3–3. The portion of the beam to the right is now inclined with respect to that at the left. The angle of inclination is $d\theta$. The angle $d\theta$ is a small angle and is equal to its tangent.

$$d\theta = \frac{Mc\ ds}{IEc} = \frac{M\ ds}{EI}$$

As the part to the right rotated, point B moved downward to point B'. If $d\theta$ is a small angle, the horizontal movement of B is negligible (zero), and the vertical movement is

$$\delta_b = d\theta(x - ds) = \frac{M\ ds\ x}{EI}$$

Now imagine that a moment M' exists at another section on the same beam. An additional "kink" will occur, as shown in Fig. 6–2. The angles

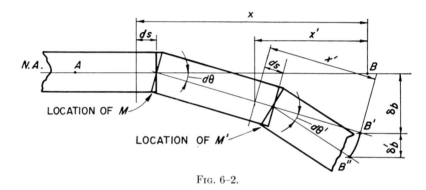

FIG. 6–2.

$d\theta$ and $d\theta'$ are both small angles, so that point B'' is, for practical purposes, vertically beneath point B. The vertical movement δ_b' due to the moment M' is $d\theta'(x' - ds)$.

The total change of slope between A and B is

$$d\theta + d\theta' = \frac{M\ ds}{EI} + \frac{M'\ ds}{EI}$$

The total vertical movement of point B (with reference to a horizontal line through point A) is

$$\delta_b + \delta_b' = \frac{M\ ds\ x}{EI} + \frac{M'\ ds\ x'}{EI}$$

The condition of bending moment existing at only one or two isolated sections is, of course, imaginary. The practical case usually involves bending moment over much or all of the length of the member. Provided the total angle change remains small, the angle changes $d\theta$ and the displacements δ_b can be added for each element of length having bending moment. The total angle change between A and B is

$$\sum_{a}^{b} \frac{M \ ds}{EI}$$

The total vertical deflection of point B, relative to a tangent at point A, is

$$\Delta_b = \sum_{a}^{b} \frac{M \ ds \ x_b}{EI}$$

The two equations above are the mathematical statements of the moment-area principle. The summation of the Mds/EI values is an area, and the summation of the $Mx_b \ ds/EI$ values is the moment of that area about point B. Thus, the two parts of the moment-area principle may be stated in words as follows:

1. *The change of slope between two points on the elastic curve is equal to the area of the M/EI diagram between the two points.*
2. *The deflection of one point on the elastic curve, relative to a tangent to the curve at another point, is equal to the moment of the M/EI area between the two points about the point for which the deflection is desired.*

The two statements above are very easy to apply. Deflections and slopes can be found easily by using them. Yet a slipshod understanding of their exact meaning can just as easily lead to mistakes. The best way to avoid these mistakes is to start out *by memorizing the two statements, word for word*. That may sound a little childish. In the author's experience though, the students who start by memorizing the statements accurately have the least difficulty in applying them. This has been the case both in the "Elements" classes and in the advanced courses in statically indeterminate structures.

EXAMPLE 6–1. Find the deflection and slope at the end of the beam in Fig. 6–3(a). Consider the effect of the concentrated load only. The properties E and I of the beam are uniform over the entire length. The bending moment diagram is shown in Fig. 6–3(b). The areas to be considered are the M/EI areas. The M/EI values are given by the ordinates of Fig. 6–3(c). The elastic curve, giving the shape of the deformed beam, shows in part (d).

The slope at A does not change with application of the load. Therefore, point A is used as a reference point. The slope at B is equal to the change of slope between A and B. This slope change can be solved using the first moment-area principle. The slope change between A and B is

$$\theta_b = \sum_a^b \frac{M\,ds}{EI} = \text{Area of } M/EI \text{ diagram between } A \text{ and } B$$

$$= \frac{1}{2} \times L \times \frac{PL}{EI} = \frac{PL^2}{2EI}$$

If the dimensions used are all in pound and inch units, the unit of the angle θ is

$$\frac{\text{lb} \times \text{in.}^2}{\dfrac{\text{lb}}{\text{in.}^2} \times \text{in.}^4} = \text{dimensionless} = \text{radians}$$

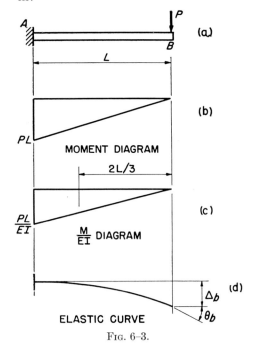

MOMENT DIAGRAM

$\frac{M}{EI}$ DIAGRAM

ELASTIC CURVE

Fig. 6-3.

Since the tangent to the elastic curve at A remains horizontal, it is used as a reference line for the deflection Δ_b. The deflection of B relative to the tangent at A is equal to the moment of the M/EI area between A and B about B (the point for which the deflection is desired).

$$\Delta_b = \sum_a^b \frac{M\,ds\,x_b}{EI} = \frac{1}{2} \times L \times \frac{PL}{EI} \times \frac{2L}{3} = \frac{PL^3}{3EI}$$

If inches are used for all linear dimensions in the above equation, the unit of Δ_b will be inches. If feet are used, the answer will be in feet. Whatever units are used, there must be a consistent use of those units in all the factors: P, L, E, and I.

EXAMPLE 6–2. A simple beam with two symmetrically placed concentrated loads is shown by Fig. 6–4(a). What is the deflection at the
center, and what is the slope at the support? The material is steel having a
modulus of elasticity E of 30,000,000
psi, and a moment of inertia about
the neutral axis of the cross section
equal to 446 in.[4]

The moment diagram and M/EI
diagram are shown by Fig. 6–4(b)
and (c), respectively. Because E and
I are constants throughout the
length of the beam, it is possible to
leave E and I as letter symbols until
the final step, making the numerical
substitution at the last minute.

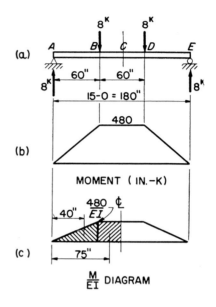

Fig. 6–4(d) shows the elastic
curve. The beam and loading are
symmetrical about the centerline;
therefore the elastic curve will
remain horizontal at the center.

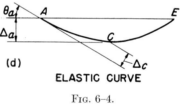

The slope at the support is the
same as the change of slope between
the end and the centerline. By the
first moment-area principle this
slope change is equal to the shaded
area in Fig. 6–4(c).

$$\theta_a = \sum_a^c \frac{M\,ds}{EI} = \left(\frac{1}{2} \times 60 \times \frac{480}{EI}\right)$$
$$+ \left(30 \times \frac{480}{EI}\right) = \frac{28{,}800}{EI}$$

Substituting for E and I,

$$\theta_a = \frac{28{,}800}{30{,}000 \times 446} = 0.00215 \text{ radian}$$

(Note that kip units were used in E since kip units had been used in M.)

The deflection desired is the vertical movement of point C. The only
good reference point is the center point C, since it is the location of the
only tangent that remains horizontal. The tangent at point C moves
downward during loading, but does not rotate. The amount of the
downward movement is shown as Δ_a on Fig. 6–4(d). It is the same as
the upward movement of point A relative to the tangent at point C.
Thus, if we apply the second moment-area principle exactly as it is

worded, the deflection Δ_a is equal to the moment of the shaded M/EI area *about point A*. (If the moment of the area about C were used, the value of the deflection of point C from a tangent at point A would be found. Ordinarily this would be somewhat useless. See dimension Δ_c on Fig. 6–4(d).

$$\Delta_a = \sum_a^c \frac{M \ ds \ x_a}{EI} = \left(\frac{1}{2} \times 60 \times \frac{480}{EI} \times 40\right) + \left(30 \times \frac{480}{EI} \times 75\right)$$

$$= \frac{1,656,000}{EI}$$

Substitution for E and I (in inch and kip units) gives

$$\Delta_a = \frac{1,656,000}{30,000 \times 446} = 0.124 \text{ in.}$$

EXAMPLE 6–3. How much deflection will occur at the center of the same beam (that of Example 6–2) if it receives uniform live and dead load of 500 lb per ft, in addition to the two concentrated loads?

The problem can be solved most easily using the principle of super-position. The total deflection is that due to the concentrated loads alone plus that due to the uniform load alone. Fig. 6–5 shows the beam and its

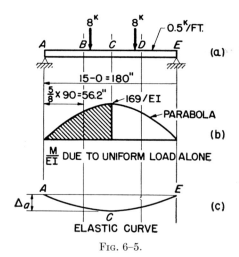

FIG. 6–5.

M/EI diagram for the uniform load alone. The bending moment M at the center is

$$\frac{wL^2}{8} = \frac{0.5 \times (15)^2}{8} = 14.1 \text{ ft-k}$$

or

$$14.1 \times 12 = 169 \text{ in.-kips}$$

The deflection at the center is equal to the deflection Δ_a of point A relative to the tangent at point C.

$$\Delta_a = \sum_a^c \frac{M \, ds \, x_a}{EI} = \frac{2}{3} \times 90 \times \frac{169}{EI} \times 56.2 = \frac{570,000}{EI}$$

$$\Delta_a = \frac{570,000}{30,000 \times 446} = 0.0426 \text{ in.}$$

The total centerline deflection is

$$\Delta_a = 0.124 + 0.043 = 0.167 \text{ in.}$$

6–3. Beams with Variable Section. The three examples shown thus far could be solved much more quickly by the use of handbook formulas. But it is necessary that the moment-area method be illustrated using the simplest of examples. When the method is known and understood, it can then be applied to problems that are beyond the scope of the usual

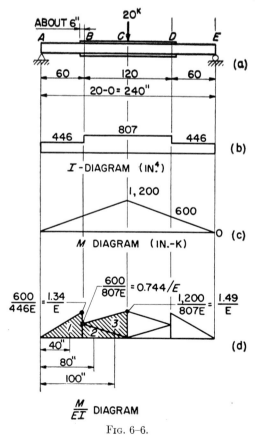

Fig. 6–6.

handbook formula. One such case is the member with a variation of I values along its length. The next example can be solved easily by moment area, but its solution is beyond the usual collection of formulas.

EXAMPLE 6–4. A beam which supports a load at its center deflects too far. As a cure, cover plates are placed on its flanges over a part of the length. The beam is shown in Fig. 6–6(a). What will be the deflection at the center, now that the beam is reinforced? (The load will be removed while the plates are installed.)

The ends of reinforcing plates are not completely effective. For purposes of computing deflections it can be assumed that the moment of inertia I changes abruptly at about 6 in. from the end of the plate. (Actually the effective I changes gradually from that of the unreinforced beam to that of the reinforced one. The abrupt change at the assumed 6-in. distance, however, works very well.) A diagram giving the moment of inertia at various points along the beam is shown in Fig. 6–6(b).

The moment diagram shows in part (c). The maximum M is $20 \times 20/4 = 100$ ft-kips, or 1,200 in.-kips. Since I is a variable, the M/EI diagram has a different shape than the moment diagram. It is shown in Fig. 6–6(d). The value of E is constant, and it is carried as a letter symbol until the final step of the solution.

The tangent which has no change in slope during loading is at the center point C. The tangent at C, then, is the reference line for deflection. The deflection desired is that of point A relative to a tangent to the elastic curve at C. This will be equal to the moment of the shaded M/EI area about point A. The shaded area is divided into convenient geometrical shapes, in this case three triangles. The solution is made in tabular form.

Item	M/EI Area	Lever Arm to A	Moment of M/EI Area About A
1	$40.2/E$	40	$1,608/E$
2	$22.3/E$	80	$1,784/E$
3	$44.7/E$	100	$4,470/E$

$$\sum_{a}^{c} \frac{M \, ds \, x_a}{EI} = 7,862/E$$

$$\Delta_a = \frac{7,862}{30,000} = 0.262 \text{ in.}$$

6–4. Gradually Changing Moment of Inertia. Occasionally tapered sections are encountered in which the value of I varies continuously along the length. The M/EI diagram for such members may have complex curves. It may not lend itself to division into simple geometric areas, as in Example 6–4.

When this is the case, the complex area should be divided along its length into a number of shorter elements. Little error will result if these small elements of area are considered "rounded off" into rectangles and triangles. In the usual case, division of the length into ten increments is accurate enough. For greater accuracy, more increments should be used. Complete details on this type of problem are beyond the common needs of the non-civil engineer, but they may be easily studied and understood from textbooks on statically indeterminate structures.[1]

6–5. Elastic-Weight Principle. Fig. 6–7 shows a beam with an unsymmetrical load. The elastic curve is shown with exaggerated deflections. The maximum deflection is equal to the deflection of either point A or point B from a tangent to the elastic curve at point C. Now, if the location of point C were known, the moment-area method could be used directly to find Δ_{max}. But the location of point C is *not* known. It is not at the center of the span, nor at the load point, but lies somewhere between the load and the center of the span. Thus, the moment-area method, unless modified, is not an easy tool to use in solving for the deflections of this beam.

A similar situation results when there is non-symmetry (along the length of the beam) of any sort, be it cross section, types of support, size of load, or location of load. (An exception is the cantilever beam, for which the moment-area method can easily be used.) For all such cases where the location of the point having zero change of tangent slope is unknown, the elastic-weight principle can be used. That principle will now be developed.

The exaggerated elastic curve is shown again in Fig. 6–7(b). Tangents are drawn to each end. The M/EI diagram is shown in (c).

$$\theta_a = \sum_a^c \frac{M \, ds}{EI}$$

$$\theta_b = \sum_b^c \frac{M \, ds}{EI}$$

As the location of C is not known, neither θ_a nor θ_b can be evaluated from the above. Their sum, however, can be evaluated. It is equal to the angle change between A and B, which is the entire M/EI area.

$$\theta_a + \theta_b = \sum_a^b \frac{M \, ds}{EI}$$

[1] C. D. Williams, *Analysis of Statically Indeterminate Structures* (Scranton, Pa.: International Textbook Co., 1946), Chap. 2.

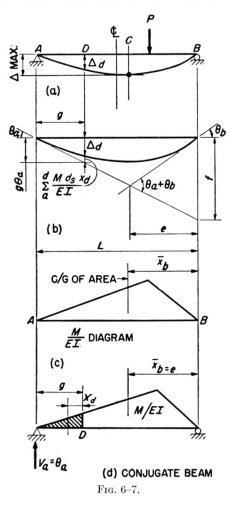

FIG. 6–7.

The angle at the intersection of the end tangents is shown as $\theta_a + \theta_b$. Remembering that the exaggerated angles shown are really small angles, two expressions for dimension f can be written. They are

$$f = e(\theta_a + \theta_b) = e \sum_a^b \frac{M\,ds}{EI}$$

$$f = \sum_a^b \frac{M\,ds\,x_b}{EI} = \bar{x}_b \sum_a^b \frac{M\,ds}{EI}\ .$$

The second expression gives the deflection of B from a tangent at A; since the angles are small, this is the same as f. The two equations above are equated to show

$$\bar{x}_b = e$$

In other words, the center of gravity of the M/EI area is at the same location as the intersection of the end tangents.

By the geometry of Fig. 6–7(b),

$$\theta_a = \frac{f}{L}$$

Substituting $e(\theta_a + \theta_b)$ for f,

$$\theta_a = \frac{e}{L}(\theta_a + \theta_b) = \frac{e}{L}\sum_a^b \frac{M\,ds}{EI}$$

In Fig. 6–7(d) the M/EI area is shown as a load on an imaginary simple beam. This imaginary beam is called the "conjugate beam." By using the equations of equilibrium, reactions for this conjugate beam can be determined. The left reaction is

$$V_a = \frac{e}{L}\sum_a^b \frac{M\,ds}{EI}$$

Thus the reaction at A for the imaginary conjugate beam is the same as the slope θ_a for the actual beam.

The slope at all other points can now be determined. For example, the slope at point D of the actual beam is equal to the slope at A minus the M/EI area between A and D. Also, the shear on the imaginary, or conjugate, beam is equal to the reaction at A (same as θ_a) minus the M/EI area between A and D (shaded). Thus the slope of the actual beam is equal to the shear at the corresponding point on the conjugate beam.

Going back to Fig. 6–7(b), the deflection of all points can be computed. For example, at section D, the tangent to end A has moved downward a distance $g\theta_a$. Point D has deflected upward with respect to this tangent an amount $\sum_a^d \frac{M\,ds\,x_d}{EI}$. The difference between the movement of the tangent and the deflection of D from the tangent is the desired actual deflection Δ_d.

$$\Delta_d = g\theta_a - \sum_a^d \frac{M\,ds\,x_d}{EI} = gV_a - \sum_a^d \frac{M\,ds\,x_d}{EI}$$

The above equation shows Δ_d equal to the moment (about D) of the conjugate-beam reaction V_a and all M/EI area between A and D. That quantity would be the *bending moment on the conjugate beam*, caused by the use of the M/EI areas as loads. These imaginary loads are called elastic weights; the principle is called the elastic-weight principle.

If the derivation is reread carefully it should be seen that the exact shape of the moment diagram, the end support conditions for the actual beam, and the question of uniformity of cross section did not enter the picture. The actual span used could be one with an end fixed, one with either uniform or non-uniform cross section, or merely the portion between two adjacent supports in the case of a beam with overhangs or of a continuous beam. For example, in Fig. 6–8 are shown several beams. The beam used in the derivation could represent any of the members shown solid in Fig. 6–8. The only limitation is that the beam

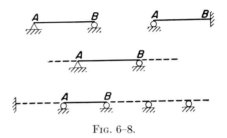

Fig. 6–8.

AB of the derivation must have supports at both A and B. The elastic-weight principle can be applied to the portion between two adjacent supports of *any* beam. The conjugate beam, however, is always a simple beam. Its span is equal to the distance between the supports of the actual beam.

The two parts of the elastic-weight principle will now be stated. Again, the student is encouraged to memorize the statements. Memorization should help much in the accurate application of the principle.

1. *The slope of the elastic curve at any point between two supports on a beam is equal to the shear at the corresponding point of a simple conjugate beam which has the M/EI area of the actual beam as its load.*

2. *The deflection of any point between two supports of a beam is equal to the bending moment at the corresponding point of a simple conjugate beam which has the M/EI area of the actual beam as its load.*

EXAMPLE 6–5. What is the deflection under the load for the beam of Fig. 6–9? What is the maximum deflection? Neglect the effect of the weight of the beam itself. The material is steel, having E of approximately 30,000,000 psi.

The reactions and bending moment are computed. The bending moment under the load is 360 in.-kips. The M/EI diagram is shown in Fig. 6–9(b), acting as the load on a conjugate beam. The factors E and I are constants for this problem, so they are left as letter symbols until the final steps. The elastic weights are shown in kip and inch units.

The reactions for the conjugate beam must be computed. The M/EI diagram is divided into two triangles for this purpose.

Item	Elastic Weight (M/EI Area)		X_a	Moment About A	X_b	Moment About B
1	$\dfrac{1}{2} \times \dfrac{360}{EI} \times 60 =$	$10,800/EI$	40	$432,000/EI$	200	$2,160,000/EI$
2	$\dfrac{1}{2} \times \dfrac{360}{EI} \times 180 =$	$32,400/EI$	120	$3,888,000/EI$	120	$3,888,000/EI$
		$43,200/EI$		$4,320,000/EI$		$6,048,000/EI$

$$V_a = \theta_a = \frac{6,048,000}{240\,EI} = 25,200/EI$$

$$V_b = \theta_b = \frac{4,320,000}{240\,EI} = 18,000/EI$$

$$\text{Check:}\ \Sigma = 43,200/EI$$

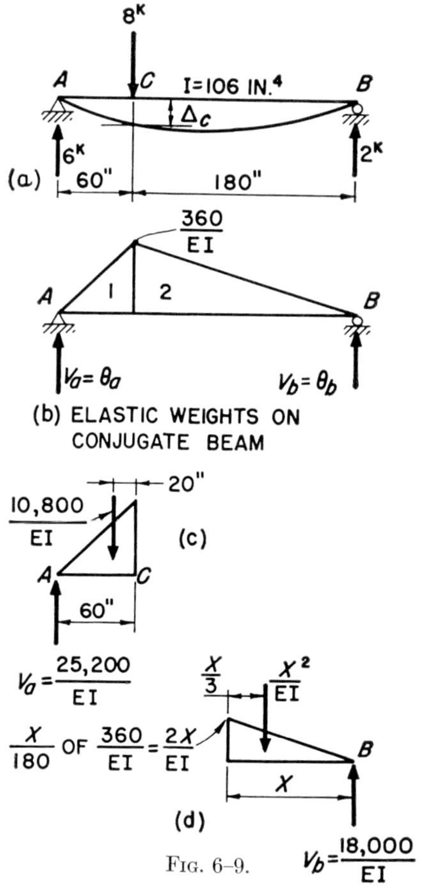

(a)

(b) ELASTIC WEIGHTS ON CONJUGATE BEAM

(c)

(d)

Fig. 6-9.

The portion of conjugate beam to the left of point C is isolated in Fig. 6–9(c). The bending moment at point C on the conjugate beam is computed.

$$\frac{25{,}200 \times 60}{EI} - \frac{10{,}800 \times 20}{EI} = \frac{1{,}512{,}000 - 216{,}000}{EI} = \frac{1{,}296{,}000}{EI}$$

This bending moment for the conjugate beam is numerically equal to the deflection for the actual beam. Thus, substituting for E and I,

$$\Delta_c = \frac{1{,}296{,}000}{30{,}000 \times 106} = 0.407 \text{ in.}$$

The maximum deflection occurs somewhere between point C and the center of the beam. The maximum deflection is numerically equal to the maximum bending moment for the conjugate beam. The maximum bending moment due to the elastic weights occurs where the shear due to the elastic weights is zero. Fig. 6–9(d) shows an isolated portion of the conjugate beam. The section was cut X inches from point B. By similar triangles [or by reference to the actual beam in Fig. 6–9(a)] the ordinate of the elastic weight at the section is equal to $2X/EI$.

The downward elastic weight on the isolated portion (area of the triangle) is $\frac{X}{2}\left(\frac{2X}{EI}\right)$ or X^2/EI. The shear at the section is the sum of the elastic-weight reaction V_b and the elastic load.

$$V_x = -\frac{18{,}000}{EI} + \frac{X^2}{EI}$$

Letting V_x be zero, the equation gives $X = 134$ in. The bending moment at 134 in. from B on the conjugate beam is equal to the maximum deflection for the actual beam.

$$\Delta_{max} = \frac{18{,}000 \times 134}{EI} - \frac{(134)^2}{EI}\left(\frac{134}{3}\right) = \frac{1{,}610{,}000}{EI}$$

$$= \frac{1{,}610{,}000}{30{,}000 \times 106} = 0.506 \text{ in.}$$

EXAMPLE 6–6. What is the maximum deflection for the beam shown in Fig. 6–10? The moment of inertia is given by the diagram in Fig. 6–10(b). The material is steel with E of approximately 30,000,000 psi.

The location of the point having zero slope, or maximum deflection, is unknown. Thus, the elastic weight principle is used. Fig. 6–10(c) shows the moment diagram. (The weight of the beam is negligible as

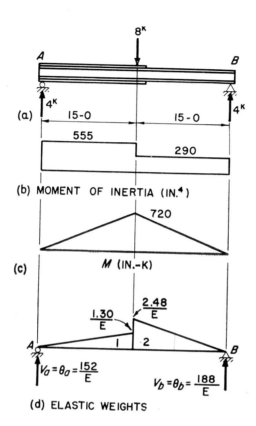

(a)

(b) MOMENT OF INERTIA (IN.^{4})

(c) M (IN.-K)

(d) ELASTIC WEIGHTS

$\frac{X}{180}$ of $\frac{2.48}{E} = \frac{0.0138X}{E}$

(e)

Fig. 6-10.

compared to the 8-kip load.) In part (d) the M/EI diagram is shown as a load on the conjugate beam. The elastic-weight reactions are now computed.

Item	Elastic Weight (M/EI Area)	X_a	Moment About A	X_b	Moment About B
1	$\frac{1}{2} \times \frac{1.30}{E} \times 180 = 117/E$	120	$14,040/E$	210	$28,080/E$
2	$\frac{1}{2} \times \frac{2.48}{E} \times 180 = 223/E$	240	$53,520/E$	120	$26,760/E$
	$340/E$		$67,560/E$		$54,840/E$

$$V_a = \theta_a = \frac{54,840}{360E} = 152/E$$

$$V_b = \theta_b = \frac{67,560}{360E} = 188/E$$

Check: $\Sigma = 340/E$

A quick comparison of the size of area number 2 and V_b shows that the shear due to the elastic weights becomes zero somewhere between the center and end B of the conjugate beam. This will be the point of maximum deflection in the actual beam. The portion of conjugate beam between this point and end B is shown isolated in Fig. 6–10(e). The shear at the section is

$$V_x = -\frac{188}{E} + \frac{0.0069X^2}{E} = 0$$

$$X^2 = 27,250$$

$$X = 165 \text{ in.}$$

The maximum deflection occurs at 165 in. from end B. It is equal to the bending moment at the corresponding point on the conjugate beam.

$$\Delta_{max} = \left(\frac{188}{E} \times 165\right) - \left(\frac{0.0069 \times (165)^2}{E} \times \frac{165}{3}\right)$$

or

$$\Delta_{max} = \frac{188}{E}(165 - 165/3) = \frac{20,680}{E}$$

Substituting 30,000 kips per sq in. for E,

$$\Delta_{max} = \frac{20,680}{30,000} = 0.69 \text{ in.}$$

EXAMPLE 6–7. What is the centerline deflection for the beam of Fig. 6–11? The beam is subject to both a concentrated load and an appreciable uniform load.

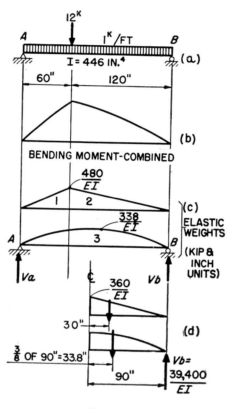

FIG. 6–11.

The moment diagram is shown in Fig. 6–11(b). The diagram is neither a parabola nor a triangle, but a combination of the two. To use the diagram as an elastic weight would be complicated. The principle of superposition can be used, however, to simplify the work. The deflection at any point is equal to the deflection caused by the uniform load plus that caused by the concentrated load. Thus, the elastic weights can be divided into a triangular load and a parabolic one, as in Fig. 6–11(c). The student should verify the moment values shown.

The elastic-weight reactions are computed in a tabular manner.

Item	Elastic Weight (M/EI Area)	X_a	Moment About A	X_b	Moment About B
1	$\dfrac{1}{2} \times \dfrac{480}{EI} \times 60 = 14{,}400/EI$	40	$576{,}000/EI$	140	$2{,}016{,}000/EI$
2	$\dfrac{1}{2} \times \dfrac{480}{EI} \times 120 = 28{,}800/EI$	100	$2{,}880{,}000/EI$	80	$2{,}304{,}000/EI$
3	$\dfrac{2}{3} \times \dfrac{338}{EI} \times 180 = 40{,}500/EI$	90	$3{,}645{,}000/EI$	90	$3{,}645{,}000/EI$
	$83{,}700/EI$		$7{,}101{,}000/EI$		$7{,}965{,}000/EI$

$$V_a = \theta_a = \frac{7{,}965{,}000}{180\ EI} = 44{,}300/EI$$

$$V_b = \theta_b = \frac{7{,}101{,}000}{180\ EI} = 39{,}400/EI$$

$$\text{Check:} \ \Sigma = 83{,}700/EI$$

The elastic loads to the right of the center of the conjugate beam are shown in Fig. 6–11(d). The bending moment at the center is now computed.

$$\text{Reaction:} \ \frac{39{,}400}{EI} \times 90 \qquad = +3{,}546{,}000/EI$$

$$\text{Triangle:} \ -\frac{1}{2} \times \frac{360}{EI} \times 90 \times 30 = \ -486{,}000/EI$$

$$\text{Half Parabola:} \ -\frac{20{,}250}{EI} \times 33.8 = \ -684{,}500/EI$$

$$M_{ctr} = \Delta_{ctr} = \ 2{,}375{,}500/EI$$

Substituting 30,000 kips per sq in. for E, and 446 in.[4] for I,

$$\Delta_{ctr} = \frac{2{,}375{,}500}{30{,}000 \times 446} = 0.177 \ \text{in.}$$

EXAMPLE 6–8. The beam of Example 3–7 and Fig. 3–14 is shown again in Fig. 6–12. How much movement occurs at point D when the hoist weight and lifted load are applied? The moment of inertia I of the beam is 34.1 in.[4].

The hoist and lifted load weigh 2.2 kips. Fig. 6–12(b) shows the moment diagram for the hoist loads alone.

The problem must now be treated in two parts. The portion of beam between supports A and B is analyzed by elastic weights. The overhanging portion BD is then analyzed by moment area. If portion AB alone were to bend, point D would deflect: if part BD alone were to bend, D would deflect. Both portions have bending moment, and the bending of each portion will have an effect on Δ_d.

A conjugate beam for the part between supports A and B is shown in Fig. 6–12(c). The elastic weight is treated as an upward load, since

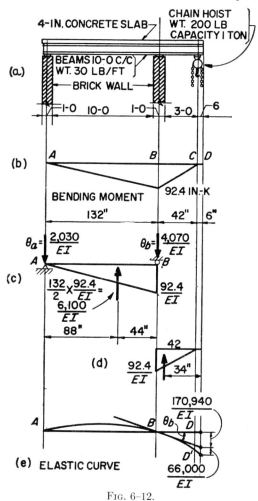

Fig. 6–12.

the tension is on the top side of the beam. The elastic-weight reactions are downward, $2{,}030/EI$ at end A, and $4{,}070/EI$ at end B. The shear in the conjugate beam just to the left of B is $+4{,}070/EI$. (See Art. 3–3 for algebraic sign of shear.) Since the shear is positive the change of slope is positive. θ_b is a *clockwise* rotation of $4{,}070/EI$. As a result of this rotation, the tangent to the beam at point B slopes downward toward the right as shown in Fig. 6–12(e).

If no bending occurred in length BD, point D would remain on this tangent and would move downward $48 \times \theta_b$, or $195,000/EI$. The bending moment in length BD causes point D to depart from the tangent to point B. This portion of the deflection, computed by moment-area, is

$$\sum_b^d \frac{M \, ds \, x_d}{EI} = \frac{92.4}{EI} \times \frac{42}{2} \times 34 = \frac{66,000}{EI}$$

The total deflection is the sum of the two parts.

$$\Delta_d = \frac{195,000 + 66,000}{30,000 \times 34.1} = 0.255 \text{ in.}$$

In problems of this type it is very important to determine whether the rotation (as at point B) is clockwise or counterclockwise. Had θ_b been counterclockwise, the final deflection would be the difference of the two parts, rather than the sum.

6–6. Other Methods.   There are many other methods of determining deflections. For example the elastic-weight and moment-area methods can be used graphically. Other mathematical methods involve consideration of the mechanical work done by loads which cause deflection and of the strain energy stored in the deflected member.

However, the two methods which have been shown in this chapter are sufficient. Any beam deflection problem can be solved by using them. There may, of course, be a few problems which are more easily solved by one of the other methods. But in general the moment-area and elastic-weight principles are easy to apply. They are also among the easiest to understand and remember.

6–7. Use of Handbook Tables.   Handbooks often give deflection equations for the more common types of loading. The good engineer will certainly use these time-saving equations whenever possible. By use of the principle of superposition and the handbook formulas, many deflection problems can easily be solved.

The real mark of a good engineer is not in his use of the handbook tables, however. A quality which identifies the good engineer is his ability to solve the case which lies outside the limits of his handbook. To cultivate that quality, he must practice first on the simpler forms. Before one learns to run, he must learn to stand and to walk. The student is cautioned, therefore, to make only judicious use of the handbook, especially while he is learning the basic facts of the subject.

6–8. Solutions of Statically Indeterminate Structures Using Deflection Computations.   A simple beam and its loads are shown by Fig. 6–13(a). Imagine that the deflection at point B has been computed by the elastic weight method and is equal to 0.75 in. downward. The same simple beam is shown in Fig. 6–13(b) with an upward load of 8 kips at point B. The deflection in this case is 0.75 in. upward. Now, if both of these types of load were applied at the same time, the total deflection at point B would be zero (by superposition). This condition is shown by Fig. 6–13(c). The shape of the beam is the same as it would be if loaded by condition (a) only, but provided with a third support at point B. Such a beam is shown in Fig. 6–13(d). The center reaction is 8 kips upward. In other words, the center reaction is large enough to reduce to zero the deflection that would occur at that point if the support were removed.

The beam of Fig. 6–13(d) is statically indeterminate to the first

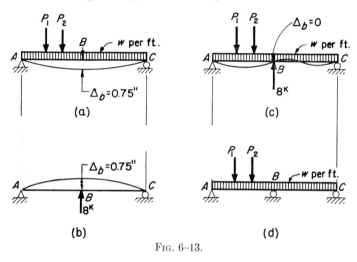

Fig. 6–13.

degree. A knowledge of deflections was used above to solve for one reaction. The remaining reactions can be solved using the equations of equilibrium.

The basic method illustrated above can be used to solve many problems in statically indeterminate structures. The steps in its application are as follows:

1. Remove enough reactions (either forces or moments) to reduce the structure to a simple structure. Use this same simple structure in the balance of the solution.
2. Apply the actual loads to this simple structure. Compute the deflections caused at points where reaction forces were removed. (Components of deflection parallel to the removed force are required.) Where the removed reaction was a moment, compute the angle of rotation at the point of that reaction.

3. Apply to the simple structure, one at a time, the reaction forces or moments which were removed. For each such loading, compute the deflections (or rotations) at the point of *each* removed reaction. The deflections (or rotations) thus computed are functions of the unknown reaction which is used as a load on the imaginary simple structure.
4. Compute the required size of the removed reactions necessary to return the deflections (or rotations) of the simple structure to zero. Where more than one reaction was removed, this operation involves simultaneous equations to solve for the effects of the simultaneous application of the removed reactions as loads.
5. Solve for the remaining unknown reactions by statics.
6. Total reactions, shears, and bending moments may be solved by superposition of the values from the various loadings of the imaginary simple structure.

The outline of steps as given above is rather detailed and it may, therefore, not be perfectly clear at first reading. A few simple examples should make the meaning clear, however.

Consider the beam of Fig. 6–14(a). It has 4 unknown reactions and is statically indeterminate to the first degree. Removal of one reaction,

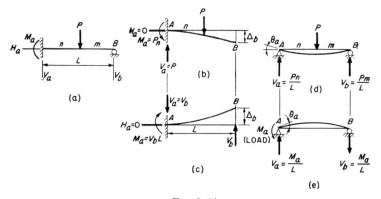

FIG. 6–14.

V_a or V_b, or M_a, will leave a simple structure. Any one of these can be removed. The beam with reaction V_b removed is shown by Fig. 6–14(b). The actual load is applied and the deflection Δ_b computed. In (c) an upward load V_b is applied. The deflection at B caused by this load is computed, the expression for the deflection containing the unknown force V_b. Equating the downward Δ_b due to load P to the upward Δ_t due to the force V_b gives an elastic equation. This equation can be solved to find the reaction V_b required to hold end B at the same height as the support. Knowing now the value of V_b in Fig. 6–14(a), it is possible to compute the remaining 3 reactions. Or, by superposition, the reaction M_a for the actual beam is equal to that for Fig. 6–14(b) plus that for (c); V_a for the actual beam is the algebraic sum of that shown in (b) and that shown in (c).

As an alternate method of solution, the moment reaction M_a is removed, leaving the simple beam of Fig. 6–14(d). End A of the simple beam rotates through an angle θ_a which can be computed by the moment-area method. In (e), the same simple beam is subjected to a moment M_a as a load. This causes end A to rotate as shown, the amount θ_a being solved as an expression involving M_a. The moment M_a is made just large enough to cause a rotation θ_a equal but opposite to the rotation θ_a caused by the load P. Thus, the simultaneous action of loads P and M_a results in the simple beam having zero slope at end A. The moment M_a required to hold the simple beam in that position is the same as the moment M_a for the actual beam of Fig. 6–14(a).

The method presented here is perfectly general and can theoretically be used to solve any statically indeterminate structure. When the degree of indeterminateness is high, however, the method becomes rather cumbersome. In such cases, more elaborate methods are used.[1] Usually, these more elaborate methods can be derived from the basic general method described above.

EXAMPLE 6–9. Assume that the beam of Example 6–7 and Fig. 6–11 is an existing one and that the addition of a center support is planned. Assume that the loads will be removed or that the center support will be jacked into place, so that the deflection at the center will be zero. With three supports, what will be the value of each reaction? What will be the maximum bending moment?

The simple beam and the actual loads are shown in Fig. 6–15(a). The deflection at the center point C was solved in Example 6–7 and is 0.177 in., or $2,375,500/EI$.

The same simple beam is shown in Fig. 6–15(b), but with a single upward force V_c at the center. Using the moment-area method and the diagram of moment due to force V_c, the deflection at C is

$$\Delta_c = \sum_a^c \frac{M\,ds\,x_a}{EI} = \frac{90 \times 45V_c}{2EI} \times 60 = 121{,}500\,V_c/EI$$

[1] C. D. Williams, *Analysis of Statically Indeterminate Structures* (Scranton, Pa.: International Textbook Co., 1946).

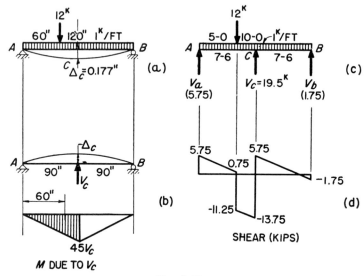

Fig. 6–15.

The total deflection caused by both conditions of loading acting together is zero, so that

$$\frac{121{,}500\,V_c}{EI} = \frac{2{,}375{,}500}{EI}$$

This equation is an "elastic equation." The elastic equation is merely a statement regarding the shape of the deformed structure; in this case it is the statement that the deflection at point C is zero. Solving the equation gives

$$V_c = \frac{2{,}375{,}500}{121{,}500} = 19.5 \text{ kips}$$

Fig. 6–15(c) shows the beam with three supports. The reaction at the center support is now known; those at the ends must be solved.

$\Sigma M_a = 0$

$(12 \times 5) + (15 \times 7.5) - (19.5 \times 7.5) - 15 V_b = 0;$

$\qquad\qquad\qquad\qquad V_b = 1.75 \text{ kips, upward}$

$\Sigma M_b = 0$

$15 V_a + (19.5 \times 7.5) - (12 \times 10) - (15 \times 7.5) = 0;$

$\qquad\qquad\qquad\qquad V_a = 5.75 \text{ kips, upward}$

Check by ΣV: $-12 - 15 + 5.75 + 19.5 + 1.75 = 0$ (Checks)

The shear diagram is drawn in Fig. 6–15(d). There are three points of zero shear, each indicating points of either maximum or minimum moment. The bending moment at each of these points is computed using the shear diagram.

At the 12-kip load, $M = 5.0\left(\dfrac{5.75 + 0.75}{2}\right) = 16.25$ ft-kips

At support C, $M = 16.25 - 2.5\left(\dfrac{11.25 + 13.75}{2}\right) = -15.0$ ft-kips

$$\text{(compression on bottom)}$$

At 1.75 ft from B, $M = 1.75 \times 1.75/2 = 1.53$ ft-kips

The maximum bending moment is the positive moment of 16.25 ft-kips at the location of the concentrated load.

EXAMPLE 6–10. What are the reactions for the fixed-end beam of Fig. 6–16? There are six reactions, and actually the beam is statically indeterminate to the third degree. The horizontal reactions are of negligible amount, however, and they are usually not solved in a structure of this type. The end moments and vertical reactions number four. Only two static equations are effective in solving for those reactions; therefore, two elastic equations must be added. The elastic equations, stated in words, are

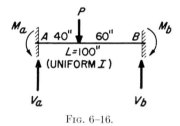

FIG. 6–16.

1. The slope at end A is zero
2. The slope at end B is zero

The problem is solved in computation-sheet form in Fig. 6–17. The first step is the reduction of the structure to a simple structure. The simple structure is then subjected to three loading conditions: first to the actual loads alone, then to the end moment M_a alone and finally to the end moment M_b alone. Since the reactions which were removed from points A and B are moments, the rotations, rather than deflections, at A and B are computed for each of the three conditions of load. The mathematical expressions for the rotations (slopes) are used in writing the two elastic equations. Note that care was taken to designate the direction of each rotation as it was solved.

After the elastic equations are solved simultaneously for reactions M_a and M_b, static equations are used to complete the solution.

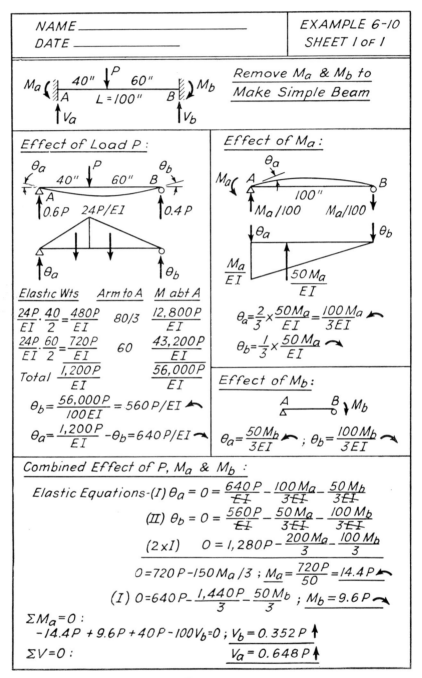

NAME _____

DATE _____

EXAMPLE 6-10

SHEET 1 OF 1

M_a $\quad$ 40" $\quad$ P $\quad$ 60" $\quad$ M_b
A $\quad$ $L = 100"$ $\quad$ B
V_a $\quad$ V_b

Remove M_a & M_b to
Make Simple Beam

Effect of Load P:

θ_a $\quad$ P $\quad$ θ_b
40" $\quad$ 60" $\quad$ B
A
$0.6P$ $\quad$ $24P/EI$ $\quad$ $0.4P$

θ_a $\quad$ θ_b

Elastic Wts	Arm to A	M abt A
$\frac{24P}{EI} \cdot \frac{40}{2} = \frac{480P}{EI}$	80/3	$\frac{12,800P}{EI}$
$\frac{24P}{EI} \cdot \frac{60}{2} = \frac{720P}{EI}$	60	$\frac{43,200P}{EI}$
Total $\frac{1,200P}{EI}$		$\frac{56,000P}{EI}$

$\theta_b = \frac{56,000P}{100EI} = 560P/EI$

$\theta_a = \frac{1,200P}{EI} - \theta_b = 640P/EI$

Effect of M_a:

θ_a
M_a $\quad$ A $\quad$ 100" $\quad$ B
$M_a/100$ $\quad$ $M_a/100$

θ_a $\quad$ θ_b

$\frac{M_a}{EI}$ $\quad$ $\frac{50 M_a}{EI}$

$\theta_a = \frac{2}{3} \times \frac{50 M_a}{EI} = \frac{100 M_a}{3EI}$

$\theta_b = \frac{1}{3} \times \frac{50 M_a}{EI}$

Effect of M_b:

A $\quad$ B $\quad$ M_b

$\theta_a = \frac{50 M_b}{3EI}$; $\theta_b = \frac{100 M_b}{3EI}$

Combined Effect of P, M_a & M_b:

Elastic Equations-(I) $\theta_a = 0 = \frac{640P}{EI} - \frac{100 M_a}{3EI} - \frac{50 M_b}{3EI}$

(II) $\theta_b = 0 = \frac{560P}{EI} - \frac{50 M_a}{3EI} - \frac{100 M_b}{3EI}$

(2×I) $\quad 0 = 1,280P - \frac{200 M_a}{3} - \frac{100 M_b}{3}$

$0 = 720P - 150 M_a/3$; $M_a = \frac{720P}{50} = 14.4P$

(I) $0 = 640P - \frac{1,440P}{3} - \frac{50 M_b}{3}$; $M_b = 9.6P$

$\Sigma M_a = 0$:
$-14.4P + 9.6P + 40P - 100 V_b = 0$; $V_b = 0.352P$

$\Sigma V = 0$:
$V_a = 0.648P$

Fig. 6-17.

PROBLEMS

6-1. What is the deflection of the outer end of the cantilever beam shown by Fig. 6–18? The material is
aluminum alloy having E of 10,500,000 psi. The
cross section has a moment of inertia of 7.49 in.^{4}

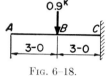

Fig. 6–18.

6-2. A wood beam has a 2-kip vertical load at each one-third point of its 10-ft
span. The cross section is 6 × 10 nominal ($5\frac{1}{2}$ × $9\frac{1}{2}$ in. actual) placed with
the greater dimension vertical. The material is southern yellow pine, hav-
ing $E = 1,600,000$ psi. What is the centerline deflection and the end slope?

6-3. A low dolly is to be made to carry a bin of steel scrap. The bin and its
contents weigh 17 kips. The proposed dolly is shown in Fig. 6–19. The

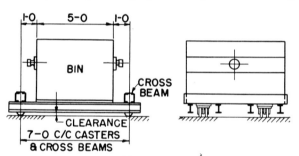

Fig. 6–19.

four I-beams share the 17-kip load equally and transmit it to the cross
beams and casters at the ends. The clearance between the dolly and the
floor is limited, so it is important to know how far the I-beams will deflect.

The I-beams are steel. It is hoped to use a section having I equal to
6.7 in.^{4} (for each beam). Assume them to be loaded uniformly over 5 ft
of their length. What is the maximum deflection of the I-beams?

6-4. The steel beam shown in Fig. 6–20 has an
overhang at each end. The portion between
supports is reinforced by cover plates. Use
the moment-area method to compute the
deflection at C and at A. Neglect the weight
of the beam. It may help to sketch the elastic curve before starting the solution.

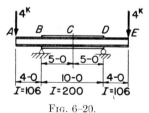

Fig. 6–20.

6-5. An outdoor crane and runway are shown by Fig. 6–21. Revisions to the
yard layout include locating a driveway next to the right row of columns.
The existing diagonal bracing for the right row of columns must be
removed. This leaves the columns with no lateral support, so overhead
bracing must be provided, as shown dotted. The designer has selected a

section for the brace consisting of two steel angles, each $5 \times 3\frac{1}{2} \times \frac{1}{2}$, arranged as shown by section A–A. This section has been checked for strength and found satisfactory. A minimum of two in. of clearance must be provided between the brace and the highest point of the moving crane. At what elevation should the top of the brace be placed where it joins the columns?

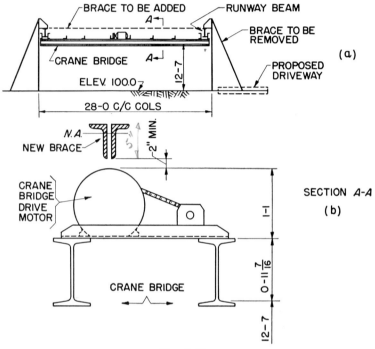

FIG. 6–21.

6–6. A high catwalk is to be built between the roof trusses of your plant. The trusses are 20 ft apart. The only loads on the catwalk will be a small dead load plus about 200 lb for the weight of one man. The cross section of the catwalk is shown by Fig. 6–22. Excessive deflection will have a bad effect

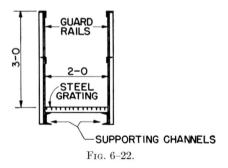

FIG. 6–22.

on the man who must use the catwalk. How much deflection will his weight cause? Assume that he can stand so as to put his entire weight on one of the supporting channels. Each channel has I of 1.6 in.[4]. What will happen when his weight shifts from one side to the other as he walks?

6–7. What is the deflection at point $\dot{C}$ of the steel beam in Fig. 6–23? The moment of inertia of the cross section is 290 in.[4].

6–8. What is the maximum deflection in the beam of Problem 6–7?

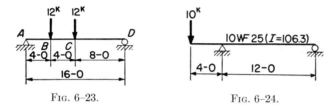

FIG. 6–23. FIG. 6–24.

6–9. What is the deflection at end A of the beam in Fig. 6–24?

6–10. What is the maximum upward deflection for the beam of Fig. 6–24?

6–11. A self-supporting jib crane is shown in Fig. 6–25. How much deflection is caused at A by the weight of the hoist, trolley, and lifted load? The mast

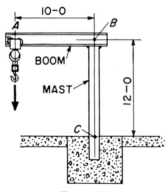

FIG. 6–25.

is a pipe section with I of 430 in.[4], and the boom is an I-beam with I of 442 in.[4]. The hoist is of 2-ton capacity and weighs 300 lb. The trolley weight is 90 lb. Assume the mast fixed at C. (Suggestion: Solve in two parts. First find the movement of A caused by bending moment in the mast only.)

6–12. Assume that a support is to be placed at end A of the beam of Problem 6–1. What will be the values of the reactions? Compute the maximum positive bending moment.

6–13. A light cross member between two heavy verticals of a welded steel machine frame is shown in Fig. 6–26. Assume that you intend to sell the

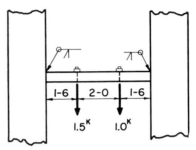

Fig. 6–26.

owner some added equipment which will load the cross member as shown. As a sales engineer you are called upon to verify that the new equipment will not damage the supporting structure. Find the reactions and draw shear and moment diagrams for the cross member.

6–14. A plating tank is to be supported on a low platform as shown in Fig. 6–27. The weight of the tank and its contents cause a load of 300 lb per ft on

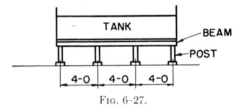

Fig. 6–27.

the main beam of each side. What are the loads in each post? Draw shear and moment diagrams for the main beam.

CHAPTER 7

DESIGN IN STEEL—MEMBERS

The chapters up to this point have dealt with the portion of structural engineering theory known as "analysis." From this point on the portion known as "design" will be considered. Design, as explained in Chapter 1, may be subdivided into "functional design" and "detail design." The art of functional design is more the result of experience and natural capabilities than of formal study. The fundamentals of detail design, though, can be learned by formal study.

In detail design, the main job is the selection of materials of the proper kind, shape, and size, to do the job. In metals the selection, or design, can be broken into the design of members and the design of connections. This chapter covers the design of members, while Chapter 8 will cover the design of connections.

7–1. Factors Affecting Detail Design. Occasionally the selection of the kind, shape, and size of material for a member or connection is controlled by one factor only. Often, however, many factors are considered before the selection is made.

Strength is a factor which often controls the final selection. Members and connections must be strong enough to provide a reasonable factor of safety against failure from all expected loads. Dead load, live load, impact, and wind load must often be considered, both separately and in combination. In some cases other unusual loads must also be included.

Rigidity is another important factor. Either excessive deflection or lateral vibration may be objectionable features. Both of these can be reduced by the use of a more rigid member. (See Chapter 6.) Quite often a particular size of member will have adequate strength as a beam, but a larger and stronger section is required in order to avoid excessive deflection.

The weight of the section must usually be considered. In general, a heavier member, in itself, is a more costly one. The heavier member adds to the dead load, so that other supporting members may in turn need to be heavier. When other factors do not conflict, it is a good design practice to select the lightest and most economical section that fills the need. In aircraft, of course, the selection of the lightest section possible is of paramount importance, even if the cost of the structure is somewhat higher. In aircraft, every pound of dead load removed provides approximately a pound of additional "pay load" capacity.

Sometimes the choice of the lightest safe section for each member results in a large conglomeration of shapes and sizes on the same job. Individually the sections may be the most economical, while collectively they may not be most economical. Because of the small quantities of each section the unit cost may be high. Fabrication costs may be higher because of the great variety of connection details. In such cases it is often desirable to limit the number of different sections used. Some may then be stronger and heavier than needed, but economy and a better appearance will be the result.

Appearance is becoming increasingly important. This is particularly so in structures which are to be viewed by the general public. Appearance is important also where it may affect the decisions of prospective customers. Where competing types of equipment are equally well designed and adapted to the customer's need, the well-proportioned type, having a neat, trim appearance, will very likely be the better seller.

Psychological factors sometimes affect the selection. A structure visible to the public should not only *be* strong enough; it should also *look* strong enough. Equipment should not only *be* durable; it should also *look* durable.

Space is sometimes limited. As a result it may be impossible to select the most economical sections. Smaller but heavier sections will be needed in order to meet the strength and rigidity requirements.

The service conditions must often be considered. These would include conditions of corrosive atmosphere, extremes of temperature, and exposure to severe weather.

The desired length of useful life should affect the design. A temporary structure could certainly be designed lighter than one expected to serve and endure for fifty years. Specifications sometimes take this into account by showing a different set of allowable stresses for temporary structures than for permanent ones.

Availability of material may affect the selection. The lightest section may be available only after a long wait or only from a great distance away. A heavier section, available immediately and from a local source of supply, might be a better choice.

Other factors often affecting the selection are the problems of fabrication, assembly, and maintenance.

7–2. Factor of Safety and Allowable Stresses.   The factor of safety of a structure is the number of times by which its load could be multiplied before causing failure. Failure, of course, must be defined. Failure may be defined either as the collapse or breaking of the structure, or as the permanent deformation of the structure. Thus the factor of safety could be defined in two ways, as follows:

1. F.S. $= \dfrac{\text{Ultimate load}}{\text{Actual load}}$

or

2. F.S. $= \dfrac{\text{Load causing permanent set (yield)}}{\text{Actual load}}$

Either type of factor of safety may be used. Most specifications provide for the use of a factor of safety with respect to yielding.

There are two ways in which the factor of safety can be applied in design. They are:

1. Multiply the expected load by the desired factor of safety. The stresses due to the increased load are then compared with the ultimate strength (or yield strength, depending on the type of safety factor used). This design procedure is used in aircraft design.

2. Divide the ultimate (or yield) strength of the material by the desired factor of safety. Use this reduced unit stress as an *allowable stress*. The stresses caused by the expected loads must not exceed this allowable value.

The second method is common to structural work other than aircraft. It is used in the AISC and ACI specifications.

The factor of safety chosen by the committees responsible for the various specifications varies. In general, if the type of service is more severe, the loads more uncertain in amount, or the responsibility to the public greater, then the factor of safety will be a little higher. For example, the allowable unit tensile stress is 20,000 psi in the AISC Specification (buildings), but only 18,000 psi in the AREA railway bridge or the AASHO highway bridge specifications. Thus, the factors of safety with respect to yield are

$$\frac{33,000}{20,000} = 1.65 \text{ for the AISC}$$

or

$$\frac{33,000}{18,000} = 1.83 \text{ for the AREA or AASHO Specifications}$$

Remember, the different factors do *not* denote disagreement. Each factor of safety is appropriate to the type of structure covered by that specification.

7–3. Classification of Members. Structural members are classified according to the type of load they receive. The main types are three in number, as follows:

1. Tension members—those having an axial tensile load only
2. Compression members—those having an axial compressive load only
3. Beams—members having transverse loads only

Members may also have transverse load (bending) in combination with either tension or compression.

The types of rolled steel section should be considered now, and their method of designation should be noted. The common types are listed below.

1. PLATE. A plate is a flat piece having a width of 6 in. or more. In specifying plates the number of pieces required is given first, then the symbol for plate. This is followed by the width and the thickness in inches, and by the length. Length is given in feet and inches for lengths of ten inches or over.

   Example: 2 Pl 9 $\times$ $\frac{1}{2}$ $\times$ 6–4

2. BAR. A bar is merely a plate of less than 6-in. width.

   Example: 1 Bar 5 $\times$ $\frac{3}{8}$ $\times$ 0–11

3. WIDE FLANGE SECTION. A wide flange section has the shape of a letter "I." See Fig. 7–1(a). The inner and outer surfaces of the

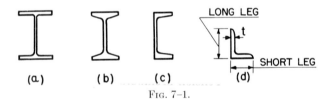

(a)   (b)   (c)   (d)

LONG LEG

t

SHORT LEG

FIG. 7–1.

flanges of this section are generally parallel. This feature makes fabrication easier. Beveled washers and tapered fillers are unnecessary. In specifying a wide flange section, the following sequence is followed: the number of pieces, the nominal depth of the section, the symbol **WF**, the weight in pounds per linear foot, and the length.

   Example: 1–10**WF**21 $\times$ 19–11$\frac{1}{2}$

4. AMERICAN STANDARD BEAM. This is popularly called the "I-beam." It too has the shape of a letter "I." See Fig. 7–1(b). The inner surface of the flange is sloped, however. The angle

between it and the flat outer surface is about 7 degrees. This causes troubles in certain types of connections. The I-beam is now avoided for many uses in favor of the newer wide flange sections. The designation is like that for a wide flange section, but with the symbol I instead of **WF**.

Example: 2–12 I 31.8 × 5–10

5. CHANNEL. A channel is shown by Fig. 7–1(c). Its flange surfaces are sloped, as in the I-beam. The channel is popular where one perfectly flat side is desired, as in steel framing around an opening in a floor or in a door frame. The order of designation is like that for a **WF** or I, but with the symbol ⌐.

Example: 1–8 ⌐ 11.5 × 10–0.

6. ANGLE. An angle is shown in Fig. 7–1(d). The inner and outer surfaces are parallel. An angle is designated in the following order: number of pieces required, the symbol ∟, the long-leg dimension, the short-leg dimension, the thickness, and the length. When an unequal-leg angle is used, the design and detail drawings should show the position of the angle; i.e., which leg is flat or which is outstanding.

Example: 2 ∟s 4 × 3 × $\frac{5}{16}$ × 13–$4\frac{1}{2}$

A selected list of rolled sections is given in the Appendix of this book. The list has been condensed to eliminate the sections which would usually not be encountered by the non-civil engineer.

There are many other sections available, such as ship channels, zees, tees, sheet piles, and bulb angles. The dimensions and properties of these may be found in a handbook such as *Steel Construction*, by the American Institute of Steel Construction.

Tension Members

7–4. Tension Member Sections. Fig. 7–2 shows a few of the shapes of cross section commonly used for tension members. The simplest kind is the round bar, Fig. 7–2(a), often used for hangers, bracing, and

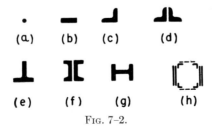

FIG. 7–2.

tie rods. The advantage of the round rod is its adjustable length. With ends threaded and supplied with nuts or a turnbuckle it can be tightened as necessary. The flat bar in (b) is simple to make, but is not adjustable and lacks stiffness. For very short members in tension it is a good section. For more stiffness an angle (c) may be used. The tension members in the bottom chords and web members of light trusses are usually double-angle sections, as in (d). In welded trusses, the tee-shaped tension member of (e) is quite common. In heavier trusses, the tension members often have sections as shown in (f), (g), or (h). The member of (h) is built up of angles and flat plates. The dotted lines indicate tie plates. They are located at frequent intervals along the length, and serve to hold the various elements of the section in the correct position.

7–5. Design of Tension Members. The unit stress caused by axial load in a straight uniform tension member is assumed to be uniform over the entire cross-sectional area. Stated mathematically, $f = P/A$. In this equation, f is the unit tensile stress, P is the applied axial load, and A is the area of the cross section. (An axial load is longitudinal, and acts at the center of gravity of the cross-sectional area.)

To design a tension member having no holes, merely select one with an area A large enough that the unit stress f does not exceed the allowable tensile stress given by the specification applicable. This is best accomplished by rearranging the equation to read

$$\text{Required } A = P/\text{allowable } f$$

7–6. Net Areas. If a tension member of non-uniform cross section is loaded to ultimate failure, the break will occur at the part having the smallest cross-sectional area. For instance, in the member of Fig. 7–3(a) failure will occur as indicated, across the section at a hole. The threaded rod of (b) would break where the section has the least area, which is at the bottom of the threads.

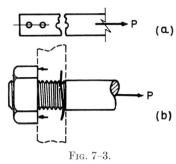

(a)

(b)

Fig. 7–3.

The minimum area, at the potential breaking points, of these members is called the *net area*. To design the members, a uniform stress distribution is assumed on the net area. The equation then becomes

$$\text{Required } A_{net} = P/\text{allowable } f$$

The net area of a member with holes is equal to the gross or total area minus the area removed from the cross section by the holes. How much area should be deducted for the effect of holes? If the holes were drilled to exact size, it would be correct to use the actual hole diameter in computing the deduction. However, holes for structural rivets are usually punched, so that the hole has rather jagged sides. Material is damaged beyond the edge of the hole. Since the damaged material does not contribute to the strength of the member, it, too, is deducted. In structural steel specifications, the deduction is made for a hole $\frac{1}{16}$ in. larger in diameter than the specified size of hole. Further, the specified hole for rivets is $\frac{1}{16}$ in. larger than the nominal diameter of the rivet. Thus for $\frac{3}{4}$-in. rivets, a $\frac{13}{16}$-in. diameter hole is punched, and an assumed effective hole diameter of $\frac{7}{8}$ in. is used in computing the net area. For $\frac{7}{8}$-in. rivets, the actual hole diameter is $\frac{15}{16}$ in., and the effective hole diameter for computing net area is one inch.

In addition to the increase of stress due to a reduced area over which the load is distributed, there may be concentrations of stress at the edge of the hole. In other words, the stress distribution may not be strictly uniform as is indicated by the equation $f = P/A$. Unless many thousands of repetitions of load will occur, however, the effect of the concentration of stress is ignored in steel design. If the number of repetitions is high, a fatigue failure might result. In such cases, the effect of the concentration of stress would need to be considered.[1]

EXAMPLE 7–1. What size of threaded rod would be required in the jib crane of Fig. 2–12? In Example 2–10 the tensile force in the rod was found to be 6,910 lb, including live load, dead load, and impact. Use the AISC Specification.

By Section 15 of the Specification the allowable unit tensile stress for threaded parts, on the nominal area at the root of the threads, is given as 20,000 psi.

$$\text{Required } A_{net} = 6,910/20,000 = 0.346 \text{ in.}^2$$

Table 3 of Appendix B shows the areas for various sizes of threaded rod. One $\frac{7}{8}$-in. rod will be satisfactory. It provides a net area of 0.419 in.^{2}. The next smaller size, $\frac{3}{4}$-in., would provide less than the required 0.346 in.^{2}.

EXAMPLE 7–2. A steel angle is used to hang the supporting members of a belt conveyor from the roof members. The hanger is shown in Fig. 7–4(a). The total load applied to the hanger angle is 1,800 lb. Is the angle satisfactory according to the AISC Specification?

Fig. 7–4(b) shows the effective cross section of the member. The effective hole size is $\frac{1}{8}$ in. larger than the rivet size, or $\frac{3}{4}$ in. diameter. Appendix

---

[1]C. D. Williams and E. C. Harris, *Structural Design in Metals*, (New York; The Ronald Press Co., 1949), Chap. 10.

A gives the properties of the common sizes of steel angle. From that table we find the gross area of the $2 \times 2 \times \frac{1}{4}$ angle to be 0.94 sq. in. The net area is the gross area minus the area removed by the hole.

$$A_{net} = 0.94 - \left(\frac{1}{4} \times \frac{3}{4}\right) = 0.75 \text{ in.}^2$$

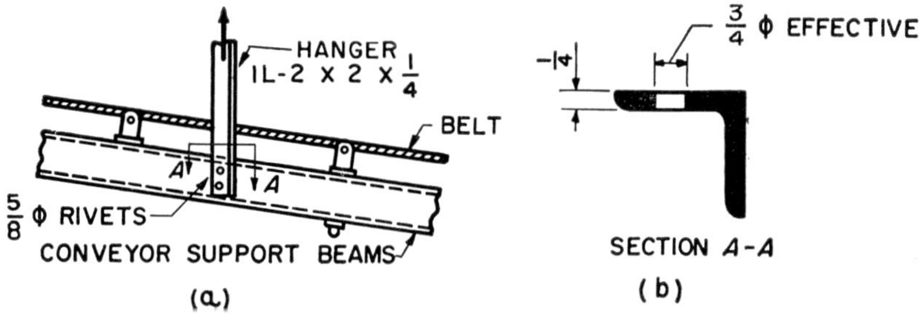

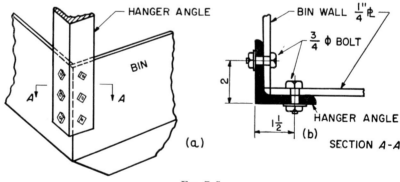

Fig. 7–4.

The actual stress on the net area is now computed.

$$\text{Actual } f = 1{,}800/0.75 = 2{,}400 \text{ psi}$$

Section 15 of the Specification gives 20,000 psi as allowable. Since the actual unit stress does not exceed the allowable, the section satisfies the strength requirement of the specification.

It might seem advisable at first to save by using a smaller size of angle. However, a smaller angle might be more difficult to obtain. Smaller sized rivets would be necessary in a narrower leg.

The Specification is often referred to in these examples. It is important for the student to refer to the Specification and read it also. Much important design information is contained in the Specification.

EXAMPLE 7–3. A bin for storage of granular material is to be suspended from the roof steel of a factory building. It is planned to use one

Fig. 7–5.

hanger at each corner of the bin, as shown in Fig. 7–5(a). The bin will be connected to the hanger using $\frac{3}{4}$-in. bolts. The total weight of the bin and its contents is 64 kips. Each hanger will take one-fourth of the total, or 16 kips. Select an angle for the hanger. Use the AISC Specification.

$$\text{Required } A_{net} = \frac{16}{20} = 0.80 \text{ in.}^2$$

The size of angle must be selected by trial. Deduction must be made for the area removed by two $\frac{7}{8}$-in. holes.

Try a $3 \times 3 \times \frac{1}{4}$ angle (Symbol: $1 \llcorner 3 \times 3 \times \frac{1}{4}$).

$$A_{net} = 1.44 - 2\left(\frac{1}{4} \times \frac{7}{8}\right) = 1.00 \text{ in.}^2 \quad \text{Satisfactory}$$

Try $1 \llcorner 2\frac{1}{2} \times 2\frac{1}{2} \times \frac{1}{4}$.

$$A_{net} = 1.19 - 2\left(\frac{1}{4} \times \frac{7}{8}\right) = 0.75 \text{ in.}^2 \quad \text{Too small}$$

Try $1 \llcorner 3 \times 2\frac{1}{2} \times \frac{1}{4}$.

$$A_{net} = 1.31 - 2\left(\frac{1}{4} \times \frac{7}{8}\right) = 0.87 \text{ in.}^2 \quad \text{Satisfactory}$$

The lightest angle to satisfy the strength requirements of the Specification is the $3 \times 2\frac{1}{2} \times \frac{1}{4}$. (Thinner angles were not tried. One-quarter inch is usually the minimum thickness accepted for such members.) One thing to check before calling for the use of this particular angle is the question of space for punching the holes and for installing the bolts. This part of the subject is covered in Chapter 8. It is separated only for instruction purposes. In practice, the details of the connection should be considered when selecting the section. In this particular case, there will be sufficient room for the bolts if they are located as shown on section A–A.

Therefore, use $1 \llcorner 3 \times 2\frac{1}{2} \times \frac{1}{4}$.

7–7. Effect of Staggered Holes. In the examples just given, if the members were loaded to ultimate failure, the line of fracture would be transverse to the member. It would be like the break shown in Fig. 7–6(a).

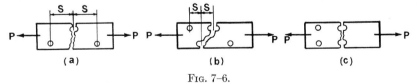

FIG. 7–6.

In the members shown in Fig. 7–6, there are two rows of holes. In (a) the holes are staggered, so that failure is on a transverse section. The net area of the member is equal to the gross area minus a deduction for one hole.

In (c) the holes are opposite, not staggered. The section of failure is through two holes. The net area is the gross area minus deductions for two holes. Obviously the bar of (c) is weaker than that of (a).

In (b) the holes are staggered, but not so much as in (a). This condition is intermediate between (a) and (c). If the stagger S is not too large, failure will occur along a diagonal path between holes, as shown in (b). If we start with a bar as shown in (a) and gradually reduce the stagger S until detail (c) is reached, the strength changes. But it does not change abruptly from the strength of (a) to the strength of (c). There is gradual transition in strength. For bars in which failure of type (b) occurs, the strength is between that of (a) and (c).

The exact analysis of stress conditions in (b) is very difficult, and does not lend itself to engineering design procedures. The strength of (b) is known to be greater than that of (c). The length of the diagonal path between the holes is greater than the transverse distance between the holes of (c). The failure surface of (b) is subject to a combination of tensile and shearing stresses. That of (c) is subject only to tensile stress. The design methods used for type (b) are empirical.

In aircraft work the effect of stagger is often considered to be too uncertain. The full deduction for both holes is required unless the stagger is large enough to insure failure of type (a).

In structural steel specifications the most used method recognizes the greater strength of the diagonal path between holes. In that method, the strength is computed as if the holes were opposite, then a compensating amount is added to cover the effect of the diagonal path. The resulting total is called the *effective* net area. This method is given by Section 19(c) of the AISC Specification as follows:

"In the case of a chain of holes extending across a part in any diagonal or zigzag line, the net width of the part shall be obtained by deducting from the gross width the sum of the diameters of all the holes in the chain, and adding, for each gage space in the chain, the quantity

$$\frac{s^2}{4g}$$

where s = longitudinal spacing (pitch) in inches of any two successive holes

g = transverse spacing (gage) in inches of the same two holes.

The critical net section of the part is obtained from that chain which gives the least net width."

The application of this method will be illustrated by the next two examples.

EXAMPLE 7–4. What is the allowable tensile load for the plate shown in Fig. 7–7? Use the AISC Specification.

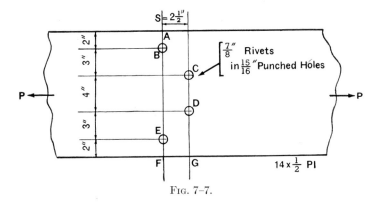

FIG. 7–7.

The effective net widths are computed as follows:

$$\text{Line } A\!-\!B\!-\!C\!-\!D\!-\!E\!-\!F: \; 14 - (4 \times 1) + \frac{(2.5)^2}{4 \times 3} + \frac{(2.5)^2}{4 \times 3} = 11.04$$
$$\qquad\qquad\qquad\qquad\qquad\qquad\qquad\qquad\qquad\qquad\qquad\qquad \textit{Controls}$$

$$\text{Line } A\!-\!B\!-\!C\!-\!D\!-\!G: \quad 14 - (3 \times 1) + \frac{(2.5)^2}{4 \times 3} = 11.52$$

$$\text{Line } A\!-\!B\!-\!D\!-\!G: \quad 14 - (2 \times 1) + \frac{(2.5)^2}{4 \times 7} = 12.22$$

$$\text{Line } A\!-\!B\!-\!D\!-\!E\!-\!F: \quad 14 - (3 \times 1) + \frac{(2.5)^2}{4 \times 7} + \frac{(2.5)^2}{4 \times 3} = 11.74$$

$$\text{Line } A\!-\!B\!-\!E\!-\!F: \quad 14 - (2 \times 1) = 12.00$$

The path which has the least effective net width, and consequently which determines the tensile strength of the member, is path $A\!-\!B\!-\!C\!-\!D\!-\!E\!-\!F$. The maximum allowable tensile load P, with the AISC allowable unit stress of 20,000 psi, is equal to $20,000 \times 11.04 \times 0.5 = 110,400$ lb.

EXAMPLE 7–5. The bottom chord of an existing roof truss consists of 2 ∟ $4 \times 3 \times \frac{3}{8}$, as shown in Fig. 7–8(a). A new air-conditioning unit is to be supported by the truss. The total stress in the end panel of the bottom chord will then equal 78 kips. Is the chord strong enough to take this new total load? There are holes for $\frac{3}{4}$-in. rivets in each leg of the angles. The holes are staggered as shown. Use the AISC Specification.

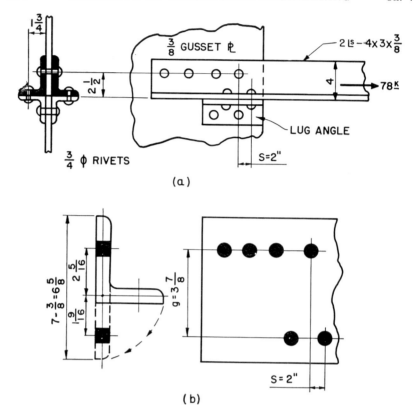

FIG. 7–8.

The angle is assumed to be bent flat as shown in Fig. 7–8(b). If this were possible, the length along the centerline of the legs would remain unchanged. The material on the inside would be stretched, that on the outside compressed. The angle is thus the equivalent of a flat plate $6\frac{5}{8}$ in. wide and $\frac{3}{8}$ in. thick. The strength of the angle in tension will be computed using the plate dimensions.

For failure through one hole only, the net area per angle is

$$A_{net} = 2.48 - \left(\frac{3}{8} \times \frac{7}{8}\right) = 2.15 \text{ in}^2.$$

For failure through two holes, along the diagonal path, the effective net width is

$$W_{net} = 6.62 - \left(2 \times \frac{7}{8}\right) + \frac{(2)^2}{4 \times 3.87} = 5.13 \text{ in.}$$

Effective $A_{net} = 5.13 \times \frac{3}{8} = 1.92 \text{ in.}^2$ per angle

The path through two holes gives the smaller effective net area and controls the strength. The allowable load on the member is

$$2 \times 1.92 \times 20 = 76.8 \text{ kips}$$

This is a little less than the expected load of 78 kips. Whether to accept it as satisfactory depends on several conditions. Is the 78-kip figure conservative? Does it include all the probable loadings? Are the loads which were used fairly accurate? If so, the slight overstress that would result is not serious. It is common in building work to allow overstress of from 3 to 5 per cent. The specifications do not suggest this, however. The decision and responsibility is strictly up to the engineer. Most engineers would call the angles analyzed in this example satisfactory.

7–8. Limiting Slenderness for Tension Members. The design of tension members, as illustrated by the previous examples, considers only their strength against computed loads. Another important factor is stiffness or rigidity. A reasonable amount of stiffness is usually desired in order to prevent lateral vibration of the member, and to strengthen it against unpredicted lateral loads. Stiffness will also help to minimize sagging due to the member's own weight.

Stiffness is usually measured by the "slenderness ratio." This ratio is equal to L/r, in which L is the length of the member between points where it is supported against lateral movement, and r is the radius of gyration of the cross section of the member. A high L/r ratio indicates a slender member, and a low L/r a stiff member. The stiffness of a member can be controlled by limiting the allowable L/r values. For example, in Section 16(a) of the AISC Specification the L/r ratio is limited to 240 for main tension members, and to 300 for secondary tension members. For bracing rods, however, no control of stiffness is given. Rods, therefore, should be used only where sagging and some vibration are not objectionable, or where a high tension is always present so that lateral vibration movement is minimized.

The difference between main and secondary members should be explained at this point. A main member is one that carries computed dead load and live load. Its presence in the structure is essential to the support of those loads. A member whose only function is to brace against wind loads, to brace other members during erection, or to brace other members against lateral buckling movement is called a secondary member.

EXAMPLE 7–6. Assume that the bin of Example 7–3 is to be located 10 ft below the roof members. (See Fig. 7–5.) Is the slenderness of the angle selected within the specification requirements?

The hanger angle is a main member. Its L/r ratio must be limited to 240. The radii of gyration about various axes are shown in the tables of the Appendix. The angle is not braced except at its ends; its center portions are free to move laterally in any direction. The critical L/r value is obtained using the minimum r, that about axis Z–Z. For a $3 \times 2\frac{1}{2} \times \frac{1}{4}$ angle, this is given as 0.53 in.

$$\frac{L}{r} = \frac{10 \times 12}{0.53} = 226$$

This is less than 240, so the angle selected is satisfactory.

Compression Members

7–9. Types of Compression Failure. Compression members can be classified according to the manner in which they would fail if subjected to ultimate axial loads. A compression member having a short length relative to its lateral dimensions will usually fail under ultimate axial load by crushing of its material, as shown in Fig. 7–9(a). If the material is brittle, failure may include actual fracture in diagonal or longitudinal directions; if it is ductile, a gradual bulging of the member will occur. Failure occurs without bending. Such a short member is often called a "compression block." A load producing yield-point stress in the material is usually considered as the critical load, inasmuch as this is the limit of the useful value of the compression block.

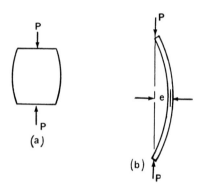

A long column is one having great length relative to its least lateral dimension. Failure of such a column under axial load consists of a sudden lateral bending or buckling, as shown in Fig. 7–9(b). For each column there is a limiting load P, known as the "Euler limiting load," which is critical for the column. When the critical load has been reached, the column may fail suddenly by buckling, even though the load does not produce an average unit stress as high as the yield point of the material.

The true dividing line between the long column and the compression block is at the length at which yield-point stress in the material is produced by the Euler load. For constant-section, round-end structural steel columns, the dividing line is at the length for which the ratio L/r is approximately 90.

FIG. 7–9.

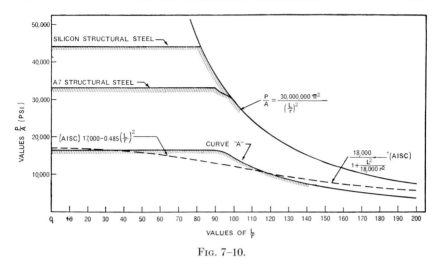

FIG. 7–10.

Fig. 7–10 shows a typical curve for the limit of axial stress in a structural steel column. When the unit stress reaches the proportional limit, the value of E decreases and the Euler curve varies from the common form. In the case of a material that has yield-point stress and proportional limit practically equal, the curve of limiting axial stress would be of the type shown for silicon structural steel.

7–10. Design of Axially Loaded Columns. Imagine a column to be straight and to have a moderate axial load P. The unit stress for this column is uniform over the cross section and is equal to P/A. Let some small lateral movement now be caused, for example, by a temporary small sidewise blow. When the force causing the lateral movement is released, the column should return to the straight condition. Now imagine the load P to be increased by increments, and the same small lateral displacement caused. The column will straighten out under each load until finally a value of P is reached which will cause the column to *remain* in the slightly deflected position. This load is called the Euler limit of load. If P is reduced slightly, the column will straighten again. If P is increased slightly, the column will bend farther and collapse completely. When the Euler limit of load is present, the deflected column is in a state of unstable equilibrium; a slight change of load either way causes the position of the column to change. The Euler limit of load is an ultimate load. The Euler limit of load can be defined as *the axial load which will just maintain some small given lateral deflection of an initially straight column.*

For a column of uniform cross section and having round ends, the Euler limit of load is $P = \pi^2 EI/L^2$. (See any strength of materials textbook.) The average unit stress at this load is called the Euler limit of stress. Substituting Ar^2 for I, the Euler limit of stress is

$$\frac{P}{A} = \frac{\pi^2 E}{\left(\dfrac{L}{r}\right)^2}$$

Fig. 7–10 shows the Euler curve for steel columns with round (or pinned) ends and constant cross section. For columns of very low slenderness ratio L/r, the ultimate P/A becomes very high. A horizontal line is drawn at P/A equal to the yield strength, about 33,000 psi. Columns with an Euler limit of more than the yield strength of the material will fail by yielding rather than by buckling. There is a short transition curve joining the yield-strength line to the Euler curve because the modulus of elasticity E of structural steel decreases slightly near the yield point.

The P/A values on the upper curves are limiting values. Columns should be designed having a factor of safety with respect to those values. There are many types of design curves and formulas in common use. The ones given by the AISC Specification, Section 15(a), are shown as the lower curve of Fig. 7–10. The design equations represented by that curve are

Allowable $P/A = 17,000 - 0.485(L/r)^2$, for L/r between zero and 120,

Allowable $P/A = \dfrac{18,000}{1 + \dfrac{1}{18,000}\left(\dfrac{L}{r}\right)^2}$, for L/r between 120 and 200

Comparison of the upper and lower curves will show that the AISC equations provide a safety factor of about 2.

7–11. Effect of Condition of End Support. The end conditions of a column affect the manner in which it can buckle. A column with pinned or round ends will curve as shown in Fig. 7–11(a). The Euler equation given in Art. 7–10 was derived for this type of column.

If both ends are fixed against rotation, the column will buckle to the curve of Fig. 7–11(b). Points of contraflexure are located a distance $0.5L$ apart. The portion between these points of contraflexure has the same shape as the entire length in Fig. 7–11(a). In applying the Euler equation, it would seem proper to substitute $0.5L$ for L, giving

$$\frac{P}{A} = \frac{4\pi^2 E}{\left(\dfrac{L}{r}\right)^2}$$

In practice, however, it is extremely difficult to produce a true fixed-end condition. Thus in the design of columns, it is usual to assume all columns as having pinned ends. Any partial fixity present then serves to increase the factor of safety.

The exception to the above assumption is the column type shown in Fig. 7–11(c). This column is free to move laterally at the top. Its curve

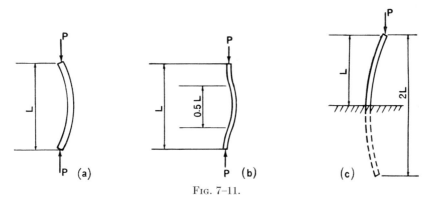

FIG. 7–11.

is shown by the solid lines. Below the support a dotted reflection of the upper curve is shown. The total curve has the same shape as the curve of Fig. 7–11(a). In applying the Euler equation to columns of type (c), $2L$ should be used as an effective length to replace L in the equation. Specifications do not remind the designer of this fact, and if it is forgotten, the factor of safety may be reduced to *less than one*. Remember, when one end is free to move laterally, use *twice* the actual length for the term L in the design formulas.

7–12. Types of Column Sections. In Fig. 7–12 a few of the many types of cross section suitable for columns are illustrated. The solid lines of the illustrations indicate elements which extend for the full effective length of the member. The dotted lines represent intermittent lacing or tie plates, the function of which is to join the main elements together, making them act as a unit.

The single angle of Fig. 7–12(a) is commonly used for relatively light axial loads. The **WF** section of part (b) is the most usual section employed for building columns. Columns of the shape shown by part (c) are made of large pipe for building use and of steel or aluminum tubing for aircraft use. Part (d) shows the popular "hat section" of aircraft, which is usually formed by bending a flat sheet to the shape shown.

A column load may be so great that sufficient area cannot practically or economically be provided by a simple section such as illustrated by parts (a) to (d); or the slenderness ratio L/r of such a section may be so great as to reduce the permissible average unit stress P/A to an undesirably low value. In either case a good solution is frequently found to be the use of a section consisting of several simple elements connected together so as to function as a single unit. Parts (e) to (t), inclusive, of Fig. 7–12 illustrate such built-up sections.

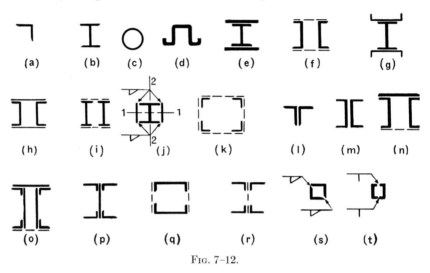

Fig. 7–12.

Parts (e) to (j), inclusive, show built-up sections that are well adapted for use as building columns. Type (j) is a welded type in which the added plates serve to equalize the stiffness of the member about both axes by increasing the lower radius of gyration of the core section. The four-angle section with lacing shown in part (k) is often observed on crane booms or on small masts or towers. Types (l) and (m) are commonly used as compression members on light trusses and as struts or compression bracing. Types (n) and (o) are well adapted for use as compression chords or as end posts of larger trusses, particularly bridge trusses. Types (p), (q), and (r) are used for building columns and for web members of larger trusses. Parts (s) and (t) illustrate but two of the many possible combinations of elements made practical by welding. Such sections are often valuable for structural parts of cranes or other machinery.

EXAMPLE 7–7. What is the axial load capacity of a 10WF33 section, used as a column? The length is 14 ft. The column is laterally supported at its ends only. Use the AISC Specification.

The column will buckle in the direction of least stiffness. The radii of gyration for the section are given by the tables as 4.20 in. about axis X–X, and 1.94 in. about axis Y–Y. The ratio L/r is

$$\frac{14 \times 12}{4.20} = 40.0 \text{ for axis } X\text{-}X$$

or

$$\frac{14 \times 12}{1.94} = 86.5 \text{ for axis } Y\text{-}Y$$

The larger L/r ratio determines the allowable capacity and the direction of buckling that would occur at ultimate load. This column would buckle as shown in Fig. 7–13, so that it bends about axis Y–Y as a neutral axis.

$$\text{Allowable } \frac{P}{A} = 17{,}000 - 0.485(86.5)^2 = 13{,}370 \text{ psi}$$

From the tables of **WF** sections, the area of the section is 9.71 sq in. The allowable axial load is

$$P = 9.71 \times 13.37 = 130 \text{ kips}$$

EXAMPLE 7–8. Suppose that the column of the previous example is an existing one used to support the floor of a storage area. The plant superintendent wishes to increase the floor load if possible. You, as

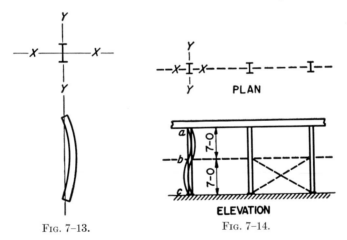

FIG. 7–13.   FIG. 7–14.

engineer, have found the floor system to be adequate. With the new load applied, this column will receive 154 kips of axial load. The column can be strengthened by bracing in one plane only. The bracing members can be located as shown dotted in Fig. 7–14. Will such bracing be adequate to raise the capacity of the column to 154 kips?

The mid point b of each column cannot move in the plane of the bracing. Such movement would require the stretching of one diagonal brace and a shortening of the other. Buckling in the plane of the bracing would occur in two loops, as shown. Each individual loop is a curve of the type for which the column formulas are written. Thus, for buckling about the Y–Y axis, L is 7 ft 0 in. For buckling about the X–X axis, however, L is the full 14 ft 0 in., since point b is not prevented from moving perpendicular to the plane of the bracing.

For axis X–X,

$$\frac{L}{r} = \frac{14 \times 12}{4.20} = 40.0$$

For axis Y–Y,

$$\frac{L}{r} = \frac{7 \times 12}{1.94} = 43.3$$

The larger value of L/r controls.

$$\text{Allowable } \frac{P}{A} = 17{,}000 - 0.485(43.3)^2 = 16{,}090 \text{ psi}$$

$$\text{Allowable } P = 9.71 \times 16.09 = 156 \text{ kips}$$

Thus, the capacity of the braced column is sufficient for the proposed increased loading.

It is important to realize that the use of the horizontal bracing members alone would not prevent movement of point b. That point on all columns could move in the same direction and the capacity of each column would be the same as it is without bracing. A system of diagonals must be used in combination with the horizontal struts. Usually, diagonals in every fourth bay (space between columns), with struts in every bay, will suffice.

EXAMPLE 7–9. Select a **WF** section to use for a column 13 ft long having 120 kips of axial load.

The design of a column is a trial-and-error procedure. This is sometimes more elegantly referred to as *successive approximation*. Such a process should not be frowned upon as unscientific or inaccurate. On the contrary, it is a process used in much engineering and scientific work. For example, long division and the extraction of square roots are trial-and-error methods.

The allowable P/A is not known until L/r is known, and L/r is not known until the selection of a section is made. Something must be assumed in order to get started. A 13-ft column is not very long so why not assume some middle-of-the-road value of L/r, say about 50? For L/r of 50, the allowable P/A would be $17{,}000 - 0.485(50)^2 = 15{,}790$ psi, or about 16 kips per sq in. If L/r were 50, the required area would then be $120/16 = 7.50$ sq in. A section with an area somewhere near 7.5 sq in. will be tried.

Trial No. 1: Try 12**WF**27 (A = 7.97 sq in.).

$$\text{Maximum } \frac{L}{r} = \frac{13 \times 12}{1.44} = 108$$

$$\text{Allowable } \frac{P}{A} = 17{,}000 - 0.485(108)^2 = 11{,}340 \text{ psi}$$

$$\text{Actual } \frac{P}{A} = \frac{120{,}000}{7.97} = 15{,}050 \text{ psi} \quad \text{Not Satisfactory}$$

Since the actual stress would exceed the allowable, the 12**WF**27 is unsatisfactory. For the next trial, use a section with either larger r, or larger A, or both.

Trial No. 2: Try 10**WF**33 (A = 9.71 sq in.).

$$\text{Maximum } \frac{L}{r} = \frac{13 \times 12}{1.94} = 80.5$$

$$\text{Allowable } \frac{P}{A} = 17{,}000 - 0.485(80.5)^2 = 13{,}860 \text{ psi}$$

$$\text{Actual } \frac{P}{A} = \frac{120{,}000}{9.71} = 12{,}350 \text{ psi} \quad \text{Satisfactory}$$

The actual stress would not exceed the allowable, so the 10**WF**33 would be satisfactory. There are many other sections that will work, however. The object is usually to find the lightest satisfactory section. Further trials should be made on lighter sections.

Trial No. 3: Try 8**WF**31 (A = 9.12 sq in.).

$$\text{Maximum } \frac{L}{r} = \frac{13 \times 12}{2.01} = 77.6$$

$$\text{Allowable } \frac{P}{A} = 17{,}000 - 0.485(77.6)^2 = 14{,}080 \text{ psi}$$

$$\text{Actual } \frac{P}{A} = \frac{120{,}000}{9.12} = 13{,}150 \text{ psi} \quad \text{Satisfactory}$$

The next lighter sections are the 10**WF**29 and 8**WF**28, both of which have much lower r values than the 8**WF**31. They will prove to be unsatisfactory. Use the 8**WF**31.

Even when the first guess is extremely poor, the designer can arrive at the most economical section after two, three, or four trials at the most. He can use the amount of error on the first trial as a guide to how much heavier, or lighter, the second trial section should be.

Courtesy of Cleveland Electric Illuminating Co.

ELECTRIC SUBSTATION, A COMPLEX ASSEMBLY OF STRUCTURAL MEMBERS—COLUMNS, TENSION MEMBERS, BEAMS, TRUSSES, AND CONCRETE FOOTINGS.

7–13. Limiting Slenderness for Columns. An upper limit on the slenderness ratio L/r is provided by specifications. The slenderness is limited so as to insure reasonable stiffness, reduce vibration effects, and minimize damage from accidental side loads. The last reason is particularly important. The axial load on a column is eccentric where the column is deflected laterally by accidental sidewise load, or where the section has a slight initial crookedness. The bending moment caused by the eccentricity tends to bend the column still farther. In a tension member, the opposite is true; the axial load tends to straighten the member and reduce the eccentricity. Consequently, L/r limits for columns are more conservative than for tension members.

The AISC Specification, Section 16, controls slenderness as follows:

"(a) The ratio of unbraced length to least radius of gyration L/r for compression members . . . shall not exceed:

For main compression members 120

For bracing and other secondary members in compression . 200

"(b) The slenderness of a main compression member may exceed 120, but not 200, provided that it is not ordinarily subject to shock or vibratory loads and provided that its unit stress under full design loading shall not exceed the following fraction of that stipulated under Section 15(a)(2) for its actual ratio L/r:

$$1.6 - \frac{L}{200r}.\text{"}$$

Prior to 1946 the AISC Specification did not contain provision (b). As a result steel columns of excessive weight were often used where they were obviously much too strong. The choice of section was controlled by limiting L/r to 120, even though the expected load was quite small. The use of provision (b) will be illustrated by Example 7–10.

EXAMPLE 7–10. Select a section for a building column 18 ft long, subject to an axial compressive load of 25 kips. Lateral support is provided at the ends only. Use the 1946 AISC Specification.

The use of AISC Specifications previous to the 1946 issue would result in the selection of an 8WF31 for this member. The selection would be controlled not by stress considerations but by the requirement that the slenderness ratio L/r not exceed 120 for main members. The 8WF31 is the lightest section for which L/r is not over 120, but its axial load capacity is 104 kips, or over four times the load to be applied.

It will now be shown that, by application of the 1946 AISC Specification provision for main compression members with L/r of over 120, much saving is possible. The following analysis is for a 5WF18.5 section:

$$A = 5.45 \text{ in}^2.$$

$$r_{\min} = 1.28 \text{ in.}$$

$$\frac{L}{r} = \frac{12 \times 18}{1.28} = 169$$

The allowable P/A for secondary members with $L/r = 169$ is

$$\frac{18,000}{1 + \dfrac{1}{18,000}(169)^2} = 6,960 \text{ psi}$$

For a main member having L/r of 169, the stress P/A allowed is the product of 6,960 and the quantity $1.6 - 169/200 = 0.755$.

The allowable P/A for the column is $0.755 \times 6,960$, or 5,250 psi.

The actual P/A for the section is $25,000/5.45$, or 4,590 psi. The allowable exceeds the actual; therefore, the section is satisfactory. A saving of 225 lb of steel per column is made possible by use of the provision quoted.

7–14. Local Buckling. The column failure considered thus far is the buckling of the member as a whole. In thin materials, however, it is possible for failure to start as local buckling. This may occur under a load too small to buckle the column as a whole. Local buckling occurs as a wrinkle or a series of wrinkles. It is affected by the properties of the cross section but not by the length of the member. Local buckling could occur at the edge of a thin flange, or near the center of a wide thin web. Consideration of local buckling is extremely important in aircraft structures, since aircraft compression members are frequently formed by bending thin sheets. It is important also in other applications where stiffened flat sheets act in compression.

There are two methods in common use for the designing of members which might buckle locally. Both methods recognize that the controlling factors are the ratio of transverse width to thickness, and the edge support condition for the element (flange or web) in question.

One method, used in aircraft and in the design of aluminum structures, consists of determining the critical local buckling stress, as well as that for over-all buckling. Whichever critical stress is lower is then used in design.

In structural steel, however, the method is to proportion the member so that local buckling will *not* occur at less than the load causing failure of the column as a whole. This is accomplished for flanges by limiting the ratio of the outstanding width to the metal thickness. Local buckling of webs and wide plates may also occur, and this can be prevented by limiting the ratio of transverse width to thickness. These limitations are described by Section 18, parts (b) and (c) of the AISC Specification.

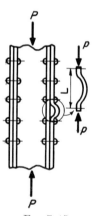

FIG. 7–15.

In a compression member consisting of parts riveted together, a lengthwise local buckling of an element between rivets might occur. This type of failure is shown by Fig. 7–15. In this case, the short buckled element is acting like a small buckled column. Obviously its L/r ratio should be kept low to insure that it will not buckle at loads less than those causing failure of the column as a whole. Since the small element is rectangular in cross section, its L/r ratio can be controlled by limiting the ratio L/t. (For a rectangle of depth t, $r = 0.289t$.) This type of control is given in Section 23(b) of the AISC Specification.

The student should study the sections (18 and 23) mentioned above.

EXAMPLE 7–11. As an alternate to hanging the bin of Example 7–3 from the roof steel it might be supported by columns from below. The bin could be tied laterally to the building columns so that the four bin columns could be considered pin-supported at both ends. This is shown by Fig. 7–16(a). A supply of 6 × 6 × $\frac{3}{8}$ angles is available in the plant. Would these be satisfactory as bin columns? Each column will have 16 kips axial load.

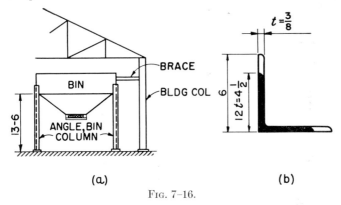

(a)   (b)

Fɪɢ. 7–16.

Fig. 7–16(b) shows the cross section of one post. The ratio of outstanding leg width to thickness is $6/0.375 = 16$. The maximum ratio allowed for single-angle struts is 12. Therefore, the 6 × 6 × $\frac{3}{8}$ angle cannot be considered fully effective. The effective size is limited to $12t$ for each leg, or $4\frac{1}{2}$ × $4\frac{1}{2}$ × $\frac{3}{8}$ (shown shaded). The properties of a $4\frac{1}{2}$ × $4\frac{1}{2}$ × $\frac{3}{8}$ angle will be used. The radius of gyration r is obtained by interpolation from the tables of properties as 0.89 in.

$$\frac{L}{r} = \frac{13.5 \times 12}{0.89} = 182$$

This is in excess of the 120 limit for main members. Therefore, the additional reduction of Section 16(b) must be applied.

Allowable $\dfrac{P}{A} = \dfrac{18,000}{1 + \dfrac{(182)^2}{18,000}} = 6,340$ psi, for secondary members

$$1.6 - \frac{L}{200r} = 0.69$$

Allowable $\dfrac{P}{A} = 6,340 \times 0.69 = 4,370$ psi, for main members

The effective area of a $4\frac{1}{2}$ × $4\frac{1}{2}$ × $\frac{3}{8}$ angle is

$$\frac{3}{8}\left(9 - \frac{3}{8}\right) = 3.24 \text{ sq in.}$$

Allowable $P = 3.24 \times 4.37 = 14.2$ kips

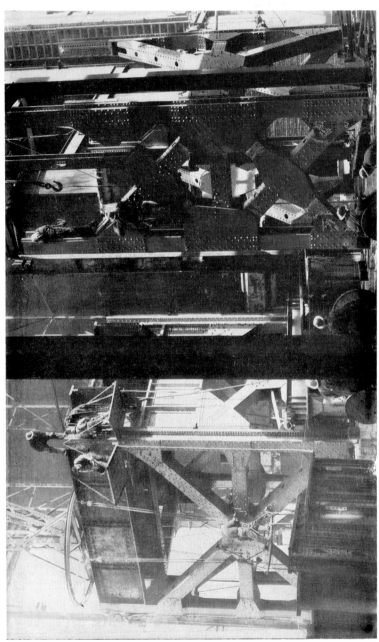

Courtesy of Cleveland Electric Illuminating Co.

TURBINE SUPPORTS. STRUCTURAL STEEL SUPPORTS FOR MECHANICAL EQUIPMENT IN AN ELECTRIC POWER PLANT.

The $6 \times 6 \times \frac{3}{8}$ angle is not satisfactory. If bracing could be provided so as to reduce the unbraced length L, it might be made satisfactory.

EXAMPLE 7–12. Would the angles of Example 7–11 be satisfactory if braced at the mid-point in one plane only? This bracing is shown in Fig. 7–17(a).

A section of one column is shown in Fig. 7–17(b). The mid-point of the length is braced against any movement having a component in the

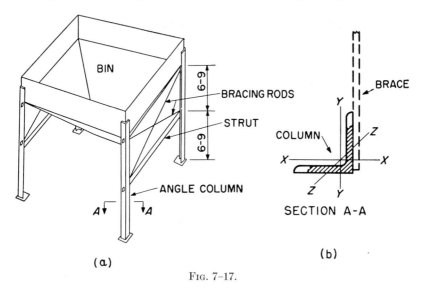

FIG. 7–17.

Y-direction. The mid-point can move only in the X-direction. Buckling of the entire 13 ft 6 in. length would occur about axis Y–Y only. The length above or the length below the braced point could buckle in any direction. Thus two L/r values must be computed and compared. The interpolated value of r for axis Y–Y of a $4\frac{1}{2} \times 4\frac{1}{2} \times \frac{3}{8}$ effective angle is 1.39 in.

$$\text{For axis } Y\text{-}Y, \frac{L}{r} = \frac{13.5 \times 12}{1.39} = 116.5, \quad \textit{Controls}$$

$$\text{For axis } Z\text{-}Z, \frac{L}{r} = \frac{6.75 \times 12}{0.89} = 91$$

$$\text{Allowable } \frac{P}{A} = 17,000 - 0.485(116.5)^2 = 10,420 \text{ psi}$$

The effective area is still limited to 3.24 sq in., that of a $4\frac{1}{2} \times 4\frac{1}{2} \times \frac{3}{8}$ angle.

$$\text{Allowable } P = 3.24 \times 10.42 = 33.8 \text{ kips}$$

If so braced, the 6 × 6 × $\frac{3}{8}$ angles would be satisfactory. They would not be the most economical in weight of material. The fact that they are on hand, however, could make their use the most economical solution with regard to the total cost.

Flexural Members

7–15. Types of Failure in Beams. A beam has transverse loads which cause bending moment and shear. A beam may fail through bending alone. In such a failure it would deflect excessively and finally collapse through crushing of the metal on one side or through fracturing of the metal on the other side. It might fail also by a column-like action of the compression side of the member. In this failure there would be a sidewise or lateral buckling of the compression side. Complete collapse might follow the lateral buckling.

The shear in a beam could cause failure. The shear failure might be observed as a fracture, but it is more likely to be observed as a bulging or as a buckling of the parts having high shearing stress.

Local failures can occur at points where large concentrated loads or reactions are applied to the member. These usually are crushing types of failure. In some members the local failure may take the form of buckling.

The design of a beam consists merely of finding the lightest satisfactory section having the proper factor of safety against all of the above types of failure. The manner of doing this is shown in the articles which follow.

Excessive deflection, while usually not a dangerous failure, is a failure of the member to serve the desired purpose. It must be considered and guarded against.

7–16. Flexural Stresses. In any text on strength of materials a derivation of the flexure formula may be found. That formula is

$$f = My/I$$

in which f = unit flexural stress (psi)

M = bending moment at the section in question (in.-lb)

y = distance from center-of-gravity axis of the cross section to the point for which f is desired (in.)

I = moment of inertia (in.^{4}) of the cross-sectional area about the center-of-gravity axis of the section (axis perpendicular to the plane of the loads)

The derivation of the flexure formula will not be repeated here, but the limiting assumptions upon which it is based will be reviewed. Those assumptions are:

1. A cross section that is plane before bending of the beam remains plane when the beam is bent.
2. The stress does not exceed the elastic limit. Therefore, stress is proportional to strain.
3. The cross section of the beam is symmetrical about an axis in the plane of the loads.
4. The beam is homogeneous and straight.

In a beam having bending moment and shear only, with no axial loads, the flexural stress at the center of gravity is zero, since $y = 0$ in the flexure formula. A line drawn through the points of zero stress, either transverse or longitudinal, is called the "neutral axis." When no axial load is present, the neutral axis of a beam coincides with the center of gravity of the cross section. The neutral axis and the intensity of flexural stress are illustrated in Fig. 7–18.

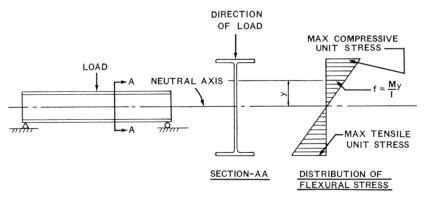

Fig. 7–18.

7–17. Design of Laterally Supported Beams for Flexure. When a beam is supported so that deflection is possible in the plane of the loads but is prevented in a transverse direction, it is said to be "laterally supported." The flexure formula, $f = My/I$, is sufficient for determining a section for a laterally supported beam.

The largest flexural stress occurs at the extreme outside portions, since y for those parts is greatest. The maximum y value is usually called c, so that the "extreme fiber stress" is Mc/I. For a particular section I and c are constants, and so is the ratio I/c. This ratio is called the "section modulus," abbreviated as S. The flexure formula then reads $f = M/S$. Tables of section properties give the values of section modulus S for each section. To design for bending, it is necessary only to select a section having the section modulus of sufficient magnitude so that f does not exceed the allowable flexural stress. For this purpose the flexure formula is rearranged as follows:

$$\text{Required } S = M/F_b$$

in which F_b is the allowable flexural stress.

Note that an unsymmetrical section may have a c distance to the extreme fibers of the compression side different from that of the tension side. Thus two different section modulus values exist.

Steel beam sections are usually either wide flange sections or American Standard beam sections. (See Fig. 7–1.) These sections are good in flexure because a large majority of the material is in the flanges—far from the neutral axis. This causes the moment of inertia I to be large in proportion to the amount of metal used. This advantage is present to an even greater degree in the wide flange section than in the I-beam.

The channel, shown in Fig. 7–1(c) is used as a beam, even though it is in violation of assumption three in the derivation of the flexure formula. The channel should be braced so as to prevent its twisting when used as a beam.

Beam sections can be built up from simpler shapes. For example, a plate and four angles can be riveted together in the shape of an I-section. Three plates can be welded to form an I-shape. Other common built-up sections will be shown later in this chapter.

EXAMPLE 7–13. Select a wide flange section to support a 10-kip load at the center of a 20-ft simple span. The beam is laterally supported.

The bending moment due to the concentrated load is

$$\frac{PL}{4} = \frac{10 \times 20}{4} = 50 \text{ ft-kips} \quad \text{or} \quad 12 \times 50 = 600 \text{ in.-kips}$$

The weight of the member is not yet known, so a weight must be assumed. Assuming that the member to be selected will weigh 30 lb per ft, the bending moment due to its own weight is

$$\frac{wL^2}{8} = \frac{0.030 \times (20)^2}{8} = 1.50 \text{ ft-kips} \quad \text{or} \quad 12 \times 1.5 = 18 \text{ in.-kips}$$

The total bending moment is $600 + 18 = 618$ in.-kips.

The allowable flexural stress is 20,000 psi, according to the AISC Specification. The required section modulus is

$$S = \frac{M}{F_b} = \frac{618}{20} = 30.9 \text{ in.}^3$$

Several **WF** sections can be found having this section modulus or a slightly higher one. Possible choices are 8**WF**35 with S of 31.1 in.[3],

10W⟍29 with S of 30.8 in.³, or 12W⟍27 with S of 34.1 in.³. Unless limited space is a criterion, the 12W⟍27 would be used.

Notice that the deeper sections provide equal bending strength (section modulus) with less weight. The 12W⟍27, however, is the lightest of the 12-in. nominal size W⟍ sections. The lightest beam of the next deeper series (14-in.) will weigh more than the lightest of the 12-in. series. Thus, the 12W⟍27 is the lightest W⟍ section suitable.

The assumed weight used in computing the bending moment M was fairly accurate. Had the original guess been a poor one, it would be necessary to correct it, compute a new bending moment, and make the selection again.

7–18. Lateral Instability of Beams.   Thus far, only beams which are laterally restrained to prevent deflection perpendicular to the plane of the load have been considered. If the lateral restraint or lateral support were removed, the ultimate strength of the beam might be reduced.

When an axial compressive load is gradually applied to a long slender bar, that bar remains straight for a time; but when the load becomes great enough, it suddenly deflects sidewise. When this buckling occurs, the bar has passed its ultimate load, corresponding to the Euler limit for a column.

If the compressive flange of a beam is sufficiently narrow, it may buckle in sómewhat the same manner. Fig. 7–19 illustrates both deflec-

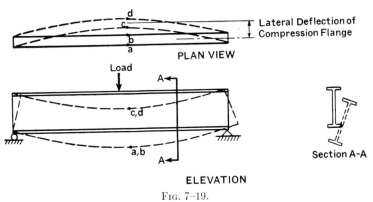

FIG. 7–19.

tion in the plane of the load and lateral deflection, or buckling. Lateral buckling occurs in the compression flange only. The tensile stresses of the opposite flange tend to cause it to remain in a straight line. Consequently, lateral buckling is a combined action like that of a column and that of torsion or twisting of the beam.

The compression flange of a beam may be considered as a column. The columns discussed in previous articles of this chapter have load applied at the ends only. That load is of constant amount throughout the length of the column. The top flange of a simple beam has zero stress at points of zero bending moment, and maximum stress at points of maximum bending moment. The load in the flange is equal to the flange area times the average stress in the flange at that section. For a beam with a single concentrated load, the flange load varies from zero at one end, to a maximum at the center, and back to zero at the other end. A column loaded with this variable load would have a different critical buckling stress than a column loaded at the ends only. Thus, while the top flange may buckle laterally as a column, its behavior cannot be predicted by the usual column formulas.

Any complete mathematical expression for the critical compressive flexural stress in the flange of a beam would need to include all of the following factors:

1. Shape of the moment diagram. (This determines the variation of compressive load in the flange.)
2. Conditions of end restraint for the compression flange.
3. Position and types of intermediate support.
4. The properties of the flange itself.
5. Torsional properties of the section.
6. Modulus of elasticity of the material.
7. Position of the load, whether at the top flange, center of web, or bottom flange.

Equations for the allowable compressive flexural stress become very complex if all of the above factors are included.[2] In structural steel design it is the custom to consider only two or three of the most important factors. The constants of the commonly used equations are conservative so that neglecting the other factors does not lead to unsafe designs.

One type of equation in common use is a parabolic equation. For example, the AREA Specification (railway bridges) gives the allowable compressive flexural stress as

$$F_b = 18,000 - 5\left(\frac{L}{b}\right)^2$$

In this expression L is the laterally unsupported length of compression flange, and b is the width of the compression flange, both in the same units. Most specifications which have formulas including L and b as the only variables limit the ratio L/b to a stated maximum, usually 40.

[2]See C. D. Williams and E. C. Harris, *Structural Design in Metals* (New York: The Ronald Press Co., 1949), Chap. 4.

The reasons for limiting L/b are the same as those given for limiting the slenderness ratio L/r of columns.

The AISC Specification considers more of the factors. It gives the allowable compressive flexural stress as

$$F_b = \frac{12,000,000}{Ld/bt}, \text{ but not over 20,000 psi}$$

In this expression d is the depth of the section and t is the thickness of the compression flange. The terms L and b are the same as in the AREA formula.

If the flexural compressive stress allowed by the AISC Specification is plotted against values of Ld/bt, a curve like that shown by Fig. 7–20 results. (Notice the similarity of this curve to the one given earlier

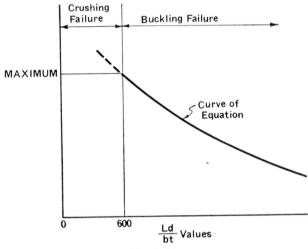

FIG. 7–20.

in this chapter for compression members.) For ratios of Ld/bt less than 600, failure is by yielding. The factor of safety in that range is $33,000/20,000 = 1.65$. Above Ld/bt of 600, failure is by lateral buckling. The curve in that region provides approximately the same factor of safety (1.65) with respect to the critical buckling stress.

The length L to be used in the formulas for allowable stress is the distance in inches between points of lateral support, or the distance from the point of contraflexure to either a lateral support or another point of contraflexure. The length L to be used for a cantilever beam, laterally free at its outer end, is *twice* the actual length of the cantilever.

Tests and experience have shown that the simpler formulas are safe when used within the limits of the specification, even though they may not always give the most economical design. Methods of analysis that include more of the variables may eventually find their way into specifications for the design of steel.

7–19. Design of Laterally Unsupported Beams for Flexure. No matter which specification is used, there is no direct method of choosing a section for a laterally unsupported beam (except by using a table of beam sections and allowable loads). Selection must be made by successive approximation. A trial section is chosen and the computed unit stress is compared with the allowable unit stress. If the computed unit stress exceeds the allowable, the beam is unsatisfactory. A stronger section must then be chosen for a second trial. As many trials are made as are needed to determine the lightest section for which the computed stress does not exceed the allowable.

EXAMPLE 7–14. Consider again the beam of Example 7–13, but with no lateral support for the compression flange. The weight of the member is unknown, as before. Also unknown is the allowable compressive flexural stress. The solution may be started by assuming a weight of section and an allowable unit stress.

Assuming 30 lb per ft for the weight of the beam, as before, the total bending moment M is 618 in.-kips. Assuming an allowable unit stress of 15,000 psi.

$$\text{Required } S = \frac{618}{15} = 41.2 \text{ in}^3.$$

For the first trial a 14**WF**30 having S equal to 41.8 in.[3] will be used. For this section d is 13.86 in., the flange width b is 6.73 in., and t is 0.383 in. The allowable compressive stress is

$$F_b = \frac{12,000,000}{240 \times 13.86/6.73 \times 0.383} = 9,300 \text{ psi}$$

The computed flexural stress is $618,000/41.8 = 14,800$ psi. The computed stress exceeds the allowable; therefore, the 14**WF**30 is not satisfactory.

For the second trial, try a 16**WF**36. For this section, S is 56.3 in.[3], d is 15.85 in., b is 6.99 in., and t is 0.428 in.

$$F_b = \frac{12,000,000}{240 \times 15.85/6.99 \times 0.428} = 9,450 \text{ psi}$$

$$\text{Computed } f_b = \frac{M}{S} = \frac{618,000}{56.3} = 11,000 \text{ psi}$$

Again the trial section is unsatisfactory. A section with about 16 per cent additional strength is required.

For the third trial, try a 16WF40, having S of 64.4 in.^{3}, d of 16.0 in., b of 7.0 in., and t of 0.503 in.

$$F_b = \frac{12,000,000}{240 \times 16/7 \times 0.503} = 11,000 \text{ psi}$$

$$f_b = \frac{618,000}{64.4} = 9,600 \text{ psi}$$

The computed stress does not exceed the allowable, so the 16WF40 is satisfactory in flexure. However, it is not the lightest safe section. A strength increase can be affected by either a higher S or a higher F_b. If the search were continued a 10WF33 would be found as the lightest section having the required bending strength. For this section

$$F_b = \frac{12,000,000}{240 \times 9.75/7.96 \times 0.433} = 17,700 \text{ psi}$$

$$f_b = \frac{618,000}{35.0} = 17,600 \text{ psi}$$

Using the AISC allowable stress, there is no logical sequence to follow in picking trial sections. When a satisfactory section has been found, then only lighter ones should be checked until the lightest suitable section is determined. This may require several trials. The work may, of course, be lessened by the use of design curves, when and if they are available.

EXAMPLE 7–15. A 10 I 25.4 is connected between building trusses as shown by Fig. 7–21. The beam serves as a short monorail for unloading trucks at a doorway where there is no dock. Its top flange is connected to the bottom-chord bracing between trusses at point C. The beam is thus laterally supported at the ends and at the center. What live load is permitted under the AISC Specification? What capacity of chain hoist should be provided?

The solution is shown on the computation sheet of Fig. 7–21.

The span is 20 ft, but the laterally unsupported length is one-half of the span, or 120 in. For t in the AISC expression for the allowable flexural stress the mean flange thickness of 0.491 in. is used. The computed F_b exceeds 20,000, indicating that failure would start through yielding rather than buckling. The allowable F_b is limited to 20,000 psi.

The total allowable live load is 7.88 kips. A 3-ton hoist should be used. The hoist and trolley would weigh about 450 lb, giving a total of 6,450 lb. The next larger hoist is of 4-ton capacity. Its use would lead to overloading of the beam.

| NAME _____ | EXAMPLE 7-15 |
| DATE _____ | SHEET I OF I |

Roof Truss

Monorail Beam

A   C   B

10 I 25.4   Chain Hoist

20-0 Span

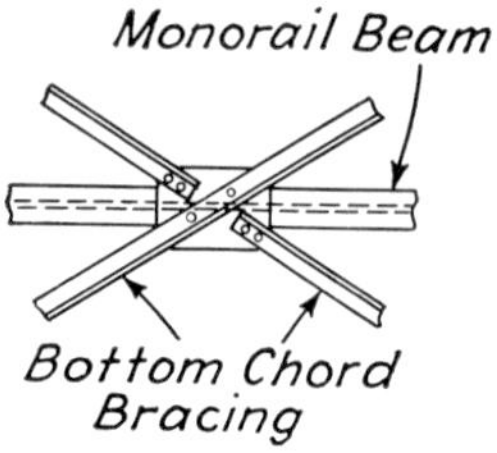

Bottom Chord Bracing

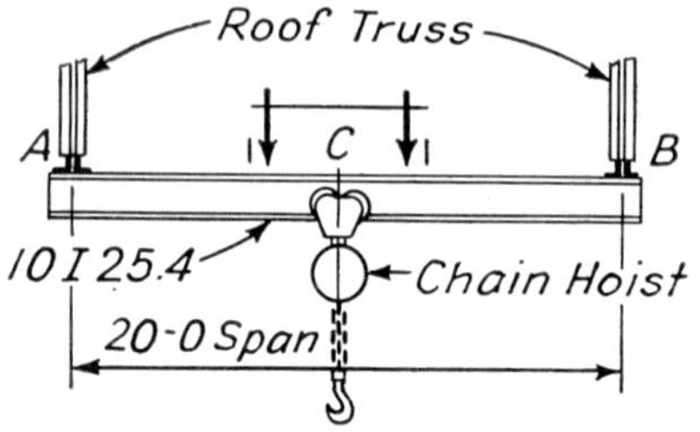

Sect. 1-1

Capacity of Monorail (Assume no impact)

Span = 20-0

L Between Lat. Supports = 10-0 = 120"

$$\text{Allowable } F_b = \frac{12,000,000}{120 \times 10/4.66 \times 0.491} = 22,900 \; ;$$

Use 20,000 psi

Allowable $M = SF_b = 24.4 \times 20$ $= 488$ in.-k $= 40.7$ ft-k

M from DL $= 0.0254 \times \overline{20}^2 /8$ $= 1.3$

M Allowed for Hoist, Trolley, & Lifted Load $= 39.4$ ft-k

$M \doteq PL/4$ (Trolley Wheelbase Short)

$P = 4M/L = 4 \times 39.4/20 = 7.88$ k

Wt of Trolley & Hoist (3-Ton) $\doteq 450$ lb

3-Ton Lifted Load $= 6,000$

Total $= 6,450$ lb $<$

7,880 OK

∴ Use 3-Ton Maximun Size of Hoist

Fig. 7-21.

7–20. Effect of Holes in Beams.   A hole in the flange of a beam causes an increase of stress. If the hole is located at or near the section of highest flexural stress, its presence may affect the ultimate strength of the beam. The increase it causes in the stress can be considered as being of two types. The first is the increase caused by redistribution of the flexural stresses to a cross section whose area and moment of inertia are smaller than those for the adjacent section without holes. The second is the concentration of stress near the edge of the hole. Stress concentration occurs at any sudden change of section and results from the inability of the material to redistribute the stresses uniformly over the reduced area. The conditions are analogous to those of water passing a rock in a stream. At the obstruction, the average velocity of the water increases because the area of the channel is reduced. However, the velocity at the section containing the obstruction does not increase uniformly. Next to the obstruction the velocity is much increased, while at other points on the cross section the velocity is only slightly affected.

In ordinary work the general redistribution is considered and the stress concentration ignored. When loads are repeated millions of times, however, fatigue failure may occur. In those cases, the stress concentrations should be considered.[3]

Analysis of stresses in a beam with holes depends on the effect the holes have on the position of the neutral axis. The flexure formula is based on a neutral axis located at the center of gravity of the effective area of the cross section. At a section where holes occur in one flange only, the center of gravity of the remaining (net) section is shifted from the position it occupies in the gross section. It is consistent with the use of the flexure formula to assume that the neutral axis is at the center of gravity of the net section and to use the moment of inertia about that neutral axis.

But if the condition just described were true, the neutral axis of a beam having holes in one flange would shift abruptly at each hole location. It would move from the center of gravity of the gross section to that of the net section, and back again to that of the gross. Fig. 7–22(a) illustrates this condition. Recalling that the neutral axis is the locus of points of zero flexural stress, it seems impossible that such fluctuation of the neutral axis can occur. Stress conditions cannot change abruptly enough to allow a complete redistribution of stress within the short length of beam occupied by the hole. If the hole extended over the entire length of beam, the neutral axis would, of course,

[3]See C. D. Williams and E. C. Harris, *Structural Design in Metals* (New York: The Ronald Press Co., 1949), Chap. 10.

remain at the net center of gravity. However, if holes occur only at intervals along the beam, a smooth fluctuation of the neutral axis position is more probable. In a beam with widely spaced holes, the neutral axis probably remains close to the gross center of gravity but shifts in the direction of the net center of gravity at the holes. As the space between the holes is decreased, the amount of shift probably

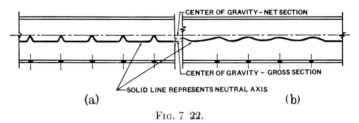

CENTER OF GRAVITY – NET SECTION

CENTER OF GRAVITY – GROSS SECTION

SOLID LINE REPRESENTS NEUTRAL AXIS

(a)   (b)

Fig. 7–22.

increases until, for very closely spaced holes, the neutral axis remains close to the net center of gravity. In any case, the neutral axis is not a sharply deformed line, as in Fig. 7–22(a), but a smoothly fluctuating curve, as shown in Fig. 7–22(b).

Although the neutral axis probably does not shift all the way to the net center of gravity, it is usually regarded as a safe practice to assume that it does so shift. The computations of the shift and of the net properties, however, are slightly cumbersome, so that simpler methods have been devised.

Of the simpler methods, the one prescribed by the AREA Specification (and others) is most logical. It is easy to understand and easy to apply. The AREA Specification describes the method as follows:

"426. Plate girders, I-beams, and other members subject to bending that produces tension on one face, shall be proportioned by the moment-of-inertia method. The neutral axis shall be taken along the center of gravity of the gross section. The tensile stress shall be computed from the moment of inertia of the entire net section and the compressive stress from the moment of inertia of the entire gross section."

The AISC Specification permits rivet holes to be neglected up to a specified limit. If the rivet holes in a flange do not remove more than 15 per cent of the gross area of that flange, they are neglected. If the rivet holes remove over 15 per cent of the area of a flange, the excess over 15 per cent is considered removed when computing the net properties. The deduction is made for both flanges if rivet holes are present in both flanges. (For countersunk rivet holes and for holes other than rivet holes, the full amount of the holes is considered when computing net properties.) The student should study Section 26(a) of the AISC Specification. The AISC Specification does not indicate whether a shift of neutral axis is to be assumed when the holes are in one flange only.

The three methods mentioned will be illustrated in the examples which follow.

EXAMPLE 7–16. A 12W▪27 has two holes for $\frac{7}{8}$-in. rivets in each flange at the section of maximum bending moment. How is its bending strength affected, as indicated by the three methods mentioned in Art. 7–20?

a) *By the Theoretical Method*: The rivet holes in the compression flange are filled by the rivets. The compressive stress from the flange is carried across the hole as compression in the rivet shank. These holes are assumed to have no weakening effect. The holes in the tension flange weaken the section. The center of gravity of the net section is computed first. See Fig. 7–23.

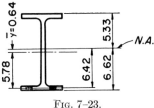

FIG. 7–23.

Item	Area	y (from gross c/g)	Ay
12W▪27	7.97	0	0
2 holes, each 1.0×0.40	−0.80	5.78	4.62
	$\Sigma A = 7.17$		$\Sigma(Ay) = 4.62$

$$\text{Shift of Neutral Axis} = \bar{y} = \frac{\Sigma(Ay)}{\Sigma A} = \frac{4.62}{7.17} = 0.64 \text{ in.}, \quad \text{Upward}$$

The shifted neutral axis is labeled N.A. on Fig. 7–23. The moment of inertia of the net section about the line N.A. is equal to the I of the gross section about that same line minus the I of the area removed by the holes.

$$I_{net} = 204.1 + 7.97(0.64)^2 - 0.80(6.42)^2 = 174.4 \text{ in.}^4$$

The section moduli for the tension and compression flanges are:

$$S_t = 174.4/6.62 = 26.4 \text{ in.}^3$$

and

$$S_c = 174.4/5.33 = 32.7 \text{ in.}^3$$

b) *By the AREA Method*: For computing the compressive stress, the unreduced section is used. S_c is 34.1 in.[3].

For computing the tensile stress, both the top and bottom holes are assumed to reduce the strength. The neutral axis is not shifted.

$$I_{net} = 204.1 - 4 \times 1.0 \times 0.40(5.78)^2 = 150.6 \text{ in.}^4$$

$$S_t = 150.6/5.98 = 25.2 \text{ in.}^3$$

Courtesy of Shaw-Box Crane & Hoist Division, Manning, Maxwell & Moore, Inc.

30-Ton Overhead Cranes Serving Press Room in Manufacturing Plant. Vertical-Plane Bracing Between Columns and Horizontal-Plane Bracing Between Bottom Chords of Roof Trusses.

c) *By the AISC Method*: The flange is 6.50 in. wide. Fifteen per cent of 6.50 is 0.97 in. Two inches of flange width are removed by holes. The excess over 15 per cent is a width of 2.00 − 0.97 = 1.03 in. Holes totaling 1.03 × 0.4, or 0.412 sq in. must be considered for each flange.

$$I_{net} = 204.1 - 2 \times 0.412(5.78)^2 = 176.6 \text{ in}^4$$

$$S_t = S_c = 176.6/5.98 = 29.5 \text{ in}^3$$

d) *Comparison of the Methods*: The section modulus values for the tension and compression sides are as follows:

	S_t	S_c	% Reduction of Bending Strength
a) By the theoretical method . . .	26.4	32.7	22.6
b) By the AREA method	25.2	34.1	26.1
c) By the AISC method	29.5	29.5	13.5
d) For the beam without holes . . .	34.1	34.1	0

Notice that the AREA values for S are very close to those obtained by the theoretical method. The value for tension is about 4.5 per cent lower (more conservative), and that for compression about 4.3 per cent higher (less conservative) than the theoretical values. The AREA method is certainly easier to apply than the theoretical method. The close correlation of results between the first two methods show that the AREA method may be safely applied in any structural design problem.

The use of the AISC method should be limited to those cases governed by the AISC Specification. Those cases are defined in the Preface and the Title of the Specification.

EXAMPLE 7–17. A small factory building is to be revised to provide a parts crib and a storage balcony. The arrangement desired is illustrated in Fig. 7–24(a). A concrete block wall is to support steel beams at 10-ft centers. The steel beams are to support wood joists and a wood floor. A monorail beam will be bolted to the bottom flange of the cross beams using $\frac{3}{4}$-in. bolts.

The live load on the balcony is 125 lb per sq ft. The weight of the flooring and joists is 12 lb per sq ft of floor. The maximum total reaction of the monorail on the cross beam is 1,700 lb. As plant engineer you are required to select a section for the beam. Use the AISC Specification.

The length required in bearing on the wall at each end is not yet known; therefore, the span of the beam is not known either. A common length of embedment in such walls is 6 or 8 in. Assume the bearing length to be 6 in. at each end. The span will be measured from the center of one bearing length to the center of the other, or 18 ft 6 in. The beam and its known loads are shown in Fig. 7–24(b).

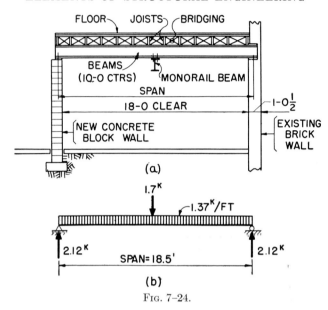

(a)

(b)

Fig. 7–24.

The bending moment at the center is computed.

Uniform load from floor, $M = 1.37(18.5)^2/8$ $= 58.6$

Concentrated load, $M = 1.7 \times 18.5/4$ $= 7.9$

Wt of beam, assume 30 lb per ft, $M = 0.03(18.5)^2/8 =$ $\underline{1.3}$

Total $M = \overline{67.8}$ ft-k

The beam may be considered as laterally supported provided the sub-flooring is laid diagonally, or made of plywood, or provided the joists are framed between the beams so as to prevent twisting of the beams. Thus F_b is 20 kips per sq in., and

$$\text{Required } S = 12 \times 67.8/20 = 40.7 \text{ in.}^3$$

This value of S must be furnished by a beam having two $\frac{7}{8}$-in. holes out of the tension flange. The holes are for bolts; thus, the entire amount of their area must be considered. Sections having a gross S of over 40.7 in.^{3} will be tried. It will be assumed that the neutral axis does not shift.

Trial No. 1:

Try a 14**WF**30

Area of 2 holes $= 2 \times 0.875 \times 0.383 = 0.670$ in.^{2}

Distance, center of flange to neutral axis $= \frac{1}{2}(13.86 - 0.38) =$ 6.74 in.

I (net) $= 289.6 - 0.67(6.74)^2 = 259.2$ in.^{4}

S (net) $= 259.2/6.93 = 37.4$ in.$^3 < 40.7$ Not Satisfactory

Trial No. 2:

Try a 14WF34

Area of 2 holes $= 2 \times 0.875 \times 0.453 = 0.794$ in.^{2}

Distance, center of flange to neutral axis $= \frac{1}{2}(14.0 - 0.45) = 6.77$ in.

I (net) $= 339.2 - 0.794(6.77)^2 = 302.8$ in.^{4}

S (net) $= 302.8/7.0 = 43.3$ in.$^3 > 40.7$ Satisfactory

The 14WF34 is the lightest section that is satisfactory in bending.

7–21. Shear in Beams.   Most texts on strength of materials give the derivation of the formula $v = VQ/Ib$. In this formula v is the intensity of shearing stress at the point in question; V is the total shear at the section; Q is the statical moment of the area between the extreme fiber and the point in question, about the center-of-gravity axis of the entire cross section; b is the width or thickness (perpendicular to the plane of loading) at the point in question; and I is the moment of inertia of the entire cross section about the center of gravity.

If a shearing unit stress of intensity v occurs on one plane, an equal unit shearing stress occurs on a plane through that point perpendicular

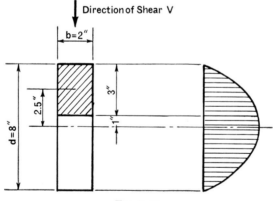

FIG. 7–25.

to the first plane. The shear formula may then be used to determine either horizontal or vertical shearing stresses in a beam.

To illustrate the application of the formula, find the shearing stress in the beam section of Fig. 7–25 at a point one in. above the center of gravity of the section when the total shear V is 10,000 lb. The value of

Q is the moment of the shaded area about the center of gravity of the entire section.

$$Q = 2 \times 3 \times 2.5 = 15.0 \text{ in}^3.$$

$$I = \frac{2(8)^3}{12} = 85.3 \text{ in}^4.$$

The unit shear at one in. from the center of gravity is $v = VQ/Ib$, or

$$v = \frac{10,000 \times 15}{85.3 \times 2} = 879 \text{ psi}$$

If v is computed for points at various distances from the center of gravity and the values are plotted, a parabola results, as shown on the right part of Fig. 7–25. The shearing stress at the center of gravity is more intense than at other fibers and is equal to $3V/2bd$, where d is the depth of the section. The quantity V/bd is the average shearing stress. It is important to remember that for any rectangular section acting as a beam the maximum unit shear is 1.5 times the average unit shear.

In a beam having relatively large flanges and a thin web, such as an I-beam, the intensity of shear varies as shown by Fig. 7–26. From

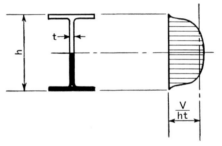

Fig. 7–26.

this figure it can be seen that the flanges do little to resist the shear V, whereas the web resists most of the shear. To illustrate this fact, assume that the section shown is a 14WF30 and that the total shear V is 10,000 lb. To determine the intensity of shear at the center of gravity, let Q be the moment of the half beam about the center of gravity of the entire section. Dimensions and properties of the half beam may be found in the AISC Manual under the heading "Structural Tees Cut from WF Beams." The section which is one-half of a 14WF30 is listed as ST7WF15. The distance from the center of gravity of the tee to the outer fibers of the flange is 1.59 in., the depth of the tee is 6.93 in., and its area is 4.41 sq in. Therefore,

$$Q = 4.41(6.93 - 1.59) = 23.5 \text{ in}^3.$$

At the center,

$$v = \frac{VQ}{Ib} = \frac{10{,}000 \times 23.5}{289.6 \times 0.27} = 3{,}000 \text{ psi}$$

Compare the above value with that obtained when it is assumed that the shear is distributed uniformly over the web and that the flanges offer no help in resisting shear. By this assumption $v = V/ht$.

If h is the over-all depth of the section, then

$$v = \frac{10{,}000}{13.86 \times 0.27} = 2{,}670 \text{ psi}$$

If h is the clear depth of the web between flanges,

$$v = \frac{10{,}000}{13.09 \times 0.27} = 2{,}830 \text{ psi}$$

The answers obtained from the approximate assumption of uniform distribution are, respectively, 11.0 and 5.7 per cent lower than those found by use of the shear formula. For other sections of the I-beam or channel type, the error resulting from the use of the approximate method is similarly small. Since the error is small, it is possible to design beams of this type with safety using the approximate method, providing the allowable unit shearing stress is established with the knowledge that the approximate method will be used. Shear is checked by this method in the majority of structural designs, but the reader should again be reminded that the error will be great if the approximate method is used for a section not having relatively large flanges and a light web.

It is usually assumed in the design of flanged beams that the allowable unit shearing stress on webs given by the Specification is the average shear rather than the maximum intensity, assuming that the web takes all of the shear.

In the preceding example, h was taken first as the over-all depth and then as the clear depth between flanges. Engineers do not all use the same values. It is probably more common, however, to use the over-all depth for rolled beams and the web dimensions for plate girders.

EXAMPLE 7–18. Is the section selected in Example 7–17 (Fig. 7–24) satisfactory in shear?

The allowable unit shear stress (average) in a beam web is 13,000 psi, according to Section 15(a) of the Specification. The 14WF34 is 14.0 in. deep and has a web thickness of 0.287 in. The total end shear is

$$V = 2{,}120 + (34 \times 18.5/2) = 2{,}434 \text{ lb}$$

$$v = V/ht = 2{,}434/14 \times 0.287 = 605 \text{ psi}$$

The actual average unit shear is less than the allowable, so the 14**WF**34 is satisfactory in shear.

In this example, bending is more critical than shear. This is usually the case. Therefore, it is generally the better procedure to select a section for bending, then check it for shear. The cases in which shear might control the selection are those having heavy loads near the ends of a span, or those in which the loads are unusually heavy and the span short. In these cases a required web area (ht), as well as a required section modulus, should be determined in advance of making the selection.

7-22. Web Crippling. A heavy load or reaction concentrated on a short length of beam may cause one of the types of web failure shown in Fig. 7-27. These types of failure result from compressive stresses in the vertical elements of web directly above or below the concentrated reaction or load.

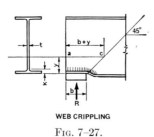

WEB CRIPPLING

Fig. 7-27.

In Fig. 7-27 is shown the failure known as either "web crushing" or "web crippling." Obviously, the reaction R is transmitted not only to the vertical strip directly above the length b but, by shearing stress, to the adjacent strips of web. It is assumed by most specifications that the vertical compressive load is distributed over the width from a to c of Fig. 7-27, where c is a point on a line drawn from the edge of the load or reaction at an angle of 45° to the flange. The unit vertical compressive stress at a distance y from the flange is given by

$$f_c = \frac{R}{\text{Area}} = \frac{R}{(b + y)t}$$

in which t is the thickness of the web at y distance from the flange.

If web crushing or crippling occurs, it does so at the points of highest compressive stress. This stress occurs where the area $(b + y)\,t$ is least. The area is least where the web meets the fillet of the beam, at distance k from the edge. (Dimension k is given by the tables of section dimensions in the Appendix.) The unit stress at this point is given as

$$f_c = \frac{R}{(b + k)t}$$

from which

$$\text{Required } b = \frac{R}{f_c t} - k$$

If the load or reaction does not occur near the end of the beam, distribution is assumed along a 45° line at each end of length b, so that

$$f_c = \frac{R}{(b + 2k)t}$$

or

$$\text{Required } b = \frac{R}{f_c t} - 2k$$

The equations for web crippling are most often used to determine the required length of bearing b. This is the length over which the load or reaction must be spread so that f_c will not exceed the allowable value. The AISC Specification permits f_c to be not more than 24,000 psi.

EXAMPLE 7–19. Assume that you have selected a 14**WF**30 beam to carry loads which cause a reaction of 30 kips. The end is to be supported on a bearing plate, as shown by Fig. 7–27. What is the required bearing length b to avoid web crippling?

The 45-degree distribution is in one direction only. The tables of **WF** sections give a web thickness of 0.270 in., and a distance k of $\frac{7}{8}$ in.

$$\text{Required } b = \frac{30}{24 \times 0.27} - \frac{7}{8} = 3.76 \text{ in.}$$

EXAMPLE 7–20. What bearing length is required for the beams selected in Example 7–17 (Fig. 7–24)? The 14**WF**34 has t of 0.287 in. and k of 15/16 in. The end reaction is 2.43 kips, as computed in Example 7–18.

$$\text{Required } b = \frac{2.43}{24 \times 0.287} - \frac{15}{16} = -0.58 \text{ in.}$$

The negative answer may be confusing. Its meaning is that it is not possible to cause web crippling of this section with a reaction as low as 2.43 kips.

When a ridiculously small bearing length is computed, what should be done? First, the bearing length to use may be affected also by the strength of the masonry on which the bearing plate rests. (This will be discussed in detail in a later article.) Next, the bearing length provided must be large enough for the erection crew to "hit" when the beam is installed. It should be large enough also so that slight errors in location will not cause trouble. For example, the walls in Fig. 7–24 are 18 ft 0 in. apart according to the drawings. There is a tolerance on their location, however. They may be one-half, or even one inch farther apart. If provision were made for only one-half inch of bearing at each end, and if the walls were one inch too far apart, the erection crew would soon be sending someone to get the "beam stretcher." In general, bearing lengths of less than two in. are rare. Where bearing plates on masonry are used, 4 in. is usually the minimum.

7-23. Web Buckling. There are two main types of buckling failure that may occur in the webs of beams. These are called "vertical buckling" and "diagonal buckling."

Vertical buckling is illustrated by Fig. 7–28. It occurs when the vertical compressive stress near the center of the beam height exceeds the critical buckling stress of the web acting as a column. Such action is limited to points where concentrated loads or reactions occur.

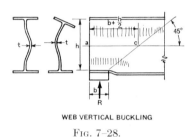

WEB VERTICAL BUCKLING

FIG. 7–28.

The possibility of vertical buckling depends, of course, on the L/r ratio for the vertical strip of web. This ratio can be measured in terms of the ratio h/t. Experiments have led to the conclusion that there is no possibility of vertical buckling in the standard rolled steel sections. Consequently, this type of failure is usually ignored in steel beam design. In aluminum structures it must be considered.[4] In built-up steel beams, having deep or thin webs, vertical buckling may be possible. In those cases it is prevented by the use of bearing stiffeners. The design of bearing stiffeners will be illustrated later in this chapter.

The type of web failure called "diagonal buckling" is the result of shear in the web. Fig. 7–29 shows a small element from the web of a

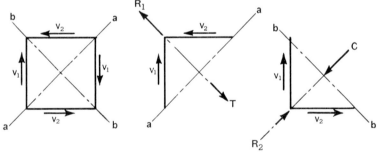

FIG. 7–29.

beam. It is acted upon by the shearing forces shown. It is assumed that the element is taken from a region where the flexural stresses are zero. On the left and right sides equal unit shearing stresses v_1 occur, which are caused by the external shear V in the beam. To maintain equilibrium of the element, equal shearing stresses v_2 occur at right angles to v_1 and in such direction that the moment couple of stresses v_2 is equal to

[4]See *Alcoa Structural Handbook*, Pittsburgh, Pa.: (Aluminum Co. of America).

and opposite to that of v_1. Thus, when a unit shearing stress occurs in one direction, an equal unit shearing stress exists in a direction perpendicular to the first. This is true for any element of material, from a beam web or elsewhere.

Consider the element cut along line a–a. In order that the triangular portions formed may be in equilibrium, it is necessary that an internal tension T exist to balance the resultant R_1 of the shearing forces v_1 and v_2. If the element is cut on line b–b, a compressive force C is necessary to insure equilibrium.

The web of a beam has flexural and shearing stresses and, as a result of shear, has diagonal tension and diagonal compression stresses. In the web of the beam of Fig. 7–30, for example, tensile stresses occur parallel

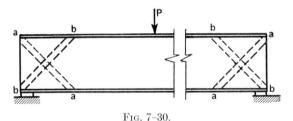

Fig. 7–30.

to the strips marked a–a, while along strips b–b the stress is compressive. At the ends of the beam, where the bending moment is zero, the intensity of the tensile or compressive stress is the same as that of the unit shearing stress at that point, but in diagonal directions. In regions where the flexural stresses in the web ($f = My/I$) are appreciable, the diagonal tensile or compressive stresses are combinations of the flexural stresses and the tensile or compressive stresses due to shear. Thus, the directions of the maximum web tensile or compressive stresses (principal stresses) vary according to the proportions of the shearing and flexural stresses in the web.

If the unit compressive stress on the line b–b is high enough, that element will buckle as a column. Such buckling (diagonal buckling) causes a series of waves or wrinkles approximately parallel to line a–a.

The intensity of shearing stress required to cause diagonal buckling depends on the column properties of the diagonal compressive strip b–b. The L/r of that strip is proportional to the ratio h/t, in which h is the clear vertical height of the web. Again, the standard rolled steel sections (WF, I, and ⌐) are proportioned so that diagonal buckling is not critical. In other words, shearing stresses equal to the factor of safety times the allowable shearing stress, cause diagonal compressive stresses that are below the critical buckling stress for the inclined web strips.

For built-up beams, however, the ratio h/t may exceed 70. When h/t exceeds 70, it may be necessary to consider diagonal buckling. Diagonal buckling can be controlled by reducing h/t, by keeping the shearing stress low, or by using stiffeners, as shown in Fig. 7–31.

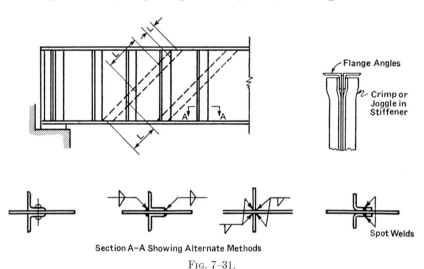

Section A–A Showing Alternate Methods

Fig. 7–31.

For additional information on the design of webs and stiffeners in built-up members, the student is referred to a text covering plate girder design.[5]

7–24. Bearing Stiffeners. Occasionally it is necessary to add stiffeners, such as shown by Fig. 7–32, to a member at points of concentrated

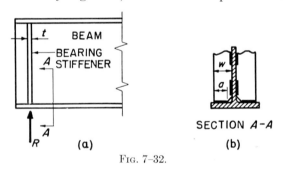

Fig. 7–32.

load or reaction. This might be necessary for two purposes, as follows:

1. To prevent vertical buckling in a built-up beam

[5]C. D. Williams and E. C. Harris, *Structural Design in Metals*, (New York: The Ronald Press Co., 1949), Chaps. 4 and 6.

2. To prevent web crippling where it is not possible to provide the required length of bearing

It is the second purpose that is more apt to affect the non-civil student.

The function of the bearing stiffener is to receive the reaction or load directly at its end, acting as a compression member. Through the welds or rivets which connect the stiffener to the web, the vertical force is transferred into the web. Thus an intense vertical compressive force in the web is avoided. The load is immediately distributed over the height of the web as shear.

The design of the stiffener is, then, the design of a compression member. Consider the ways in which such a member might fail.

1. It might be crushed at its end, where the vertical load is transferred to it through the flange of the beam.
2. It might fail through high compressive stress farther up in the stiffener.
3. Its outer edge might wrinkle in a local buckling failure.
4. In an extremely high member the entire beam, stiffeners included, might buckle as in vertical buckling, shown by Fig. 7–28.

Prevention of the first type of failure is accomplished by limiting the bearing stress on the contact area. The AISC Specification in Section 15(a)(5) shows two values for this stress. The one to use depends on the manner in which the contact end is made smooth. The contact area is of width a only (Fig. 7–32). Even if an attempt were made to fit the fillet, only the flat area should be considered.

The second type of failure is prevented by limiting the average stress on the gross area of the stiffener. Under the AISC Specification, 20,000 psi is permitted [Section 15(a)(2)].

Local buckling is avoided by limiting the ratio of outstanding width to thickness, w/t. It is usual to allow a maximum of 16 for this ratio on stiffeners. [See Section 18(b).]

The fourth type of failure is important only in built-up members, such as very deep plate girders.

EXAMPLE 7–21. Assume that you have selected a 14WF30 beam for the support of a heavy bin. The end reaction of the beam is 40 kips. Only $1\frac{1}{2}$ in. of bearing length is available. Are stiffeners needed? If so design them.

The required length of bearing, without stiffeners, is

$$b = \frac{40}{24 \times 0.27} - \frac{7}{8} = 5.30 \text{ in.}$$

This is more than can be provided. Stiffeners are required.

The stiffeners will be assumed to carry the entire reaction of 40 kips. (If necessary in order to obtain a reasonable stiffener design, the bearing value of the $1\frac{1}{2}$-in. length of web could be deducted. For this member, the amount that could be carried by the beam web is 15.4 kips, leaving 24.6 kips to the stiffeners. This refinement is usually ignored.)

The end-bearing area required for the stiffeners is

$$A_b = \frac{40}{27} = 1.48 \text{ in.}^2, \quad \text{assuming fitted stiffeners}$$

The gross area required is

$$A_g = \frac{40}{20} = 2.00 \text{ in.}^2$$

The stiffener is generally made as wide as is convenient and practical. A standard bar size is usually selected, so that the stiffener comes close to the edge of the flange, but does not project beyond it. The maximum width of space available is dimension a of "Dimensions for Detailing" in the Appendix. For a 14**W**F30 this is $3\frac{1}{4}$ in. A 3-in. bar is the maximum practical width.

The minimum allowable thickness is given by Section 18(b) as $\frac{1}{16}$ of the 3-in. dimension, or $\frac{3}{16}$ in.

To provide a gross area A_g of 2.00 sq in. by two stiffeners, the required thickness is $2.00/2 \times 3 = 0.333$ in.

By subtracting the flange thickness from the k distance, the fillet radius is obtained as $r = \frac{7}{8} - \frac{3}{8} = \frac{1}{2}$ in. Thus the flat width of flange bearing against the stiffener is only $3 - 0.50 = 2.5$ in. per bar. To provide an end bearing area A_b of 1.48 sq in., the thickness must be

$$1.48/(2 \times 2.5) = 0.296 \text{ in.}$$

The largest of the three thickness requirements is 0.333 in. The stiffener bars used would be $3 \times \frac{3}{8}$ minimum.

The balance of the design is a connection problem. The weld joining the bars to the web is required to transfer the stiffener load into the web. The design of welded connections will be presented in Chapter 8.

7–25. Reinforcement of Beams.   Quite often it is necessary to use built-up or reinforced members. Reasons for using such members are:

1. A built-up section may be less expensive than a suitable single section.
2. The weight of a built-up section may be less than that of a single section. For aircraft structures and some bridges, this may be sufficient reason to use a built-up section even though the cost will be increased.

3. No single section having the necessary dimensions and properties may be available.

4. The loading for an existing structure may be increased. Reinforcement of the existing members may be more practical than replacing them with new sections.

The last two reasons are the ones most apt to affect the work of the non-civil engineer.

Fig. 7–33 shows several types of built-up beam. Reinforcement of one flange only, as in (a), is common where only one flange is accessible

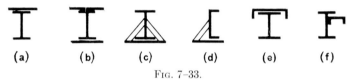

(a)   (b)   (c)   (d)   (e)   (f)

Fig. 7–33.

for connection of the added plate. The top flanges of crane runway girders and monorail beams are often reinforced in this manner. The use of a plate wider than the flange may permit a higher allowable compressive flexural stress.

When both flanges are accessible, plates may be added to both, as in (b).

Types (c) and (d) are often used for lintels. A lintel is a beam which spans the opening for a door or window in a masonry wall. The bottom plate forms a smooth surface above the opening, and it supports the masonry above. The diagonal bars prevent the extended plate from being bent downward under the weight of the masonry. The ends of a lintel are usually supported by bearing upon the solid wall adjacent to the opening. When the ends of the member extend to the steel columns and are supported by the columns, the member is called a spandrel beam.

Type (e) is very common for use as crane girders and as monorail beams. The added channel serves several purposes. It increases the section modulus, it may increase the allowable compressive stress, and it provides strength against lateral loads. With the channel on the side as in (f) the lateral resistance is provided. However, this section is not symmetrical about the plane of the vertical loads. Unless well braced, it will twist when loaded. The analysis of such a beam when not braced against twisting is quite difficult; the non-civil engineer would usually not be required to analyze it.

The design of reinforced beams that are symmetrical about the plane of the loads is relatively simple. A procedure for the design follows:

1. Select a trial section consisting of a rolled beam section and its reinforcement. Except for sections that are symmetrical about

both axes, such as that of Fig. 7–33(b), a direct solution is not possible. The first selection must be an estimate.

2. Locate the center-of-gravity axis of the combined section and compute the moment of inertia about that axis.

3. Compute the maximum tensile and compressive unit stresses for the combined section and compare them with the stresses permitted by the Specification.

4. Repeat steps 1, 2, and 3 as required to determine a satisfactory section.

5. If it is desired to use reinforcement only at the points where the section modulus of the unreinforced beam is insufficient, determine the points of cutoff for the reinforcement. Since the flange dimensions affect the allowable unit compressive flexural stress, a beam with reinforcement extending over less than the entire span might have a different allowable stress than one with full-length reinforcement. Specifications do not provide for the determination of the allowable stress for such members. A value of the allowable compressive stress for such a beam can be approximated by a procedure given by C. D. Williams.[6] Otherwise, an approximate value of the allowable compressive stress can be obtained by using a ratio of L/b (or Ld/bt) intermediate between that of the unreinforced beam and one with full-length reinforcement. The effective ratio used should be a weighted average value which considers the relative lengths of reinforced and unreinforced sections.

6. Check for resistance to shear failure, web crippling, and web buckling, as required.

7. Determine the longitudinal shear at the connection of the reinforcement to the beam and design the welded, riveted, or bolted connections of the reinforcement to the beam.

One refinement should be considered. Reinforcement must occasionally be added to a beam while the beam continues to carry some load, such as the dead load of a floor system. Assume that a plate is added to the bottom flange of such a beam. The original section carries the dead load before the reinforcing plate is installed, and continues to carry it afterward. The reinforcing plate will be stressed only when *additional* loads occur, which raise the bending moment at the section in question to more than the dead load bending moment.

EXAMPLE 7–22. In Example 7–17 a 14**WF**34 was selected for the beam supporting the storage balcony and the monorail (see Fig. 7–24).

---

[6] C. D. Williams, *Analysis of Statically Indeterminate Structures*, (3d ed.; Scranton, Pa.: International Textbook Co., 1943), Chap. 9.

Often one must use materials that are on hand, rather than use the lightest section. Assume that several pieces of 10WF21 are available in the plant. How could these be reinforced to make them usable? Assume also that clamps have been designed so that the monorail below can be attached without making holes in the bottom flange of the beam.

From Example 7–17, the total bending moment at the center of the span is 67.8 ft-kips. The beam is laterally supported, and F_b is 20,000 psi.

$$\text{Required } S = \frac{67.8 \times 12}{20} = 40.7 \text{ in}^3.$$

If a plate is added to each flange, the neutral axis will remain at the center of the base section. In this case it is quite easy to compute the required plate size directly.

Assume that $\frac{1}{4}$-in. plates will be used.

$$c = \frac{9.90}{2} + 0.25 = 5.20 \text{ in. from N. A. to extreme fiber}$$

$$\text{Required } I = S \times c = 40.7 \times 5.20 = 212 \text{ in}^4.$$

This is the moment of inertia of the combined section, and is equal to the I of the 10WF21, plus the I of the two plates about the center of gravity of the WF section. Call the area of each plate A.

$$212 = 106.3 + 2A(5.20 - 0.25/2)^2$$

$$51.5A = 105.7$$

$$\text{Required } A = 2.05 \text{ in}^2. \text{ per plate}$$

This could be provided by a $\frac{1}{4}$-in. plate $8\frac{1}{2}$ in. wide. Such a plate might be a little too wide to be practical. If so, a new thickness should be assumed and the process repeated. For example, if a $\frac{3}{8}$-in. plate were assumed, the required area A would be 2.10 sq in. per plate. One $6 \times \frac{3}{8}$ plate on each flange would suffice.

EXAMPLE 7–23. An existing building has a concrete floor slab supported on 12WF27 beams as shown in Fig. 7–34(a) and (b). The floor and the beams were originally designed for a live load of 125 lb per sq ft. A new contract requires that some rather heavy raw materials be stored on this floor. If possible, the superintendent would like to stack all of these materials in a few bays so as to conserve valuable space. To do so would raise the floor live load to 200 lb per sq ft. You, as an engineer for the company have found the floor slab to be strong enough to take the new load. The 12WF27 beams, however, are not strong enough. How can they be reinforced to do the job?

Obviously, it would be hard to reinforce the top flange. It would be easy, though, to weld a plate to the bottom flange, as shown in Fig. 7–34(c). The section will be unsymmetrical; thus, a direct solution like that of the previous example will not be possible. The trial and error procedure will be necessary.

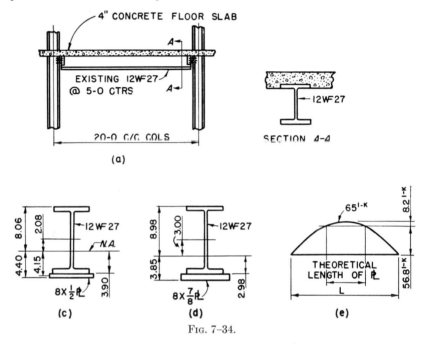

Fig. 7–34.

All live load will be kept off the floor while the reinforcing plate is being installed. Thus the plate will assist in supporting all of the live load. The dead load, however, will be active during installation of the plate. The dead load will not stress the plate. The dead load will be supported entirely by the 12WF27.

Dead load per foot of beam: Concrete slab $\frac{1}{3} \times 150 \times 5 = 250$ lb per ft

Beam and plate, estimated $= \underline{50}$

$w = 300$ lb per ft

$$M_{DL} = \tfrac{1}{8} \times 0.30(20)^2 = 15.0 \text{ ft-kips}$$

Live load per foot of beam $= 200 \times 5 = 1,000$ lb

$$M_{LL} = \tfrac{1}{8} \times 1.00(20)^2 = 50.0 \text{ ft-kips}$$

Trial No. 1: Try an $8 \times \frac{1}{2}$ plate. (This width will project beyond the flange of the 12WF27 far enough to permit easy welding.)

Item	Area	y (from WF c/g)	Ay	$\bar{y}$	$A\bar{y}^2$	I_0
12WF27 8 × 1/2 Pl	7.97 4.00	0 6.23	0 24.92	2.08 4.15	34.5 68.8	204.1 0
Σ	11.97		24.92		103.3	204.1

$$\bar{y} = \frac{24.92}{11.97} = 2.08 \text{ in.} \quad \text{(below ctr of WF)}$$

The tabulations to the right of the double line above give the moment of inertia I_0 for each element about its own center of gravity, and the quantity $A\bar{y}^2$ for transposition to an axis at the center of gravity of the combined section. In complex sections, the tabular form saves much time. The student may have to make some extra effort in order to become familiar with the tabular method, but he should find the time very well spent.

$$I = \Sigma I_0 + \Sigma(A\bar{y}^2) = 204.1 + 103.3 = 307.4 \text{ in}^4.$$

$$S_t = 307.4/4.40 = 69.8 \text{ in}^3.$$

$$S_c = 307.4/8.06 = 38.1 \text{ in}^3.$$

The stresses will now be checked for the top flange.

$$\text{DL stress, } f = M_{DL}/S_{WF} = 12 \times 15.0/34.1 = 5.3$$

$$\text{LL stress, } f = M_{LL}/S_c = 12 \times 50.0/38.1 = 15.7$$

$$\text{Total compressive stress} = 21.0 \text{ kips/in}^2.$$

Since the allowable of 20 kips per sq in. is exceeded, an 8 × ½ plate is not satisfactory.

Trial No. 2: Try an 8 × ⅞ plate.

Item	Area	y (from WF c/g)	Ay	$\bar{y}$	$A\bar{y}^2$	I_0
12WF27 8 × 7/8 Pl	7.97 7.00	0 6.42	0 44.9	3.00 3.42	71.7 82.0	204.1 0
Σ	14.97		44.9		153.7	204.1

$$\bar{y} = 44.9/14.97 = 3.00 \text{ in.}$$

$$I = 153.7 + 204.1 = 357.8 \text{ in}^4.$$

$$S_t = 357.8/3.85 = 93.0 \text{ in}^3.$$

$$S_c = 357.8/8.98 = 39.9 \text{ in}^3.$$

Stress on compression side:

$$f_{DL} = 12 \times 15.0/34.1 = 5.3$$

$$f_{LL} = 12 \times 50.0/39.9 = \underline{15.0}$$

$$\text{Total compressive stress} = 20.3 \text{ kips/in}^2_{.}$$

The section is slightly overstressed, but the stress is well within the customary 5 per cent tolerance. An $8 \times \frac{7}{8}$ plate will be satisfactory provided that enough weld can be applied to connect it to the 12**WF**27. That phase of the problem will be considered separately in Chapter 8.

The maximum bending moment exists at one section only. Elsewhere, the need for the reinforcing plate is not so serious; in some parts it is not needed at all. How long should the reinforcing plate be? It should be used wherever the total bending moment is greater than the allowable for the unreinforced 12**WF**27 beam.

The allowable bending moment for the 12**WF**27 is

$$M = F_b S = 20 \times 34.1 = 682 \text{ in-kips,} \quad \text{or} \quad 56.8 \text{ ft-kips}$$

Fig. 7–34(e) shows the moment diagram, which is parabolic. The total bending moment at the center is $50 + 15 = 65$ ft-kips. A plate is required in the length where M exceeds 56.8 ft-kips.

$$L = 20.0 \sqrt{\frac{8.2}{65}} = 7.1 \text{ ft}$$

This is the theoretical length in which the plate is needed. It would be extended slightly more at each end to provide room for connecting the ends. The total length used would be about 8 ft.

The moment diagram is always used to determine cover plate lengths. When the diagram is not a regular shape, such as the parabola of this example, it should be drawn to scale and the length of plate determined graphically. When moving loads are involved, a *diagram of maximum moments at each section* should be used instead of a moment diagram.

The web of the 12**WF**27 should be checked for shear. The end shear under the new loading is

$$V = 10(300 + 1,000) = 13,000 \text{ lb}$$

$$v = \frac{13,000}{11.95 \times 0.24} = 4,530 \text{ psi} < 13,000$$

The member is satisfactory in shear.

7–26. Combined Axial Load and Flexure. A common design problem is that of members having simultaneous bending moment and axial load. Consider the member shown in Fig. 7–35(a). The eccentric load P can be replaced by an axial load of the same amount and a bending moment Pe, as shown in Fig. 7–35(b). At any section, such as at a–b, equilibrium of the section is maintained by an internal force and an internal moment equal to, but in opposite direction to, the external force and moment, respectively. At any point on the section, the total

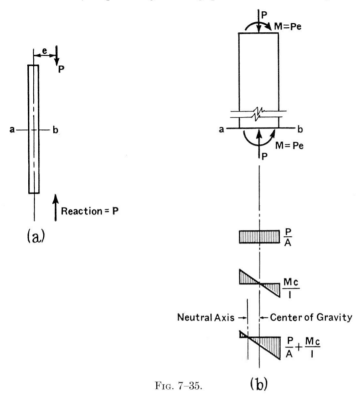

FIG. 7–35.   (b)

stress is the sum of the stresses caused by axial load and by bending moment.

At point a,

$$f = \frac{P}{A} - \frac{Mc}{I}$$

and at point b,

$$f = \frac{P}{A} + \frac{Mc}{I}$$

or for any point on section a–b,

$$f = \frac{P}{A} \pm \frac{My}{I}$$

These conditions would prevail provided neither the yield strength nor the critical buckling stress had been reached.

For a member in which the allowable bending stress is equal to the allowable axial load stress, the choice of a safe section consists of finding one for which the maximum combined stress $P/A \pm Mc/I$ does not exceed the allowable. Because of the number of variables, direct choice of section is not feasible, except for sections of regular shape, such as round, square, hexagonal, etc. For the usual case, successive trials must be made to determine the most economical safe section.

If the allowable stress in bending is not equal to that for axial load, to what value should the total or combined stress be limited? It is certainly conservative to require that the combined stress be no larger than the smaller of the allowable stresses in bending or axial load. Some specifications do require that the combined stress be so limited.

A more popular method is one in which the combined stress is a compromise between the bending and axial allowables. By this method, if the major part of the combined stress is due to axial load, the allowable combined stress lies between the bending and axial load allowables, but closer to that for axial load; if bending causes the larger part of the combined stress, the allowable value lies closer to that for bending.

The AISC Specification, Section 12(a), provides such a compromise. The student should read that section carefully. This method of determining the limit of stress is based on the rationalization that, if a certain percentage of the strength of the member has been used for axial load, the remaining percentage may be used for bending moment. It will be noted that if $f_b = 0$, f_a may equal F_a; if $f_a = 0$, f_b may equal F_b; if $f_a = \frac{1}{3}$ of F_a, f_b may be $\frac{2}{3}$ of F_b; etc. Since both F_a and F_b are based on empirical formulas, no rational derivation of the relationship seems possible.

7-27. Design of Members Subject to Combined Compression and Flexure.
In the usual problem there is no direct method of selection possible. Design is accomplished by trying various sections until the lightest suitable one is determined.

Any section at all could be used for the first trial. It is better though to use a little judgment in choosing the first trial section. If the first guess is a "wild" one, many more trials may be needed in order to converge upon the satisfactory section. How can the first trial section be picked? There are some guides that one may use.

1. The L/r limitation can be used to find a minimum allowable value of r.
2. The section must obviously be stronger than would be needed if axial load alone existed.
3. The section must be stronger than needed for bending alone.

EXAMPLE 7–24. A 10W33 column is laterally braced at its ends only. The length is 15 ft. A load of 55 kips is applied to a seat connection 2 ft from the top of the column as shown in Fig. 7–36(a). Is the section satisfactory under the AISC Specification?

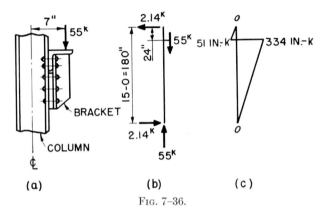

FIG. 7–36.

Fig. 7–36(b) shows the free-body diagram, and part (c) the moment diagram. Normally, unless the load is applied at a considerable distance from the end, the bending moment is assumed to be the product of P and e. In this case, the moment would be taken as

$$7 \times 55 = 385 \text{ in.-kips}$$

The custom is obviously a conservative one. The usual excuse for using it though, is merely the failure to recognize the support condition and the shape of the moment diagram. In this example, it will be assumed that the support conditions are known and recognized. The 334 in.-kip moment will be used.

$$L/r = 180/1.94 = 92.8$$

$$\text{Allowable } F_a = 17,000 - 0.485(92.8)^2 = 12,830 \text{ psi}$$

$$\text{Actual } f_a = 55,000/9.71 = 5,660 \text{ psi}$$

$$\text{Allowable } F_b = \frac{12,000,000}{180 \times 9.75/7.96 \times 0.433} = 23,600 \text{ psi}$$
$$(\text{Use } 20,000 \text{ psi.})$$

$$\text{Actual } f_b = 334,000/35 = 9,550 \text{ psi}$$

$$\frac{f_a}{F_a} + \frac{f_b}{F_b} = \frac{5.66}{12.83} + \frac{9.55}{20} = 0.441 + 0.477 = 0.918 < 1.0$$

Therefore, the column is satisfactory.

Courtesy of Link-Belt Co.

Ash Storage Bin with Semi-automatic Skip Hoist. Notice Structural Supports, Including Columns, Bracing, and Concrete Footings.

EXAMPLE 7–25. A cylindrical steel bin with a conical bottom is to be supported by four posts. The easiest way to connect the posts to the bin is by welding as shown in Fig. 7–37. The total weight of the bin and its contents is 128 kips. The bin is located inside a building, so that wind forces need not be considered. The bin can be tied laterally to the

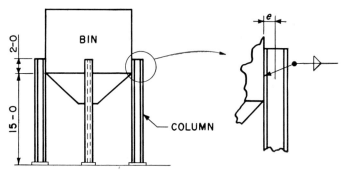

FIG. 7–37.

building steel, so that the columns can be considered supported at each end. Design the post using the AISC Specification.

The load per post is 32 kips. An effective length of 16 ft will be used. The load is applied to one flange of the column. The eccentricity e is one-half of the column depth and is unknown until a selection has been made.

Trial No. 1: Try an 8WF24. (This is selected because its axial load capacity is more than 32 kips, and its L/r ratio does not exceed the permissible L/r.)

$$L/r = 192/1.61 = 119$$

$$F_a = 17,000 - 0.485(119)^2 = 10,100 \text{ psi}$$

$$f_a = 32,000/7.06 = 4,530 \text{ psi}$$

$$F_b = \frac{12,000,000}{192 \times 7.93/6.5 \times 0.398} = 20,400 \quad (\text{Use } 20,000 \text{ psi.})$$

$$f_b = M/S = 32,000 \times 3.97/20.8 = 6,100 \text{ psi}$$

$$\frac{f_a}{F_a} + \frac{f_b}{F_b} = \frac{4.53}{10.1} + \frac{6.10}{20} = 0.449 + 0.305 = 0.754 < 1.0$$

Therefore, the 8WF24 is satisfactory. Another trial will be made to see if a lighter satisfactory section can be found.

Trial No. 2: Try a 6WF20.

$$L/_r = 192/1.50 = 128$$

$$F_a = \left[\frac{18,000}{1 + \frac{(128)^2}{18,000}}\right]\left[1.6 - \frac{128}{200}\right] = 9,040 \text{ psi}$$

$$f_a = 32,000/5.90 = 5,420 \text{ psi}$$

$$F_b = \frac{12,000,000}{192 \times 6.20/6.02 \times 0.367} = 22,300 \quad (\text{Use } 20,000 \text{ psi.})$$

$$f_b = 32,000 \times 3.10/13.4 = 7,400 \text{ psi}$$

$$\frac{f_a}{F_a} + \frac{f_b}{F_b} = \frac{5.42}{9.04} + \frac{7.40}{20} = 0.600 + 0.370 = 0.970 < 1.0$$

Examination of the tables of sections shows that all lighter sections have smaller values of section modulus and radius of gyration, except the 8WF17. That has a slightly higher section modulus. However, it proves to be unsatisfactory. The 6WF20 is the lightest acceptable section.

PROBLEMS

Use the AISC Specification unless otherwise noted.

7–1. Select an angle to resist 30 kips tension. The connections will be made by a single row of $\frac{3}{4}$-in. rivets in one leg.

7–2. What is the allowable tensile load for the member shown in Fig. 7–38. The member is a $14 \times \frac{5}{8}$ plate, and the rivets are $\frac{3}{4}$ in.

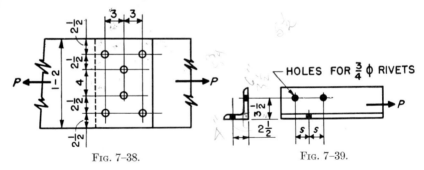

FIG. 7–38.   FIG. 7–39.

7–3. A $6 \times 4 \times \frac{1}{2}$ angle is shown in Fig. 7–39. Determine the allowable tensile load for the angle when the stagger s is $1\frac{1}{2}$ in. What is the minimum value of the stagger that may be used to insure that the angle strength will be controlled by the net section through one hole only?

7–4. A flat plate is used as a tension member and is connected to a gusset plate as shown in Fig. 7–40. Compute the allowable tensile load for the member.

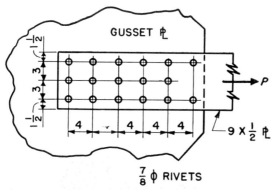

FIG. 7–40.

(Suggestion: How much of the total load P is in the $9 \times \frac{1}{2}$ plate at the section having three holes?)

7-5. A balcony is to be added near the outside wall of an existing industrial building. To avoid cluttering the main floor with new columns (posts), it is decided to hang one edge of the balcony from the roof trusses. Fig. 7–41(a)

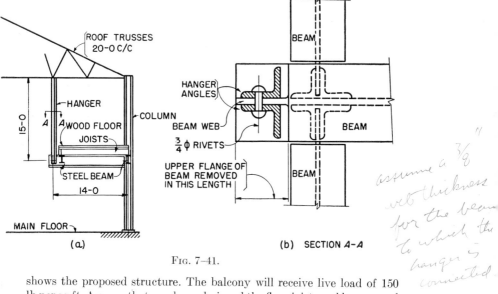

FIG. 7–41.

shows the proposed structure. The balcony will receive live load of 150 lb per sq ft. Assume that you have designed the floor joists and beams, and that the floor system weighs 30 lb per sq ft of floor.

The hanger can consist of a single angle or two angles, as in Fig. 7–41(b). Assume that a single row of $\frac{3}{4}$-in. rivets will connect the floor system to the hanger. Select

a) The most economical single angle

b) The most economical two-angle section

7–6. Compute the axial load capacity for a 10W^F49 used as a column, 22 ft long, supported at the ends only.

7–7. If the length of the column in Problem 7–6 is increased to 27 ft, what is the capacity?

7–8. Fig. 7–42 shows existing columns which form a tower supporting a bin in a factory building. The columns are braced on all four sides of the tower as shown. The load per column is 35 kips. To obtain clearance for new elec-

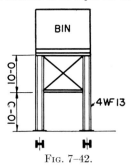

Fig. 7–42.

trical equipment, it is desired to remove the diagonal bracing from the near face of the tower. Will the columns be satisfactory with this bracing removed?

7–9. Select a section for a column 18 ft long between supports, to carry an axial load of 27 kips.

7–10. Plant expansion makes it necessary to construct another bin arrangement like that in Fig. 7–42. In the new one, bracing can be used on all four sides of the tower. A search of the stockpile shows four 6 × 6 × 3/8 in. angles, each 20 ft 0 in. long. It would pay to use these as the corner columns of the bin support tower, rather than buy new W^F sections. What would be the capacity per angle if braced as shown in Fig. 7–42? At what vertical spacing should the bracing be placed in order to permit the use of these angles?

7–11. Select members for the sign support truss of Problem 4–13, shown in Fig. 4–28. Assume that all connections will be made by welding, so that no deductions are needed for rivet or bolt holes. The wind can blow either way. The entire vertical weight of the sign is only 2 kips; this can be assumed to stress the two main verticals only. Use single angles or double angles, whichever is more practical. Note Section 15(d) of the AISC Specification. Note also that the long sloping member has support perpendicular to the plane of the truss at the upper and lower ends only. In the plane of the truss, the member has lateral support at each panel point.

7–12. Design the members for the truss that was analyzed in Example 4–5 and shown in Fig. 4–12. Assume that the bottom chord members will be laterally braced by cross members at each panel point. Single angle members may be used if practical. Assume that the connections will be made using ½-in. bolts in 17/32-in. drilled holes.

7-13. Select a W section to support a uniform load of 1,200 lb per ft, in addition to its own weight, over a 16-ft span, laterally supported.

7-14. A 14W30 is used as a simple beam of 25-ft span. The only loads are its own weight and a concentrated load at mid-span. Lateral support is provided at the ends and at the center of the span. What is the maximum allowable concentrated load?

7-15. Select an American Standard Beam section for use as a monorail beam. The span is 20 ft, laterally unsupported. A 2-ton electric hoist, weighing 650 lb is to be used. The hoist will be carried by an 8-wheel trolley weighing 140 lb. The wheels are arranged in four pairs, with 12-in. spacing between pairs. See the AISC Specification for the impact allowance.

7-16. A self-supporting jib crane is shown by Fig. 7–43. The boom is an American Standard Beam, and the mast is a heavy welded pipe. What size of boom

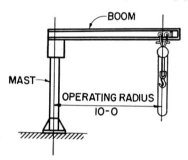

Fig. 7–43.

is required for a 2-ton crane? Assume a chain hoist and trolley weighing 300 lb. Allow 20 per cent of the lifted load for impact.

7-17. A type of support frequently used for medium-sized transformers is shown in Fig. 7–44. Select a size of channel for the main beams of such a platform.

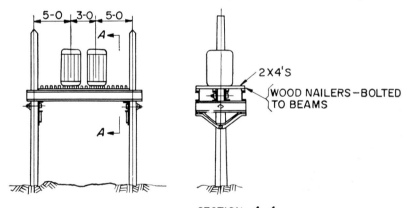

SECTION *A–A*

Fig. 7–44.

The floor consists of yellow pine 2 × 4's, placed with the $3\frac{5}{8}$-in. dimension vertical, and spaced at $3\frac{1}{4}$-in. centers. The transformers weigh 1,500 lb each. The weight of the transformers should be assumed to act entirely on the two center beams. An allowance should be made for the weight of men working on the platform. Allow for two 200-lb men. During installation of the system, their weight could easily occur at the same location as the transformer. For convenience of detail, the outer beams will probably be of the same section as the center beam. Assume 2 × 4's are 4 ft long.

7–18. While installing a new lighting system in a customer's building, you find it necessary to drill holes in several of the roof purlins. Two holes of $\frac{1}{2}$-in. diameter will be needed in the tension flange at the center of the purlin span. The owner has no engineer in his employ. As the electrical contractor, you are responsible for any damage these holes may cause. What will be the flexural stresses at the section containing the hole? You have measured the purlin section and have identified it as 10B15. The purlins have a 20-ft span, and are 8 ft apart. The roofing is 5-ply felt and gravel. The roof is supported by gypsum plank about 2 in. thick. The local building code specifies a snow load of 25 lb per square foot of horizontal projection. The roof is nearly flat.

7–19. Compute the maximum allowable uniform load per foot for a 14W⁻34 beam having a span of 6 ft 6 in.

7–20. A 21W⁻62 is used as a short beam to support an 80-kip load at mid-span. What bearing length is required at the end? At the load?

7–21. Fig. 7–45 shows two steel beams used as "skids" on which to place a heavy piece of equipment. After adjusting to the correct position, the equipment

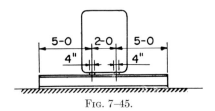

Fig. 7–45.

is welded to the beams. What section is required? Consider all types of beam failure. The equipment weight is 60 kips.

7–22. Assume that the beam of Problem 7–20 has been made with a 3-in. bearing length. It now becomes necessary to move the 80-kip load over one support. Welded stiffeners are required to prevent crippling. Design the stiffeners.

7–23. An existing $1\frac{1}{2}$-ton monorail system has been found inadequate. It is planned to increase its capacity to 2 tons. The existing monorail beams are 8 I 18.4 on 18-ft simple spans. Design reinforcement to permit the use of these beams with the new system. (A plate or a channel on the top flange is suggested.) The new hoist will weigh 600 lb. and the trolley 150 lb. The trolley will have four pairs of wheels with 9 in. of space between pairs. Allow 25 per cent of the lifted load for impact.

7-24. An existing building into which your company moves has 4-in. concrete floor slabs. The slabs are supported by 14WF30 simple beams spaced 8 ft apart. The span of the 14WF30 beams is 25 ft. In one area of the building, the beams have an 8 × ½ plate welded to the bottom flange. The record prints of the design drawings do not show these plates, so the plates were apparently installed after the building was completed. What is the allowable live load per square foot of floor in the area of the reinforced beams. (Consider only the strength of the beams; assume that the floor slab is to be analyzed separately.)

7-25. What would be the theoretical point of cutoff for the plates of Problem 7-24 in order that the reinforced beams carry the load you have computed?

7-26. Some 8WF17 beams are to be reinforced so that they can resist a bending moment of 32 ft-kips. The beams will be laterally supported. They can be removed for welding so that reinforcement can be added to both flanges. Design the reinforcement.

7-27. A 10WF33 column is eccentrically loaded by a beam that is connected to one flange near the top of the column. The column is 18 ft long and is laterally supported at the ends only. What is the allowable load?

7-28. Select a WF section for a column 20 ft long to support an 18-kip load with a 16-in. eccentricity at mid-height of the column. Lateral support is provided at the top and bottom.

7-29. A jib crane is shown in Fig. 7-46. The mast has swivel connections at the top and bottom so that the entire crane can rotate about a vertical axis.

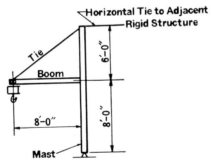

Live Load = 4,000 Lb
Trolley and Hoist = 1,000 Lb
Impact = 20% of Live Load Only

Fig. 7-46.

Select sections for the mast and boom. In each case try to find the most economical section of the type suggested. An American Standard beam is suggested for the boom, and a WF section for the mast. Select the boom first, using an estimated boom weight. Then design the mast, using the corrected boom weight. Assume the entire vertical load to occur at the top of the mast. The hoist and load should be placed at the center of the boom when designing the boom. For the mast design, it should be moved to the outer end.

7–30. A steel column for the support of a transformer is shown in Fig. 7–47. The problem is to select a section for the column. The transformer weight is

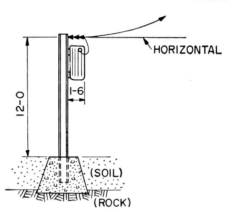

FIG. 7–47.

500 lb. The total wire pull is normally 210 lb. A $\frac{1}{2}$-in. thickness of ice on the transformer will weigh 60 lb. The weight of the wire used is 0.16 lb per ft. The outside diameter of the insulated wire is $\frac{1}{2}$ in. Assume that a $\frac{1}{2}$-in. thickness of ice can form on the wires also.

CHAPTER 8

DESIGN IN STEEL—CONNECTIONS

A structural member is usually but one of many members which are connected to each other to form a complete structure. It is important that each of these members be selected with due regard to safety and economy. But—a chain is no stronger than its weakest link. Similarly, the structure is no stronger than the weakest detail. Thus, it is equally important that much care be given to designing the *connections* by which these individual members become parts of the structure. Structural failures are more common in the connections than in the main members themselves.

8–1. Types of Connector. The common types of connector in structural steel work are rivets, bolts, and welds.

The rivets used in structural steel are usually of the button-head variety. Table 1 of Appendix B shows this shape of rivet head. Sometimes limited space requires that the heads be flattened or countersunk.

Rivets are usually driven hot. The rivet as received from the manufacturer has one head. After heating the rivet is inserted in the work. The manufactured head is held in place using a "bucking bar." The riveting gun, an air-operated hammer having a die of the proper shape, is used to upset the rivet shank forming another head. During this operation the shank is also upset along its length so that the hole is practically filled by the shank.

In shop fabrication, the hot rivets are often driven by pneumatic or hydraulic rivet presses. These upset the shank and form the head with a single stroke of the machine.

The common sizes of structural steel rivets are $\frac{5}{8}$ in., $\frac{3}{4}$ in., $\frac{7}{8}$ in., and 1 in. The size refers to the diameter of the shank before driving. The $\frac{3}{4}$-in. size is the one most commonly used in building work.

The holes for hot-driven rivets are made $\frac{1}{16}$ in. larger in diameter than the nominal size of the rivet. When the thickness of the material is not more than the hole diameter plus $\frac{1}{8}$ in., the hole can be punched. If the material is thicker, the hole is drilled. When very high-class workmanship is needed, as in bridges or large traveling cranes, the holes may be subpunched and then reamed to the correct size and proper alignment.

Bolts are often used in structural steel. Generally the rivet is preferable, and bolts are limited to special cases. Bolts are used for temporary connections, for tensile loads where the specification does not permit sufficient tension in rivets, for connections where clearances do not permit driving of rivets, for connections where the noise of riveting is objectionable, and for connecting members that must be removable.

Both hexagonal and square-shaped bolt heads and nuts are available. In the common sizes, $\frac{5}{8}$, $\frac{3}{4}$, and $\frac{7}{8}$ in., the square head is usually used. The threads do not extend over the full length; as much as possible of the bolt shank is left unthreaded. A washer should be used under the nut so that none of the material connected by the bolt is in contact with the sharp threads.

For common bolts, the hole is $\frac{1}{16}$ in. larger than the bolt shank diameter. For important work, turned bolts are used in holes subpunched and reamed to the correct size.

There are many welding processes; broadly, they are divided into "pressure processes" and "non-pressure" processes. The non-pressure processes are commonly called "fusion" welding. The two types of fusion welding commonly used in structural steel are gas welding and arc welding. In these processes the base metal is heated to the fusion temperature and additional molten metal is added.

Gas welding is accomplished by using an oxyacetylene flame to fuse the base metal and to melt the welding rod.

In the arc welding process an electric current passes through a cable from a direct-current generator to the welding rod which is held by the operator. The current passes from the welding rod through the metal being welded, and thence through another cable back to the generator. The operator touches the welding rod to the work, causing current to flow, and then draws the rod slightly away from the work

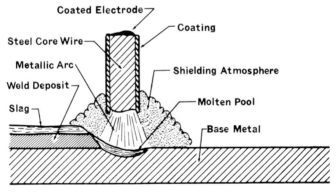

Fig. 8-1.

causing an arc to form. The heat developed by the arc melts the welding rod and the metal of the parts being welded (base metal). The metal from the welding rod is added to the parts and mixes with the molten base metal.

Many different welding rods are manufactured to provide for varying requirements, such as differences in materials; position of work—overhead, vertical, or flat; and the size of the weld material to be added. Because of the superior quality of the weld, most specifications require the use of coated rods. The coating is melted by the heat of the arc and provides a vapor shield around the area being fused. This vapor shields the molten metal, preventing its contamination from contact with the air, and confines the atmosphere of the arc, permitting more nearly complete ionization of the metal particles forming the arc. The coating also serves as a flux carrying impurities to the surface of the molten metal. It forms a slag coating over the weld to protect it from the air during the cooling process. Fig. 8–1 shows the principle elements of the shielded metallic arc. The slag should be removed after the weld has cooled. Since the slag is brittle, it breaks up very easily with light tapping of a hammer.

8–2. Riveted and Bolted Connections.   The usual riveted or bolted joint is a shear type of connection, such as shown by Fig. 8–2(a). There

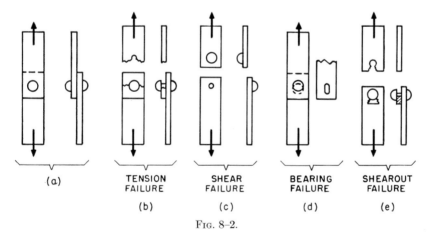

(a)

TENSION
FAILURE

SHEAR
FAILURE

BEARING
FAILURE

SHEAROUT
FAILURE

(b)

(c)

(d)

(e)

Fig. 8–2.

are four basic ways in which such a connection may fail. Those failures are illustrated in parts (b), (c), (d), and (e) of the figure.

Failure (b), due to tensile stress in the member itself, was covered in Chapter 7. While it is actually a failure of the member, it is often effected by the design of the connection.

In the shear failure (c) the shank of the rivet is broken. The shearing

Courtesy of Chicago Bridge and Iron Co.

1,000,000-GALLON RADIAL-CONE BOTTOM TANK, 100 FEET TO BOTTOM. SUPPORT IS BY TUBULAR COLUMNS. DIAGONAL BRACING AND STRUTS ASSIST IN RESISTING HORIZONTAL LOAD.

stress is assumed to be uniform over the shank area. The allowable shearing load for one rivet is

$$R = A \text{ (shank)} \times \text{Allowable unit shear} = Af_s$$

The allowable unit shearing stresses for hot-driven rivets are established for computation using the area of the original shank before driving. Thus, although a $\frac{3}{4}$-in. rivet may swell to $\frac{13}{16}$-in. diameter when it is driven, the $\frac{3}{4}$-in. diameter is used when computing the strength.

The bearing failure of (d) is the result of compression of the rivet shank against the member material at the side of the hole. The failure consists of distortion of the rivet hole (or, rarely, of the rivet) by load. As a connection is loaded to failure, a shear failure is sudden and complete. The bearing failure, however, is gradual and progressive. No obvious point of failure exists, and the bearing failure must be a defined one. It is usual to define a bearing failure as a permanent increase of the hole diameter by some stated percentage of its original diameter. For example, the *Alcoa Structural Handbook* gives bearing values for rivets which are based on the assumption that a 2 per cent permanent elongation of the hole diameter constitutes a bearing yield failure.

Fig. 8–3 shows two types of joint, a single-lap and a double-lap. The intensity of the bearing stresses (compression) between the rivet shank and the connected material is shown shaded. In the single-lap joint

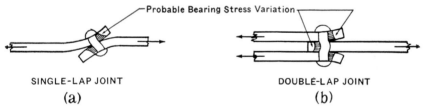

SINGLE-LAP JOINT

(a)

DOUBLE-LAP JOINT

(b)

Fig. 8–3.

there is considerable distortion, and the bearing stress varies much. In the double-lap joint there is less distortion and the bearing stress is more nearly uniform, particularly for the inner plate. In each type, the *average* bearing stress can be computed as

$$f_{br} = \frac{\text{Rivet load transferred to material in question}}{\text{Shank diameter (nominal)} \times \text{Material thickness}}$$

This could be stated also,

$$\text{Allowable } R = tdf_{br}$$

In each of the above f_{br} is the average bearing stress. For a single-lap joint, the average may be much lower than the maximum. For the inner plate of a double-lap joint there is less difference between maximum and minimum. Some specifications give one allowable bearing stress, set low enough for safe use with either the single- or the double-lap joint. The AISC Specification, however, gives an allowable of 32,000 psi for a single-lap (single shear) connection, and 40,000 psi for the inner plate of the double-lap (double shear) connection. Sometimes the more descriptive term "enclosed bearing" value is used in place of double-shear bearing value; and "non-enclosed" bearing value is used in place of single-shear bearing value. Thus in Fig. 8–3, the 32,000-psi value would be used to determine the bearing capacity in either plate of the single-lap joint, or in the outer plates of the double-lap. The 40,000-psi value would be used with the inner plate of the double-lap.

The value of a bolt is computed in the same manner, but usually with different allowable unit stresses for unfinished bolts.

EXAMPLE 8–1. What is the allowable load for one $\frac{3}{4}$-in. rivet joining two $\frac{3}{8}$-in. plates in a single-lap joint, as in Fig. 8–3(a)?

Shear Value: In a shear failure, the shank is broken in one place only. This is called a single-shear connection.

$$A = \pi\left(\frac{0.75}{2}\right)^2 = 0.4418 \text{ sq in.}$$

$$f_s = 15,000 \text{ psi} \quad [\text{AISC Specification, Section 15(a)(4)}]$$

Shear value = $0.4418 \times 15 = 6.63$ kips

Bearing Value:

$$f_{br} = 32,000 \text{ psi}$$

$$A_{br} = \frac{3}{4} \times \frac{3}{8} = \frac{9}{32} \text{ sq in.}$$

Bearing value = $\frac{9}{32} \times 32 = 9$ kips

The shear value is smaller and controls the strength. The maximum load allowed for one such rivet is 6.63 kips.

EXAMPLE 8–2. What is the allowable load per rivet in the double-lap joint of Fig. 8–3(b)? Assume $\frac{3}{4}$-in. rivets, a $\frac{1}{2}$-in. inside plate, and $\frac{1}{4}$-in. outer plates.

Shear Value: In a shear failure the rivet shank would be broken in two places. (Assume the center plate to move to the right.) This is called a double-shear connection.

$$A = 2\pi\left(\frac{0.75}{2}\right)^2 = 0.8836 \text{ sq in.}$$

$$f_s = 15,000 \text{ psi}$$

Double shear value $= 0.8836 \times 15 = 13.25$ kips

Bearing Value—Inner Plate: The entire joint load enters the center plate through bearing.

$$f_{br} = 40,000 \text{ psi}$$

$$A_{br} = \frac{3}{4} \times \frac{1}{2} = \frac{3}{8} \text{ sq in.}$$

Bearing value $= \dfrac{3}{8} \times 40 = 15$ kips

Bearing Value—Outer Plates: One-half of the joint load is carried through bearing into each outer plate. The bearing capacity of the *two* plates is computed.

$$f_{br} = 32,000 \text{ psi}$$

$$A_{br} = 2 \times \frac{3}{4} \times \frac{1}{4} = \frac{3}{8} \text{ sq in.}$$

Bearing value $= \dfrac{3}{8} \times 32 = 12$ kips

The bearing value of the outer plates is the lowest. Therefore, it is the controlling value. The allowable load per rivet is limited to 12 kips.

8–3. Edge Distance of Rivets and Bolts.　Control of the distance of a rivet or bolt from the edge of the material is necessary if a shear-out failure is to be prevented. This type of failure was shown by Fig. 8–2(e).

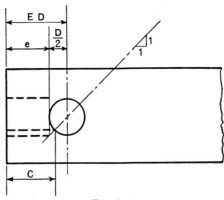

Fig. 8–4.

Control is also necessary to prevent the bulging of the edge material under the pressure caused by driving a rivet.

In Fig. 8–4, the resistance of the piece to shear-out is probably equal to the shearing strength of 2 areas of length c and width t, where t is the thickness of the material. Occasionally, when available space is limited, this assumption is used to determine the required edge distance for pins. The driving of a rivet, however, causes stresses of varying and uncertain magnitude in the metal surrounding the hole, so this assumption as to required edge distance might be unsafe.

For rivets and bolts, the shear-out strength may be considered equal to the shearing strength of 2 areas having length e and width t. The dimension e is often called "net edge distance." Stated as an equation, the required edge distance is

$$\text{E.D.} = \frac{R}{2tf_s} + \frac{D}{2}$$

in which R is the capacity of the rivet or bolt, D is the diameter of the hole, and f_s is the allowable unit shearing stress of the material in the member. Occasionally the use of this formula indicates a required edge distance so low that splitting or bulging of the edge may occur during punching or during driving of the rivet. A lower limit of one and one-half times the nominal diameter is often used in such cases. The same lower limit of edge distance is often specified for bolts in material thicknesses for which the computed required edge distance is low.

Most structural specifications quote minimum edge distances for rivets of various size, irrespective of the material thickness. When the theoretical method described above gives a larger value of edge distance, the larger value should be used.

The AISC Specification has two controls for minimum edge distance. In Section 23(e) a table is given showing the edge-distance requirements for punched holes. Observance of the limits in this table should prevent damage during punching of the hole or during driving of the rivet. In Section 23 (f) is an empirical formula for edge distance in rivets carrying load. The use of this formula is intended to prevent shear-out failure. Generally, the empirical method gives slightly more conservative results than the theoretical method described above. The edge distance for the punched hole by Section 23(e), or that for the rivet by Section 23(f), whichever is the larger, should be used.

A maximum allowable edge distance is given by many specifications, in order to avoid undesirable gaps at the edges of parts being joined.

EXAMPLE 8–3. What edge distance is required on the plates of Example 8–2, according to the AISC method?

For the Outer Plates: The ends of the plate are sheared. The edge distance of a punched hole from a sheared edge is given by the Specification as $1\frac{1}{4}$ in. minimum.

By Section 23(f),

$$\text{Required E.D.} = \frac{0.4418}{1/4} = 1.77 \text{ in.}$$

For the Inner Plate:

$$\text{Required E.D.} = \frac{2 \times 0.4418}{1/2} = 1.77 \text{ in.}$$

The requirement of Section 23(f) controls. A $1\frac{3}{4}$-in. edge distance would be used in each plate.

EXAMPLE 8–4. What edge distance would be required according to the theoretical method described in Art. 8–3?

The minimum of $1\frac{1}{4}$ in. would still be effective to prevent bulging of the plate during punching and driving.

The edge distance requirement will be computed for the outer plate. An allowable shear stress of 13,000 psi will be used for the plate; this is the same as permitted in beam webs. The allowable load for the rivet was shown in Example 8–2 to be 12 kips. The load carried by the rivet in the outer plate is 6 kips.

$$\text{Required E.D.} = \frac{R}{2tf_s} + \frac{D}{2}$$

$$= \frac{6}{2 \times \frac{1}{4} \times 13} + \frac{3/4}{2} = 1.30 \text{ in.}$$

Under this method a $1\frac{3}{8}$-in. edge distance would be used.

8–4. Spacing of Rivets and Bolts. Spacing is controlled by three things. (1) If the holes are close enough together, a shear-out failure occurs in which the material between holes is pushed toward one of the holes, the rivet or bolt in that hole pushing more material toward the next, and so on. The spacing must be sufficiently large so that the shearing strength of two planes, each having an area equal to the thickness of the material times the net distance between holes, be equal to or greater than the load on one rivet or bolt. (2) The spacing must also be sufficiently large so that the rivet heads, or the bolt heads or nuts, do not interfere. And (3) the spacing must be large enough to permit easy installation. If the spacing is too small, interference may result between the tool used and the adjacent nut or head.

Spacing is usually limited by the specification to a stated number times the nominal diameter. For example, the AISC Specification states: "The minimum distance between centers of rivet holes shall preferably be not less than three times the diameter of the rivet."

To prevent gaps between the layers of material connected and to prevent local buckling of compression members, limiting maximum spacings are also given.

8–5. Assumptions Used in the Design of Riveted and Bolted Connections.

Certain assumptions are made to facilitate the design. These have been proved to provide a conservative design for static loads. Much research is being carried on, however, and modifications in design methods may occur from time to time.

The usual assumptions made are as follows:

1. The friction between the parts connected is to be ignored. Since much frictional resistance to slipping of the plates may exist, this assumption is conservative. The amount of the friction is hard to predict, particularly in bolted connections. In hot-driven riveted joints it may be very high. The cooling of the rivet shank results in high tensile forces in the shank. These forces cause compression between the plates.

2. All rivets or bolts in a group that is not loaded eccentrically receive equal loads. (Or, if the rivets are not all of the same strength, they share the load in proportion to their strengths.) At design loads this assumption is often incorrect. Tests have shown, however, that at the ultimate load for the joint, the distribution of the load among the rivets is very nearly uniform. Thus, this assumption is justified for joints in which fatigue failure is not critical.

3. Rivets are assumed to fill the holes in which they are driven. The bearing capacity of a rivet is dependent on contact between the rivet shank and the member material. Poor alignment of the holes in the parts being joined would prevent contact in some of the rivets. Those rivets would be ineffective until some slipping had occurred so as to bring them into bearing.

4. The tensile force in the plate being connected is assumed to be uniformly distributed over the net area. This was discussed in Chapter 7.

5. The strength of compression members is unaffected by holes having rivets. If the rivet fills the hole, the compressive stress is transmitted right through the rivet material. If the rivet does not completely fill the hole, this defect is eliminated by compressive deformation of the member.

8–6. Riveted or Bolted Connections for Axially Loaded Members.

The design of a connection for an axially loaded member can be broken into four steps, as follows:

1. Select the size of connector to be used. (This may be a trial selection only, to be confirmed by the results of the other steps.)
2. Determine the controlling strength R of a single connector of the size selected. For rivets or bolts this will be either the bearing value or the shear value, whichever is smaller.
3. Compute the number of connectors required. If P is the total load to be transferred, the required number $n = P/R$.
4. Determine the arrangement and spacing of the connectors. It is usually best to make the connector group as compact as possible.

Very often the size of connector is fairly well known in advance. For example, in most building work the rivets are of $\frac{3}{4}$-in. diameter. Thus the procedure may start with the second step listed above.

EXAMPLE 8–5. A $5 \times \frac{3}{4}$ steel bar carries 45 kips tension. It is to be connected to a $\frac{3}{8}$-in. gusset plate using $\frac{3}{4}$-in. rivets. Design the connection.

Value of One Rivet:

Shear = 6.63 kips   *Controls*

Bearing on gusset plate = $\frac{3}{4} \times \frac{3}{8} \times 32 = 9$ kips

Number required = $45/6.63 = 6.79$ *Use 7 rivets minimum.*

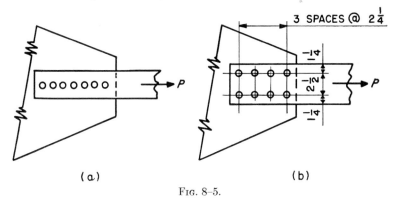

(a)   (b)

FIG. 8–5.

The rivets could be arranged in a single row along the center of the bar, as shown by Fig. 8–5(a). The objection to this arrangement would be that it is not compact. Too much overlap of the member with the gusset plate is needed. Check now to see whether the rivets could be placed in 2 rows. The net area of the member would be

$$A_{net} = \tfrac{3}{4}[5 - (2 \times \tfrac{7}{8})] = 2.44 \text{ sq in.}$$

Allowable axial load $P = F_a A_n = 20 \times 2.44 = 48.8$ kips

The member has sufficient strength when 2 rows of holes are removed. The rivets could be arranged as in Fig. 8–5(b). Eight rivets, rather than

7, would be used. The spacing would be limited to not less than 3 diameters, which is $2\frac{1}{4}$ in. The transverse spacing is made $2\frac{1}{2}$ in., which leaves just the required $1\frac{1}{4}$-in. edge distance on each side of the bar.

EXAMPLE 8–6. In Example 7–5 the bottom chord of a roof truss was analyzed to determine whether it is adequate for the added load of a new air-conditioning unit. It was found to be satisfactory. The connection of the chord to the end gusset plate is shown by Fig. 7–8. Is the connection satisfactory?

The "lug angle" shown in Fig. 7–8 is occasionally used to reduce the length of a connection. There is some question as to its effectiveness. There are 6 rivets passing through one angle of the main member. If the lug angle were very stiff, all 6 of these rivets could share the load equally. However, the lug angle may deform, causing the rivets through the main member and lug angle to take slightly less than $\frac{1}{6}$ of the load each. If it is necessary to use lug angles, certain precautions should be taken. The angle should be placed close to the end of the connection at which the stress in the member is highest and where greater movement will occur under load. The lug angle should be made as stiff as practical. It should contain as few rivets as necessary, but yet be as long as is practical so that greater stiffness will result. The total number of rivets through the gusset plate should be conservatively determined.

Value of one $\frac{3}{4}$-in. rivet:

    Single shear = 6.63 kips

    Double shear = 13.25 kips

    Bearing on gusset = $\frac{3}{4} \times \frac{3}{8} \times 40$ = 11.25 kips   *Controls*

At ultimate load all rivets will be loaded alike. The limiting load is that load causing enclosed bearing of 11.25 kips per rivet on the gusset plate. Each rivet which passes through the member and gusset plate has 2 shear planes. Each rivet passing through the member and lug angle has one. There are 12 shear planes in all.

    Load per shear plane = 78/12 = 6.5 kips

    Load per rivet in member and gusset = 2×6.5 = 13.0 kips

This exceeds the enclosed bearing value of 11.25 kips per rivet. The connection is not satisfactory.

8–7. Bending of Rivets. Normally, bending in rivets can be neglected. Bending is prevented to some extent by friction between the members being connected. Further, the allowable unit stresses for rivets are established by tests in which that same bending is present. Consequently, no harm is done by neglecting its effect in our computations for most riveted connections.

However, if the rivet has a large grip, as shown in Fig. 8–6, bending may be so great that its effect cannot be ignored. It is difficult to compute the amount of bending moment for two reasons. The exact amount of displacement of each layer of material cannot be predetermined,

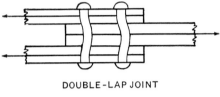

DOUBLE-LAP JOINT

FIG. 8–6.

because it is limited by an uncertain amount of friction. If the displacement could be determined, the problem of computing the bending moment would still be statically indeterminate. Any analysis made to determine the exact effect of rivet bending would be too cumbersome to use for usual design and probably would be inaccurate.

A practical way of handling the problem of bending in long rivets is to use extra rivets. Most specifications indicate the number of extra rivets as a percentage of the basic number required. For example, see Section 22(d) of the AISC Specification.

8–8. Types of Welded Connection. There are two main types of weld produced by the arc-welding process. These two are the "butt" weld and the "fillet" weld. Because of different manners in which the welded parts meet, these welds may have a variety of shapes.

Fig. 8–7 shows several types of butt weld, and the symbols which

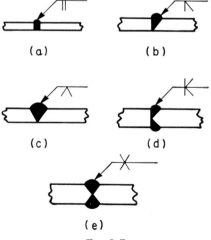

FIG. 8–7.

are used on engineering drawings to designate the welds. A key to the standard welding symbols of the American Welding Society is given by Appendix C.

A square butt weld is shown in Fig. 8–7(a). The shaded area represents weld metal added. This weld is limited to thin material; otherwise the plates must be held apart a greater distance to permit the weld metal to flow and fill the space completely.

The most common butt welds used in structural work are the "single-bevel" and "single-vee" butt welds shown by (b) and (c), respectively. The prepared slot at the edges to be joined is filled with weld metal. The slot makes the full thickness of material accessible to the welder and helps to insure good penetration by the weld metal.

The cost of welding varies with the amount of weld metal used. When more metal must be deposited, the welder's time and the current consumption also are increased. In thick material the single-bevel and single-vee butt welds may be quite expensive. A saving is sometimes made possible by use of the "double-bevel" or the "double-vee" butt welds of Fig. 8–7(d) and (e). In these welds the groove on one side is welded; then the work is turned and the groove on the other side is filled. Another advantage to these types is that warping can be controlled more easily than with the single-bevel or single-vee varieties.

Other types, including the single and double-J and U welds are rarely used in structural work. These are illustrated in Appendix C. Their use is mainly in such things as welded beds for heavy machinery.

A "fillet" weld is shown by Fig. 8–8. The fillet weld is the most common weld in structural work. Dimension W is called the weld size.

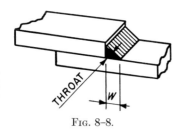

FIG. 8–8.

Fillet welds of $\frac{3}{16}$-, $\frac{1}{4}$-, and $\frac{5}{16}$-in. size can be made with a single pass of the welding electrode. For a larger weld, the slag is removed and additional passes are made to provide the desired size. Fillet welds for strength purposes must be at least $\frac{3}{16}$ in.; smaller sizes may be used for non-structural purposes, such as sealing. The least dimension through the triangular cross section is called the "throat" dimension. This dimension is important in determining the strength of the weld.

8–9. Strength of Butt Welds. A butt weld is shown in Fig. 8–9. The weld shown has "reinforcement," which is an additional deposit of weld metal causing the throat dimension to be greater than the thickness of the plate. Butt welds are commonly referred to as 100, 125, or 150 per cent butt welds, according to whether the throat dimension is equal to or is 25 or 50 per cent more than the material thickness.

If concentrations of stress are neglected, the tensile load shown may be assumed to be distributed uniformly over the cross section of the

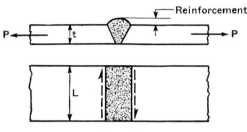

Fig. 8–9.

weld. The weakest point in the weld is at its thinnest point, so that the effective cross-sectional area is the product of the weld length L and the plate thickness t.

The tensile value of the butt weld in pounds per inch is equal to $f \times t$, where f is the allowable unit tensile stress for either the weld material, or the member material, whichever is lower.

If the load is compressive, the value of the weld per inch is given by the same product, but with f equal to the allowable unit compressive stress for the weld or for the member material, whichever is lower.

The joint may be subject to shearing load as shown dotted in Fig. 8–9. In this case the value of the connection in pounds per inch is equal to tf, in which f is the allowable unit shearing stress in either the weld material or the member material, whichever is weaker.

If strength is determined by the plate thickness, why bother to "reinforce" a butt weld?

The surface of a weld is not so smooth as that of the original material and may contain slag inclusions, etc. The probability that the strength of the joint will be affected by such irregularities is lessened by the deposit of extra metal on the joint. Further, it would require an excellent welder, indeed, to produce a flush joint having in no place a thickness less than that of the material being welded. It is much easier to make a butt weld having reinforcement. For butt welds having static loads, or loads without vibration or frequent variation, some reinforcement is advantageous. For members having often repeated or vibrating loads, however, it is well to insure full section by providing reinforcement and then grinding the weld flush so that its throat dimension is equal to the material thickness. If the reinforcement is not removed, a concentration of stress, which might become a nucleus for fatigue failure, will occur at the point where the bead meets the member.

8–10. Strength of Fillet Welds. A fillet weld may be loaded in two ways. Fig. 8–10(a) shows fillets having their axes parallel to the direction of stress in the member. Each weld transfers load from one bar to the other by means of shearing stress parallel to its axis. Distribution of the shearing stress is assumed to be uniform over the length of the weld, although it is easily shown that uniform distribution cannot occur at stresses below the elastic limit. The maximum stress in the weld is a shearing stress at the throat and parallel to the axis. In failure, the weld should break on a longitudinal plane through the throat of the weld.

Fig. 8–10(b) shows fillet welds transverse to the direction of stress. Welds of this type break through the throat as the result of combined shearing and tensile or compressive stresses. Computation of the principal stresses in the weld is complicated by many variable conditions (such as the degree of contact between the two members) in the connection. Tests show that the load-carrying capacity of a transverse fillet weld is about one-third greater than that of a longitudinal one of the same dimensions. For design purposes, it is usual to assume that the strength per linear inch of fillet is its shearing strength, regardless of the direction of load on the weld.

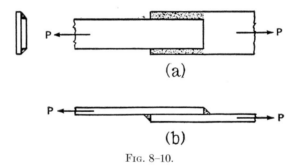

(a)

(b)

Fig. 8–10.

The design strength per linear inch of fillet weld is equal to the throat dimension multiplied by the unit shearing strength of the weld material. For a normal fillet weld the cross section is a right isosceles triangle, so that the throat dimension is the weld size W divided by $\sqrt{2}$.

Using the AISC allowable unit shearing stress of 13,600 psi for weld metal on structural steel for buildings, the following allowable loads per inch of fillet weld are obtained:

(Load per inch $= 13{,}600 \times W/\sqrt{2}$)
For $\frac{3}{16}$-in. fillet weld, 1,800 lb per in.

For $\frac{1}{4}$-in. fillet weld, 2,400 lb per in.
For $\frac{5}{16}$-in. fillet weld, 3,000 lb per in.
For $\frac{3}{8}$-in. fillet weld, 3,600 lb per in.
For $\frac{1}{2}$-in. fillet weld, 4,800 lb per in.

In transferring stress from one member to another, a transverse fillet weld is subject to concentrations of stress, somewhat as shown in Fig. 8–11(a). If the load is vibratory or so often repeated that considera-

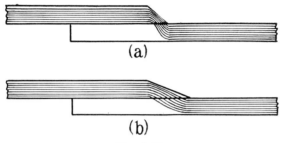

(a)

(b)

Fig. 8–11.

tion of fatigue is necessary, the concentration may be reduced by use of a fillet having unequal legs, as shown in Fig. 8–11(b). In such a weld the transition from bar to fillet and from fillet to bar is more gradual, so that the stress distribution is more nearly uniform. The rough weld surface may be ground smooth to further remove possible fatigue nuclei. The designer may call the attention of the fabricator to these precautionary measures by using appropriate standard welding symbols on the detail drawings.

The ends of a fillet weld are tapered; thus, the throat dimension at the ends is less than elsewhere. For this reason, twice the fillet size is added to the computed length of each fillet weld. The length given on detail drawings, however, is the net or computed length. The welder provides that length of full-sized section, and adds $2W$ to that length for end tapers.

Because of the previously mentioned unequal distribution of stress along a fillet placed parallel to the load, the ends of the weld are subject to more than the average shear. To reduce the stress at the ends, the fillet should, where possible, be continued for a short distance around

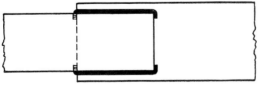

Fig. 8–12.

the corner of the member, as shown in Fig. 8–12. The length of the "return" is usually not less than twice the weld size W.

8–11. Allowable and Effective Size of Fillet Weld. The heat generated by the welding process and the subsequent cooling cause expansion and shrinkage of both the original material and the weld material. If the amount of shrinkage in the two materials is unequal, initial or residual stresses occur in both the original material and the weld. Because the amount of expansion and shrinkage is controlled by the total amount of heat generated by the welding process, it is affected by the size of the fillet weld and by the thickness of the original material. Placing of a small weld on thick material does not generate enough heat to cause appreciable expansion of the original material. The weld tends to contract during cooling, but it is restrained from contracting fully by its attachment to the cooler thick material. Residual stress in the weld results. If the weld size is increased, the greater heat causes the expansion to be more nearly uniform. Less residual stress may occur.

In addition to this mechanical effect of the welding heat, there is a metallurgical effect. Steel, if very rapidly cooled from temperatures above 1500°F, becomes brittle and loses its ductility. A small weld on very thick material is cooled very rapidly by conduction of heat away from the welded area by the thick base material. Such rapid cooling can be prevented by preheating the base material or by using a larger size of weld.

To avoid both the undesirable effects just described, specifications require that the size W of fillet welds be *not less* than those shown by the following tabulation:

Size of Fillet Weld (Inches)	Maximum Thickness of Part (Inches)
$\frac{3}{16}$	$\frac{1}{2}$
$\frac{1}{4}$	$\frac{3}{4}$
$\frac{5}{16}$	$1\frac{1}{4}$
$\frac{3}{8}$	2
$\frac{1}{2}$	6
$\frac{5}{8}$	Over 6

The maximum size of fillet weld is limited by three considerations. The first is the destruction of the original material by the heat generated in placing a large-sized weld with a single pass of the electrode. The maximum size weld that could be used without such destruction depends on the type of material being connected and the type of weld metal.

For structural steel, destruction of the original material is unlikely if the weld size is limited by the second consideration, efficiency. As the fillet size is increased, the amounts of weld material, current (or gas), and labor required to deposit the weld increase at a much greater rate than the strength per unit length of fillet. Therefore, from a cost standpoint, the most efficient fillet size is generally the smallest that is practical to use. For strength purposes, welds as small as $\frac{3}{16}$ in. are permitted.

To avoid excessive length of weld, larger fillets may be used, *up to that size for which the strength of the welds is equal to that of the base material*. An increase beyond this size is not effective, and the additional weld metal used is wasted.

The beam shown by Fig. 8–13 will be used to illustrate determination of the maximum effective size of fillet weld. At the end connection the

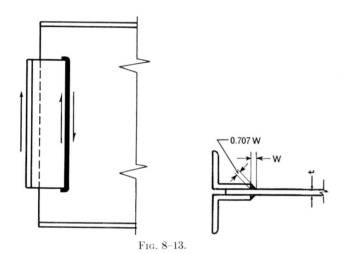

Fɪɢ. 8–13.

shearing stress per inch of weld is equal to that per inch height of web, or half of that amount if welds occur on both sides of the web.

The value of two welds (per inch) $= 2W \times 0.707 f_{sw}$

The shear value of the web (per inch) $= t f_{sb}$

The terms f_{sw} and f_{sb} represent the allowable unit shearing stress in the weld and in the beam, respectively. When the maximum effective size W is used, $2W \times 0.707 f_{sw} = t f_{sb}$. The maximum effective

$$W = (t f_{sb})/(1.414 f_{sw}).$$

If the weld were on one side only of the web, the maximum effective W would be twice the value given by the above equation. Substituting the AISC allowable of 13,600 for f_{sw} and 13,000 for f_{sb} in the preceding equation, the maximum effective W is limited to about $1.4t$ for welds on one side only of material of thickness t, or to about $0.7t$ each for welds on both sides.

The third consideration that may control the size of some fillet welds is the shape and thickness of the edge along which it is deposited. Since the base material melts during welding, it is difficult to produce a good fillet weld of nominal size equal to the thickness of the edge. To insure full throat thickness for such a weld, it is necessary to build up with weld metal at rounded edges or where square edges have been melted by the welding heat. Unless it is absolutely necessary to use weld sizes equal to the thickness of the edge, the following maximum sizes are recommended:

1. For nominally square edges: $\frac{1}{16}$ in. less than the edge thickness
2. For rounded edges, such as the toes of angles or of channel flanges, three-fourths of the nominal edge thickness.

8–12. Prevention of Bending of Fillet Welds. Fillet weld joints should be designed so that the individual welds do not have high bending stress. Fig. 8–14(a) shows undesirable connections in which the fillets are subject to bending. The effect on the fillets is similar to that which

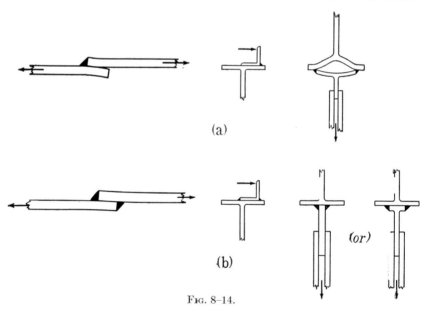

(a)

(b)

Fig. 8–14.

would be caused by driving a wedge between the members of the connections so as to pry them apart. Welds so loaded will not develop their full rated strength. Corrected details are shown in Fig. 8–14(b).

8–13. Welded Connections for Tension and Compression Members. Tension and compression members are usually connected by overlapping the member with a gusset plate, as shown in Fig. 8–5, or by overlapping the members on each other. Fillet welds are usually placed along the sides of the member as shown in Fig. 8–10(a). Occasionally they are used at the ends, as in Fig. 8–10(b). When the space is limited and the load high, a combination of end welds with side welds may be used.

It is the usual practice to "balance" the welds. By this is meant that the welds are located so that the center of gravity of the weld group is in line with the tensile or compressive load. Thus the joint is centrally loaded. The load is assumed distributed uniformly over the throat areas of the welds comprising the joint.

Tests have shown that the balancing may be an unnecessary refinement when the load is static. For shock, vibratory loads, or often repeated loads, however, balancing still is desirable. The usual practice is to balance the welds whenever possible.

EXAMPLE 8–7. What length and size of weld is required for the connection shown in Fig. 8–15? Use 13,600 psi for the allowable shearing stress in the weld.

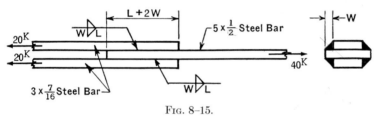

FIG. 8–15.

The minimum allowable W is $\frac{3}{16}$ in. The maximum effective W is $0.7 \times \frac{1}{2}$, or 0.35 in. Lengths will be determined for fillet sizes from $\frac{3}{16}$ in. to $\frac{3}{8}$ in. The load per weld is 10,000 lb.

For $W = \frac{3}{16}$, strength per inch = 1,800 lb

For $W = \frac{1}{4}$, strength per inch = 2,400 lb

For $W = \frac{5}{16}$, strength per inch = 3,000 lb

For $W = \frac{3}{8}$, strength per inch = $0.35 \times 0.707 \times 13,600 = 3,360$ lb

The net length required per weld:

$$L = \frac{10,000}{1,800} = 5.6, \text{ for } W = \tfrac{3}{16} \quad \text{(Specify } 5\tfrac{3}{4} \text{ in.)}$$

$$L = \frac{10,000}{2,400} = 4.2, \text{ for } W = \tfrac{1}{4} \quad \text{(Specify } 4\tfrac{1}{4} \text{ in.)}$$

$$L = \frac{10,000}{3,000} = 3.3, \text{ for } W = \tfrac{5}{16} \quad \text{(Specify } 3\tfrac{1}{2} \text{ in.)}$$

$$L = \frac{10,000}{3,360} = 3.0, \text{ for } W = \tfrac{3}{8} \quad \text{(Specify } 3 \text{ in.)}$$

One of the "rounded-off" lengths above would be indicated on the detail drawings using the AWS symbols. Thus for example, a length of $3\frac{1}{2}$ in. and a size of $\frac{5}{16}$ in. might be indicated. The welder will add $2W$ to the indicated length to provide for end tapers. The over-all lengths would then be:

$$6\frac{1}{8} \text{ in. for } \tfrac{3}{16}\text{-in. weld}$$

$$4\frac{3}{4} \text{ in. for } \tfrac{1}{4}\text{-in. weld}$$

$$4\frac{1}{8} \text{ in. for } \tfrac{5}{16}\text{-in. weld}$$

$$3\frac{3}{4} \text{ in. for } \tfrac{3}{8}\text{-in. weld}$$

If possible, the right end of each weld should be wrapped around the corner of the bar, as shown in Fig. 8–12.

EXAMPLE 8–8. In Example 7–3 hanger angles were designed for supporting a bin. The load per angle is 16 kips. A $3 \times 2\frac{1}{2} \times \frac{1}{4}$ angle was selected.

Assume that the upper end of this hanger is to be connected to the roof truss by a $\frac{3}{8}$-in. gusset plate, as shown in Fig. 8–16. Design a balanced welded connection.

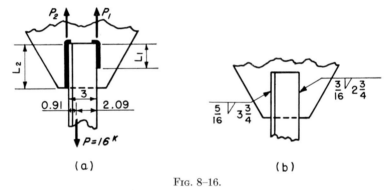

(a)   (b)

FIG. 8–16.

The downward load of 16 kips in the hanger is resisted by upward reactions P_1 and P_2 in the welds. First, compute moments of the forces shown about the line of action of force P_1. The 16-kip force P is assumed to act at the center of gravity of the angle. This is shown by the tables of Appendix A to be 0.91 in. from the back of the angle.

$$3P_2 - (16 \times 2.09) = 0$$

$$P_2 = 11.1 \text{ kips}$$

$$\Sigma V = 0$$

$$P_1 = 16.0 - 11.1 = 4.9 \text{ kips}$$

Welds must be provided to resist the reactions P_1 and P_2. The maximum size W that can be used conveniently on the toe (at P_1) is $\frac{3}{4}$ of the angle thickness, or a $\frac{3}{16}$-in. fillet. This is also the minimum size permitted for load-bearing welds. A $\frac{3}{16}$-in. fillet will be tried in both locations. The value in shear for one inch of $\frac{3}{16}$-in. weld is 1.8 kips.

Required $L_1 = 4.9/1.8 = 2.72$ in.   Use $L_1 = 2\frac{3}{4}$ in. (net).

Required $L_2 = 11.1/1.8 = 6.16$ in.   Use $L_2 = 6\frac{1}{4}$ in. (net).

To use these welds the angle must overlap the plate by at least $6\frac{1}{4}$ in. The added length for end tapers could be placed in short "returns" as shown in Fig. 8–16(a).

As a second possibility, assume that it is not possible to provide more than 4 in. of overlap. What can be done?

One solution is to increase the size W of the weld on the heel. Try a $\frac{5}{16}$-in. weld, which has a shear value of 3.0 kips per inch.

Required $L_2 = 11.1/3.0 = 3.70$ in.   Use $L_2 = 3\frac{3}{4}$ in. (net).

This solution is shown using the standard welding symbols in Fig. 8–16(b).

EXAMPLE 8–9. Compute the length of fillet weld required in a balanced joint for the steel member shown in Fig. 8–17. Weld is to be

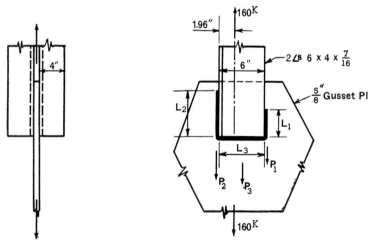

FIG. 8–17.

placed on the back, toe, and end of the member. Use the AISC allowable stresses for the weld and base material.

A number of solutions are possible, depending on the weld sizes used. This solution illustrates one possible combination.

The maximum effective W is $0.7 \times \frac{5}{8}$, or 0.44 in. The maximum practical W on the toe is $\frac{3}{4}$ of $\frac{7}{16}$, or approximately $\frac{5}{16}$ in. Using $\frac{5}{16}$-in. fillets on the toe and end,

$$P_1 + P_2 + P_3 = 160 \text{ kips}$$

$$P_3 = 2 \times 6 \times 3.0 = 36 \text{ kips}$$

Taking moments about the back of the angles,

$$6P_1 + 3P_3 = 160 \times 1.96$$

Then,

$$P_1 = 34.2 \text{ kips}$$

and

$$P_2 = 160 - 34.2 - 36 = 89.8 \text{ kips}$$

The weld required is as follows:

Location	W (In.)	Value in Kips (per Inch)	Net Length in Inches (per Angle)	Gross Length in Inches (per Angle)
Toe	$\frac{5}{16}$	3	5.7	6
Back	$\frac{1}{2}$ (effective = 0.44)	4.2	10.7	$11\frac{1}{4}$
End	$\frac{5}{16}$	3	6.0	6

In determining the gross lengths required, only $1 \times W$ is added to the net length of each weld at the toe and at the back of the angles, since those welds are tapered at one end only. The welds at the end of the member have no end tapers, and the required gross length is the same as the net.

8–14. Eccentrically Loaded Shear Connections.

Connections of this type are quite common, and the non-civil engineer is very apt to encounter them in his own professional practice. Probably the most common of these connections is the bracket, shown by Fig. 8–18(a).

In this particular bracket the connectors are shown as rivets. The derivation to be made, however, is perfectly general. The connectors may be considered as rivets, as bolts, or as unit lengths of weld. All of the connector units shown are assumed to be of the same size and strength.[1] The load P on the bracket is not in line with the center of the group of connectors. The distance from P to the center of the group is the eccentricity e. The eccentric load P can be replaced by a force P acting through the center of the group of connectors, and a twisting moment Pe. These might be called the "components" of the original load P. The centrally applied force and the moment are shown by Fig.

[1]For the derivation of a method of analysis to be used when different sizes of connector occur in the same joint, refer to C. D. Williams and E. C. Harris, *Structural Design in Metals*, (New York: The Ronald Press Co., 1949), Chap. 5.

8–18(b). By this figure it can be seen that the connection is deformed in two ways. First, all the units are pushed in the direction of force P. Second, the group of connectors are rotated clockwise about the center of the group. By the principle of superposition, the load that would be

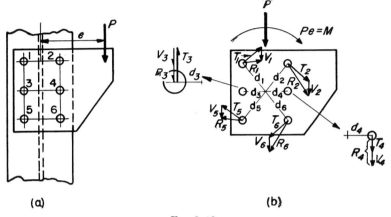

(a)   (b)

Fɪɢ. 8–18.

caused in one of the connectors by the vertical force P alone, combined with the load that would be caused in that same connector by the moment Pe alone, must equal the load caused in the connector when P and Pe act together.

The vertical force P, acting alone and centrally located, would stress all the connectors equally. Stated mathematically,

$$V = P/n$$

in which V is the shearing force per connector caused by the direct load P, and n is the number of connectors. The shear V is parallel to the force P; in this case it is vertical.

The center of rotation of the connection when acted upon by the moment Pe is at the center of gravity of the group of connectors. As the bracket rotates slightly the connectors are pushed in a direction perpendicular to a line drawn from the connector to the center of rotation. Connector number 1 is pushed in the direction of T_1, connector number 2 in the direction of T_2, etc., as shown by Fig. 8–18(b). The force T in each connector is proportional to the distance the connector is moved by the rotation; this in turn is proportional to the distance d from the connector to the center of rotation. Thus

$$T_2 = T_1 \frac{d_2}{d_1}; \quad T_3 = T_1 \frac{d_3}{d_1}; \quad \text{etc.}$$

The sum of the moments of all of the T-forces about the center of rotation must be equal to the applied moment Pe. (For equilibrium, $\Sigma M = 0$.)

$$Pe = T_1d_1 + T_2d_2 + T_3d_3 \cdots + T_nd_n$$

Expressing all T-forces in terms of T_1 changes this to

$$Pe = T_1d_1 + T_1d_2^2/d_1 + T_1d_3^2/d_1 \cdots + T_1d_n^2/d_1$$

$$Pe = \frac{T_1}{d_1}(d_1^2 + d_2^2 + d_3^2 \cdots + d_n^2) = \frac{T_1}{d_1}\Sigma d^2$$

Solving for the force T_1 gives

$$T_1 = \frac{Ped_1}{\Sigma d^2} = \frac{Md_1}{J}$$

The term Σd^2 or J is the polar moment of inertia of the connector group about its center of gravity. Similarly, $T_2 = Md_2/J$, $T_3 = Md_3/J$, etc.

Each connector now has a shearing load V parallel to the applied load P, and a shearing load T due to the moment Pe. These shearing forces V and T are shown on each connector of Fig. 8–18(b). The total shear on each connector unit is the resultant R. The resultant R can be determined either graphically or analytically. In the design of a connection of this type, R should be limited to the controlling allowable load per connector unit.

EXAMPLE 8–10. What is the allowable load P for the bracket shown in Fig. 8–19? Assume that the plate of the bracket has ample strength, so that the strength of the connection itself is the only consideration.

The eccentricity e is measured from the center of gravity of the rivet group to the line of action of the load P.

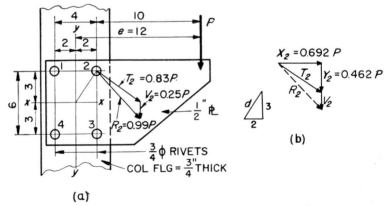

FIG. 8–19.

$$e = 12 \text{ in.}$$
$$M = Pe = 12P$$
$$J = I_x + I_y$$

In computing I and J, one rivet is taken as a unit of area. The equation $T = Md/J$ then gives T in pounds per rivet, rather than in pounds per square inch.

$$I_x = 4(3)^2 = 36$$
$$I_y = 4(2)^2 = \overline{16}$$
$$J = \overline{52}$$

Examine Fig. 8–18(b) closely. It shows that the connector units having the highest load R are those at the ends of the row closest to the line of action of the eccentric load P. (Connectors 2 and 6 for Fig. 8–18.) Similarly, the rivets having the highest load in this example are numbers 2 and 3. For either rivet,

$$d = \sqrt{(2)^2 + (3)^2} = 3.6 \text{ in.}$$

$$T = \frac{Md}{J} = \frac{12P \times 3.6}{52} = 0.83P$$

$$V = \frac{P}{n} = 0.25P$$

Vectors for T_2 and V_2 are drawn on the picture of the bracket in Fig. 8–19(a). The value of R_2 is scaled from the force triangle.

$$R_2 = 0.99P$$

The force triangle for R_3 will be like that for R_2, but in a different position. R_3 also is equal to 0.99P.

The controlling value for a $\frac{3}{4}$-in. rivet in $\frac{1}{2}$-in. material is the single shear value of 6.63 kips per rivet. The allowable load P is that load which makes R_2 equal to 6.63 kips.

$$6.63 = 0.99P$$

$$\text{Allowable } P = 6.70 \text{ kips}$$

The graphical solution is easy to perform since so often the connection is sketched to scale when the problem is started. It is then quite convenient to apply the force vectors directly to the scale drawing and to determine the resultants graphically.

The analytical solution may be convenient when the tools for making a scaled sketch are not at hand. A simple short cut in the analytical solution will now be illustrated.

To compute R analytically, it is desirable to find the horizontal and vertical components of the T force. For force T_2 call the components X_2 and Y_2, as shown in Fig. 8–19(b). By similar triangles,

$$X_2 = T_2\left(\frac{3}{d}\right) \quad \text{and} \quad Y_2 = T_2\left(\frac{2}{d}\right)$$

Substituting Md/J for T

$$X_2 = \frac{3M}{J} \quad \text{and} \quad Y_2 = \frac{2M}{J}$$

This could be stated in words as follows: To solve for the horizontal component of T, use the equation $T = Md/J$, but substitute for the term d the vertical component of distance d. To solve for the vertical component of force T, substitute the horizontal component of the distance d.

For rivet number 2 of this problem.

$$X_2 = 3 \times 12P/52 = 0.692P$$

$$Y_2 = 2 \times 12P/52 = 0.462P$$

The total vertical component is the sum of V_2 and Y_2 or $0.712P$.

$$R_2 = \sqrt{(0.692P)^2 + (0.712P)^2} = 0.993P$$

From this point on, the solution is the same as was illustrated using a graphical solution of the force triangle.

EXAMPLE 8–11. An air hoist is to be used for rapid operation of a dipping section in a monorail. It is planned to attach the hoist to the building column using a bracket as shown in Fig. 8–20(a). What size W of fillet weld must be used to attach the bracket?

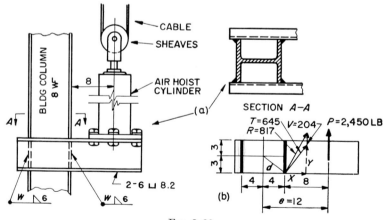

FIG. 8–20.

The weight of the lift section and its live load cause 1,100 lb of tension in the cable. About 25 per cent should be added for impact caused by the rapid starting or stopping of the hoist. The air hoist itself weighs 600 lb. The column itself has been checked and is sufficiently strong to resist the bracket loads.

The total upward pull on the hoist is that of the four parts of cable shown, or $4 \times 1{,}100 \times 1.25 = 5{,}500$ lb. Deducting for the weight of the hoist, the net upward load on the bracket is 4,900 lb. One channel of the bracket is shown in Fig. 8–20(b). The load per channel is 2,450 lb. Each channel is attached to the column by two welds.

The most highly stressed portions of weld are at the upper and lower ends of the weld closest to the line of action of the load P. The eccentricity e is 12 in.

In computing the load for fillet welds, n is taken as the number of inches of fillet length, and the weld size is considered unity when computing J. The values of V and T thus obtained are in pounds per linear inch of weld.

$$J = I_x + I_y$$

$$I_x = 2 \times \frac{1}{12} \times (6)^3 = \quad 36$$

$$I_y = 2 \times 6 \times (4)^2 \quad = 192$$

$$J = \overline{228}$$

For the lower extremity of the right weld, $d = 5$ in., and

$$T = Md/J = 2{,}450 \times 12 \times 5/228 = 645 \text{ lb per in.}$$

or,

$$X = 2{,}450 \times 12 \times 3/228 = 387 \text{ lb per in.}$$

$$Y = 2{,}450 \times 12 \times 4/228 = 516 \text{ lb per in.}$$

$$V = 2{,}450/12 = 204 \text{ lb per in.}$$

$$V + Y = 720$$

$$R = \sqrt{(387)^2 + (720)^2} = 817 \text{ lb per in.}$$

The weld size selected must have a strength of at least 817 lb per in. The smallest weld permitted by the specification is a $\frac{3}{16}$-in. fillet, which has a value of 1,800 lb per in. Thus the $\frac{3}{16}$-in. weld would be acceptable. (Many engineers, however, prefer to avoid using welds as small as $\frac{3}{16}$-in. These engineers would probably specify $\frac{1}{4}$-in. welds. Their reluctance to specify the smaller size is justifiable. A small defect in a small weld means a large percentage reduction of strength. The same defect in a larger size weld is less serious. In other words, it is easier to guarantee good quality in the larger size of weld.)

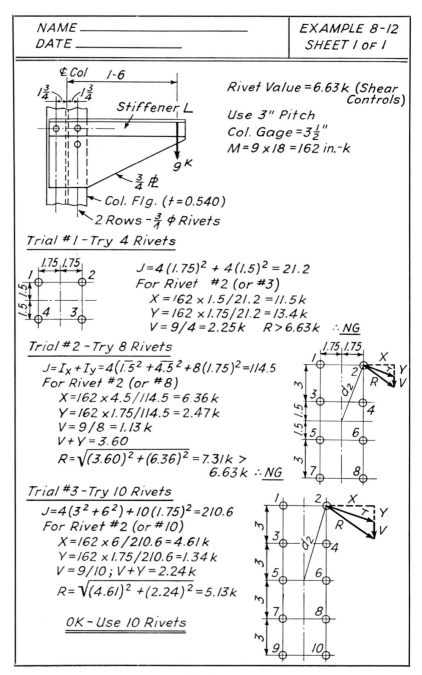

NAME _____

DATE _____

EXAMPLE 8-12

SHEET 1 OF 1

℄ Col   1-6

Stiffener L

9^k

$\frac{3}{4}$ ⌀

Col. Flg. $(t=0.540)$

2 Rows $-\frac{3}{4}$ ⌀ Rivets

Rivet Value $=6.63k$ (Shear Controls)

Use 3" Pitch

Col. Gage $=3\frac{1}{2}$"

$M=9 \times 18 =162$ in.-k

Trial #1 - Try 4 Rivets

$J=4(1.75)^2 + 4(1.5)^2 = 21.2$

For Rivet #2 (or #3)

$X = 162 \times 1.5/21.2 = 11.5k$

$Y = 162 \times 1.75/21.2 = 13.4k$

$V = 9/4 = 2.25k$ $R > 6.63k$ ∴ __NG__

Trial #2 - Try 8 Rivets

$J=I_x + I_y = 4(1.5^2 + 4.5^2) + 8(1.75)^2 = 114.5$

For Rivet #2 (or #8)

$X = 162 \times 4.5/114.5 = 6.36k$

$Y = 162 \times 1.75/114.5 = 2.47k$

$V = 9/8 = 1.13k$

$V + Y = 3.60$

$R = \sqrt{(3.60)^2 + (6.36)^2} = 7.31k > 6.63k$ ∴ __NG__

Trial #3 - Try 10 Rivets

$J=4(3^2 + 6^2) + 10(1.75)^2 = 210.6$

For Rivet #2 (or #10)

$X = 162 \times 6/210.6 = 4.61k$

$Y = 162 \times 1.75/210.6 = 1.34k$

$V = 9/10 ; V+Y = 2.24k$

$R = \sqrt{(4.61)^2 + (2.24)^2} = 5.13k$

__OK - Use 10 Rivets__

Fɪɢ. 8-21.

EXAMPLE 8–12. A vertical load of 9 kips is to be connected to a building column by a bracket as shown in Fig. 8–21. Design the connection using $\frac{3}{4}$-in. rivets.

It is possible to develop an equation giving directly the number of rivets required. It is usually quicker, however, to solve the problem by trial-and-error. That process is used here, the complete solution being shown in computation-sheet form by Fig. 8–21.

Two rivets would be enough to resist the vertical force centrally located. Since the load is eccentric, more than two rivets will be needed. For the first trial, use 4 rivets. A vertical spacing of 3 in. is assumed. In computing the T-force for the corner rivet, X- and Y-components are used so that the mathematical solution for the resultant R is simplified.

The computations for the first trial show that both X and Y for rivet No. 2 exceed 6.63 kips, so the resultant rivet load R is obviously greater than 6.63 kips. Four rivets are not enough.

Two more trials are made before a satisfactory design is obtained. Ten rivets, arranged as shown for Trial No. 3, are found satisfactory. The resultant R for rivet No. 2 or No. 10 is only 5.13 kips, and the vertical spacing might be reduced somewhat in order to save bracket material. There is advantage though in sticking to common spacings such as $2\frac{1}{2}$ in., 3 in., etc.

8–15. Brackets with Rivets in Tension. A bracket of this type is shown by Fig. 8–23(a). The moment Pe tends to rotate the bracket clockwise, pulling it away from the column at the top and pressing it against the column at the bottom. The method of analysis to be used depends on the state of initial tension in the connectors. If hot-driven steel rivets are used, the method shown in this article is suitable. For bolts or cold-driven rivets, see Art. 8–16.

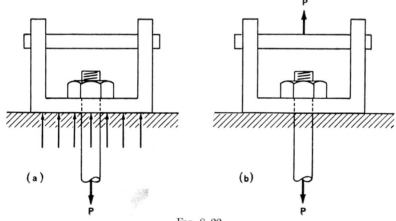

FIG. 8–22.

Courtesy of American MonoRail Co.

MATERIALS-HANDLING SYSTEM FOR BAR STORAGE YARD. MONORAIL IS SUPPORTED BY TRIANGULAR-SHAPED FRAMES WITH BRACING ABOVE.

The effect of initial tension on a single rivet will be considered first. Fig. 8–22(a) shows a fitting attached by a single rivet which has a total initial tensile force P. This force is caused by the contraction of the rivet shank during cooling. There will be compressive forces between the fitting and the support totaling P in amount. Now let a force P be applied to the fitting as shown in Fig. 8–22(b), just removing the compression between the fitting and the support. The tension in the rivet is obviously equal to P.

For applied loads up to the full amount of the initial tension, there is no appreciable change in rivet stress. Applied loads exceeding the initial tension force do affect the rivet stress.

Tests[2] have shown that the initial tensile stress in hot-driven steel rivets is in the order of 24,000 psi. Thus, in the bracket of Fig. 8–23(a) there is considerable initial pressure between the bracket material and

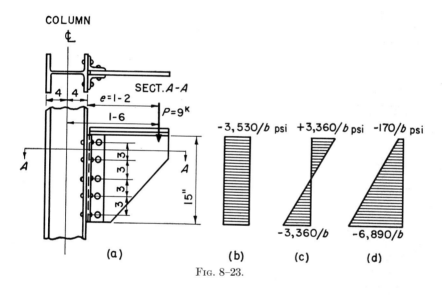

Fig. 8–23.

the column face. As the moment Pe rotates the bracket, the pressure at the top is reduced, while at the bottom it is increased. No appreciable change occurs in the tensile force in the upper rivets until all pressure between bracket and column at the location of the top rivets is removed.

The allowable shearing stress for rivets was established by test. The rivets tested had initial tension also. It is logical, then, to allow bracket rivets to be stressed in shear up to the full allowable shear value, provided the bracket rotation does not increase the tensile load on the

[2]Wilbur M. Wilson and John V. Coombe, "Fatigue Tests of Connection Angles," *University of Illinois Engineering Experiment Station Bulletin*, **317** (Oct. 1949).

rivets. When the bracket and rivet group are so designed that compression between the bracket and the support exists at all points, the rivets are loaded exactly as they would be if the load were not eccentric. That is, they have their initial tension and the applied shear.

The application of this reasoning to design will be illustrated by the example which follows.

EXAMPLE 8–13. Assume that the bracket designed in Example 8–12 is to be moved, placing it normal to the column flange as in Fig. 8–23(a). The holes are already in the column. Will 10 rivets still be sufficient?

So as to allow a safety factor, only one-half of 24,000 psi, or 12,000 psi will be used for the initial tensile stress. The area of one $\frac{3}{4}$-in. rivet shank is 0.442 sq in. The total initial tensile force for the ten rivets is $12,000 \times 0.442 \times 10 = 53,000$ lb. The total initial compressive force is also 53,000 lb. Fig. 8–23(b) shows the compressive force per sq in. of contact surface as $53,000/15b = 3,530/b$ lb. In this expression b is the width of the contact surface.

As the bracket rotates, a change of pressure occurs at all points except those at the center of rotation. The change of pressure can be expressed by the flexure formula. The change at the extreme top or bottom is M/S, in which S is the section modulus of the contact area.

$$S = \frac{b}{6}(15)^2 = 37.5b$$

$$M/S = 9,000 \times 14/37.5b = 3,360/b$$

The diagram for the change of pressure due to moment is shown in Fig. 8–23(c). The combination of the initial compressive stresses plus the change of pressure is given by Fig. 8–23(d). Compression still exists over the entire surface, and the shear per rivet is less than the allowable 6.63 kips. Therefore, the bracket is satisfactory. With freedom of choice as to rivet spacing, however, it might be possible to design a more economical bracket. The design can be made by trial, or by a direct procedure if desired.[3]

8–16. Riveted or Bolted Brackets Without Initial Tension. When the initial tension in the shank of the bolts (or cold-driven rivets) is slight, rotation of the bracket will separate it from the support at the top. When this condition occurs, it is necessary to adopt an entirely different method of analysis. With this method there are no applicable allowable stress values given by the specifications. It is sometimes necessary to compute principle stresses.

[3]C. D. Williams and E. C. Harris, *Structural Design in Metals* (New York: The Ronald Press Co., 1949), Art. 5–17, p. 179.

For a detailed description of the method and examples of its application, the student is referred to Chapter 5 of the textbook *Structural Design in Metals*, by C. D. Williams and E. C. Harris.

8–17. Web Connections for Beams. Perhaps the most frequently used but least understood connection is the beam web connection shown in Fig. 8–24(a). It consists usually of two angles, shop connected

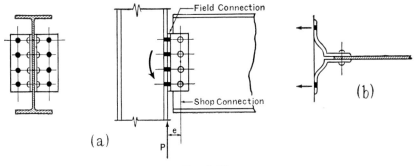

Fɪɢ. 8–24.

to the web of the supported beam and field connected to the supporting member. It is the intent to provide by this detail a simple-beam connection which permits rotation of the end of the beam. For end rotation to occur, it is necessary that the upper part of the connection angles deform in bending, as illustrated by Fig. 8–24(b). It can be shown that, for this deformation to be great enough to permit the end of the beam to rotate as a simply supported end, the angles will be stressed in bending beyond the yield-point stress. It is probable that, with the application of load to the beam, the angles undergo permanent deformation. That deformation permits rotation almost as great as needed for the simple-support condition. A small end moment is produced by the connection, although the amount of the end moment is not great enough to be of benefit in the design of the beam. Although web connections are satisfactory for beams having nearly static loads, such connections for beams having loads applied and removed a large number of times have frequently resulted in fatigue failure near the fillet at the upper end of the angles.

Since the intent is to make rotation as easy as possible, this should be kept in mind when selecting the angle thickness. A good guide for the thickness of such angles is found in the standard web connections of the AISC Manual. Those standards use $\frac{7}{16}$-in. thick angles for beams over 18 in. deep, and $\frac{3}{8}$-in. thick angles for connecting beams 18 in. or less in depth.

Since only slight end moment is provided by the connection, the field rivets or bolts are assumed to act in vertical shear only. It is assumed also that the small moment Pe on the shop rivets or bolts is resisted by friction between the beam web and the connection angles. The shop rivets or bolts are then assumed subject to vertical shear only.

The design procedure is as follows:

1. Determine the number of shop rivets or bolts required. The value of one connector is usually controlled by bearing on the web, but it may be controlled instead by double shear or by bearing on the angles.

2. Determine the number of field rivets or bolts required. The

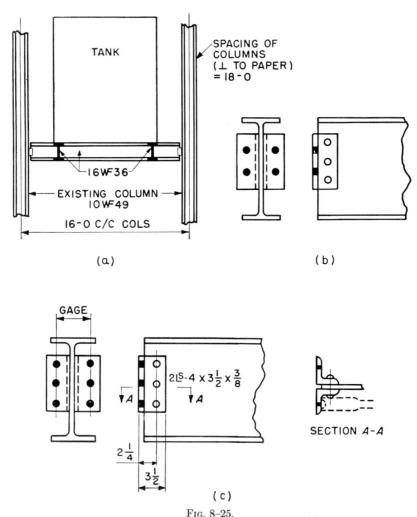

Fig. 8–25.

value of one connector may be controlled by shear, by bearing on the connection angle, or by bearing on the supporting member.

3. Specify the number of rivets or bolts of each type to be used, so that the detail and fabrication of the joint is practical. For example, if it is determined in steps (1) and (2) that 4 shop rivets and 5 field rivets are required, 4 shop rivets and 8 field rivets would be used, as in Fig. 8–24(a).

EXAMPLE 8–14. A water tank is designed to be supported overhead in an existing building. The support can be provided using existing building columns with new beams installed as shown in Fig. 8–25(a). The tank dimensions are 10 ft wide, 12 ft long, and 10 ft high. The weight of the steel plate and braces for the tank has been computed as 11,500 lb. Two 16WF36 beams support the tank and carry its load to a second pair of 16WF36 beams. Each beam of this second pair is to be supported by the columns, as shown in Fig. 8–25(a). Design a web connection for joining these beams to the building columns. Use $\frac{3}{4}$-in. rivets.

The first step is to compute the load to be carried by one connection.

$$
\begin{aligned}
\text{Wt of water} &= 62.4 \times 10 \times 12 \times 10 = 74{,}900 \text{ lb} \\
\text{Wt of tank} &= 11{,}500 \text{ lb} \\
2\text{--}16\text{WF}36 \times 16\text{--}0 = 2 \times 36 \times 16 &= 1{,}152 \text{ lb} \\
2\text{--}16\text{WF}36 \times 18\text{--}0 = 2 \times 36 \times 18 &= 1{,}296 \text{ lb} \\
\text{Details—about } 5\% \text{ of beam wts} &= \underline{122 \text{ lb}} \\
\text{Total load} &= 88{,}970 \text{ lb} \\
\text{Load per connection} = \tfrac{1}{4} \text{ of } 88{,}970 &= 22{,}240 \text{ lb}
\end{aligned}
$$

The connection angles will be shop-riveted to the web of the 16WF36, one on each side. The values of one $\frac{3}{4}$-in. shop rivet are:

Double shear $= 2 \times 0.442 \times 15 = 13.25$ kips

Enclosed bearing on 0.299-in. web $= 0.75 \times 0.299 \times 40 = 8.97$ kips
Controls

Bearing on two $\frac{3}{8}$-in. angles $= 2 \times 0.75 \times 0.375 \times 32 = 18.0$ kips

Number of shop rivets required $= 22.24/8.97 = 3$ minimum

Field rivets will connect the angles to the flange of the 10WF49 column. The values of one field rivet are:

Single shear $= 0.442 \times 15 = 6.63$ kips   *Controls*

Bearing on $\frac{3}{8}$-in. angle $= 0.75 \times 0.375 \times 32 = 9.0$ kips

Number of field rivets required $= 22.24/6.63 = 4$ minimum

If economy of rivets were extremely important, the minimum numbers of each kind could be used, arranged as shown in Fig. 8–25(b). The normal practice, however, is to use a few extra field rivets so located that each vertical row has the same spacing and number of rivets. Fig. 8–25(c) shows the connection as it would normally be made.

The spacing of the rows of field rivets (gage) must be selected by several considerations, as follows:

1. The gage must be suitable for the column. Sufficient edge distance on the column flanges must be provided.
2. Sufficient edge distance must be provided on the angles.
3. Driving clearance must be provided. Section A–A of Fig. 8–25(c) shows the driving tool dotted. The field rivet should be out far

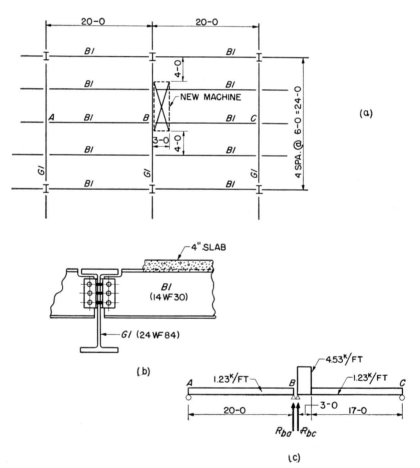

Fig. 8–26.

enough on the angle so that the shop rivet head does not interfere with the tool. (See Appendix B, Table 1.)

The tables of *Dimensions for Detailing* (Appendix A) show $5\frac{1}{2}$ in.
to be a usual gage for the 10W F49 column. This value satisfies the
other requirements above and would be used.

EXAMPLE 8–15. It is planned to install a new machine on the second
floor of an existing building. Will the connections be satisfactory for
the increased load? The layout of the floor and beams is shown by Fig.
8–26(a). Beams *B1* are connected to the girders *G1* by standard web
connections, as shown by Fig. 8–26(b). Other data are as follows:

> Floor: 4-in. reinforced concrete slab
> Floor live load: 150 lb per sq ft
> Rivet size: $\frac{3}{4}$ in.
> Weight of new machine: 20,000 lb

A free-body diagram of beams *AB* and *BC* is shown by Fig. 8–26(c).
The load per foot of beam is computed first.

$$\text{Slab weight} = 6 \times 50 = \quad 300$$
$$\text{Beam weight} \qquad\qquad = \quad\;\; 30$$
$$\text{Live load} = 6 \times 150 = \quad 900$$
$$\text{Load per foot} = w = \; = 1{,}230 \text{ lb or } 1.23 \text{ kips per ft}$$

The machine load is resisted by two beams *B1* only. To conform to
the AISC Specification, Section 10(c), 20 per cent of the machine weight
should be added for impact. Floor live load will not be included in the
dotted area occupied by the machine.

Load per foot of beam under machine:

$$\text{Slab dead load} = 6 \times 50 \qquad\qquad = \quad 300$$
$$\text{Beam dead load} \qquad\qquad\qquad = \quad\;\; 30$$
$$\text{Floor live load} = \frac{150 \times 4 \times 2}{6} = \quad 200$$
$$\text{Machine dead load} = \frac{20{,}000}{2 \times 3} \; = 3{,}333$$
$$\text{Impact} = 0.2 \times 3{,}333 \qquad\qquad = \quad\;\; 667$$
$$w = 4{,}530 \text{ lb, or } 4.53 \text{ kips per ft}$$

For beam *AB*, the reaction at *B* is

$$R_{ba} = 1.23 \times 10 = 12.3 \text{ kips}$$

For beam BC, the reaction at B is

$$R_{bc} = \frac{1}{20} [(1.23 \times 17 \times 8.5) + (4.53 \times 3 \times 18.5)] = 21.5 \text{ kips}$$

Three shop rivets must transmit the 21.5-kip reaction of beam BC to the two angles. The values of one of these rivets are:

Double shear $= 2 \times 0.442 \times 15 = 13.25$ kips

Enclosed Bearing on 0.270-in. web $= 0.75 \times 0.270 \times 40 = 8.1$ kips
Controls

Allowable reaction on shop rivets $= 3 \times 8.1 = 24.3$ kips

This value exceeds the expected 21.5 kips; thus, the shop rivets are satisfactory.

The field rivets must carry $21.5 + 12.3 = 33.8$ kips to the web of the girder $G1$. Of this, 21.5 kips tends to shear the rivets on one side of the girder only. The shear value of the six rivet shanks on that one side is $6.63 \times 6 = 39.8$ kips. The field rivets are satisfactory in shear. Their bearing value on the web of the girder $G1$ should now be checked.

Enclosed bearing value on 0.470-in. web $= 0.75 \times 0.470 \times 40$

$$= 14.1 \text{ kips per rivet}$$

Value of six rivets in bearing $= 6 \times 14.4 = 84.6$ kips

This allowable exceeds the expected 33.8 kips; thus, the connection is satisfactory for the increase of load.

8–18. Welded Web Connections for Beams.   A welded web connection is shown in Fig. 8–27. The welds connecting the angles to the web of the beam in Fig. 8–27(a) are shop welds. Those on the outer edges of

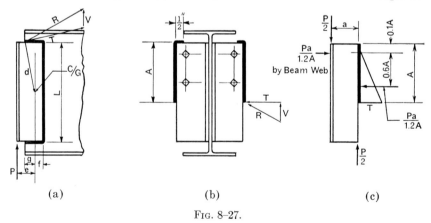

(a)   (b)   (c)

Fig. 8–27.

the angles, Fig. 8–27(b) are the field welds. Erection bolts are used to support the weight of the beam while the field welding is being done.

There are no initial tensile forces to clamp the angles against the beam web as was the case in the riveted web connection. Consequently, the eccentricity e of the reaction P from the center of gravity of the shop welds must be considered. The stress T per inch of weld due to the moment Pe is computed. The stress V per inch due to the vertical force P alone is also computed. T and V are combined vectorially to give the resultant stress R per inch of weld. The most highly stressed weld increments are those at the top or bottom, closest to the line of action of the applied force P. A force triangle giving R for the shop welds is shown on Fig. 8–27(a).

An equation could be derived relating the length L of the vertical shop welds and the resultant R. The equation would be very complex, however, and a direct solution for the required length L would not be practical. Design by successive approximation is the better method. (Curves can be plotted to simplify the design of connections in which the angle-leg dimension is standardized.) The computations for the shop welds are shown in the next example.

In the analysis of the field welds, Priest[4] recommends that a moment be considered, in addition to the direct vertical effect. This moment may be a little difficult to visualize unless the equilibrium of a single angle is considered. In Fig. 8–27(b) the field welds are shown on the outer edges of the angles. The total upward reaction for the beam is P. Each field weld, then, pushes the angle to which it is attached upward with a force of $P/2$. Fig. 8–27(c) shows one of these angles. The field weld applies an upward force $P/2$ to the right edge, while the beam pushes downward with a force $P/2$ on the left edge. Thus the equation $\Sigma V = 0$ is satisfied for the angle. The two vertical forces, however, form a counterclockwise couple $Pa/2$. Since the angle actually does not rotate in service, an equal but opposite couple must exist in order to satisfy the equation $\Sigma M = 0$. Pressure of the beam web near the top of the angle prevents movement of the top toward the web. The only thing that can possibly resist movement of the angle away from the beam at the lower end is a horizontal force in the weld. The location of these two horizontal forces is not known. It seems reasonable, though, to assume that the resultant pressure of the beam web against the angle is very near to the top of the angle. Priest recommends that the upper force be assumed to act at $0.1A$ from the top. Priest also recommends that the weld below that point be assumed to exert horizontal resistance in proportion to its vertical distance below that point. Thus, the horizontal

[4]H. Malcolm Priest, *The Practical Design of Welded Steel Structures* (New York: American Welding Society, 1943).

resistance per inch of weld would vary from zero at $0.1A$ from the top, to the value T at the lower edge. The resultant of the horizontal weld stresses would lie at $0.3A$ from the bottom. The clockwise couple of the two horizontal forces H on one angle should equal the counterclockwise couple $Pa/2$.

$$0.6AH = Pa/2$$

$$H = Pa/1.2A$$

The horizontal stress T per inch at the lower end of the field weld is twice the average, so that

$$T = \frac{2H}{0.9A} = \frac{Pa}{0.54A^2}$$

The vertical stress per inch of field weld is

$$V = P/2A$$

The maximum stress per inch is the resultant of T and V, or

$$R = \sqrt{T^2 + V^2} = \frac{P}{A}\sqrt{\frac{1}{4} + \left(\frac{a}{0.54A}\right)^2}$$

This equation can be solved for the required length A of field weld with a given weld size and allowable stress R.

End rotation of the beam causes the upper end of the angles to bend in a manner that might easily tear the field weld. Two precautions can be taken to prevent this action. A short return of the field welds, say $\frac{1}{2}$ in., can be made along the upper edge of each angle. The return would reinforce the weld at the point where the tearing action is most severe. The other method is to locate the field erection bolts near the top of the

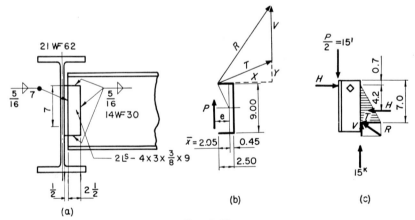

Fig. 8–28.

angles and to leave them tightly installed after field welding. While such bolts would prevent the tearing or bending of the field welds, it would be difficult to be certain that the bolts would not later be loosened or removed. Also, they would reduce the flexibility of the connection slightly. The weld returns are the more satisfactory solution.

EXAMPLE 8–16. The floor in your plant has web-angle connections as shown in Fig. 8–28. It is planned to increase the floor loads permanently so as to increase the beam reactions to 30 kips. Are the connections satisfactory?

The center of gravity of the shop welds is computed first. See Fig. 8–28(b).

$$\bar{x} = \frac{(9.0 \times 2.5) + (2 \times 2.5 \times 1.25)}{9.0 + 2(2.5)} = 2.05 \text{ in.}$$

$$J \text{ (per weld)} = I_x + I_y$$

$$J = \frac{1}{12}(9)^3 + 2[2.5 \times (4.5)^2]$$

$$+ [9 \times (0.45)^2] + 2\left[\frac{(0.45)^3}{3}\right] + 2\left[\frac{(2.05)^3}{3}\right]$$

$$J = 169.5 \text{ per weld}$$

$$M = Pe = 30 \times 2.55$$

$$= 76.5 \text{ in.-kips total, or } 38.2 \text{ in.-kips per weld}$$

$$T = Md/J$$

The components of T are

$$X = 38.2 \times 4.5/169.5 = 1.01 \text{ kips per in.}$$

$$Y = 38.2 \times 2.05/169.5 = 0.46 \text{ kips per in.}$$

$$V = 30/28 = 1.07 \text{ kips per in.}$$

$$R = \sqrt{(1.53)^2 + (1.01)^2} = 1.83 \text{ kips per in.}$$

Shop welds occur on each side of the web of the 14W̱F30. Thus the effective weld size is limited to 0.7 × the web thickness. (See Art. 8–11.)

$$\text{Effective } W = 0.7 \times 0.270 = 0.189 \text{ in.}$$

Allowable load per inch, $R = 13.6 \times 0.189/\sqrt{2} = 1.82 \text{ kips per in.}$

The expected 1.83 kips per in. exceeds the allowable by less than one per cent. The shop welds would be considered satisfactory for the increased reaction.

The field weld and one angle are shown in Fig. 8–28(c).

$$15 \times 4 \text{ (counterclockwise)} = 4.2H \text{ (clockwise)}$$

$$H = 14.3 \text{ kips}$$

$$T = 2 \times 14.3/0.9 \times 7 = 4.54 \text{ kips per in.}$$

$$V = 30/14 = 2.14 \text{ kips per in.}$$

$$R = \sqrt{(2.14)^2 + (4.53)^2} = 4.54 \text{ kips per in.}$$

The field weld size is only $\frac{5}{16}$ in., however, and the allowable R per in. is 3 kips. The expected resultant of 5.00 kips per in. is considerably more than the allowable. Thus, the field welds are not satisfactory for the new increased loads.

No value can be given to the bolts. They would not come into full bearing until movement had occurred. This movement would not occur in sufficient amount until after the welds had failed.

8–19. Standard Web Connections.   To simplify design procedure and to reduce the large variety of sizes of web connection that might be designed for use on a single structure, engineers have established standard sizes of connections. For riveted building construction, the AISC manual, *Steel Construction*, gives tables of standard riveted web connections for varying nominal depths of beam section. The tables give also the maximum safe load for each connection. It is an acceptable and usually economical practice to use the standard connection, even though it may be much stronger than required for the expected loads. When very heavy reactions are encountered, it may be necessary to design a special connection.

Web connections are made by the following combinations of shop and field methods:

1. Shop riveted and field riveted
2. Shop riveted and field bolted
3. Shop bolted and field bolted
4. Shop welded and field welded
5. Shop welded and field bolted
6. Shop welded and field riveted

8–20. Beam Connections to Resist Moment.   Web connections provide simple support for a beam. Sometimes it is necessary to support the beam so that end rotation is prevented. This results in an end moment which must be carried by the connection. Several types of end connections to resist moment are shown in Fig. 8–29.

The riveted connection of Fig. 8–29(a) is used where large moments

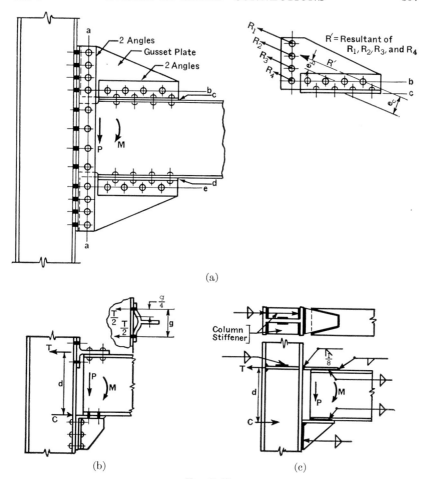

Fig. 8–29.

occur and where sufficient space is available. The field rivets are analyzed by the method given in Art. 8–15, initial tension being considered. The shop rivets on line a–a have vertical loads that are due to the reaction P and horizontal loads due to the moment M. The total load on each of these rivets is the resultant R of the V and T forces. The upper gusset plate is loaded by forces R_1, R_2, R_3, and R_4, from the four top rivets of line a–a. The gusset is held in equilibrium by the shop rivets of line b. These rivets must resist the force R' and a moment $R'e_b$. Similarly, the rivets of line c must resist force R' and a moment $R'e_c$, Line c also is analyzed considering initial tension.

Thus, while the connection appears quite complicated, it is actually only an accumulation of shorter design problems. Each of the shorter problems is easy to solve. When it is divided into a series of easy problems, the complete problem itself becomes simpler.

When space is limited, or when the moment is smaller, details of the types shown by Fig. 8–29(b) or (c) may be used. In each the moment M is resisted by a couple. The couple consists of a force T transmitted by a tee-clip or by a plate attached to the top flange, and a force C transmitted by the bracket or by a clip on the bottom flange. Forces C and T are each equal to M/d. The vertical force P is resisted either by a bracket as shown or by a web connection.

For additional details on the design of end-moment connections the student is referred to the textbook *Structural Design in Metals*, by C. D. Williams and E. C. Harris.

8–21. Flexibility of Welded Connections for Simple Beams. If a beam is designed as a simple beam, its end connections must be arranged to permit easy rotation of the end of the beam. If they are not, then either the connection, the beam itself, or the supporting structure will be overstressed.

Occasionally the urge to simplify welded beam connections has led to rigid designs, without providing for the effects of end moment. For example, the simplest kind of beam connection, shown by Fig. 8–30(a), is a complete welding of the beam section to the support. The connection is obviously rigid, permitting only that rotation which results from bending of the column. Such a connection is proper if provision is made for end moment.

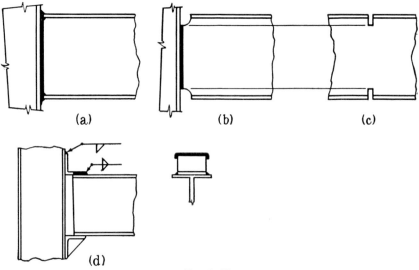

Fig. 8–30.

That shown by Fig. 8–30(b) is only a partial development of the beam section by the welds. Yet, it cannot permit free end rotation of the beam. If rotation of the ends is prevented, an end moment develops which may be as great as two-thirds of the simple-beam moment for which the section is selected. Since almost the entire section is needed to resist that amount of bending moment, the reduced section at the welds is certain to be overstressed. The effect is similar to that which would occur if the flanges and web were cut at the point of maximum bending moment, as shown by Fig. 8–30(c). This connection has been used for building work—often without ill effects. Why? Three explanations may be given. Since building loads are largely static, a yielding of overstressed connection material may occur, thus permitting greater rotation. In some cases, a large portion of the load may be present before welding, so that the rotation required after welding is reduced. Ultimate collapse does not occur, but the factor of safety for some parts is reduced. Since a uniform factor of safety is desirable, it is considered best to design flexible connections, or to consider the effect of their rigidity in the design of both the connections and the members they connect.

The connection of Fig. 8–30(d) is merely a beam-seat connection with a top angle added. The top angle is often used, either to prevent over-turning of the beam or to provide some resistance to end moments due to wind loads. Yet it is usually considered as a simple-beam connection. Obviously, it cannot be a simple-beam connection and provide end-moment resistance. As the beam end rotates under vertical loading, the top angle is bent away from the column. For the usual amounts of end rotation, the bending stresses in the angle exceed the yield point. The angle permanently deforms, permitting end rotation of the beam but causing a slight end moment to remain in the beam. The angle could aid in resisting end moments due to wind, but only if those moments did not exceed the amount needed to cause yield-point stress in the angle. The weld connecting the angle to the column should be located near the upper edge only. If it were extended all the way down the sides of the angle, the flexibility of the connection would be destroyed. The weld, as shown by Fig. 8–30(d), however, is subject to bending like that shown by Fig. 8–14(a). Field bolts or a top weld having $\frac{1}{2}$-in. returns along the vertical edges would be better. That this connection is used with success can probably be explained by the three reasons given in the preceding paragraph.

While it has some faults, the connection of Fig. 8–30(d) may be considered satisfactory for static loads. That of Fig. 8–30(a) should be used only if the resulting end moment is considered in the design. That of Fig. 8–30(b) should be avoided.

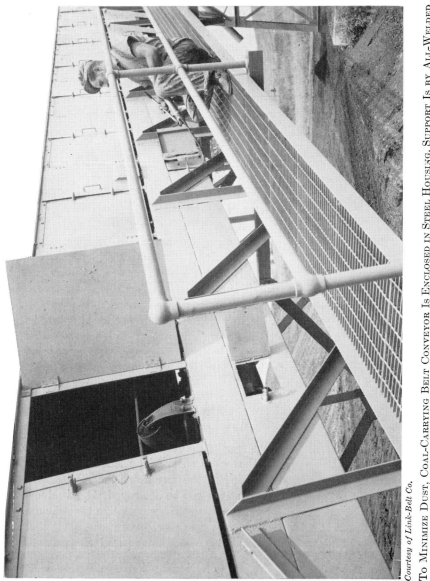

Courtesy of Link-Belt Co.

To Minimize Dust, Coal-Carrying Belt Conveyor Is Enclosed in Steel Housing. Support Is by All-Welded Steel Trusses.

A simplification of the top angle is a flat plate, connected as shown by Fig. 8–29(c). If this is used, however, the beam end cannot rotate freely. While such a connection is good for continuous beams, it is not a simple beam connection.

8–22. Fillers. Filler plates are often needed to fill spaces between parts which are riveted or bolted to each other. A connection requiring filler plates is shown in Fig. 8–31.

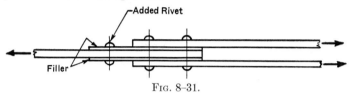

FIG. 8–31.

The allowable stresses for rivets are established for connections transferring load from one layer of material to the adjacent layer. If additional layers, such as fillers, intervene, there is more than the usual tendency for slipping of the plates and for bending of the rivets. Under such conditions, the rivet strength may be reduced.

Slippage and rivet bending can be reduced by connecting the filler to one of the parts with additional rivets beyond those required if fillers are absent. The number of added rivets required is often controlled by the specifications, but if it is not, the following procedure is recommended:

1. Compute the load in the filler, assuming that the load of the member to which it is connected is divided uniformly over the combined cross-sectional area of the member and the filler.
2. Provide enough extra rivets to transfer this computed load to the filler. The added rivets are usually installed through the extended filler and one of the members, as shown in Fig. 8–31. The added rivets may, however, go through the filler and both members, if it is more convenient or economical.

If the effect of friction between the materials is neglected, this procedure is a logical and a safe one to use. Tests have shown, however, that the maximum number of added rivets, through the filler and one member, that is effective is about one-third of the number required for the same connection without fillers. Added rivets beyond that number cause no increase in the static strength of the joint.

If the load is vibratory or often repeated, so that the friction may be destroyed, it would be well to use the method previously outlined in this article, even though the number of added rivets thus obtained exceeds one-third the number required for the joint without fillers.

8–23. Bearing Plates for Beams.   At the ends of beams which rest on masonry or concrete, bearing plates are usually used. The bearing plate serves two purposes. It spreads the vertical reaction over a large enough area so that the masonry is not crushed. It also facilitates erection of the beam by providing a bearing surface that is easily adjusted to the correct height and leveled.

A typical bearing plate is illustrated by Fig. 8–32. If the masonry is extended over the beam (as indicated by dotted lines), some form of

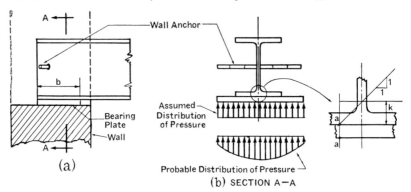

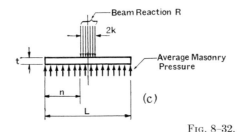

Fig. 8–32.

wall anchor is used. The type shown is called a "government anchor" and consists of a bent steel rod. A pair of short clip angles connected to the web might be used instead of the rod. No structural strength is assumed to be provided by the anchor. Its purpose is to prevent longitudinal movement of the beam with respect to the wall.

The beam reaction causes pressure between the masonry and the bearing plate. The intensity of pressure p is assumed for design purposes to be uniform over the area of the plate. A small upward deflection of the outer edges of the plate does occur, of course, relieving the pressure near the outer edges and increasing the pressure near the center, as shown in Fig. 8–32(b). Because of the deflection of the beam itself, there is an increase in pressure along the edge of the bearing plate nearest the center of the beam span and a corresponding decrease at the edge near the end of the beam. The allowable average unit compressive stresses in the masonry are low in order to compensate for these non-uniformities of pressure distribution. The design of bearing plates resulting from the assumption of uniform distribution of bearing stress is generally on the safe side.

After the area of plate has been selected so as to prevent crushing of the masonry, the thickness of plate must be chosen to prevent bending of the plate itself. If the beam flange and the bearing plate were both perfectly flat and in contact with each other at all points, both would act to resist bending caused by the upward pressure p. This perfect condition is improbable.

Thus, the usual method of design for bearing plates assumes that the entire resistance to bending is provided by the bearing plate. The critical section of the plate is assumed to be at a distance k from the center of the web. (See Appendix A, "Dimensions for Detailing," for dimension k.) The load on the plate by this assumption is as shown by Fig. 8–32(c).

At the assumed critical section a–a of Fig. 8–32(b), the bending moment is

$$M = pn(n/2) = pn^2/2$$

for a strip of plate one in. wide. The plate thickness t selected must provide the necessary section modulus to resist this bending moment.

EXAMPLE 8–17. A heavy piece of equipment is to be supported by beams as shown in Fig. 8–33(a). One end of each beam is to be rested

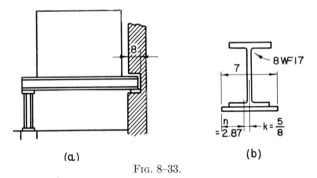

(a)   (b)

FIG. 8–33.

on an existing brick wall. Pockets can be cut by removing two courses of brick. The pockets will be about 8 in. deep. The beam size is 8WF17 and the end reaction 10 kips. Design a bearing plate.

Section 15(c) of the AISC Specification gives 250 psi as the allowable bearing stress on the masonry. The required bearing area is

$$A = 10,000/250 = 40 \text{ sq in.}$$

Several shapes of plate can be selected to provide this area. The length parallel to the beam, however, should not exceed about 6 in. The edge of the plate must be kept back from the face of the masonry, since the bearing pressures are actually so much higher than the average at that edge of the plate. A plate 6 in. by 7 in. will provide adequate area.

With the plate placed as in Fig. 8–33(b), dimension n is $3\frac{1}{2} - \frac{5}{8} = 2\frac{7}{8}$ in. The actual average pressure p is

$$10,000/6 \times 7 = 238 \text{ psi}$$

$$M = 0.238 \times (2.87)^2/2 = 0.98 \text{ in.-kips per inch strip of plate}$$

Required $S = M/F_b = 0.98/20 = 0.049$ in.^{3} per inch strip of plate

$$S = \tfrac{1}{6}t^2$$

Required $t = \sqrt{6 \times 0.049} = 0.542$ in.

A plate $6 \times \frac{5}{8} \times 7$ would be satisfactory.

8–24. Column Base Plates. A typical column base plate detail is shown in Fig. 8–34. The plate may be welded to the column as illustrated

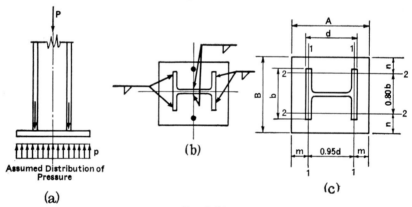

Assumed Distribution of
Pressure

(a)

(b)

(c)

Fig. 8–34.

in (b), or it may be riveted by means of angles connected to the flanges or to the flanges and the web of the column. If the column end is milled, its connection to the plate need be strong enough only to hold the parts together. If the column is not milled, the connection is required to transmit the entire column load to the plate.

For an undeformed plate, the upward pressure p would be uniformly distributed over the entire area $A \times B$. Because of elastic deformation of the plate and the supporting material, there is actually a reduction of pressure near the edges of the plate and an increase near the portion beneath the column flanges and web. As with beam bearing plates, the allowable masonry bearing pressure is low to permit safe use of the assumption that the pressure distribution is uniform. The plate design based on this assumption is conservative.

The downward pressure P is concentrated on the area of contact between the column and the plate. The assumed uniform pressure p tends to bend upward those portions of plate which project beyond the outline of the column. The projecting portions are considered as uniformly loaded cantilever beams. The bending moment is maximum near the point where the flange contacts the plate. It is usually assumed that the maximum moment occurs on the sections marked 1–1 and 2–2 in Fig. 8–34(c).

The maximum moment would occur at a line of zero shear. This line would fall within the area of contact between the column and the plate. Since the unit pressure on this area is much greater than the unit pressure on the masonry, the line of zero shear will be near the outer face of the column. The values $0.95d$ and $0.80b$ are arbitrary but are selected to meet average values.

For section 1–1,

$$M = \frac{pm^2}{2} \text{ per inch strip of plate}$$

Similarly, for section 2–2,

$$M = \frac{pn^2}{2} \text{ per inch strip of plate}$$

Whichever value of moment is the larger is used in determining the required thickness of plate.

The analysis just described is for columns with negligible bending moment at the lower end; i.e., in effect, pin-connected. Columns connected by two anchor bolts as shown in Fig. 8–34 will resist practically no end moment. If end moment does occur, the column base will rotate or deform slightly so as to relieve the column of its moment. To make a column base to resist high end moment, very heavy details are required; usually at least four anchor bolts are used. The design of such a base is quite complicated compared to that for a pinned-end column.

EXAMPLE 8–18. An 8WF24 is selected for a column to support a die rack. Each column will have an axial load of 60 kips. The columns will rest on new concrete footings. Design a base plate for these columns.

Bearing area required = 60,000/600 = 100 sq in.

There are many possible plate shapes that will satisfy the requirement of bearing area. The minimum thickness of plate will be obtained if the plate size is selected so that dimensions m and n are equal. One plate dimension of course, should be of some whole-inch dimension so as to avoid cutting. In some cases the outline of the plate may be affected by the footing shape or by required clearances. Various sizes of plate will be compared below.

For the 8**WF**24: $0.95d = 7.53$ in.; $0.80b = 5.20$ in.

Plate Size	m (in.)	n (in.)
10 × 10	1.23	2.40
11 × 9	1.73	1.90
12 × 8½	2.23	1.65

If clearances or footing shape do not prevent it, the 9 × 11 plate would be used. Dimension n is slightly larger than m and will control the thickness selection.

$$\text{Actual } p = 60{,}000/9 \times 11 = 606 \text{ psi}$$

$$M = 0.606 \times (1.90)^2/2 = 1.10 \text{ in.-kips per in. strip of plate}$$

$$\text{Required } S = 1.10/20 = 0.055 \text{ in.}^3$$

$$S = \tfrac{1}{6}t^2$$

$$\text{Required } t = \sqrt{6 \times 0.055} = 0.574 \text{ in.}$$

This solution indicates that a 9 × ⅝ plate, 11 in. long, is satisfactory. In practice, however, plates less than ¾ in. thick are seldom used for column bases. Experience has shown that thinner plates are too easily damaged in handling, in tightening of the anchor bolts, etc. Most engineers would use a ¾-in. plate for this column.

8–25. Connection of Reinforcement to Beams. The reinforcement of beams through the addition of plates or other shapes to the beam flanges was presented in Art. 7–25. In order for the reinforcement to be effective, adequate connections must be provided to join it to the original section. These connections should be strong enough to transmit into the reinforcement the stresses it is to receive when the member is loaded.

A mental picture of the nature of the stress to be transferred can be obtained from Fig. 8–35. In Fig. 8–35(a) a beam with a reinforcing

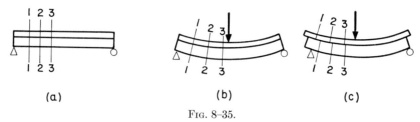

(a)   (b)   (c)

Fig. 8–35.

plate is shown. The plate is attached to the beam. Loading causes the beam to bend, as shown exaggerated in Fig. 8–35(b). The cross sections 1–1, 2–2, and 3–3 are sloping, but they are otherwise the same as in the unloaded beam. Assume now that all the connectors joining the reinforcement has failed. The reinforcing plate will slide with respect to the original beam, as shown in (c). The reinforcement will now be ineffective in strengthening the beam. The failure that has occurred is called a "horizontal shearing failure."

It is necessary to know the amount of the horizontal shearing stress at the plane of contact between the beam and the reinforcement. When this is known, the connectors can be selected and spaced so as to prevent the horizontal shearing failure.

A portion of a reinforced beam is shown by Fig. 8–36(a). The flexural stresses for the combined section are shown. The stresses at opposite

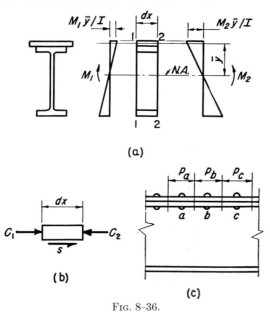

(a)

(b)

(c)

FIG. 8–36.

ends of the portion are different, since M_1 is not equal to M_2. The stress at any point is My/I. For example, at the center of gravity of the reinforcing plate on section 1–1,

$$f_1 = M_1 \bar{y}/I$$

in which $\bar{y}$ is the distance of the center of the plate above the neutral axis of the combined section.

Fig. 8–36(b) shows an enlarged view of the cover plate removed from the short section of beam. Compressive stresses should occur at each

Courtesy of American MonoRail Co.

SWINGING JIB CRANE MOUNTED ON EXISTING BUILDING STEEL. BUILDING COLUMN
MUST RESIST THRUST FROM BOOM OF CRANE.

end of the element of plate. The average stress on the left end is $f_1 = M_1\bar{y}/I$, and the average on the right is $f_2 = M_2\bar{y}/I$. The resultant of the compressive stresses on the left is called C_1, and is equal to the average stress f_1 times the area of the flange cross section; or

$$C_1 = f_1 A = M_1\bar{y}A/I$$

Similarly,

$$C_2 = M_2\bar{y}A/I$$

Unless M_1 and M_2 are equal, C_1 will not balance C_2. The plate element will be held in equilibrium by a horizontal shearing force at its plane of contact to the beam. This force is shown as s in Fig. 8–36(b). For equilibrium,

$$s = C_2 - C_1$$

$$= M_2\bar{y}A/I - M_1\bar{y}A/I = \frac{\bar{y}A}{I}(M_2 - M_1)$$

The term $\bar{y}A$ is the moment of the plate area about the center of gravity of the combined section. This is called Q in the usual shear formula. The term $(M_2 - M_1)$ is the change of bending moment between sections 1–1 and 2–2. In Chapter 3 it was shown that the change of bending moment is equal to the area of the shear diagram between the two sections. Thus, if the shear is fairly constant in the short length dx,

$$M_2 - M_1 = V\,dx$$

Both of these substitutions are made in the expression for the shear force s to give

$$s = \frac{VQ\,dx}{I}$$

If dx is unity, the intensity of horizontal shear *per inch of beam length* is

$$v = VQ/I$$

Connectors are usually placed at intervals of a few inches along the beam. If the connectors are p inches apart, the connection at one cross section must resist all of the horizontal shear for p inches of plate length. Thus, in Fig. 8–36(c), the pair of rivets at section a must resist all the shear between the plate and the beam in length p_a. This amount of shear is $p_a v$, or $p_a VQ/I$. Using R to designate the load in the connectors at a section,

$$R_a = p_a VQ/I$$

$$R_b = p_b VQ/I, \text{ etc.}$$

The connectors can be loaded to their full allowable shear (or bearing) strength. The "pitch" p should be selected so as to avoid overloading the connectors. The maximum allowable pitch is

$$p = RI/VQ$$

In the above expression, R is the allowable load for the connector or connectors joining the plate to the beam at the cross section in question; I is the moment of inertia of the complete cross section, V is the maximum shear that can occur at that section; and Q is the static moment (about the center of gravity of the combined section) *of the area to which the connectors in question must transfer stress.*

Occasionally the use of the equation developed above will give a required pitch that is ridiculously high or low. If the pitch required is very small, it may be impossible to install the necessary connectors. The only cure is to redesign the reinforced beam section, selecting a combination that can be connected practically.

When the equation gives a very large pitch, other practical considerations may control. These are the requirements for sealing and for prevention of local buckling of the reinforcing plate. The AISC Specification covers these requirements in Section 23(b) for rivets, and in Section 25(b) for welds.

EXAMPLE 8–19. An 8WF17 is reinforced by two full-length $7 \times \frac{3}{4}$ plates, one on each flange as shown in Fig. 8–37(a). It is used on a 14-ft simple span. The dead load is 400 lb per ft and the movable live load

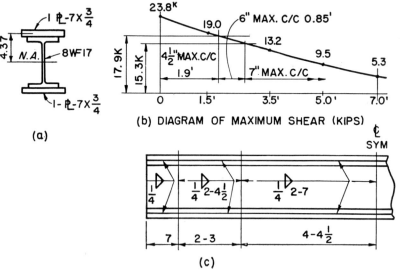

(a)

(b) DIAGRAM OF MAXIMUM SHEAR (KIPS)

(c)

FIG. 8–37.

3,000 lb per ft. Design the connection of the plates to the **WF** section, using $2 \times \frac{1}{4}$ fillet welds.

The smallest spacing will occur where V is largest—at the end of the span in this case.

$$\text{Maximum } V = 7(0.4 + 3.0) = 23.8 \text{ kips}$$

The moment of inertia of the combined cross section is

$$I = 56.4 + [2 \times 7 \times 0.75 \times (4.37)^2] = 257 \text{ in}^4.$$

Welds should be opposite, one at each edge of each flange. Thus the term R will be the shear value for 4 in. of $\frac{1}{4}$-in. fillet weld.

$$R = 4 \times 2.4 = 9.6 \text{ kips}$$

$$Q = 7 \times 0.75 \times 4.37 = 23.0$$

The required spacing of the welds is

$$p = RI/VQ = 9.6 \times 257/(V \times 23) = 107/V$$

At the end of the beam this will be

$$p = 107/23.8 = 4.50 \text{ in.}$$

For strength purposes the welds should be spaced at $4\frac{1}{2}$-in. centers. Section 25(b) of the AISC Specification limits the clear distance between welds for the compression flange to 16 times the thickness of the thinner part joined. This would be

$$16 \times 0.308 = 4.92 \text{ in.}$$

The center-to-center distance of the $2 \times \frac{1}{4}$ welds must not exceed $4.92 + 2 = 6.92$ in., or approximately 7 in. The strength requirement controls, so the pitch will be limited to $4\frac{1}{2}$ in.

Since the strength requirement of $4\frac{1}{2}$ in. is much below the Specification maximum pitch of 7 in., it may be advisable to increase the spacing for sections having lower shear V. To facilitate this, a diagram of maximum shear is drawn in Fig. 8–37(b). This is *not* a shear diagram. Its values are not simultaneous. An ordinate at a section gives the maximum shear that can occur at the section. To plot the diagram, maximum shears are computed for various sections (see Chapter 5), ordinates are plotted, and a smooth curve is drawn between them.

The pitch can be changed continuously along the beam, but this is seldom practical. A better design is one in which the smaller pitch ($4\frac{1}{2}$ in.) is maintained until a reasonable change can be made, for example, to a pitch of 6 in. The shear V for which a 6-in. pitch may be used is equal to or less than

$$V = RI/pQ = 9.6 \times 257/(6 \times 23) = 17.9 \text{ kips}$$

The pitch can be changed to 7 in. where the shear does not exceed

$$V = 9.6 \times 257/(7 \times 23) = 15.3\,\text{kips}$$

Horizontal lines are drawn on the curve of Fig. 8–37(b) at ordinates of 17.9 kips and 15.3 kips. The change of spacing can be made where these lines intersect the curve. The lengths in which each of the three spacings are suitable are shown below the diagram.

Since the 6-in. spacing is shown over such a small length it may be more practical to limit the detail to two spacings. Either the 6-in. or the 7-in. spacing could be eliminated. A detail in which the 6-in. spacing is eliminated is shown by Fig. 8–37(c). The end weld is made $5\frac{1}{4}$ in. (or more) long to conform to Section 25(b) of the AISC Specification.

EXAMPLE 8–20. In Example 7–23 reinforcement for 12WF27 floor beams in an existing building was designed. The object of the reinforcement was to increase the capacity of the floor system to allow live load of 200 lb per sq ft. The reinforcement selected was an $8 \times \frac{7}{8}$ plate to be welded to the bottom flange. The theoretical length of plate required is 7.1 ft; the actual length 8.0 ft. Design the welded connections.

The beam is shown by Fig. 8–38. The plate is $\frac{7}{8}$ in. thick, thus the weld size must be at least $\frac{5}{16}$ in. [Section 24(c)]. The flange of the

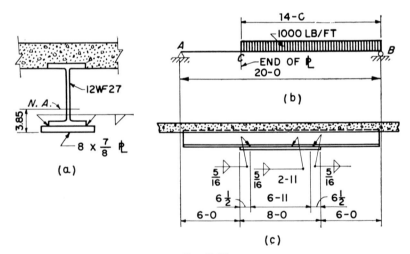

FIG. 8–38.

12WF27 is $\frac{3}{8}$ in. thick. The welds are placed against the edge of the flange and should be $\frac{1}{16}$ in. smaller than the flange thickness, or $\frac{5}{16}$ in. maximum. Therefore, $\frac{5}{16}$-in. fillets will be used.

The dead load will not stress the plate. The welds must transfer to

the plate only the stress due to live load. The maximum stress transfer per in. of length will occur where V is maximum. This will be at the end of the plate when live load is placed as shown in Fig. 8–38(b).

$$V_c = R_a = \frac{1}{20}(14,000 \times 7) = 4,900 \text{ lb}$$

The area to which stress must be transferred is that of the plate, or 7.0 sq in. The moment of this area about the center of gravity of the combined section is

$$Q = 7.0 \times 3.42 = 23.94$$

The horizontal shear between plate and beam is VQ/I.

$$v = 4.9 \times 23.94/357.8 = 0.328 \text{ kips per in.}$$

The value of two $\frac{5}{16}$-in. welds is $2 \times 3.0 = 6$ kips per in. For each inch of beam only $0.328/6 = 0.0546$ in. of weld is required for strength. If 2-in. lengths of weld were used, the required spacing would be $2.0/0.0546 = 36.6$ in., or

$$p = RI/VQ = 12/0.328 = 36.6 \text{ in.}$$

The requirements of the specification are now considered. Section 25(b) allows the clear distance between welds on the tension side of the beam to be either 24 times the thickness of the thinner part, which is the beam flange, or 12 in. whichever is smaller.

$$\text{Clear distance required} = 24 \times 0.40 = 9.6 \text{ in. maximum}$$

The specification requirement controls, and the horizontal shear requirement does not. The welds can be $2 \times \frac{5}{16}$ fillets with a center-to-center spacing of $9.6 + 2 = 11.6$ in. The weld at the end of the member should be as long as the width of the 12**WF**27 flange, which is $6\frac{1}{2}$ in. These requirements are given by the detail drawing of Fig. 8–38(c).

PROBLEMS

Use the AISC Specification unless otherwise noted.

8–1. Two $3 \times \frac{3}{16}$ bars are to be connected to one $3 \times \frac{5}{16}$ bar in a double-lap joint like that of Fig. 8–3(b). Design the joint to carry the tensile capacity of the member, using $\frac{1}{2}$-in. rivets.

8–2. What spacing and end distance are required for the rivets of Problem 8–1?

8–3. A Fink truss supporting a factory roof has a center vertical member, as in Fig. 8–39. In order to lift a machine, it is planned to attach a block and tackle to the truss at point A. The rivets are $\frac{3}{4}$ in. The force to be applied

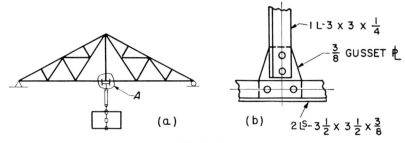

FIG. 8–39.

is 4 tons. You have checked the strength of critical members and have found them safe. Is the riveting at point A satisfactory?

8–4. A $3 \times 1\frac{1}{2}$ bar is connected in a double-lap joint to two $3 \times 1\frac{1}{4}$ bars. The load to be transferred by the joint is 39 kips. Design the joint using $\frac{3}{4}$-in. rivets.

8–5. In repairing a large electric motor, it is found necessary to lift the rotor by crane. No lifting device is available, and limited headroom prevents merely using two wire-rope slings, so a spreader bar is made as shown in Fig. 8–40.

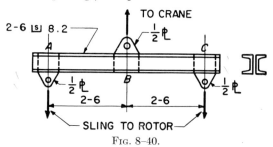

FIG. 8–40.

The rotor weighs 8,400 lb. Design riveted connections using $\frac{1}{2}$-in. rivets. What edge distance is required for the 2-in. hole in the center plate?

8–6. When monorail beams are added to an existing structure they are often connected using clamps such as shown in Fig. 8–41. What is the working

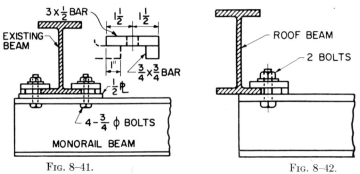

FIG. 8–41.   FIG. 8–42.

capacity of the clamp shown? (In computing the bolt loads, assume that the lever arms may be measured to the center of the $\frac{3}{4}$-in. bar and to the center of the overlap of the clamp and beam flange.)

8-7. Design a clamp of the type shown in Fig. 8–42, where the monorail is a 12I 31.8, the roof beam is 18W⊏50, and the reaction is 7.0 kips.

8-8. Complete the truss design which was started in Example 4–5 (Fig. 4–12) and which was continued in Problem 7–12. Design connections for the truss members you have selected. If the connections are impractical, it may be necessary to revise the selection of members.

8-9. Design a balanced welded connection to transmit a 40-kip load from a $3 \times 3 \times \frac{3}{8}$ angle to a $\frac{3}{8}$-in. gusset plate, as follows:

(a) using side welds only; (b) using an end weld and side welds.

8-10. Two $4 \times 3 \times \frac{3}{8}$ angles have been selected by you to serve as a hanger. They are to be connected to a $\frac{1}{2}$-in. gusset plate, one on each side of the plate and with the 4-in. legs against the plate. Design a balanced welded connection for the full allowable tensile value of the member.

8-11. A catwalk is to be connected to building columns as shown in Fig. 8–43. The columns are spaced at 20-ft centers. Live load on the catwalk should be taken as 50 lb per sq ft. The grating selected weighs 9 lb per sq ft, and the guard rails each about 10 lb per ft. Is the connection satisfactory as shown?

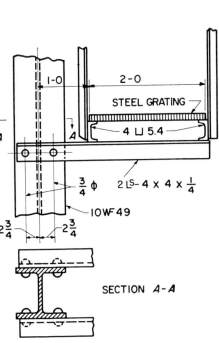

FIG. 8–43.

8–12. By use of $6 \times 3\frac{1}{2} \times \frac{5}{16}$ angles placed with the long leg vertical, four rivets may be placed in each angle of the catwalk bracket of Problem 8–11. What is the highest rivet load? Use the "Usual Gages for Angles" as shown in Appendix B.

8–13. What is the allowable load P for the welded bracket of Fig. 8–44? No end returns are possible.

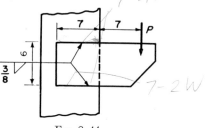

F IG . 8–44.

8–14. What is the capacity of the bracket of Problem 8–13 when weld is applied at the left edge also, with no end tapers except at the right end of the horizontal welds?

8–15. "Ears" are placed on a scrap bin so that it can be lifted by a crane. They are arc welded as shown in Fig. 8–45. What is the capacity of the connection?

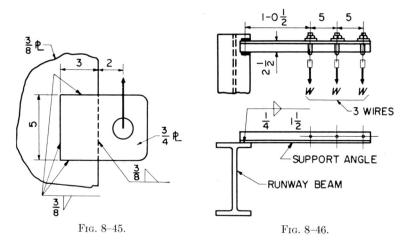

F IG . 8–45.   F IG . 8–46.

8–16. A crane runway is to have 3-wire electrification. At one end of the runway there is very limited space in which to connect the electrification support angle to the top of the girder. The length of weld is limited to the amount shown in Fig. 8–46. However, the wires must be kept in tension in order to keep them level and in contact with the sliding collectors on the crane. How much can the pull W be per wire without overstressing the welded connection?

8–17. Two 8-in. pipes, each weighing 72.4 lb per ft, are to be supported about 12 ft off the floor. Support will be provided by brackets attached to the building columns, which are 20 ft apart. It is hoped that one bracket per column will be adequate. The bracket is shown by Fig. 8–47. The pipes will carry water. What is the required net length L for the welds? $I.D. = 7''$

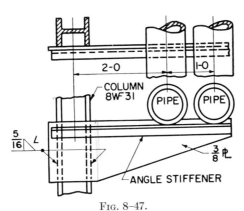

FIG. 8–47.

8–18. An existing crane runway in your plant is supported by brackets as shown in Fig. 8–48. It is planned to suspend a conveyor track from the bottom of the brackets. The bracket will then be subject to increased load. What is allowable vertical load per bracket?

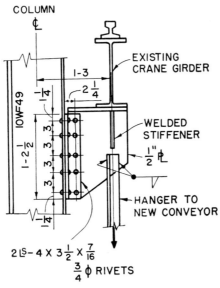

FIG. 8–48.

8–19. In another area of the building it is more practical to support the catwalk of Problem 8–11 using angles as shown in Fig. 8–49. Design the connections using $\frac{3}{4}$-in. rivets. The angles are $\frac{5}{16}$ in. thick.

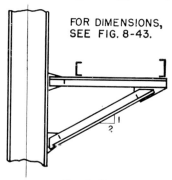

FOR DIMENSIONS, SEE FIG. 8-43.

FIG. 8–49.

8–20. A standard web connection is used to support a 21W̶62 beam on the web of a 24W̶76. What is the capacity of the connection? (The standard connection shows $2\text{l}\underline{s}$ —4 $\times$ $3\frac{1}{2}$ $\times$ $\frac{7}{16}$ $\times$ 1–2$\frac{1}{2}$ long, with five $\frac{3}{4}$-in. shop rivets, and ten field rivets.)

8–21. It is planned to add a mezzanine office area in an existing factory. Assume that you have already designed the floor beams, and that they include 16W̶36 beams which frame into the existing columns as shown in Fig. 8–50. Each 16W̶36 has a maximum reaction of 19 kips. Design web angle connections, using $\frac{3}{4}$-in. rivets. Give all necessary dimensions.

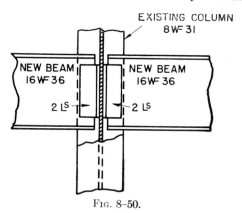

EXISTING COLUMN
8 W̶ 31

NEW BEAM
16 W̶ 36

NEW BEAM
16 W̶ 36

2 l̶S

2 l̶S

FIG. 8–50.

8–22. A manufacturing building is to be converted to suit a new process. Several existing pieces of equipment must be removed. Among these is a machine weighing about 44,000 lb. The machine is now supported by an independent pier of concrete, as shown in Fig. 8–51. The machine was installed before the building floor was completed. It can be removed by skidding it over the floor to a nearby doorway as shown. The weight of the machine

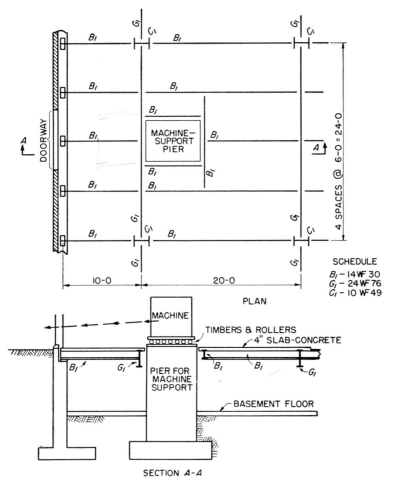

FIG. 8–51.

can be spread by timbers over an area 6 ft square. Other floor live load can be removed from the area during the moving. Will the connections withstand the load, or will shoring of the beams from the basement be necessary? Since the load is temporary and will occur only once, allow a 25 per cent overstress. The adjacent bays to the north and south are the same, but with no opening for such machines.

Details on the connections are:

Beam $B1$ to girder $G1$, web angles $4 \times 3\frac{1}{2} \times \frac{3}{8}$, 3 shop rivets through $B1$, and 6 field rivets through $G1$

Girder $G1$ to col $C1$, web angles $4 \times 3\frac{1}{2} \times \frac{7}{16}$, 6 shop rivets through $G1$, and 12 field rivets through $C1$.

All rivets are $\frac{3}{4}$ in.

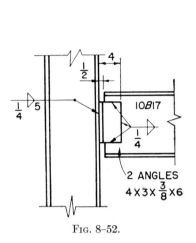

Fig. 8–52.

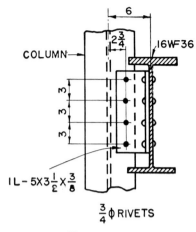

Fig. 8–53.

8–23. What is the capacity of the welded web angle connection of Fig. 8–52?

8–24. Design welded web angle connections for the beams of Problem 8–21.

8–25. A beam is connected eccentrically using a single web angle, as shown in Fig. 8–53. What is the allowable beam reaction on this connection?

8–26. Where beams are supported away from the face of a column, a detail like that of Fig. 8–54 is sometimes used. (This is seen for eave struts and span-drel beams in buildings.) What is the allowable reaction for the beam shown? (Suggestion: Analyze the field rivets by the method of Art. 8–14, and the shop rivets through the column by the method of Art. 8–15. Rotation in the plane of the column flange may be ignored; it is limited to the end rotation of the beam.)

8–27. During some minor plant alterations existing 10W$\Vdash$21 beams, including their web angle connections, are salvaged for use in another part of the building. The beam assemblies are $\frac{3}{4}$ in. too short to fill the clear space between columns at the new location. A $\frac{3}{8}$-in. filler plate will be used at each end, as shown by Fig. 8–55. Design the connection of the filler and beam to the column. The maximum reaction will be 25 kips.

8–28. In Problem 7–5(b) a double-angle hanger was designed for the support of the outer edge of a balcony. (See Fig. 7–41.) In one bay the truss detail at the upper end of the hanger makes it necessary to provide a 2-in. clear spacing between the backs of the angles. Thus, at that one location, fills must be provided at the lower end of the hanger between the angles and the web of the supported beam. The beam has been designed; a 14W$\Vdash$30 has been selected. Design and detail the connection for the beam where fills are required.

8–29. What size and thickness of bearing plate would be required to support one of the 14-in. beams of Example 8–16 on a concrete wall?

8-30. Design a bearing plate for supporting on brick masonry the end of the beam of Problem 7-21.

8-31. Design a base plate for a 12W̶40 column having an axial load of 100 kips. The footing is reinforced concrete.

8-32. The columns for an overhead bin and hopper are 4W̶13. Their axial load is 35 kips each. Design base plates to support these columns on a concrete mat.

8-33. Design welded connections for the reinforced beam of Problem 7-27.

8-34. Design welds for connecting the reinforcement to the monorail beam of Problem 7-24. (As a purely practical consideration, should the beams be left in place or should they be removed during connection of the reinforcement?)

8-35. A 12W̶36 is reinforced with a full-length 8 × 1 plate on the compression flange only. It is to be used on a span of 8 ft to support a total uniform load of 11 kips per ft. Design the welded connection of plate to beam, using intermittent $3 \times \frac{5}{16}$ fillet welds wherever the specification will allow.

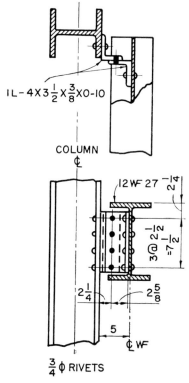

Fig. 8-54.

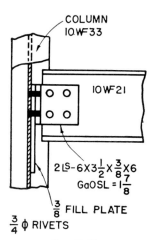

Fig. 8-55.

CHAPTER 9

DESIGN IN CONCRETE

Among our oldest building materials are those known as "cements." Many kinds of cement have been used. One very early example is found in ancient Babylon, where lime cement was used.

The cement which is in most common use today is "portland cement." This type of cement was invented in 1824 by Joseph Aspdin, an English bricklayer. With the introduction of portland cement, "concrete" became an important and reliable construction material. Concrete is a mixture of sand and stone, cemented together by a paste of portland cement and water. Essentially concrete is merely an artificial stone, one which can be cast to almost any desired shape. Its main defect is a low tensile strength.

With the development of steel a method became available by which this main defect could be overcome. Steel rods, imbedded in the concrete where tensile stress was expected were found to prevent collapse of the structure due to tensile failure of the concrete. This new composite material is the "reinforced concrete" of present day use. It is used for bridges, complete building frames, floor slabs, roof slabs, highways, airport runways, and dams. Water pipes, sewers, foundations, tanks, and even floating barges have been made of reinforced concrete. Recent developments in "prestressed" concrete (a little beyond the scope of this book) foretell its use in many new and amazing applications.

The non-civil engineer is very apt to become involved with the simpler problems of design or analysis in reinforced concrete. The applications likely to effect him are found in concrete floor and roof slabs of buildings, in concrete beams and columns of buildings, in simple foundations, and in concrete supports for machines and other equipment.

9–1. Properties of Concrete. Concrete is a mixture of aggregates, cement, and water. In a properly proportioned concrete aggregate stones of medium size fill the large spaces between the large stones, smaller stones fill the spaces between the medium ones, and a sand containing many sizes of grain occupies the remaining space to produce a fairly dense mass. In a good concrete, each grain of this graded and compacted aggregate is coated with a well-proportioned paste of cement and water, and most of the space between the smallest grains is also filled by the paste. The resulting concrete is very dense and will have good properties of strength and durability.

Concrete of the quality described above does not occur by accident.

Courtesy of Portland Cement Association.

MEASURING SLUMP OF CONCRETE.

To produce good quality concrete consistently, one must use a carefully selected and controlled mixture. There are several methods of selecting and controlling the mixture. The oldest method, one still in common use, is the "arbitrary volumes" method. In that method the proportions of stone, sand, and cement to each other are controlled by use of the ratio of the volumes of each required. For example, a 1:2:4 mix is one in which one part (by volume) of cement is mixed with two parts of sand and four parts of stone. The method may be applied by using accurate volume measures, or by the use of "a shovelful of cement, two shovelfuls of sand, etc." After the dry materials have been measured, the water is added. This may be a measured amount of water, but is more often an amount that is judged by the man at the mixer. Unless the amount of water is carefully stated and controlled, the arbitrary volumes method fails to provide control over either the strength or the durability of the concrete. The only property that is controlled is the workability (fluidity), which effects the ease of placing the concrete.

Several mixture design methods of greater accuracy have been developed. Most of these are based on the requirement that strength and workability be controlled at previously selected values. The unit compressive strength at 28 days after mixing is used as a strength measurement. Concretes having specified strengths of 2,000 or 2,500 psi are common in foundations and in older buildings. In newer buildings 28-day strengths of 3,000 psi are most common, with the occasional use of strengths as high as 4,000 psi.

The workability is controlled so that the concrete may be placed (never "poured") easily. The more complex the formwork into which the concrete is placed, the more nearly fluid it must be. If the mix is too sloppy, though, the materials may segregate during placing, the large stones falling to the bottom and the cement paste rising to the top. The degree of workability is measured by the "slump" test which is shown on the preceding page. In this test a conical form is filled with concrete. After the prescribed tamping, the form is removed. The distance which the mass of concrete drops immediately after removal of the form is called the slump. The slumps suggested for various common uses are:

	Maximum	Minimum
Reinforced foundation walls and footings	5 in.	2 in.
Plain footings	4	1
Slabs, beams, reinforced walls	6	3
Building columns	6	3
Heavy mass concrete	3	1

A mixture design method now in common use is the "trial batch" method.[1] This method is intended to guarantee the required strength and to provide the desired workability and durability.

The control of strength is considered first. It is based on the discovery

[1]*Design and Control of Concrete Mixtures* (9th ed.; Chicago: Portland Cement Association).

by Duff Abrams that for a workable and plastic mix, strength is controlled by the ratio of water to cement in the mix. With modern portland cement, the relationship between 28-day compressive strength and the water–cement ratio is as shown by Fig. 9–1. In the trial batch method, the first step is to select the water–cement ratio which gives the required strength. At the same time the weather conditions to which the concrete will be exposed are considered. The water–cement ratio selected must not exceed a specified maximum for the expected exposure.

The second step is to determine experimentally the proportions of aggregates, fine and coarse, to be added to this cement paste in order to obtain the desired workability. This can be done strictly by trial, although excellent tables are available which suggest starting mixes for various types of aggregate. Varia-

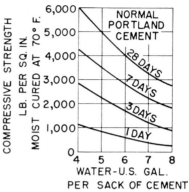

Fig. 9–1.

tions from the starting mix are made until the one is discovered which gives the required slump. The mix selected must be workable and plastic, as shown on page 336. No changes are made in the ratio of free water to cement. The amount of water must be increased slightly to compensate for absorbtion by dry aggregates, or decreased to compensate for free water on the surface of wet aggregates.

The mixture thus selected can be reproduced in quantity using accurate volumetric measurement or by weighing. The large batching plants use the latter method. A transit-mix concrete plant will provide properly proportioned concrete, although the control of the water content is usually in the hands of the truck driver. Since the water–cement ratio controls the strength and durability, one should guard against the temptation to make the mix more workable by adding more water. Excess water usually leads to poor concrete. Excess water occupies space that would otherwise be filled by cement paste. When the excess water evaporates, holes are left in the concrete. The holes reduce strength, reduce stiffness, reduce water-tightness, and invite destruction by weathering.

An apparent exception to these ideas is found in our use of "air entrained" concrete. This material was used by the ancient Romans, but has only recently been "rediscovered" and improved for modern-day use. A resin is added to the mix for the purpose of trapping small bubbles of air. Air is present in all concrete. In ordinary concrete the air bubbles

Courtesy of Portland Cement Association.

A WELL-PROPORTIONED MIXTURE. LIGHT TROWELLING GIVES A SMOOTH SURFACE AND CAUSES ALL SPACES TO BE FILLED WITH MORTAR. IT IS A WORKABLE AND PLASTIC MIX, YET AN ECONOMICAL ONE IN USE OF CEMENT.

A CONCRETE MIXTURE HAVING TOO MUCH CEMENT-SAND MORTAR. IT IS WORKABLE AND PLASTIC, BUT IS UNECONOMICAL. ITS SHRINKAGE IS APT TO BE HIGH AND THE RESULTING CONCRETE WILL LIKELY BE POROUS.

A CONCRETE MIXTURE WITH INSUFFICIENT CEMENT-SAND MORTAR TO FILL THE VOIDS BETWEEN PARTICLES OF COARSE AGGREGATE. THIS CONCRETE WILL BE HARD TO HANDLE AND PLACE. THE RESULTING CONCRETE WILL BE POROUS AND WILL HAVE A "HONEY-COMBED" SURFACE.

are interconnected, so that seepage of water is made easy. In air entrained concrete the air is trapped in small bubbles, encased in the synthetic resin. The bubbles are separated from each other. The disconnected air bubbles of air-entrained concrete do not assist the passage of water. Waterproofness and resistance to weathering is thus much improved. In some areas air-entrained concrete is now used to the exclusion of other types. Highway departments in many states require it for highways and structures. There is no significant difference in cost.

After the concrete has been designed and placed, it is desirable to control its curing conditions. A uniform and complete hydration of the cement can occur only when the concrete is kept moist. The concrete should be covered and sprinkled as required to keep it moist at all times during curing. It should be protected from temperatures below freezing.

The tensile strength of concrete is only about 10 per cent of its compressive strength.

It is to compensate for the low tensile strength that steel reinforcing bars are used. Steel bars are used where the concrete will be in tension through computed bending moments. Steel bars are also used to prevent large cracks from forming as concrete shrinks during curing, or as severe changes of temperature occur. In each case, the steel compensates for the natural weakness of concrete in tension.

Even though it must be reinforced for tension, concrete has advantages as a constructional material. It can be easily formed to the desired shape. The cost makes it a favorable competitor for metals in many cases. Its resistance to weathering and corrosion is good. Its mass is often desirable for the damping of vibrations caused by machinery or by large moving loads.

The specification most often used as a guide in the design of reinforced concrete is the *Building Code Requirements for Reinforced Concrete*, by the American Concrete Institute. This specification is often called the ACI Code. In addition to reading the examples of this chapter, the student should study the applicable sections of the ACI Code.

9–2. Stress Distribution in Steel and Concrete. A typical stress–strain curve for a concrete specimen slowly loaded in compression is shown by Fig. 9–2. The curve has no straight portion as does that for steel. The reason for the continuous curvature is that plastic flow of the concrete accompanies its elastic deformation. If special precautions are taken prior to rapid testing to eliminate the plastic action, a curve having a straight-line beginning is obtained.[2]

[2]George E. Large, *Basic Reinforced Concrete Design* (New York: The Ronald Press Co., 1950), Arts. 1–13, 1–14.

The modulus of elasticity E_c for the concrete is a property which must be known for use in design computations. E_c is equal to the slope of the stress–strain curve. The curve of Fig. 9–2 would give a constantly changing value of E_c. A compromise value is given by the ACI Code as

$$E_c = 1,000 f'_c$$

in which f'_c is the ultimate compressive strength. (This value corresponds closely to the slope of the straight-line portion of the rapid test mentioned above.) For design in the usual stress range E_c is assumed to be constant. For the computation of ultimate loads, however, its variation must be considered.

Assuming that E_c is constant, a relationship can be stated between the stresses in steel and concrete. That relationship is developed in the next paragraph. It is the basis for the conventional design methods in reinforced concrete.

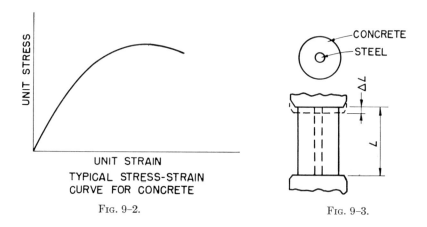

FIG. 9–2.   FIG. 9–3.

Fig. 9–3 shows a cylinder of concrete containing a bar of steel. The cross-sectional area and modulus of elasticity of the steel are A_s and E_s, respectively. For the concrete these values are A_c and E_c. As a load P is applied, both the steel and the concrete shorten an amount ΔL. The shortening of the steel is a function of the stress in the steel.

$$\Delta L = \frac{P_s L}{A_s E_s} = \frac{f_s L}{E_s}$$

For the concrete,

$$\Delta L = \frac{P_c L}{A_c E_c} = \frac{f_c L}{E_c}$$

The two values for ΔL are equal.

$$\frac{f_s L}{E_s} = \frac{f_c L}{E_c}$$

$$f_s = f_c E_s / E_c$$

The ratio E_s/E_c is assumed to be a constant for a given quality of concrete. The ratio is usually called n, so that

$$f_s = n f_c$$

This relationship of f_s and f_c at points of equal unit shortening (or elongation) will be used considerably in the work which follows.

It is often convenient in analysis to use a "transformed section." For the cylinder shown in Fig. 9–3, the total load

$$P = f_c A_c + f_s A_s = f_c (A_c + n A_s)$$

The quantity $(A_c + n A_s)$ is called the "area of the transformed section." The transformed section is one in which the steel area is assumed to be replaced by n times as much area of an imaginary material having the same modulus of elasticity as the concrete. Since all the material in the transformed section has the same E value, analysis of the unit stresses for the transformed section is quite simple.

Any composite member, whether in tension, compression, or bending, may be analyzed by means of a transformed section. The same procedure is used in the analysis of members having other material combinations—for example, steel and aluminum, or wood and steel.

9–3. Analysis of Rectangular Beams. Rectangular concrete beams are usually reinforced by a single layer of steel bars located near the tension face of the beam. This arrangement is shown in Fig. 9–4(a).

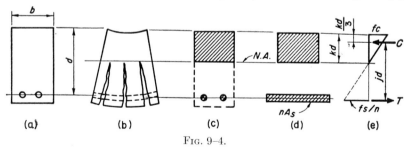

(a)　　　(b)　　　(c)　　　(d)　　　(e)

Fig. 9–4.

Occasionally beams are doubly reinforced, in which case a layer of steel is located near the compression face also.

Analysis of the beam to determine its capacity, or to determine its stresses under given loads can be made by using formulas. The formulas for reinforced concrete work are often long and cumbersome. Unless one works with the formulas regularly, it is better to use the transformed section wherever it is applicable. The transformed section is easy to use, and it helps the user to keep the nature of the analysis clearly in mind.

As the beam of Fig. 9–4 bends, the concrete on the bottom edge receives tensile stress. Concrete is weak in tension, so cracks develop on the bottom face while the tensile stresses are still quite low. As the bending moment is increased the cracks progress upward, nearly to the neutral axis. The cracks are narrow, hairline cracks, but are closely spaced. The portion of the concrete which is cracked is now ineffective in resisting bending. The entire bending moment is resisted by the remaining uncracked concrete and by the steel. It is practical to consider all concrete below the neutral axis to be cracked. The effective section is thus limited to that shown shaded in Fig. 9–4(c). This effective section has materials of two different E values. For computation purposes it will be changed to a transformed section.

The transformed section is obtained by substituting imaginary tension-resisting concrete for the steel. The area substituted is n times the steel area, and is located on the same line as the original steel. The transformed section is shown by Fig. 9–4(d).

The flexural stress on the transformed section is proportional to the distance from the neutral axis. This distribution of stress is shown in Fig. 9–4(e). (The stress distribution can be expressed also by the flexure formula $f = My/I$, provided the moment of inertia I is that of the transformed section.) The upper extreme fiber stress shown is that for the actual section as well as for the transformed section. The bottom stress shown is the stress in the imaginary material of the transformed section. The steel of the actual beam is n times as stiff as the imaginary material. The steel stress is n times the stress for the imaginary material.

The flexure formula can easily be used with the transformed section, but there is an even easier method. Fig. 9–4(e) will be used to illustrate it. The force C is the resultant of all of the compressive stresses on the cross section. That resultant is located at the center of gravity of the triangle showing the intensity of stress, or at a distance $kd/3$ from the top fiber. The resultant of the tensile stresses is force T. For practical purposes this is located at the center of the reinforcing steel. These two resultants, T and C, form an internal couple. The resisting moment of this couple is equal to the bending moment applied to the beam at that section. Thus

$$M = Cjd$$

or

$$M = Tjd$$

The dimension d is known as the "effective depth"; jd is the "lever arm of the internal couple."

EXAMPLE 9–1. What are the flexural stresses in the steel and concrete of the beam section shown in Fig. 9–5(a)? The bending moment is 45 ft-kips. The ultimate compressive strength f'_c for the concrete is 3,000 psi.

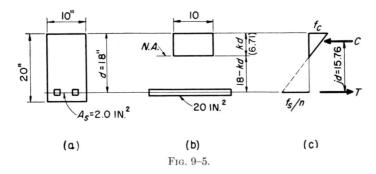

(a)   (b)   (c)

FIG. 9–5.

The transformed section is shown in Fig. 9–5(b). The modulus of elasticity E for 3,000-lb concrete is $1,000 \times 3,000$ or 3,000,000 psi. That for steel is 30,000,000 psi, and n is the ratio 30,000,000/3,000,000 or $n = 10$. The area substituted for the steel is nA_s or 20 sq in.

The dimension kd must be determined. The neutral axis of a member in bending is at the center of gravity of the cross section. In this case it is at the center of gravity of the transformed section. The moment of the area above the neutral axis (about the neutral axis) is equal to the moment of the area below.

$$10kd \, \frac{kd}{2} = 20(18 - kd)$$

$$5(kd)^2 = 360 - 20kd$$

Dividing by five, and completing the square gives

$$(kd)^2 + 4kd + 4 = 72 + 4 = 76$$

$$kd + 2 = \pm 8.71$$

$$kd = 6.71 \text{ in.}$$

Now that the neutral axis has been located, jd, the lever arm of the internal couple, can be determined.

$$jd = 18 - 6.71/3 = 15.76 \text{ in.}$$

The applied bending moment of 45 ft-kips is resisted by the internal couple, Cjd or Tjd.

$$C = T = 45 \times 12/15.76 = 34.3 \text{ kips}$$

The flexural stress in the concrete varies from zero to f_c, so that the extreme fiber stress f_c is twice the average stress. Compression exists on the area above the neutral axis, which is $10 \times 6.71 = 67.1$ sq in.

$$f_c = 2 \times C/67.1 = 2 \times 34,300/67.1 = 1,020 \text{ psi}$$

The force T is divided uniformly over the steel area of 2.0 sq in., so that

$$f_s = 34,300/2.0 = 17,150 \text{ psi}$$

EXAMPLE 9–2. Fig. 9–6(a) shows a section through a building. The concrete floor slab was originally intended to support light office-type

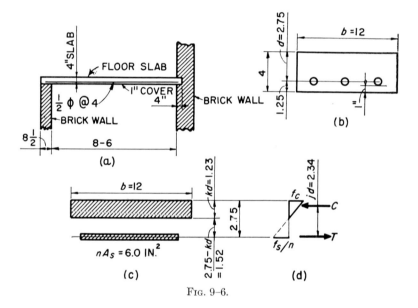

FIG. 9–6.

loads. Assume that it is now desired to convert the area to a heavier type of service. What is the allowable uniform live load per square foot of floor? The building records show that concrete with f'_c of 3,000 psi was specified, and that the allowable fiber stress for the reinforcing steel was 16,000 psi. The detail drawings also show that $\frac{1}{2}$-in. round bars were used at 4-in. centers. A cover of one inch of concrete was provided below the steel.

A slab is merely a beam of great width. To simplify the computations a strip one-foot wide is analyzed, considering only the loads on that one-foot strip. Fig. 9–6(b) shows such a strip. The distance from the bottom of the slab to the center of the bars is the cover thickness plus the bar radius, or 1.25 in. Thus the effective depth d is 2.75 in. Table 7 of Appendix B shows the area A_s to be 0.20 sq in. per bar. Each one-ft width of slab contains three such bars, so that A_s is $3 \times 0.20 = 0.60$ sq in. E for the concrete is 1,000 times f'_c, or 3,000,000 psi.

$$n = E_s/E_c = 10$$

The transformed section is shown by Fig. 9–6(c). The moment of the area above the neutral axis is equal to the moment of the area below.

$$12kd \, \frac{kd}{2} = 6.0(2.75 - kd)$$

$$6(kd)^2 = 16.5 - 6.0kd$$

Dividing by 6 and completing the square gives

$$(kd)^2 + kd + (0.50)^2 = 2.75 + 0.25 = 3.00$$

$$kd + 0.50 = \pm 1.73$$

$$kd = 1.23 \text{ in.}$$

The internal couple is shown in Fig. 9–6(d).

$$jd = 2.75 - 1.23/3 = 2.34 \text{ in.}$$

The load that can be carried depends on the amount of the internal resisting couple. Two resisting moments must be computed. Moment Cjd is the resistance that will be developed when the extreme fiber stress in the concrete reaches the allowable value. Moment Tjd is that which will be developed when the steel stress reaches its allowable of 16,000 psi. These two moments of resistance are usually not equal. When they are equal, the beam is said to have a "balanced design."

The allowable extreme fiber stress in the concrete is given by the ACI Specification as $0.45f'_c$ or 1,350 psi. When the extreme fiber is stressed to 1,350 psi, the average compressive stress will be one-half of 1,350. The total force C will be

$$C = \frac{1,350}{2} (12 \times 1.23) = 9,960 \text{ lb}$$

The resisting moment of the concrete is

$$M_c = Cjd = 9,960 \times 2.34 = 23,300 \text{ in.-lb}$$

The resisting moment of the steel is jd times the allowable value of the force T.

$$\text{Allowable } T = 0.60 \times 16{,}000 = 9{,}600 \text{ lb}$$

$$M_s = 9{,}600 \times 2.34 = 22{,}400 \text{ in.-lb}$$

The lower moment, M_s, controls. When the applied bending moment is 22,400 in.-lb, the steel is stressed to 16,000 psi, and the concrete is stressed to less than 1,350 psi. The amount of f_c can be computed by similar triangles on Fig. 9–6(d).

$$\frac{f_c}{1.23} = \frac{16{,}000/10}{1.52}$$

$$f_c = 1{,}295 \text{ psi}$$

For a simply supported beam,

$$M = wL^2/8$$

The span L is the distance center-to-center of supports, which is 9 ft $0\frac{1}{4}$ in., or 9.02 ft. When M is 22,400 in.-lb, or 1,870 ft-lb,

$$w = \frac{8M}{L^2} = \frac{8 \times 1{,}870}{(9.02)^2} = 184 \text{ lb per ft of beam}$$

The total allowable load is 184 lb per sq ft of slab. The slab itself weighs $\frac{1}{3}$ of 150, or 50 lb per sq ft. The allowable live load is, therefore, $184 - 50$ which is 134 lb per sq ft of slab.

The example thus far has considered only the flexural strength of the slab. Other things to be considered include the shear and bond strengths, which will be explained later in this chapter.

9–4. Design of Rectangular Beams. At the start of the design of a rectangular beam only the allowable stresses (f_s and f_c) and the ratio n are known. The unknowns are the effective depth d, the steel area A_s, the factors k and j for the dimensions kd and jd, and usually the width b. The unknowns are too many to permit a direct solution. Many different combinations of d, b, and A_s will be found satisfactory.

The design is started by assuming values for some of the unknowns. The remaining unknowns are then solved. If the section selected shows much variation from the assumed values, the design can be made again with better assumptions. The method thus becomes one of successive approximation. It is rarely, however, that a second trial is necessary.

It is the usual practice to start by assuming that a "balanced design" will be used. In a beam of balanced design, f_c and f_s both reach their full allowable values under the same condition of loading. The diagram of flexural stress in Fig. 9–7 shows that for any given values of f_c, f_s, and n the factor k is a constant. By similar triangles,

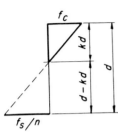

$$\frac{kd}{f_c} = \frac{d - kd}{f_s/n}$$

Solving the above gives

$$k = \frac{f_c}{f_c + f_s/n}$$

For example, when f'_c is 3,000 psi, and the allowable f_s is 16,000

FIG. 9–7.

$$k = \frac{1{,}350}{1{,}350 + 16{,}000/10} = 0.457$$

The lever arm jd is equal to $d - kd/3$; therefore,

$$j = 1 - k/3$$

For example, when f_c is 1,350 psi and f_s 16,000 psi,

$$j = 1 - 0.457/3 = 0.848$$

Using the tentative values of k and j, a width and required effective depth are next selected. After selecting a practical size for actual use, the required steel area A_s and size of steel bars are determined. The procedure will be shown by examples.

EXAMPLE 9–3. Design a rectangular reinforced concrete section for interior use to resist a total bending moment of 50 ft-kips. Use concrete having a 28-day strength (f'_c) of 2,500 psi, and intermediate grade reinforcing steel. Use the ACI Code.

$$E_c = 1{,}000 f'_c = 2{,}500{,}000 \text{ psi}$$

$$n = 30{,}000{,}000/2{,}500{,}000 = 12$$

The allowable f_c is $0.45 f'_c$ or 1,125 psi, and the allowable f_s is 20,000 psi. By similar triangles, as in Fig. 9–7,

$$\frac{kd}{1{,}125} = \frac{d - kd}{20{,}000/12}$$

$$k = \frac{1{,}125}{1{,}125 + 20{,}000/12} = 0.403$$

$$j = 1 - 0.403/3 = 0.866$$

These will be the values of k and j for a balanced design.

The internal resisting couple is shown by Fig. 9–8(a). Force C will be the average stress times the area (bkd) above the neutral axis.

$$C = \frac{1,125}{2} \times 0.403bd = 227bd$$

The moment of 50 ft-kips must be resisted by the internal couple Cjd.

$$50,000 \times 12 = 227bd(0.866d) = 197bd^2$$

Required $bd^2 = 3,040$

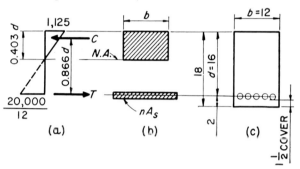

Fig. 9–8.

Many different combinations of b and d will satisfy the above equation. Possible solutions are:

For $b = 10$ in., required $d = 17.5$ in.
For $b = 12$ in., required $d = 15.9$ in.
For $b = 14$ in., required $d = 14.8$ in.

Practical considerations such as available space and economy would now determine which size to select. For greater stiffness or for the saving of steel, a section larger than those above could be used. If necessary, a smaller section could be used, although this would require additional reinforcement.

Let us assume that the section with b of 12 in. is most practical for this example. Section 507(b) of the ACI Building Code requires that reinforcing bars on beams not exposed to the weather be protected by $1\frac{1}{2}$ in. of concrete cover. Assuming that the bars to be selected will be one inch thick, the total depth of beam should be

$$15.9 + 1\tfrac{1}{2} + \tfrac{1}{2} = 17.9 \text{ in.}$$

To be practical, a 12-in. by 18-in. section will be used. Cover of $1\frac{1}{2}$ in. will be provided, making d tentatively 16 in. The section is shown in Fig. 9–8(c).

The required steel area will be computed next.

$$T = \frac{M}{jd} = 50,000 \times 12/(0.866 \times 16) = 43,300 \text{ lb}$$

Required $A_s = 43,300/20,000 = 2.16$ sq in.

Refer to Table 8 of Appendix B. The required area of steel could be provided by various bar sizes, as follows:

> 11 No. 4 bars (provides 2.20 sq in.)
> 7 No. 5 bars (provides 2.17 sq in.)
> 5 No. 6 bars (provides 2.20 sq in.)
> 4 No. 7 bars (provides 2.40 sq in.)
> 3 No. 8 bars (provides 2.37 sq in.)

Based on economy of steel only, 7 No. 5 bars would seem to be the logical choice. However, the spacing requirements of Section 305(a) of the ACI Building Code would rule out their use. To permit their use the width of beam would have to be

$$2 \times 1\tfrac{1}{2} \text{ (cover)} + (7 \times 0.625) + 6 \times 1 \text{ (spaces)} = 13\tfrac{3}{8} \text{ in. minimum}$$

Since b is only 12 in., the No. 5 bars could not be used unless arranged in two layers, one above the other. This would add to the required over-all depth of beam.

Five No. 6 bars would require a width b of

$$(2 \times 1\tfrac{1}{2}) + (5 \times 0.75) + (4 \times 1) = 10\tfrac{3}{4} \text{ in. minimum}$$

Before the final selection of the bar sizes can be made, the bond strength between the concrete and steel must be considered. This will be dealt with later in the chapter. If 5 No. 6 bars were found satisfactory in bond also, they would very likely be selected for use in this beam.

EXAMPLE 9–4. Assume that space requirements limit the beam of the previous example to 12-in. width and 16-in. over-all depth. How could such a beam be made without overstressing the concrete?

There are three ways to do this. First, a stronger concrete could be used; second, reinforcing bars could be placed on the compression side as well as on the tension side; and third, an excess of steel could be placed on the bottom, giving a design that is not "balanced." This third method will be illustrated. To avoid clouding the basic principles no new formulas or design charts will be introduced. The theory covered thus far is sufficient.

Since the design is not to be balanced one, the value of f_s in Fig. 9–9(a) is not known. Neither are the factors k and j. The effective depth d will be 14 in. if bars of one-inch thickness can be used.

$$\text{Force } C = \frac{1,125}{2}(12kd) = 6,750\,kd$$

$$M = Cjd = 6,750\,kdjd$$

$$kj = \frac{M}{6,750\,d^2} = \frac{50,000 \times 12}{6,750(14)^2} = 0.454$$

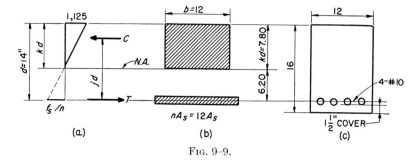

Fig. 9-9.

In Fig. 9–9(a), $jd = d - kd/3$, so that $j = 1 - k/3$.

$$k(1 - k/3) = 0.454$$

$$k^2 - 3k = -1.362$$

$$(k - 1.5)^2 = -1.362 + (1.5)^2 = 0.888$$

$$k = 1.5 \pm 0.943 = 0.557; \quad kd = 7.80 \text{ in.}$$

$$j = 1 - 0.557/3 = 0.814; \quad jd = 11.4 \text{ in.}$$

Now that the lever arm of the internal couple is known, the force T of the internal couple could be computed. Knowing T would not help, however. The steel stress f_s is not known and steel cannot be selected from knowing T alone. Instead, the steel area A_s must be chosen so as to keep the concrete stress f_c within the allowable value of 1,125 psi. The stress f_c will equal 1,125 psi if kd is 7.80 in.; it will be less than 1,125 psi if kd is larger than 7.80 in. The steel area A_s, then, must cause kd to be equal to or greater than 7.80 in. The area needed can be solved using the transformed section in Fig. 9–9(b). The neutral axis (N.A.) is at the center of gravity of the transformed section.

$$12A_s \times 6.20 = 12 \times 7.80 \times \frac{7.80}{2} = 365$$

Required $A_s = 4.91$ sq in.

Four No. 10 bars will provide an area of 5.08 sq in. They would require a beam width of $(2 \times 1\frac{1}{2}) + (4 \times 1.25) + (3 \times 1.25) = 11.75$ in. minimum. Smaller sized bars would require a width larger than the available 12 in.

9–5. Shear and Bond.   In reinforced concrete the term "shear stress" refers to the shear in the concrete. The term "bond stress" refers to the shearing stress between steel and concrete at the surface of the steel bars. The intensity of each can be computed using the flexure formula and the relationship of total shear V to the change of bending moment. (See Chapter 3.)

Concrete in shear will fail by forming tension cracks in a diagonal direction. Fig. 9–10(a) shows an example of this type of failure near the end of a beam. In Fig. 9–10(b) a small unit element of material is

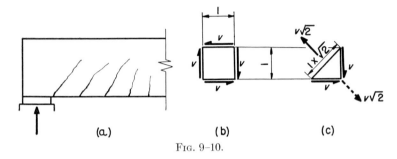

Fig. 9–10.

isolated. It is taken from a portion of the beam having shear only and no flexural stresses. The vertical shearing stresses on this element form a clockwise couple. This is balanced by a counterclockwise couple formed by horizontal shearing stresses on the top and bottom surfaces of the element. Since the two couples are equal, the horizontal shearing stress is equal to the vertical.

This element is now considered to be cut along a diagonal. One of the halves is shown in Fig. 9–10(c). The two shearing stresses can be replaced by their resultant $v\sqrt{2}$, which is shown dotted. This half-element is held in equilibrium by a tensile force $v\sqrt{2}$ normal to the inclined face. While the surfaces of the original element have unit area, the sloping surface has an area of $1 \times \sqrt{2}$. The *unit* tensile stress on that surface is then equal to v. In other words, a diagonal tensile stress is caused by shear; it is equal to the shear stress and inclined at 45 degrees to it. (A diagonal compressive stress is caused at 90 degrees to the tensile stress.) At locations having flexural stress as well as shear, the inclination of the resultant tensile force will vary from point to point. Thus the slope of the tensile cracks will vary as shown in Fig. 9–10(a).

It is customary to limit the unit shear stress to the allowable given by the specification. The real object, of course, is to limit the diagonal tensile stress, since the failure will be a tensile one as shown by Fig. 9–10(a). Concrete has a very low tensile strength; therefore, the allowable shearing (diagonal tensile) stress is low. The ACI Building Code (Section 305) allows only $0.03f'_c$. For 3,000-lb concrete, this would be only 90 psi for shear.

Computation of the unit shear is based on the flexure formula. Fig. 9–11(a) shows a slice of length dL taken from a beam. The resultant flexural forces, T and C, are shown on each end of the slice. Now, imagine this slice to be cut horizontally at a distance y above the steel. The bottom part of the slice is shown in part (b) of Fig. 9–11.

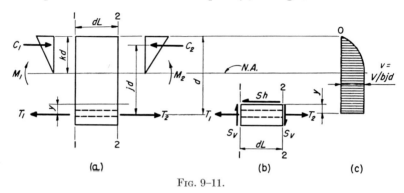

FIG. 9–11.

If the beam has shear at the section being considered, the bending moments M_1 and M_2 will be unequal. Assume that M_2 is the larger moment. Force T_2 is larger than T_1, and an additional horizontal force is required in order to satisfy the equilibrium equation $\Sigma H = 0$. The horizontal force is S_h, provided by horizontal shearing stresses on the top surface of the element. Vertical shearing forces at the ends of the element complete the picture. The intensity of shearing stress on the upper surface of the element will now be computed.

By $\Sigma H = 0$, $S_h = T_2 - T_1$.

$$T_1 = M_1/jd \quad \text{and} \quad T_2 = M_2/jd$$

$$T_2 - T_1 = \frac{M_2 - M_1}{jd} = S_h$$

In Chapter 3 rules relating load, shear, and bending moment were developed. One of these stated that the change of bending moment between two sections is equal to the area of the shear diagram between those two sections. Thus, if V is the shear at the section, and if dL is a very short length,

$$M_2 - M_1 = V \, dL$$

Substituting $V \, dL$ for $M_2 - M_1$ gives

$$S_h = V \, dL/jd$$

The shear force S_h is distributed uniformly over the area of the upper surface. This area is dL times the width b of the beam. Thus, the unit shear stress is

$$v = S_h/b \, dL = V/bjd$$

The distance y did not enter into these computations in any way. The force S_h on Fig. 9–11(b) is independent of the distance y, provided the horizontal cut is made below the neutral axis. If the cut were made above the neutral axis, though, a portion of each of the compressive forces C_1 and C_2 would appear on the isolated element, and the force S_h would become smaller. It would become zero if the horizontal cut were made at the top surface of the beam. The isolated element would then be the entire slice of Fig. 9–11(a). Obviously no shear force can exist on the upper surface of the beam.

The intensity of horizontal shear stress at various points on the cross section is shown in Fig. 9–11(c). This curve conforms to the explanation in the previous paragraph. It is also the curve of the equation $v = VQ/Ib$, in which I is the moment of inertia of the transformed section.

In designing a beam one should solve for the depth required to prevent overstress in shear. This depth and that required for flexure should be compared. A depth meeting both requirements should be selected. Then the design should be continued to compute the steel required.

When selecting the steel, it is necessary to be certain that the bond stress (horizontal shear between concrete and steel) does not exceed the allowable values. The bond stress is computed using the same method as was used for shear. In this case the steel bars are removed from the short "slice" of beam. These bars are shown isolated in Fig. 9–12. The

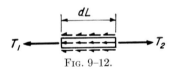

FIG. 9–12.

forces T_1 and T_2 are unequal. The bar is held in equilibrium by horizontal shearing stresses between the concrete and the steel. (The sum of these stresses corresponds to force S_h in Fig. 9–11.) These shear stresses are called "bond stresses." They are assumed to be uniform over the surface area of the bars. The surface area is equal to length dL times Σo, the sum of the bar perimeters. The bond stress intensity u is equal to $(T_2 - T_1)$ divided by this surface area.

$$u = \frac{T_2 - T_1}{dL\ \Sigma o}$$

Substituting $V\ dL/jd$ for $(T_2 - T_1)$ gives

$$u = \frac{V}{\Sigma o\ jd}$$

The tables of bar sizes give the bar perimeters, so that the above equation can be used to determine bond stress. In design, the allowable bond stress is known and the required sum of perimeters Σo is computed.

With the required A_s and Σo known, and with spacing and other practical requirements considered, the final choice of steel bars can be made.

Caution. When checking existing work, it is necessary to know the type of bar that was used. Prior to 1951, all deformed reinforcing bars had bond strengths conforming to the 1947 ACI Building Code. In 1951, a new type of reinforcing bar deformation was adopted as a standard. This new bar has *much* higher bond strength than the older type bars. It is described in ASTM Specification A305–50T. The allowable bond stresses for these "hi-bond" bars are given in the 1951 ACI Building Code. (The raised ribs on the bar surface are "deformations.")

In Appendix B, Table 7 shows the properties of the older type of bar, while Table 8 gives the properties of the newer type.

When it is certain that the newer bars will be used, the 1951 allowables should be used.

For work done during 1951 and part of 1952, either type of bar may have been used. The record plans and specifications should be consulted to determine which type was used.

For work done prior to 1951, it is reasonable to assume that the old type of bar was used. The 1947 ACI Building Code should be used in this case. The allowable bond stresses in that Code were as follows:

In beams and slabs:

 Plain bars . . . . $0.04f'_c$, but not to exceed 160 psi
 Deformed bars . . . . $0.05f'_c$, but not to exceed 200 psi

In beams, slabs, and one-way footings:

 Plain bars (hooked) . . . . . $0.06f'_c$, but not to exceed 200 psi
 Deformed bars (hooked) . . $0.075f'_c$, but not to exceed 250 psi

In two-way footings:

 Plain bars (hooked) . . . . . $0.045f'_c$, but not to exceed 160 psi
 Deformed bars (hooked) . . $0.056f'_c$, but not to exceed 200 psi

EXAMPLE 9–5. In Example 9–2 an existing floor slab was analyzed for flexure. It was found that a live load of 134 lb per sq ft could be applied. Continue this analysis now to determine whether the existing slab can resist that load in bond and in shear. The slab was built in the year 1945. Fig. 9–6 shows the slab cross section. The load per square foot of slab is 134 lb for live load plus 50 lb for dead load, or 184 lb total. The span is 9.02 ft. For a span of slab one ft wide, the maximum shear is the end reaction, or

$$V = 184 \times 9.02/2 = 830 \text{ lb}$$

Shear (diagonal tension) will be considered first. The ACI Code allows 90 psi in shear for 3,000-lb concrete. The computed actual unit shear stress is

$$v = V/bjd = 830/12 \times 2.34 = 29.6 \,\text{psi}$$

The actual stress is much less than the allowable, so the slab is satisfactory in shear.

The allowable bond stress for the old-type bars is $0.05f_c'$, which is $0.05 \times 3,000 = 150$ psi. Table 7 of Appendix B shows the perimeter of one $\frac{1}{2}$-in. round bar to be 1.6 in. Each one-ft width of slab contains 3 bars, as shown in Fig. 9–6(b), and Σo for the one-ft width is 4.8 in. The computed actual bond stress is

$$u = V/\Sigma o \, jd = 830/4.8 \times 2.34 = 73.9 \,\text{psi}$$

Thus the slab is satisfactory in bond also.

EXAMPLE 9–6. Fig. 9–13(a) shows a pit into which granular materials are dropped from small bottom-dump cars. Conveyors beneath the pit move the material to the next operation.

The 12I31.8 beams which support the track and cars have corroded rapidly and must be replaced. If new steel beams are installed, the corrosion will occur again. Concrete beams are being considered. They could be precast and cured near the site, and then hoisted into place with a light crane. This would avoid shutting down the plant during a long curing period as would be necessary if the beams were cast in place. Assume that you, as a plant engineer, have been requested to design such a beam. Intermediate grade steel and concrete having a 28-day strength of 3,000 psi will be assumed. The maximum load applied by the stringers to the transverse beam is 10 kips at each load point. Assume that this has been computed by the methods used in Chapter 5. These loads are shown in Fig. 9–13(b). The concrete beams will be made with one in. of clearance at each end, giving a 7-in. bearing length. The span will be 9 ft 7 in.

The pockets to receive the new beams are 14 in. deep. That depth can be increased or decreased if necessary.

It is now necessary to estimate the weight of the beam itself, and to compute the maximum shear and bending moment. Assuming that the beam weight w is 150 lb per ft,

$$\text{Maximum } V = 10.00 + (0.15 \times 9.58/2) = 10.72 \,\text{kips}$$

The maximum bending moment will occur at the center of the span.

$$\text{Maximum } M = (10 \times 3.04) + 0.15(9.58)^2/8 = 32.1 \,\text{ft-kips}$$

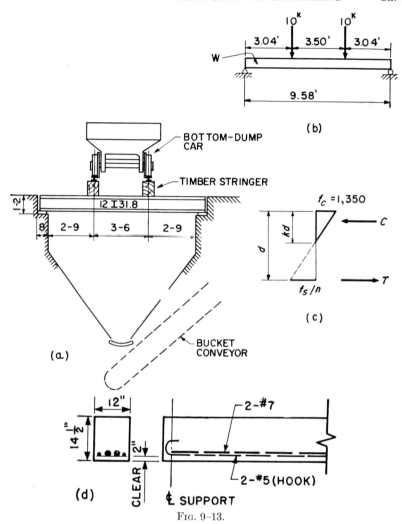

FIG. 9–13.

The allowable f_c is $0.45f'_c = 1,350$ psi. The allowable f_s is 20,000 psi. Ratio n is $30,000,000/(1,000 \times 3,000) = 10$. Using the similar triangles on the stress diagram of Fig. 9–13(c), and assuming a balanced design,

$$k = \frac{1,350}{1,350 + 20,000/10} = 0.403$$

$$j = 1 - k/3 = 0.866$$

The depth required for bending will be considered first. Use Fig. 9–13(c).

$$C = \frac{1,350}{2} \times 0.403db = 272bd$$

The bending moment of 32.1 ft-kips is resisted by the internal resisting moment of forces C and T.

$$236bd^2 = 32,100 \times 12$$
$$\text{Required } bd^2 = 1,630$$

This requirement could be satisfied by a beam having

$$b = 10 \text{ in.} \quad \text{and} \quad d = 12.75 \text{ in.}$$

or by one having

$$b = 12 \text{ in.} \quad \text{and} \quad d = 11.7 \text{ in.}$$

Assuming that one-in. bars will be used with a cover of 2 in., the over-all depths of the above sections are required to be 15.25 in. and 14.2 in., respectively. The deeper section would require that the beam pockets in the wall be deepened by chipping. The shallower section could be used with little chipping, even when "rounded off" to a practical depth. The computations will be continued using a $12 \times 14\frac{1}{2}$ beam, having d equal to 12 in. This section is now checked for shear.

$$v = V/bjd = 10,720/12 \times 0.866 \times 12 = 86 \text{ psi}$$

This is less than the 90 psi allowed by the ACI Code. Therefore the $12 \times 14\frac{1}{2}$ beam is satisfactory for both flexure and shear. The actual weight of the beam will be about $150 \times 14.5/12 = 181$ lb per ft. The weight assumed was only 150 lb per ft. Correcting this would give a maximum bending moment of 32.5 ft-kips, and a maximum shear of 10.87 kips. These corrected values will be used to continue the solution.

$$T = (32,500 \times 12)/(0.866 \times 12) = 37,500 \text{ lb}$$
$$\text{Required } A_s = 37,500/20,000 = 1.87 \text{ sq in.}$$

The new type of bar will be used so that the allowable bond stress u is 300 psi. (See the ACI Code.)

$$\text{Required } \Sigma o = V/ujd = 10,870/(300 \times 0.866 \times 12) = 3.48 \text{ in.}$$

The above area and perimeter could be provided by any of the following:

    a) 2 No. 9 bars ($A_s = 2.00$ sq in.; $\Sigma o = 7.0$ in.)
    b) 3 No. 8 bars ($A_s = 2.37$ sq in.; $\Sigma o = 9.3$ in.)
    c) 4 No. 7 bars ($A_s = 2.40$ sq in.; $\Sigma o = 10.8$ in.)
    d) 2 No. 7 and 2 No. 5 bars ($A_s = 1.82$ sq in.; $\Sigma o = 9.4$ in.)*

*When a section has bars of more than one size, bond stresses for the various sizes are not alike. The bars of (d) were selected assuming equal bond stress. The two larger bars alone provide adequate perimeter in this case, so that the section is obviously satisfactory in bond. Were it not obviously satisfactory, the following reasoning and procedure could be used:

The change of unit stress in length dL is alike for all bars. The change of bar load,

The choice of reinforcement is apparently between (a) and (d) above. The width b of 12 in. is adequate for the spacing of either. Group (d) would probably be the better choice. The bond requirements of the ACI Code do not cover the question of how the bars of this beam should terminate. The author feels that at least two of them should extend beyond the center of the support. Only 2 in. of extension can be provided. More would reduce the coverage to less than $1\frac{1}{2}$ in. The extension could be provided by hooks; the smaller size of bar is much easier to bend in this manner. The final beam using group (d) above is shown in Fig. 9–13(d). The 2 No. 7 bars could be dropped where the bending moment is low enough so that the 2 No. 5 bars are sufficient. The smaller bars supply only 0.62 sq in., which is 0.62/1.87 or 0.332 times the required A_s. If kd and jd are assumed to be unchanged where the larger bars are dropped, then the section having only 2 No. 5 bars will have a resisting moment of 0.332 × 32.5 = 10.8 ft-kips. That amount of bending moment will occur at less than one ft from the end of the beam. The No. 7 bars could, in theory, be dropped at that distance from the end. It is the custom, however, to extend the bars a little beyond the point where they are no longer needed for tension. Section 902 (a) of the ACI Code covers such extension for bars in continuous beams. A similar extension would be used in this case. A 12-diameter extension of the No. 7 bars would bring the end of the bar nearly to the center of the support. The practical solution is to make the bars full-length, as shown in Fig. 9–13(d).

9–6. Web Reinforcement. Sometimes the beam size required to prevent overstress in shear is much larger than is needed for flexure. The larger section may be undesirable. In these cases, a smaller section may be used provided it is reinforced against failure by diagonal tension.

The ideal way in which to prevent such failure would be to place steel at right angles to the possible diagonal cracks. (See Fig. 9–10.) This, of course, is not practical. The direction of the cracks changes from point to point. The bars would need to be bent into weird shapes and they would be very difficult to place. Further, with movable or moving loads, the directions of the principal tensile stresses might change. A single set of bars would be suited to one load condition only.

---

though, is proportional to the bar area or to the square of the bar diameter. The bar surface area in length dL is proportional to the diameter. Bond stress is equal to change of bar load divided by bar surface area, which is proportional to $d^2/d = d$. The allowable shear $V = jdu\Sigma o$ where one size of bar is used, or $V = jd(u_1\Sigma o_1 + u_2\Sigma o_2)$ where two sizes are used. The perimeter Σo_1 of 2 No. 7 bars is 5.4 in., and Σo_2 of 2 No. 5 bars is 4.0 in. When the bond stress u_1 is 300 psi for the No. 7 bars, u_2 will be 5/7 of 300 or 214 psi for the No. 5 bars. V allowed = 0.866 × 12[(300 × 5.4) + (214 × 4.0)] = 25,750 lb. The allowable shear V exceeds the actual, so the bars of (d) are satisfactory in bond.

There are two practical manners in which web reinforcement can be provided. The first of these is the use of bent-up bars, as shown in Fig. 9–14(a). Several bars are provided for flexure at the point of maximum bending moment. Where the moment is less, some of the bars

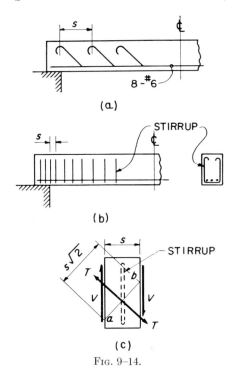

(a)

(b)

(c)
Fɪɢ. 9–14.

may be eliminated. The bars which are no longer needed are bent up, usually at a 45-degree angle. The bent-up bars are parallel to the diagonal tensile stress caused by shear. If the spacing s of the bent portions is controlled, the strength of these bars plus the tensile strength of the concrete itself will prevent the diagonal tensile cracks. The disadvantages in using bent-up bars are that the fabrication is costly, and that the correct spacing of the bends along the member may be hard to provide. The present practice is to use bent-up bars sparingly. Usually they are used only where an additional purpose is served by bending them up. For example, in continuous beams the bent-up bars are continued along the top of the beam to serve there as tensile reinforcement in regions of negative bending moment.

The second type of web reinforcement is the "stirrup." This is shown by Fig. 9–14(b). The stirrup is usually made of lighter bar material, such as No. 3 or No. 4. It is very easy to fabricate. The spacing s may be varied easily, according to the amount of shear present. Sections 803 and 806 of the ACI Code govern the design of stirrups.

Fig. 9–14(c) shows an isolated portion of beam containing one stirrup. The length of the portion is equal to s, the spacing between stirrups. The average shear in the length s is V; that amount of shear is shown on each end of the portion. The shear V causes diagonal tensile stresses which are equal to the unit shearing stress v. The diagonal tensile stresses caused by shear are inclined at 45 degrees and are perpendicular to line a–b. The total tensile force on a plane through the beam at line a–b is called T. Force T is the resultant of all the diagonal tensile stresses on that plane.

$$T = \text{unit diagonal tensile stress} \times \text{area}$$

$$T = vbs\sqrt{2} = Vs\sqrt{2}/jd$$

The force T is assumed to be resisted in two ways, as follows:

1. A portion is assumed to be resisted by the tensile value of the concrete itself. The full allowable shearing stress is used in computing the amount.
2. The balance of the force T, in excess over the amount assigned to the concrete itself, is assumed to be resisted by the steel. The horizontal component is assumed to be resisted by the main reinforcement; the vertical component by the stirrup.

The amount of the force T to be resisted by the steel is called T'. The amount by which V exceeds the shear capacity of the beam based on the concrete strength alone is called V'.

$$T' = V's\sqrt{2}/jd$$

The vertical component of T' is $T'/\sqrt{2}$, or $V's/jd$. The stirrup must resist this force. The steel area required for the stirrup is

$$A_v = V's/f_v jd$$

In this expression f_v is the allowable tensile stress for the stirrup. Under the present ACI Code, f_v is the same amount as allowed for f_s.

The most practical way to design stirrups is to determine first the size to be used. As mentioned before, this is usually a small size. The above equation is then solved for the required spacing of stirrups. The spacing can be varied according to the shear V. For ease in field work several spaces may be made alike, then a substantial change made and several more stirrups installed at that spacing. If the saving of materials were the only object, the spacing could change continuously along the length of the beam.

The total shear stress v, computed as V/bjd is allowed to rise as high as $0.08f'_c$ when stirrups are used. (Section 803, ACI Code.)

Where web reinforcement is needed at all, it should be spaced so that each potential 45-degree crack will be crossed by at least one line of web reinforcement. (If $v = V/bjd$ exceeds $0.06\ f'_c$, each potential 45-degree crack must intersect two lines of web reinforcement.) Cracks would extend from the tensile steel to approximately mid-depth. Thus, the stirrup spacing should not exceed $d/2$ (or $d/4$ where v exceeds $0.06f'_c$).

EXAMPLE 9–7. Design web reinforcement for the beam of Fig. 9–15. The loads are dead load of 600 lb per ft and a movable concentrated live

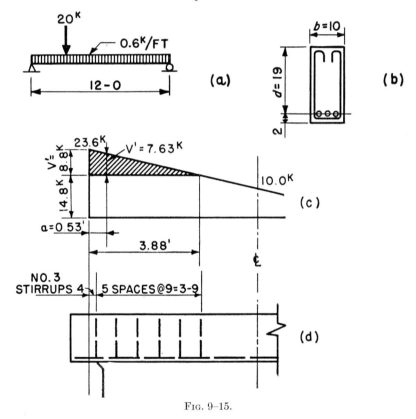

FIG. 9–15.

load of 20 kips. The beam has already been designed for flexure, and the dimensions on Fig. 9–15(b) determined. The factor j is 0.866. A 3,000-lb concrete is to be used with intermediate grade steel.

The required stirrup spacing and size depend on the amount of shear at each section. The maximum shear for each section must be considered. Fig. 9–15(c) shows a diagram of maximum shear. (This is not the same as a shear diagram; only with one fixed condition of loading would the shear diagram give the maximum shear for each section along the beam.)

Without any web reinforcement, a shear stress of 90 psi would be allowed. The total shear V that can be assumed resisted by the concrete itself is

$$vbjd = 90 \times 10 \times 0.866 \times 19 = 14,800 \text{ lb, } \text{ or } \text{ } 14.8 \text{ kips}$$

With web reinforcement the computed v is allowed to be $0.08f_c'$, or 240 psi. The allowable shear for the section reinforced by stirrups is

$$V = 240 \times 10 \times 0.866 \times 19 = 39,500 \text{ lb}$$

This is more than the maximum actual shear of 23.6 kips. Reinforcement by stirrups is permitted

A horizontal line is drawn on the curve of Fig. 9–15(c) at an ordinate of 14.8 kips. Wherever the curve is higher than this line, stirrups are required. The shear V' for which stirrups must be provided is equal to the ordinate of the shaded area.

If No. 3 bars are used, each stirrup will have the area of two No. 3 bars, or 0.22 sq in. The allowable steel stress f_v is 20,000 psi. Solving the equation for the spacing s gives

$$s = A_v f_v jd / V'$$

At the end of the beam V' is $23.6 - 14.8 = 8.8$ kips.

$$s = 0.22 \times 20 \times 0.866 \times 19/8.8 = 8.23 \text{ in.}$$

A stirrup spacing of 8 in. will be used at the end of the beam.

The unit shear v is less than $0.06f_c'$, so the stirrup spacing must not exceed $d/2$ which is $9\frac{1}{2}$ in. The spacing can be changed to $9\frac{1}{2}$ in. where V' is reduced to

$$V' = A_v f_v jd / s = 0.22 \times 20 \times 0.866 \times 19/9.5 = 7.63 \text{ kips}$$

Since the diagram of maximum shear is a straight line, the location of the section where V' is 7.63 kips can be computed easily. The distance from that section to the end is called a.

$$V_a = 7.63 + 14.8 = 22.4 \text{ kips}$$

$$a = 6(23.6 - 22.4)/(23.6 - 10) = 0.53 \text{ ft}$$

It is often convenient to draw the diagram of maximum shear to scale and to measure the distances on the diagram. This is especially true when the diagram is a curved line.

No stirrups are needed where V does not exceed 14.8 kips. This shear value occurs at 3.88 ft from the end.

The final design of the web reinforcement is shown in Fig. 9–15(d).

9–7. Design of Continuous Slabs Using the ACI Building Code.   Concrete slabs in buildings are usually continuous. For example, roof slabs extend without break over several supporting purlins. Floor slabs may span several spaces between the supporting floor beams. A continuous slab is statically indeterminate; therefore, its exact analysis is beyond the scope of this book. Continuous slabs are very common, however, and it is very likely that problems involving them will be encountered. For this reason, a brief exposure to the simple design methods of the ACI Building Code should be valuable to the non-civil engineer.

Fig. 9–16(a) shows a beam that is continuous over several spans. The beam is subject to dead load, which is constant. Most floor and

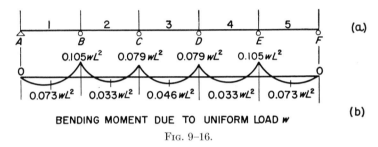

BENDING MOMENT DUE TO UNIFORM LOAD w

Fig. 9–16.

roof slabs are subject also to a uniform live load. If this live load were to occur over the entire slab at all times, simple computations could be made to determine the bending moment and shear for all sections. The moment diagram could be drawn, as in Fig. 9–16(b).

The moments shown on this diagram are not the maximum values for all points. Other conditions of loading may give higher moments. For example, if the live load is removed from spans 2 and 4, then spans 1, 3, and 5 will be allowed to deflect farther. The positive moments (tension bottom) for spans 1, 3, and 5 will then be larger than those on Fig. 9–16(b). Similarly, for the greatest positive moment in spans 2 and 4, the other spans should be left unloaded.

Another complication is the fact that the live load is movable while the dead load is not. Also, the supports for the slab are transverse beams which will deflect elastically when they receive load from the slab. Thus the supports of the slab may have unequal settlement. This action would cause further change of the bending moments in the slab.

It is easy to see that the accurate design or analysis is quite complicated. Yet the problem is a very common one. The ACI Building Code gives an approximate method which is very easy to use. The code states "Approximate methods of frame analysis are satisfactory for buildings of usual types of construction, spans and story heights." There are two limitations given for the use of the method. These are given in Section 701(c) of the code. The moment values given by the code are all functions of wl'^2, and the shear values functions of wl'. These values are *not* all simultaneous. As was shown previously, the maximum shear and moment values at various sections involve a variety of loading conditions.

The use of the simplified ACI method will be illustrated by Example 9–8.

9–8. Temperature and Shrinkage Reinforcement.

Reinforcing steel is used in concrete to prevent the formation of large localized tension cracks. Only the tensile stresses due to applied loads have been considered thus far. Two other very important causes of tensile stress and of cracks in the concrete are shrinkage and temperature change.

Concrete shrinks during curing. The shrinkage is cause by the chemical changes which occur, the evaporation of water, and the cooling of the concrete as the heat from the chemical reaction is dissipated. The amount of shrinkage varies; it is more in a mix that is "rich" in cement than in a "lean" mix. The shrinkage is usually from 0.0002 to 0.0004 in. per inch of length. If the supports of a mass of concrete do not resist the shrinkage, the mass will shrink freely and will not crack. When the mass is restrained, not free to shrink as a unit, tensile stresses are set up. The concrete then cracks to permit each portion between cracks to shrink freely. If each inch of width had its own shrinkage crack, those cracks would be quite small (0.0002 to 0.0004 in.). There is a tendency, though, for the cracks to be localized, one larger crack providing freedom to shrink for a wider strip of concrete. These larger localized cracks are detrimental. They are the starting points for disintegration through weathering.

Temperature changes have a similar effect. For example, sunlight falling on a concrete pavement or sidewalk slab will expand it. Later, as cooling occurs, the slab shrinks. If it is a small slab, there may be enough tensile strength in the concrete so that it can draw the outer portions back toward the center, overcoming the friction between the slab and the ground. If the slab is of larger extent, the friction will be too great and the concrete will develop tensile cracks during cooling. The cracks will fill with dirt, water, and ice. Repeated freezing and thawing will cause the size of the crack to increase.

Reinforcing steel is used to eliminate the bad effects of both shrinkage and temperature cracking. The steel does not prevent the cracks from occurring. It merely distributes the cracks throughout the concrete as fine, even invisible, cracks, avoiding their accumulation into larger localized cracks.

The total tensile force tending to crack the concrete as it shrinks or cools is proportional to the cross section of the concrete. The reinforcing steel, then, should also be proportional to the cross section. Another factor affecting the amount of the tensile force is the amount of the temperature change to be expected. Thus the amount of temperature steel should vary with the condition of exposure expected. Both of these variables have been considered in establishing certain standards for the amount of reinforcement. These standards are given by the ACI Code in Section 707 for roof and floor slabs, and in Section 1112(i) for walls. The amount of steel required is given as a specified factor times the area of concrete. For example, if a roof slab is 4 in. thick, with d equal to 2.75 in., the area of temperature steel shall be

$$2.75 \times 12 \times 0.0025 = 0.0825 \text{ sq in. per ft of slab width}$$

This steel should be placed at right angles to the main reinforcement. The main reinforcement is intended to prevent large shrinkage and temperature cracks in the other direction. Obviously the area of the main reinforcement should not be less than that required for shrinkage and temperature alone.

EXAMPLE 9–8. It is desired to add a small 20-ft by 27-ft mezzanine floor area to an existing building. The area is to be used as a crib for automobile parts. The maximum live load per sq ft will be about 160 lb. The floor is to be a concrete slab. It will be supported by a framework of steel beams and by the existing building columns, as shown in Fig. 9–17(a). Design the floor slab. Use intermediate grade steel and 3,000-lb concrete.

The dead load of the slab is not yet known. If a 6-in. slab is assumed, the tentative dead load is 75 lb per sq ft. The total load is then 235 lb per sq ft. The spans and loads conform to the limitations of Section 701(a), so the simplified ACI moment equations can be used.

The maximum bending moment is usually the "negative moment at exterior face of first interior support" (point C). However, the negative moment at all supports in this case is given by the special paragraph for "slabs with spans not exceeding ten feet . . ."

$$\text{Negative } M = \frac{1}{12} wl'^2 = 0.235(9)^2/12 = 1.59 \text{ ft-kips}$$

(per ft width of slab)

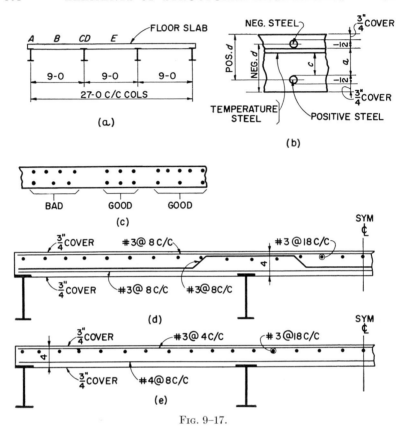

Fig. 9–17.

The depth required for moment will now be computed. Assuming that the design will be balanced, j is 0.866 and k is 0.403. With f_c of 1,350 psi, or 1.35 kips per sq in.,

$$C = bkdf_c/2 = 12 \times 0.403d \times 1.35/2 = 3.26d$$

$$M = Cjd = 3.26d \times 0.866d = 2.82d^2$$

$$d^2 = M/2.82 = 1.59 \times 12/2.82 = 6.76$$

Required $d = 2.60$ in.

The maximum shear is

$$1.15wl'/2 = 1.15 \times 0.235 \times 9/2 = 1.22 \text{ kips (per foot of slab width)}$$

The allowable unit shear is 90 psi. The required depth for shear is

$$d = V/vbj = 1,220/(90 \times 12 \times 0.866) = 1.30 \text{ in.}$$

The moment requirement controls. Concrete cover above the negative steel should be at least $\frac{3}{4}$ in. for slabs not exposed to the weather. Assuming that the bars will be $\frac{1}{2}$ in. thick, the slab thickness should be $2.60 + 0.25 + 0.75 = 3.60$ in. for a balanced design. Fig. 9–17(b) shows a cross section of the slab. Both positive and negative steel will occur at the same section. Temperature steel will occur at right angles to the main reinforcement. Before proceeding to complete the design, the probable spacing between the bars should be checked. Section 505(a) of the ACI Code requires that the clear space be not less than one inch, nor less than $1\frac{1}{3}$ times the maximum aggregate size. Three-quarter inch stone would be a logical size to use, so the one-inch clear spacing will control. The slab cross section in Fig. 9–17(b) shows the cover and the assumed bar sizes. With a $3\frac{1}{2}$-in. slab, dimension a would be one inch. The clear space c must be at least one inch though. If a 4-in. slab were used, dimension a would be $1\frac{1}{2}$ in. This would allow room for temperature steel as large as $\frac{1}{2}$ in. thick. The 4-in. slab will be used.

The estimated dead load can now be corrected. The weight of the 4-in. slab will be 50 lb per sq ft. and w will be 160 plus 50, or 210 lb per sq ft. With this corrected value of w, the negative moment and maximum shear per foot of slab width are recomputed.

$$\text{Negative } M = 0.21(9)^2/12 = 1.42 \text{ ft-kips}$$

$$V = 1.15 \times 0.21 \times 9/2 = 1.09 \text{ kips}$$

$$\text{Required negative } A_s = T/f_s = M/jdf_s = 12 \times 1.42/(0.866 \times 3 \times 20)$$

$$= 0.33 \text{ sq in. per ft width}$$

$$\text{Required negative } \Sigma o = V/ujd = 1.09/(0.3 \times 0.866 \times 3)$$

$$= 1.40 \text{ in. per ft of width}$$

Positive moments at B and E:

$$M_b = \frac{1}{14} wl'^2 = 0.21(9)^2/14 = 1.22 \text{ ft-kips}$$

$$M_e = \frac{1}{16} wl'^2 = 0.21(9)^2/16 = 1.06 \text{ ft-kips}$$

The bottom (positive) reinforcement is now computed.

$$\text{At } B, \text{ required } A_s = M/jdf_s = 0.28 \text{ sq in.}$$

$$\text{At } E, \text{ required } A_s = 0.25 \text{ sq in.}$$

In order to compute the bond requirements for the positive steel it is necessary to know the location of the points of contraflexure (zero moment). These points have variable locations because of the variety of load conditions. Roughly, they will not occur any closer to the end of the span than 15 per cent of the span length. At the point of contraflexure the positive steel is not needed for flexure. In theory it could be ended at that point. The bond stresses at that point are maximum, however. The shear at the point of contraflexure should be used to compute the bond requirements.

For the end span at the point of contraflexure,

$$V \doteq 1.09 - (0.15 \times 9 \times 0.21) = 0.81 \text{ kips}$$

For the points of contraflexure on interior spans,

$$V \doteq (0.21 \times 9/2) - (0.15 \times 9 \times 0.21) = 0.66 \text{ kips}$$

For the end span, positive steel,

$$\text{Required } \Sigma o = V/ujd = 0.81/(0.3 \times 0.866 \times 3) = 1.04 \text{ in.}$$

For interior spans, positive steel,

$$\text{Required } \Sigma o = 0.66/(0.3 \times 0.866 \times 3) = 0.85 \text{ in.}$$

All of the necessary information has been obtained. It is now possible to proceed with the selection of the main reinforcement.

The negative steel requirement could be satisfied by

$$\text{No. 4 bars at 7-in. centers } (A_s = 0.34; \Sigma o = 2.7)$$

or by

$$\text{No. 3 bars at 4-in. centers } (A_s = 0.33; \Sigma o = 3.5)$$

The positive steel requirement in the end span could be filled by

$$\text{No. 4 bars at } 8\tfrac{1}{2}\text{-in. centers } (A_s = 0.28; \Sigma o = 2.2)$$

or by

$$\text{No. 3 bars at } 4\tfrac{1}{2}\text{-in. centers } (A_s = 0.29; \Sigma o = 3.1)$$

For the interior spans, the positive steel requirement could be filled by

$$\text{No. 4 bars at } 9\tfrac{1}{2}\text{-in. centers } (A_s = 0.25; \Sigma o = 2.0)$$

or by

$$\text{No. 3 bars at 5-in. centers } (A_s = 0.26; \Sigma o = 2.8)$$

The problem now is to find some practical solution to all these possibilities. Using the most economical solution for each type of steel would result in a real "hodge-podge" of bars and spacings. It would make the field work of placing the steel and the concrete quite difficult. The "bad" arrangement in Fig. 9–17(c) shows, in part, what might happen. For easier field work and lower field cost one of the simpler bar arrangements should be used. The bottom spacing should be like, or a multiple of, the top spacing.

Two possible solutions are shown. Fig. 9–17(d) shows a solution involving bent bars. Alternate bars are bent up from the bottom at about the one-quarter points of the span. Over the supports, these bars serve as negative steel; at the center of the span they serve as positive steel. The other bars are straight ones which extend over the entire length. (The bars occur in a single layer for positive steel and another for negative. The drawing gives the impression of two layers in the top and two in the bottom. It is drawn this way so as to indicate clearly the length and shape of each bar.)

Fig. 9–17(e) shows another solution. This one uses no bent bars. It does, however, use two different sizes. If this is undesirable, a third solution would be to use a layer of No. 4 bars at 7-in. centers for positive steel and a similar layer for negative.

At right angles to the main reinforcement temperature steel must be provided. Section 707(a) of the ACI Building Code requires a temperature steel area equal to $0.002bd$.

$$A_s = 0.002 \times 12 \times 3 = 0.072 \text{ sq in. per ft of slab width}$$

This area could be provided by No. 3 bars at 18-in. centers. The temperature steel is shown on both solutions.

By now the reader has probably wondered "Isn't this a doubly reinforced member?" Yes, it is. Steel is present on both the tension and compression sides at all sections. However, this was not considered in the design. By considering only the tensile steel, we have a design that is slightly conservative. The compression steel is rarely considered in a floor slab design. If space limitations or other requirements cause trouble, then the compression steel might be considered. The method that would be used is explained in the next article and set of examples.

9–9. Doubly Reinforced Beams. Fig. 9–18(a) shows the cross section of a beam having both tensile and compressive reinforcement. The concrete above the neutral axis is in compression; the rest is assumed to be cracked and ineffective in resisting flexural stress.

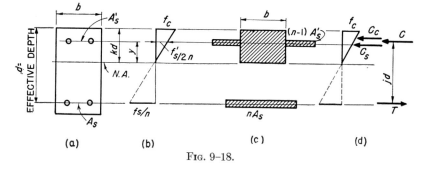

Fig. 9–18.

Fig. 9–18(b) is a diagram showing the assumed flexural stress in the concrete at various distances from the neutral axis. The stress in the concrete at height y above the neutral axis is equal to the abscissa of the diagram at that point. Steel, being n times as stiff, should have n times that stress. Thus the abscissa of the diagram should represent the steel stress f'_s divided by n. It has been found, however, that the compression steel is actually stressed to more than is indicated by the above theory. The difference is caused by shrinkage, by plastic flow of the concrete under long sustained stress, and by the errors present in the assumption of a straight-line stress variation. Accordingly, the compression steel is assumed to have twice the theoretical stress. [See Section 706(b) of the ACI Code.] The tension steel is assumed to have the theoretical stress, and the bottom abscissa in Fig. 9–18(b) is f_s/n.

The transformed section is shown by Fig. 9–18(c). Imaginary material is substituted for the steel. In the bottom, n times the steel area A_s is substituted. An area nA'_s is substituted for the compression steel. Of this quantity, an amount A'_s will fill the holes in the concrete; the remainder, $(n - 1)A'_s$, is additional area beyond the area bkd. This additional area is inserted at the same height y as the original compression steel.

Fig. 9–18(d) shows the interior forces. Force C_c is the resultant of the flexural stresses on the area bkd. Force C_s is the total flexural force on the added area $(n - 1)A'_s$. These must often be considered separately. The resultant of forces C_c and C_s is the force C. The distance of C from the resultant tensile force T is the lever arm of the internal couple, or jd.

The high compressive stresses in the compression steel would cause the top bars to buckle if they were not supported laterally. Normally the surrounding concrete gives the bars sufficient lateral support. For loads near the ultimate for the beam, the effectiveness of the concrete in preventing buckling of the bars is reduced. In order to maintain lateral support throughout the full capacity of the beam, stirrups are used. The stirrup prevents the bars from buckling away from the beam; the enclosed concrete, even when cracked, prevents buckling movement of the bars toward the center of the beam. The required stirrup size and spacing for this purpose are specified by Section 706(a) of the ACI Code. These stirrups may be considered effective as reinforcement for diagonal tension (shear) if desired.

The design or the analysis of a doubly reinforced beam can be accomplished using the same principles that have already been presented. The only difference is that the computations here may be a little more cumbersome. (Design charts and tables are convenient tools to aid the practiced designer. Their use by the student at this stage would completely obscure the principles and would accomplish nothing.)

Compression reinforcement reduces the amount of compression that the concrete must resist. As a result, the depth d can be made less than is possible with tensile reinforcement alone. The resulting beam may in itself be more expensive than the deeper beam with single reinforcement. The reduced weight may affect the design of other members, though, and permit saving there. More important, double reinforcing helps to solve problems of limited headroom. It is very convenient to use and design double reinforcement in continuous beams.

EXAMPLE 9–9. A doubly reinforced rectangular beam is shown in Fig. 9–19(a). The steel is of intermediate grade and the concrete has a

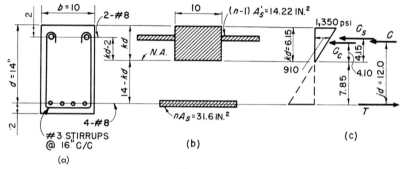

FIG. 9–19.

28-day ultimate compressive strength of 3,000 psi. What is the allowable bending moment? Stirrups are provided as required by Section 706(a) of the ACI Code.

The steel areas A_s and A_s' are 3.16 sq in. and 1.58 sq in., respectively. The ratio n is $30,000,000/3,000,000 = 10$. Fig. 9–19(b) shows the transformed section in which A_s is replaced by $10 \times 3.16 = 31.6$ sq in. of imaginary material. A_s' is replaced by 10×1.58 sq in. Part of this merely fills in the holes occupied by the steel; 9×1.58 or 14.22 sq in. is added. The neutral axis is at the center of gravity of the transformed area.

$$10kd(kd/2) + 14.22(kd - 2) = 31.6(14 - kd)$$
$$5(kd)^2 + 14.22kd - 28.44 = 442.4 - 31.6kd$$
$$(kd)^2 + 9.16kd + (4.58)^2 = 94.2 + 21.0 = 115.2$$
$$kd + 4.58 = \pm 10.73$$
$$kd = 6.15 \text{ in.}$$

The allowable unit stress in the concrete is 1,350 psi. When this stress occurs, the average is one-half as much, and the resultant force on the rectangular compressive area bkd is

$$C_c = \frac{1,350}{2} \times 10 \times 6.15 = 41,500 \text{ lb}$$

This force acts at $\frac{2}{3}$ of 6.15 in., or 4.10 in. above the neutral axis.

When the maximum f_c is 1,350 psi, concrete at the same height as the compressive steel is stressed to

$$\frac{4.15}{6.15} \times 1,350 = 910 \text{ psi}$$

By use of the modular ratio n, the steel stress would be considered as n times 910 psi. The compressive steel, however, may be taken as twice that effective in bending. (See Section 706(b), ACI Code.) The stress in the compressive steel is then $2 \times 10 \times 910 = 18,200$ psi. This does not exceed the allowable of 20,000 psi in tension, so f_s' will be taken as 18,200 psi. A portion of this stress has already been included in computing force C_c, since no holes were assumed to exist in the concrete area bkd. The amount of f_s' not yet included is $18,200 - 910 = 17,290$ psi. The compressive force increase due to the presence of the steel is

$$C_s = 17,290 \times 1.58 = 27,300 \text{ lb}$$

The moment of resistance when f_c is 1,350 psi is now computed. This will be the sum of the moments of C_c and C_s about the lower steel force T.

$$M = (41.5 \times 11.95) + (27.3 \times 12.0) = 823 \text{ in.-kips}$$

An applied moment in excess of 823 in.-kips will overstress the concrete.

The lever arm of the internal couple can now be figured. (In this case, the answer is obvious. The procedure shown, though, will be useful for beams of different proportions.)

$$C = C_c + C_s = 68.8 \text{ kips}$$
$$jd = M/C = 823/68.8 = 12.0 \text{ in.}$$

When the lower steel is stressed to the full allowable stress,

$$T = 20 \times 3.16 = 63.2 \text{ kips}$$

The moment required to stress the steel to that value is

$$M = Tjd = 63.2 \times 12.0 = 758 \text{ in.-kips}$$

A moment greater than 758 in.-kips will overstress the lower steel.

The lower resisting moment is that of the tensile steel. The allowable bending moment is, therefore, 758 in.-kips.

EXAMPLE 9–10. The beam of Example 9–9 and Fig. 9–19 will be subject to a shear V of 15 kips. Is it satisfactory in diagonal tension?

The shearing stress v as a measure of diagonal tension will be considered first. By Section 803(c), the allowable shear stress when vertical stirrups are used is limited to $0.08f'_c$, or $0.08 \times 3,000 = 240$ psi. The computed shear v for this beam is

$$v = V/bjd = 15,000/10 \times 12.0 = 125 \text{ psi}$$

Thus, the requirement of Section 803(c) is satisfied.

The stirrup size and spacing are checked next. With no web reinforcement, v equal to 90 psi is allowed. The excess over this allowable is $125 - 90 = 35$ psi. The stirrups must resist this excess. The steel area A_v provided by one stirrup is $2 \times 0.11 = 0.22$ sq in. Refer now to Fig. 9–14(c). For the beam now being considered, the stirrup spacing s is 16 in. The force T is equal to $125\ sb\sqrt{2}$. Of this amount, $90/125$ is to be resisted by the concrete, while the excess, $35/125$, is to be resisted by the steel. The vertical component of the excess is considered to be resisted by the stirrup. The load on the stirrup is then

$$35sb = 35 \times 16 \times 10 = 5,600 \text{ lb}$$

The stirrup stress is $5,600/0.22 = 25,500$ psi. The allowable stress f_v for the stirrups is only 20,000 psi, so the beam is unsatisfactory in diagonal tension. Furthermore, the spacing exceeds $d/2$, so that all potential crack lines are not crossed by a stirrup. A smaller stirrup spacing is needed.

EXAMPLE 9–11. Is the beam of Example 9–9 and Fig. 9–19 satisfactory in bond when the shear V is 15 kips?

The bond stresses permitted are given by the Code as 210 psi for the top bars and 300 psi for the bottom bars.

The bond stress for the bottom bars is computed in the usual manner.

$$u = V/\Sigma ojd = 15,000/(12.4 \times 12.0) = 101 \text{ psi}$$

The bottom bars are satisfactory in bond.

Bond on the compressive bars will usually not control the design. The bond stress for the top bars can be computed easily, though. Fig. 9–20 shows a short element of the compressive steel. If the beam has shear at the location of this element, then forces C_s and C'_s are not equal.

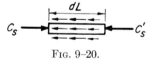

FIG. 9–20.

Force C_s (or C'_s) is only a part of the total compression force C. From Example 9–9 C_s is approximately $27.3/68.8$ of C, or $0.397C$. The difference between C_s and C'_s is then

$$0.397(C - C') = 0.397(M - M')/jd = \frac{0.397\ V\ dL}{jd}$$

The element of Fig. 9–20 is in equilibrium. The unbalance of C_s and C'_s is equal to the resultant of the bond stresses, which is $u\ dL\ \Sigma o$.

Writing the equation $\Sigma H = 0$ and substituting 15 kips for V and 6.2 in. for Σo gives

$$\frac{0.397 \times 15 \; dL}{12.0} = u \; dL \times 6.2$$

and

$$u = 0.080, \quad \text{or} \quad 80 \, \text{psi}$$

EXAMPLE 9–12. Consider again the precast beams designed in Example 9–6. There are some probable objections to the 12-in. by $14\frac{1}{2}$-in. section which was chosen. In the first place, it will be lifted during erection, most likely by a chain or sling near the middle of the beam length. This could cause failure since tensile stress would occur on the top side during lifting. Also, the beams would weigh $150 \times 1 \times 1.17 \times 10.17 = 1,780$ lb each. This is a little heavy for easy handling. Finally, a slightly shallower beam might be desirable for clearance reasons. A 12-in. depth, or less, is desirable.

Assume that you, as plant engineer, have designed the beam according to Example 9–6, and that you have just completed all the necessary detail drawings. Now somebody calls the above objections to your attention and requests that you try to rectify them and revise the drawings. The first impulse might be to "blow your top." These events, however, are common, and should be taken in stride. In engineering practice the revisions take as much time (often more) as the original work. It is just as important that the revisions receive careful attention, since they will certainly affect the final product.

In this case, the thing to do would be to consider a doubly reinforced beam. Such a beam will be designed in this example.

The selection of a section must be made by trial. The procedure will be to try a beam of some given outside dimensions and to compute the steel requirements for that beam. If the section thus selected is impractical or in any way undesirable, further trials are made as necessary to determine a suitable section. There are, of course, many possible suitable sections for the beam. In this example, only those of 12-in. over-all depth will be considered.

The computations of Example 9–6 show an end shear V of 10.72 kips and a bending moment M of 32.1 ft-kips (385 in.-kips).

The doubly reinforced beam will have vertical stirrups, so that the allowable shear stress v is $0.08f_c'$, or 240 psi. The area required for shear is

$$bd = V/vj \doteq 10,720/(240 \times 0.87) = 51.4 \, \text{sq in.}$$

As a first trial section, consider an 8-in. by 12-in. beam. This is shown by Fig. 9–21(a). If the tensile bars are more than $\frac{5}{8}$ in. in diameter, a 2-in. cover will be required. The stirrups will require $1\frac{1}{2}$ in. of cover.

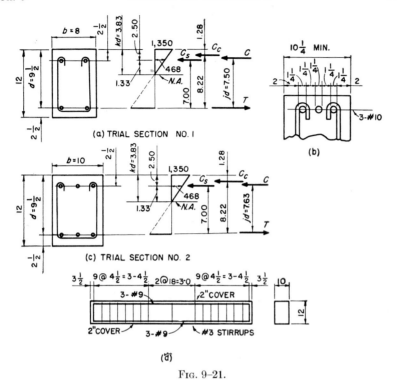

Fig. 9-21.

Assuming that the main bars will be one-inch bars, the center of the tensile steel will be $2\frac{1}{2}$ in. from the bottom, and $d = 9\frac{1}{2}$ in.

A balanced design is assumed. Dimension kd is $0.403 \times 9.5 = 3.83$ in. When f_c is at the full allowable value, the total compressive force in the concrete is

$$C_c = \frac{1,350}{2} \times 8 \times 3.83 = 20,700 \text{ lb} = 20.7 \text{ kips}$$

The resisting moment caused by stress in the concrete is the moment of C_c about the tensile steel.

$$M \text{ (concrete)} = 20.7 \times 8.22 = 170 \text{ in.-kips}$$

The compressive steel must raise the total resisting moment of the compressive forces to 385 in.-kips. The moment of the force C_s must be $385 - 170 = 215$ in.-kips. The lever arm of the compressive steel is 7 in., so that

$$C_s = 215/7 = 30.7 \text{ kips}$$

At the location of the compressive steel, f_c is $1,350 \times 1.33/3.83 = 468$ psi. The steel stress is theoretically n times 468, or 4,680 psi. The Code allows twice that value, or 9,360 psi to be used. To be exact in the application of the Code, 468 psi should be deducted from this, since no holes were assumed when the concrete force C_c was computed. A steel stress of $9,360 - 468 = 8,892$ psi will be used.

$$\text{Required } A'_s = 30.7/8.89 = 3.46 \text{ sq in.}$$

The lever arm jd can now be computed. The moment of forces C_s and C_c about the bottom steel is 385 in.-kips.

$$C = C_s + C_c = 51.4 \text{ kips}$$

$$jd = 385/51.4 = 7.50 \text{ in.}$$

Force T must equal force C.

$$\text{Required } A_s = T/f_s = 51.4/20 = 2.57 \text{ sq in.}$$

The steel requirements just computed can be met by using 3 No. 10 bars for compressive steel, and 2 No. 10 bars for tensile steel. Fig. 9–21(b) shows the spacing requirements using 3 No. 10 bars. These minimum dimensions are in accord with Sections 505(a) and 507(a) of the ACI Code. Obviously, the 8-in. width assumed for the first trial section is too narrow to permit the use of the bars chosen. Other groups of bars to satisfy the A'_s required would result in an even wider beam. Another trial section is needed.

For the second trial section, try a 10-in. by 12-in. beam. This is shown in Fig. 9–21(c). The steel requirements for this section are computed in the same manner as for the first trial.

$$C_c = \frac{1,350}{2} \times 10 \times 3.83 = 25,800 \text{ lb} = 25.8 \text{ kips}$$

$$\text{M (concrete)} = 25.8 \times 8.22 = 212 \text{ in.-kips}$$

$$\text{M (required by compressive steel)} = 385 - 212 = 173 \text{ in.-kips}$$

Use $f'_s = 8,892$ psi.

$$C_s = 173/7 = 24.7 \text{ kips}$$

$$\text{Required } A'_s = 24.7/8.89 = 2.78 \text{ sq in.}$$

$$T = 25.8 + 24.7 = 50.5 \text{ kips}$$

$$\text{Required } A_s = \frac{50.5}{20} = 2.52 \text{ sq in.}$$

$$jd = \frac{385}{50.5} = 7.63 \text{ in.}$$

$$\Sigma o \text{ required for tensile steel} = \frac{V}{ujd} = \frac{10,720}{300 \times 7.63} = 4.68 \text{ in.}$$

The steel requirements computed above can be satisfied by using 3 No. 9 bars for compressive steel and either 3 No. 9 bars or 2 No. 10 bars for tensile steel. The use of the 2 No. 10 bars saves a little steel, but there are advantages to using the 3 No. 9 bars both top and bottom. First, there is only one size of bar and errors in fabrication are thus less probable. Second, the beam will be alike top and bottom, so that no harm would result from installing it upside down. Three No. 9 bars will be used in each place, top and bottom.

The need for stirrups should now be investigated. Without web reinforcement a shear V of $90 \times 10 \times 7.63 = 6,860$ lb is allowed. The actual shear is 10,720 lb. Stirrups must be provided for the excess over 6,860 lb, which is $10,720 - 6,860 = 3,860$ lb.

Assuming No. 2 stirrups,

$$A_v = 2 \times 0.05 = 0.10 \text{ sq in.}$$

The required stirrup spacing is

$$s = \frac{0.10 \times 20,000 \times 7.63}{3,860} = 3.96 \text{ in.}$$

For No. 3 stirrups, A_v is 0.22, and the computed required spacing s is 8.7 in. A maximum spacing of $d/2$, or 4.75 in. is required to insure that each potential 45-degree crack line is crossed by one stirrup. No. 3 stirrups at $4\frac{1}{2}$-in. centers are specified for the length between the end and the first concentrated load. Between concentrated loads the shear is practically zero, and the minimum requirement of Section 706(a) is used. The No. 3 stirrups in that length are spaced at 18-in. centers.

The final design is shown by Figs. 9–21(c) and (d).

9–10. Analysis of T-Beams. When a concrete slab is supported by concrete beams, the slab and the beams are usually cast monolithically. By this, it is meant that they are cast together as one solid mass. The cross section of such an arrangement shows in Fig. 9–22(a).

As load is applied to this slab, the beams will bend downward, their top fibers shortening. The slab adjacent to the beam is forced to move with the beam. The slab deflects with the beam and its fibers shorten like those of the beam. The slab actually functions as a part of the beam. The cross section of the beam is then not rectangular, but T-shaped, as shown shaded in Fig. 9–22(a). Such a beam is called a T-beam. (Similar beam action is found in metals. For example, the stressed skin of aircraft acts together with the stiffening stringers or longerons to which it is attached.)

There are, of course, limits to the width of slab that can be assumed to act with a particular beam. As the space between beams becomes

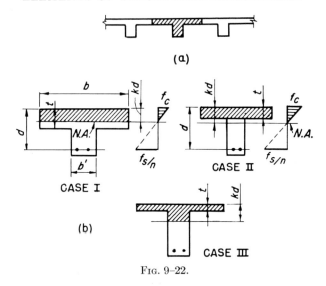

Fig. 9–22.

greater, the portions of slab farthest from the beams may not be very effective in strengthening the beam. The ACI Code gives three limiting requirements for the effective width of the T-beam. They are as follows:

1. The width to be considered effective shall not exceed one-fourth of the beam span.
2. The width of flange to be considered effective on either side of the web shall not exceed 8 times the slab thickness.
3. The slab shall not be considered effective beyond the center of the clear distance to the web of the adjacent beam.

When the extent of the effective section has been determined, the T-beam can be analyzed using the principles previously developed.

Fig. 9–22(b) shows three T-beam cross sections. Because of different proportions, these beams will behave differently. They are commonly referred to as the "three cases of T-beams."

In Case I the neutral axis is in the flange; kd is less than t. Compression exists over the rectangular shaded area.

Beams of Case II have the neutral axis slightly below the bottom of the flange; kd is slightly more than t. Compression exists over the entire rectangular flange area (shaded), and over a small section of the web. The portion of web contained between the neutral axis and the bottom of the flange is so small, however, that neglecting the compressive force on that area causes negligible error.

In Case III the neutral axis is farther down in the web and the compressive force on the stem is not negligible. Obviously there is no clear-cut dividing line between Case II and Case III. Beams of cases I and II are easier to compute than those of Case III. Fortunately, the majority of the T-beams encountered in building construction are definitely of Case I or Case II.

In analyzing rectangular beams dimensions b, d, and kd were involved. The question of the shape of the beam below the neutral axis was not considered. Since concrete below the neutral axis is unstressed in flexure, it could be removed without affecting the flexural stresses. Enough could be removed, for example, to change the beam to a T-shape. The beam would then be that shown as Case I. Still, its flexural stresses and its analysis would be unchanged. Therefore, a T-beam of Case I can be analyzed for bending as if it were a rectangular beam of width b and effective depth d.

Fig. 9–23(a) shows the cross section of a Case II beam. The transformed section for this beam is shown in (b). Compression in the small

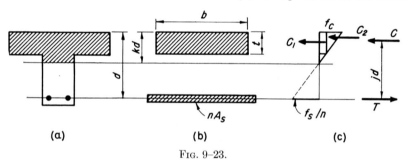

(a)   **(b)**   **(c)**

FIG. 9–23.

element of web above the neutral axis is neglected. The neutral axis is at the center of gravity of the transformed section. The moment of the flange area bt about the neutral axis is equal to that of the transformed steel area nA_s.

The flexural stress on the transformed section is shown by Fig. 9–23(c). The unit stress in the flange is variable. The amount of the resultant compressive force C can easily be computed if the stress diagram is divided into a rectangle and a triangle, as shown. C_1 and C_2 are the resultant forces due to the portions of the stress represented by the rectangle and the triangle, respectively. C is the resultant of C_1 and C_2. The balance of the analysis procedure for Case II beams is like that used for rectangular beams.

In the analysis of a beam of Case III, an additional force C_3 would be added to represent the resultant compressive force in the stem between the bottom of the flange and the neutral axis.

EXAMPLE 9–13. A simple T-beam is shown by Fig. 9–24(a). The steel is intermediate grade and the concrete has a 28-day strength of 2,500 psi. What is the allowable bending moment?

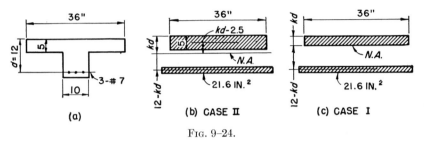

Fig. 9–24.

At the start it is not known for sure whether the beam is a Case I or a Case II beam. Fig. 9–24(b) shows the transformed section as it would be for a Case II beam.

$$n = 30,000,000/(1,000 \times 2,500) = 12$$

$$nA_s = 12 \times 3 \times 0.60 = 21.6 \text{ sq in.}$$

$$5 \times 36(kd - 2.5) = 21.6(12 - kd)$$

$$180kd - 450 = 259 - 21.6kd$$

$$201.6kd = 709$$

$$kd = 3.52 \text{ in.}$$

But if kd were 3.52 in., the neutral axis would not be below the flange as was assumed; it would be up in the flange. Therefore, this is a Case I beam and the analysis should be started again.

In Fig. 9–24(c) the transformed section for a Case I beam is shown.

$$36kd(kd/2) = 21.6(12 - kd)$$

$$18(kd)^2 = 259 - 21.6kd$$

$$(kd)^2 + 1.2kd + (0.6)^2 = 14.4 + 0.36 = 14.76$$

$$kd + 0.6 = \pm 3.84$$

$$kd = 3.24 \text{ in.}$$

This value of kd confirms the assumption that the beam is a Case I beam. The analysis would now be continued as for a rectangular beam of 36-in. width. For shear, however, the 10-in. width would be used in the equation $v = V/bjd$.

EXAMPLE 9–14. Fig. 9–25(a) shows a reinforced concrete floor slab cast monolithically with supporting T-beams. The beams are supported by the basement walls with no reinforcement provided to "fix" the ends of the beams. They will act as simple beams on a span of 16 ft 8 in. Assume that this is an existing structure built in 1940 using 3,000-lb

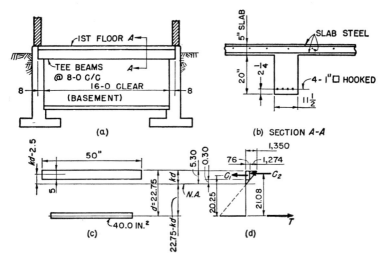

Fɪɢ. 9–25.

concrete and intermediate grade steel. The owner of the plant has requested you to determine the allowable live load per sq ft of floor,
based on the strength of the tee beams. (The floor slab would be checked
also. Assume that this has been done.)

The effective width must be found first using Section 705(a) of the
ACI Building Code.

One-fourth of the span = 12 × 16.67/4 = 50 in.
Stem thickness + 16 × slab thickness = 11.5 + (16 × 5) = 91.5 in.
Distance center to center of spaces between beams = 96 in.

The first requirement gives the smallest answer. An effective width of
50 in. will be used.

Fig. 9–25(c) shows the transformed section. It is assumed that this is
a Case II beam. The computation of the location of the neutral axis
will either verify or disprove the assumption. A_s is 4.00 sq in. and n is
10, so that the area substituted for the steel is $nA_s = 40.0$ sq in.

$$50 \times 5(kd - 2.5) = 40(22.75 - kd)$$

$$250kd - 625 = 910 - 40kd$$

$$290kd = 1,535$$

$$kd = 5.30 \text{ in.}$$

Since kd exceeds 5 in., the assumption that the beam is of Case II is
confirmed.

Refer now to Fig. 9–25(d). When f_c is the full allowable of 1,350 psi the concrete stress at the lower edge of the flange is

$$\frac{0.30}{5.30} \times 1,350 = 76 \text{ psi}$$

The compressive force in the flange is divided into two parts, as shown on Fig. 9–25(d).

C_1 (rectangle) $= 50 \times 5 \times 76 = 19,000$ lb, or 19 kips

C_2 (triangle) $= 50 \times 5 \times 1,274/2 = 159,000$ lb, or 159 kips

The moment of these forces about force T is the resisting moment M_c for the concrete.

$$M_c - (19 \times 20.25) + (159 \times 21.08) = 3,736 \text{ in.-kips}$$

The lever arm jd of the internal couple can now be computed.

$$jd = M_c/C = 3,736/178 = 21.0 \text{ in.}$$

The resisting moment for the steel is reached when f_s is the allowable value of 20,000 psi.

$$M_s = 20 \times 4.0 \times 21.0 = 1,680 \text{ in.-kips}$$

M_s controls since it is lower than M_c. The allowable bending moment is 1,680 in.-kips. The allowable load per foot of beam is now computed.

$$w = \frac{8M}{L^2} = \frac{8 \times 1,680,000/12}{(16.67)^2} = 4,040 \text{ lb per ft}$$

The shear strength will be considered next. The maximum shear occurs below the neutral axis. At this section the concrete stem is only $11\frac{1}{2}$ in. wide. The allowable shear (diagonal tension) stress is 90 psi. Based on diagonal tension, the allowable shear for the beam is

$$V = vbjd = 90 \times 11.5 \times 21 = 21,800 \text{ lb}$$

The allowable bond stress must be based on the old specification, since this structure was built prior to the development of the new-type reinforcing bars. The allowable stress u is 225 psi. The shear that will cause u to be 225 psi is

$$V = ujd\Sigma o = 225 \times 21 \times 16.0 = 75,600 \text{ lb}$$

The allowable shear is controlled by diagonal tension and is limited to 21,800 lb. The load per foot of beam to cause this shear is

$$V/0.5L = 21,800/8.33 = 2,620 \text{ lb per ft}$$

The allowable load per foot of beam is controlled by diagonal tension. The limiting 2,620 lb per ft includes all dead load and live load on a one-foot strip extending from the center of one space between beams to the center of the next space. In this case, the loads from 8 sq ft of slab are carried on one linear foot of beam.

Weight of slab $= 8 \times 150 \times 5/12$ $= 500$ lb

Weight of stem of beam $= 0.96 \times 1.67 \times 150 = 240$ lb

Total dead load $= 740$ lb per ft of beam

Allowable live load $= 2,620 - 740 = 1,880$ lb per ft of beam

This live load is for 8 sq ft of slab, so that the allowable live load per square foot of floor is $1,880/8 = 235$ lb.

9-11. Reinforced Concrete Columns. The proportions of concrete columns are such that their capacity is usually a function of their crushing strengths, rather than a function of buckling by the entire column. For that reason, this article will deal first with short columns. Later the effect of the column length will be included.

The design and analysis methods of this chapter have thus far been based on the assumption that stress is proportional to strain at working loads. The effect of the assumption is to provide a straight-line distribution of stress in beams. The assumption has been used because it makes the numerical work easy, and because the design method is then similar to the method used in designing structural steel members.

If the straight-line assumption is applied to the analysis of a concrete column, the basic relationship in Art. 9–2 and Fig. 9–3 is obtained. By that relationship,

$$f_s = nf_c$$

The total load P on the short column of Fig. 9–3 would then be

$$P = f_c A_c + f_s A_s$$

The area A_c is approximately equal to the gross area A_g. The steel area A_s can be replaced by $p_g A_g$, in which p_g is the ratio A_s/A_g, commonly called the "percentage of steel."

$$P = f_c A_g + f_s p_g A_g$$
$$= A_g(f_c + f_s p_g)$$

Assuming the straight-line variation of stress, it would seem proper to compute the column capacity from this last equation. The stresses f_c and f_s would be limited to specified maximums, and would be used in the proportions given by $f_s = nf_c$.

Tests of columns have shown, however, that the actual capacities cannot be predicted reliably by the above method. Such discrepancies are found also in comparisons of beam test data with strengths predicted from the conventional method of beam design. But in the case of columns, the discrepancies are much more serious, so that the design formulas of the ACI Code have been altered to correct for the discrepancies. The reason for the discrepancies is that the stress–strain diagram for concrete is curved over most of its length. At ultimate load for the column, the steel has been stressed to the yield point and the concrete has been stressed almost to the ultimate strength f_c'.

The present ACI equation (Section 1103) is based on a comparison of ultimate loads for columns. Its form is like that developed for the straight-line method, but the constants in the equation provide a factor of safety with respect to ultimate load for the column, rather than with respect to ultimate unit stresses for test cylinders. The ACI equation for spirally reinforced columns is

$$P = A_g(0.225f_c' + f_s p_g)$$

The terms of this equation are defined in Section 1103(a) of the ACI Code.

The cross section of a typical column is shown by Fig. 9–26(a). As the ultimate load for this column is reached, the steel yields and the

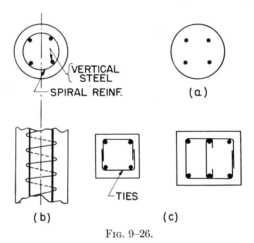

FIG. 9–26.

concrete crumbles. If the concrete were to break away from the vertical bars, those bars would have no lateral support and would buckle. A greater ultimate capacity is realized if the pieces of concrete are tied together and the bars are braced so that buckling cannot occur even after the concrete begins to break. This lateral restraint is provided in one of two ways. Spiral reinforcing can be placed around the vertical steel, as shown in Fig. 9–26(b). The other method is to use horizontal ties to brace the vertical steel, as in Fig. 9–26(c).

The spiral reinforcing of the vertical steel is quite effective in "holding the parts together" at loads near ultimate. For columns so reinforced, the allowable load P is computed from the ACI formula given above. (Section 1103.) Tied columns are easier to make, but the system is not quite so effective. The load allowed for tied columns is only 80 per cent of the amount given by the above formula. (See Section 1104 of the ACI Code.)

A complete design involves choosing the column cross section, the vertical steel, the size of spiral or tie steel, and the spacing of spirals or ties. The amount of vertical steel is limited by the specification. In the case of spirally reinforced columns one to 8 per cent may be used; for tied columns, one to 4 per cent. These limits are based on the results of tests of columns. The size and spacing of spiral steel or of ties is also controlled by specification requirements.

Buckling of the column as a whole is not considered in any of the above. Most concrete columns are "short" columns. Buckling is a factor to consider in concrete column design only when the laterally un-supported length h exceeds ten times the least lateral dimension d. The column is then classed as a "long" column. The load allowed on a long column is reduced from that for a short column of the same cross section. The reduction is given by Section 1107 of the ACI Code.

$$P' = P\left(1.3 - 0.03\,\frac{h}{d}\right)$$

In this, P' is the allowable load for the long column, and P is the load for a short column of the same cross section. The factor in parentheses gives no reduction in load allowed for h/d ratios up to 10. For ratios over 10, the allowable load P' reduces in a straight-line variation. If a graph like that of Fig. 7–10 were constructed for a concrete column, it would show a straight horizontal line for h/d-values between zero and 10, and from that point on a straight line sloping downward toward the right.

EXAMPLE 9–15. A spirally reinforced column is shown in Fig. 9–27. The laterally unsupported length of the column is 17 ft 6 in. The steel is intermediate grade and the concrete has a 28-day strength f'_c of 3,000 psi. What is the allowable axial load for the column?

The ratio of unsupported length to least lateral dimension is

$$\frac{210}{15} = 14$$

The ratio exceeds 10, so the column is treated as a long column. The allowable load will be computed first as if the column were short. Then a correction factor will be applied to determine the allowable load for the actual column.

The load allowed for a short column of the same cross section is

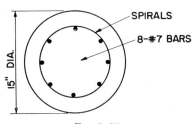

$$P = A_g(0.225f'_c + f_s p_g)$$

$$A_g = \frac{\pi(15)^2}{4} = 177 \text{ sq in.}$$

Allowed $f_s = 0.40f_y = 16,000$ psi

$$p_g = \frac{A_s}{A_g} = \frac{4.80}{177} = 0.0272$$

FIG. 9–27.

$$P = 177[(0.225 \times 3,000) + (16,000 \times 0.0272)]$$

$$= 196,000 \text{ lb, or } 196 \text{ kips}$$

To obtain the allowable load P' for the long column, the allowable for the short column is multiplied by the factor

$$\left(1.3 - 0.03\frac{h}{d}\right) = 1.3 - (0.03 \times 14) = 0.88$$

The allowable axial load for the long column is

$$P' = 0.88 \times 196 = 173 \text{ kips}$$

EXAMPLE 9–16. Fig. 9–28(a) shows the manner proposed for the installation of a new set of bins in an existing building. The bins are to

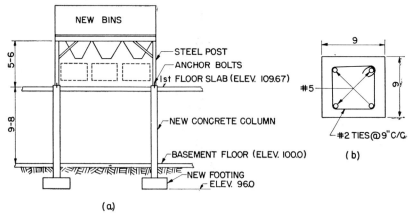

FIG. 9–28.

serve operations at first-floor level. The weight of the bins and their contents, however, is a total of 80 tons, so that support by the existing floor system is not practical. Independent support by 4 columns is proposed. Steel columns with adequate lateral bracing can be used above the first floor. In the basement, however, it is extremely damp and steel columns could corrode excessively. You have proposed the use of concrete columns up to the top of the first floor. Design tied concrete columns using intermediate grade reinforcing steel and 3,000-lb concrete. Assume that you have selected a 5-in. by 5-in. steel section for the upper column.

Each column receives 20 tons or 40 kips of load from the bin system. The weight of the column itself will be assumed as 2 kips. The design load for the column is then 42 kips. The new columns will pass through holes in the first floor slab so that they will not receive load from the floor. They will nearly fill the holes, however, so that the columns can be assumed as laterally supported at top and bottom. The length of the column will be taken as the distance from the top of the footing to the top of the first-floor slab. If a 12-in. footing thickness is assumed, the length h will be 12 ft 8 in., or 152 in.

When the column to be designed is definitely a short column, a fairly direct design procedure can be followed. This column will most likely turn out to be a long column, so that a direct approach is not possible. Many approaches can be used. The one used here is to assume a column size and then to compute the steel requirements for that column. Enough trials are made to determine a satisfactory and economical section.

The smallest practical size is determined largely by the base plate for the steel column above. The bearing plate will be of such size that the bearing pressure does not exceed 600 psi, according to Section 15(c) of the AISC Specification. The required base plate area is then $42/0.6 = 70$ sq in. A plate measuring $8\frac{1}{2}$ in. square could be used. The smallest practical concrete column to receive that base plate is one 9 inches square.

For a 9-in. by 9-in. column, h/d is $152/9 = 16.9$, and

$$P' = P(1.3 - 0.03 \times 16.9) = 0.793P$$

For a load P' of 42 kips on the long column, a section having a short-column allowable P of $42/0.793$, or 53 kips must be used.

$$P = 0.8A_g(0.225f'_c + f_s p_g)$$

$$53 = 0.8 \times 81[(0.225 \times 3) + 16p_g]$$

Required $p_g = 0.009$

The ACI Code in Section 1104(a) gives 0.01 to 0.04 as the allowable range of p_g for tied columns. The specified minimum of 0.01 controls.

$$\text{Required } A_s = p_g A_g = 0.01 \times 81 = 0.81 \text{ sq in.}$$

The minimum bar size permitted is No. 5; the minimum number permitted is four. Four No. 5 bars will provide an area A_s equal to 4×0.31, or 1.24 sq in. The column section with those bars is shown by Fig. 9–28(b).

The lateral ties must now be selected. These must be bent to fit around the 4 vertical bars, so a small size is desirable for easy fabrication. The minimum size allowed is No. 2, which is about $\frac{1}{4}$ in. in diameter.

For $\frac{1}{4}$-in. ties, the spacing is limited to:

1. 16 bar diameters $= 16 \times \frac{5}{8} = 10$ in.
2. 48 tie diameters $= 48 \times \frac{1}{4} = 12$ in.
3. The column thickness $= 9$ in.

The third requirement controls. The ties will be made of No. 2 size and will be spaced at 9-in. centers as shown.

9–12. Wall Footings. Concrete footings are used to transfer loads from the structure above into the supporting soil. Their purpose is

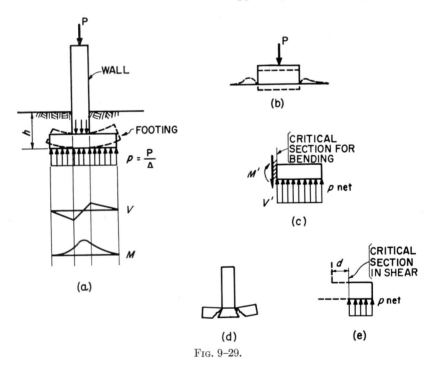

FIG. 9–29.

similar to that of bearing plates. They spread the load over a large enough area so that the weaker material (the soil) is not damaged or deformed excessively. As with the bearing plate, the design of a footing consists of two main parts. First, the footing is proportioned so as to avoid overstressing or overdeforming the soil. Second, the footing is proportioned and reinforced so as to prevent its own failure.

Fig. 9–29(a) shows a wall footing. A wall footing extends along the entire length of the wall it supports. The other common type is the spread footing shown in Fig. 9–30(a). The spread footing is usually square or rectangular in plan (top view), and is used to receive a concentrated load, such as that from a column or from a heavy machine.

To determine the size of a footing, we must first determine an allowable bearing stress for the soil. This is obviously difficult to do, since soils are so variable. In large and important work soil bearing tests are often made to determine the allowable pressure. These tests are expensive, however, and are not justified for most small jobs. The local building codes will usually list the typical soils of the area and give allowable bearing values for each. Even the best of such lists cannot cover all the possible soil types. They also leave to the user the task of identifying the soil and of matching or interpolating with the listed varieties. Table 10 of Appendix B is typical of the lists given by the building codes.

The vertical loads to be considered on a wall footing are computed as weight per linear foot of wall. The loads include:

1. Live and dead loads received by the wall from the structure above
2. The weight of the wall
3. The weight of the footing itself

The weight of the footing is not known in advance. It must be assumed, and later verified or corrected. Knowing the total load per linear foot and the allowable soil bearing pressure p per square foot, the required width of footing can be determined. Notice that the weight of the earth above the footing is not listed as one of the loads on the footing. A little thought as to the nature of soil failure should show the reason for this. In Fig. 9–29(b) a block is shown resting on soil. As the block is pushed downward the soil beneath it is compressed. Some elastic deformation and usually plastic deformation of the soil occurs. In failure, there is an upward bulging of the soil adjacent to the block. The movement is indicated by the dotted lines. This type of failure could be prevented by the application of downward pressure on the soil surface around the block. With such restraint to upward bulging of the soil, a larger force P would be required to cause failure. Added depth of soil around the block is a way of providing the restraining downward pressure. The pressure added by such soil is its own weight, and this is proportional to the depth of such soil above the bottom of the block. Thus in Fig. 9–29(a), this bulging is resisted additionally by soil of height h above the bottom of the footing. The restraining effect of this soil is at least equal to and usually greater than the added downward force it causes on the footing. Thus it is reasonable and safe in ordinary design to neglect both its added load and its added restraint to a soil failure.

The footing itself can fail in flexure, diagonal tension, or bond. All of these must be considered when designing a footing. The footing acts as a beam having upward uniform load all along the bottom and a downward force at the wall location. These loads tend to bend the footing as shown exaggerated in Fig. 9–29(a). The shear and moment diagrams for a one-ft strip of footing are shown below the footing. The point of zero shear and maximum bending moment is shown at a section beneath the center of the wall. As the footing tends to bend, however, it is aided in resisting bending by the stiffness of the wall above. In other words, it is somewhat reinforced by the wall at the section of theoretically maximum bending moment. In designing the footing it is sufficient to consider some smaller bending moment, one which is resisted by the bending strength of the footing alone. The location and amount of this critical bending moment depend on the nature of the wall above. Section 1204(b) of the ACI Code lists three cases. For example, when the wall above is concrete, the critical section for bending is assumed to be at the face of the wall. With masonry walls, which cannot participate in reinforcing the footing so effectively, the critical section is assumed to be midway between the edge and the center of the wall.

Assuming that the wall is concrete, Fig. 9–29(c) shows the portion to the right of a critical section for bending. This portion is merely a cantilever beam having upward loads. (If the wall were of brick or concrete block, the portion removed would show also some downward loads from the wall near the left end.) The bearing pressure p below does not include the effect of the weight of the earth above the footing. Thus, the downward force of the earth above the footing is not shown on the isolated portion. The "net pressure" shown is the bearing pressure minus the weight of the footing per square foot. The concrete and the reinforcing steel must provide the necessary resisting moment M' to this net pressure. The bond requirements for the steel are computed using the shear V computed at the same critical section as for bending.

A diagonal tension failure for a footing is shown in Fig. 9–29(d). The cracks are inclined so that the failure starts at about distance d

(effective depth) from the face of the wall. This has been confirmed by test. The diagonal tensile stress due to shear is computed by the equation $v = V/bjd$, using the shear V computed at the distance d from the face of the wall. The portion projecting beyond this critical section is shown in Fig. 9–29(e).

A few practical requirements should be considered. It is difficult to trim the excavation to the exact depth, and the bottom may not be smooth. This leads to the possibility of large errors in thicknesses and in coverage below the reinforcing steel. Small thicknesses and coverage should be avoided. Footings are rarely as thin as 6 in. The concrete coverage for the bars must be at least 3 in. where the concrete is placed against the ground.

The soil may not be of the same quality under the entire length of footing. Steel is sometimes placed longitudinally near the bottom of a wall footing, so that if a "soft spot" is encountered, the footing can span that spot, transferring the load to solid ground on either side. Unequal settlement and cracking may result when serious variations of soil quality are encountered. Such differences would include variation in particle size (as between sand and clay), and differences in degree of wetness or of compaction. These cases should be referred to the attention of an engineer well versed in the solution of foundation problems.

9–13. Spread Footings. Fig. 9–30 shows a spread footing. The spread footing bends like the wall footing but in two planes. The resulting shape is a rectangular "dish," pushed down by the concentrated load

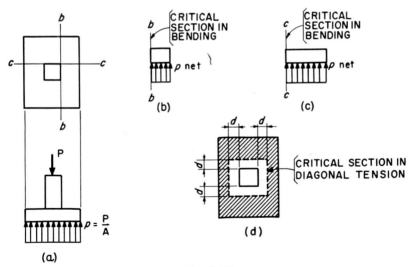

Fig. 9–30.

at the central pedestal or column, and pushed upward by the net soil pressure.

Fig. 9–30(b) shows the portion of footing outside the critical section b–b. That portion is merely a cantilever beam subject to p (net) as an upward load per square foot. Fig. 9–30(c) shows a similar portion outside of critical section c–c. Loads near the corners of the footing show on both Figs. 9–30(b) and (c). Obviously then, these corner loads are only partially effective in causing bending moment at section b–b and only partially effective at section c–c. An exact analysis would be complex. For use in selecting reinforcing steel only, a simple and economical approximation is given by Section 1204(e) of the ACI Building Code. In this approximation 85 per cent of the moment caused by the net pressure on the entire projecting portion is used. This gives an effective moment for each section, b–b and c–c. Unless the footing is square, these two values will be different. Reinforcing steel is selected separately for each section. Bond requirements are based on 85 per cent of the shear on each section, b–b and c–c. The complete unreduced moments for section b–b or section c–c are used to compute the flexural stresses in the concrete itself.

The diagonal tension failure of a spread footing is similar to that for a wall footing. Failure occurs all around the column or pedestal, however, so that a portion is "punched" out, leaving a ring around the outside. The critical section in diagonal tension is taken as a line around the pedestal at distance d away from its face. This critical section is shown dotted on Fig. 9–30(d). The area shown shaded is pushed upward with respect to the central unshaded area. The shear V to be considered in checking diagonal tension is the total net upward force on the shaded area. The diagonal tensile stress is computed from the shear equation $v = V/bjd$. The term b is normally the width of the section; in this case it is the total length of the dotted critical-section line.

In designing a spread footing, the following procedure is usually followed:

1. Assume a weight for the pedestal and footing.
2. Solve for the required base area and select a practical footing size.
3. Using the net p given by the selected size, compute the total bending moments, and find the required effective depth d. Select a practical footing thickness.
4. Check the selected footing for diagonal tension. Increase the depth if necessary.
5. Compute the reduced effective moments for each critical section, and solve for the required steel area and perimeter for each direction of reinforcement.

6. In footings that are not square, distribute the reinforcing bars according to Section 1204(g). This will be illustrated by Example 9–18.

EXAMPLE 9–17. The detail of an existing footing is shown in Fig. 9–31(a). Revisions being planned for the building above will increase the load on the footing to 92 kips. Will the footing be satisfactory?

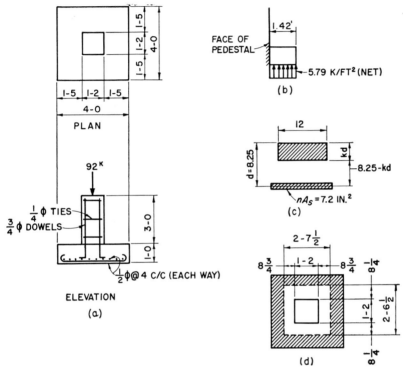

FIG. 9–31.

The building plans show that 2,500-lb concrete and intermediate-grade steel were used. The building was constructed in 1941. The soil is a compact fine sand having an allowable bearing value of 3 tons (6 kips) per sq ft.

The total load and actual soil pressure p will be computed first.

$$\begin{aligned}
\text{Load from column} &= 92.0 \text{ kips} \\
\text{Pedestal } 0.15 \times 3 \times (1.17)^2 &= 0.6 \\
\text{Footing } 0.15 \times 1 \times (4)^2 &= 2.4 \\
\hline
P &= 95.0 \text{ kips}
\end{aligned}$$

Soil pressure $p = 95.0/16 = 5.94$ kips per sq ft

This is less than the allowable 6 kips per sq ft. The footing is satisfactory in bearing.

$$p \text{ (net)} = 5.94 - 0.15 = 5.79 \text{ kips per sq ft}$$

The critical section in bending is at the face of the pedestal. The projecting portion is shown in Fig. 9–31(b). It is usually easier to work with the loads and moment for a one-ft strip, rather than those for the entire width of footing. The bending moment at this section is

$$M \text{ (per foot)} = 5.79 \times 1.42 \times 1.42/2$$

$$= 5.84 \text{ ft-kips or } 70.0 \text{ in.-kips}$$

The above value is used to check for flexural stress in the concrete. The reinforcing steel is checked using 85 per cent of the above moments or

$$0.85 \times 5.84 = 4.95 \text{ ft-kips or } 59.4 \text{ in.-kips (per ft of width)}$$

The shear V for bond requirements is computed at the same section as for bending.

$$V \text{ (per foot)} = 0.85 \times 5.79 \times 1.42 = 6.98 \text{ kips}$$

The flexural and bond strengths will now be checked. The effective depth d is $12 - 3\frac{1}{2} - \frac{1}{4} = 8\frac{1}{4}$, or 8.25 inches. The ratio n is $30,000,000/(1,000 \times 2,500) = 12$. The steel area is 0.60 sq in. per ft, and Σo is 4.8 in. per ft. (See Table 7 of Appendix B.) Fig. 9–31(c) shows the transformed section for a one-ft width. The computations for center of gravity are not shown here, but they give $kd = 2.60$ in. The section can now be checked for flexure either by comparing the stresses f_c and f_s with the allowable stresses, or by computing the resisting moment of the section and comparing it with the applied moment. The former method will be used here.

$$jd = 8.25 - 2.60/3 = 7.38 \text{ in.}$$

$$T = 0.85 M/jd = 59.4/7.38 = 8.05 \text{ kips}$$

$$f_s = 8,050/0.60 = 13,400 \text{ psi}$$

$$C = M/jd = 70.0/7.38 = 9.49 \text{ kips}$$

$$f_c = 2 \times \text{average stress} = 2 \times 9,490/(12 \times 2.60) = 608 \text{ psi}$$

These are less than the allowable stresses of 20,000 and 1,125 psi for steel and concrete, respectively. The section will be satisfactory in flexure.

The allowable bond stress for the old-type bars is 140 psi. The computed bond stress is

$$u = V/\Sigma ojd = 6,980/(4.8 \times 7.38) = 197 \text{ psi}$$

Courtesy of Cleveland Electric Illuminating Co.

STEEL GRILLAGES FOR ELECTRIC POWER PLANT.

This exceeds the allowable bond stress; therefore, the footing is not satisfactory for the increased loading.

Ordinarily the analysis would be considered complete after finding one obvious point of weakness. Here, in order to show the method, the analysis will be continued to cover shear (diagonal tension). The shear V for this use is the sum of the net upward loads on the shaded area of Fig. 9–31(d). Notice that the difference of d values for the two directions of reinforcement was considered. Often the smaller value or the average value is used in both directions.

$$\text{Shaded area} = 16.00 - (2.62 \times 2.54) = 9.35 \text{ sq ft}$$

$$V \text{ (for shear)} = 9.35 \times 5.79 = 54.0 \text{ kips}$$

$$\text{Perimeter of critical section} = 10 \text{ ft } 4 \text{ in.} = 124 \text{ in.}$$

$$v = V/bjd = 54,000/124 \times 7.38 = 59 \text{ psi}$$

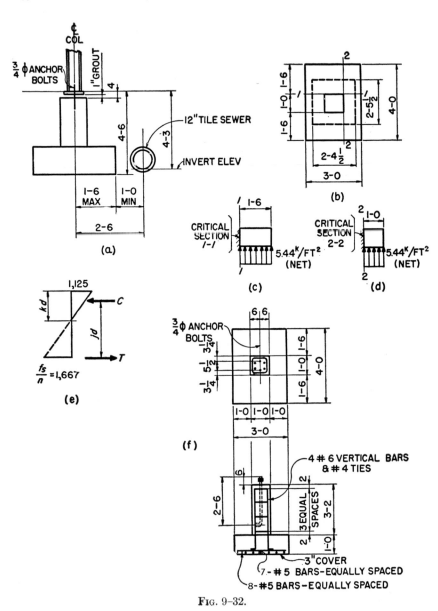

Fig. 9-32.

The allowable unit shear is 75 psi; therefore, the footing is satisfactory in diagonal tension. Bond, however, controls and the footing must be considered as unsatisfactory for the proposed increase of load.

EXAMPLE 9–18. An existing building is to have a rack installed near one wall. The rack is for storage of heavy dies. One edge of the rack will be attached to the existing building columns. Those columns and their footings have been analyzed and found satisfactory for the increased load. The other edge of the rack is to be supported by new columns on new footings. Assume that you have designed the column and must now design the footings. The new columns will each carry a total load of 65 kips. They will be 8WF31 sections on 10-in. by 11-in. base plates.

Fig. 9–32(a) shows the existing conditions. A 12-in. tile sewer is located 2 ft 6 in. from the centerline of the proposed new columns. The invert (bottom of the inside diameter) is 4 ft 3 in. below the finished floor. The bottoms of other existing interior footings are 3 ft below the finished floor. The record drawings show that 6,000 lb per sq ft was the soil bearing pressure allowed in designing the original footings.

Normally on a smaller job such as this, the designer himself will select the strength of concrete to be used. There is seldom much advantage in using a high-strength concrete for small footings. Usually a 2,500-lb concrete is used, and occasionally 3,000-lb. Assume that you have chosen to use 2,500-lb concrete and intermediate-grade steel for these footings.

The complete design of this foundation includes the design of the pedestal, as well as that of the footing itself. The pedestal is a short column. Its cross section must be at least as large as the bearing plate, and preferably a little larger. The design will be made for a 12-in. square pedestal. The height of the pedestal is about 3 ft; its weight about $\frac{1}{2}$ kip. The load for which it should be designed is $65 + 0.5 = 65.5$ kips.

$$P = 0.8 \times 144[(0.225 \times 2.5) + 16p_g] = 65.5 \text{ kips}$$

Solving the ACI column equation above gives

$$\text{Required } p_g = 0.0005$$

The above value indicates that practically no vertical steel is required for fulfillment of the strength requirements. Thus the specified minimum of $p_g = 0.01$ will be used, which makes the required $A_s = 1.44$ sq in. Four No. 6 bars will fill the requirement.

Ties must be provided. If No. 2 ties are used, they may be placed at 12-in. centers. (See Section 1104.)

Now that the pedestal dimensions are known, it is possible to proceed with the design of the footing. The bottom of the footing will be placed slightly lower than the nearby sewer so that the pressure from the footing does not damage the pipe. The soil at 4 ft 6 in. below the finished-floor level has not been disturbed, so it is safe to use the same allowable soil pressure there as was used for the other interior footings.

The total load must be estimated since the footing size is not yet known. Assuming the footing to be about one ft thick and allowing about $1\frac{1}{2}$ kips for its own weight gives

$$P = 65.5 + 1.5 = 67 \text{ kips}$$

$$\text{Required Bearing Area} = \frac{67}{6} = 11.2 \text{ sq ft}$$

There should be clear space between the footing and the sewer pipe. If the edge of the footing is placed at least one ft from the center of the pipe, clearance of about 6 in. will be provided. The maximum width of footing would then be twice 1 ft 6 in., or 3 ft, as shown on Fig. 9–32(a). Using 3 ft for the footing width, the length must be at least $11.2 \div 3 = 3.73$ ft. The design will be continued for a 3-ft by 4-ft footing.

The bearing area provided is 12.0 sq ft, so that the actual bearing pressure is

$$p = 67/12 = 5.59 \text{ kips per sq ft}$$

The plan view of the footing shows in Fig. 9–32(b). The critical sections for bending are shown as sections 1–1 and 2–2. The bending moment per foot width will be greater for strips projecting from section 1–1. One such strip is shown in Fig. 9–32(c). The upward bearing pressure is 5.59 kips per sq ft. The downward force caused by the weight of the footing is 0.15 kips per sq ft (for an assumed one-ft thickness).

$$p \text{ (net)} = 5.59 - 0.15 = 5.44 \text{ kips per sq ft}$$

For computing the required effective depth d, use

$$M = \frac{5.44 \times (1.5)^2}{2} = 6.11 \text{ ft-kips per one-ft strip}$$

The depth required for bending will now be determined. The allowable flexural stress f_c is 1,125 psi; the ratio n is $30,000,000/2,500,000 = 12$; and the allowable stress f_s is 20,000 psi. For a balanced design kd will be $0.403d$ and the lever arm of the internal couple will be $d - \frac{1}{3}kd$, which is $0.866d$. This is shown by the stress diagram of Fig. 9–32(e).

$$C = \frac{1{,}125}{2} \times 0.403d \times 12 = 2{,}720d \text{ per one-ft strip}$$

$$Cjd = M = 6.11 \text{ ft-kips} = 73{,}400 \text{ in.-lb}$$

$$2{,}720d \times 0.866d = 73{,}400$$

$$d^2 = 31.2$$

Required $d = 5.58$ in.

Three inches of concrete are required between the steel and the ground. Assuming that one-half-inch (No. 4) bars are used, the required footing thickness is $5.58 + 3.00 + 0.25 = 8.83$ in. A 9-in. depth could be used, although such thin footings are not common. A little additional thickness is not necessarily uneconomical, since the cost of the extra concrete is offset by a saving of steel. A 12-in. thickness will be used to continue the design. The effective depth d will be $12 - 3 - \frac{1}{4} = 8.75$ in. (For the reinforcement perpendicular to section 2–2, d will be less, assume it to be 8.25 in.)

The footing will be checked for diagonal tension next. A dotted line is drawn on Fig. 9–32(b) to indicate the critical section. The line is located d in. from the face of the pedestal. The shear V to be considered is the net upward load on the ring outside of this critical section.

$$\text{Area of ring} = 12.0 - (2.46 \times 2.37) = 6.17 \text{ sq ft}$$

$$V = 6.17 \times 5.44 = 33.5 \text{ kips}$$

$$b \text{ (length of section)} = 9 \text{ ft 8 in.} = 116 \text{ in.}$$

$$v = V/bjd = 33{,}500/(116 \times 7.15) = 40 \text{ psi}$$

This is much less than the allowable of 75 psi given for footings by Section 305 of the ACI Code, so the 12-in. depth will be satisfactory.

The next step is to choose steel for the footing. The bending moment for Section 1–1 is 85 per cent of 6.11, which is 5.20 ft-kips per one-ft strip. For the same strip, the shear to be used to compute bond requirements is

$$V = 0.85 \times 1.5 \times 5.44 = 6.93 \text{ kips}$$

$$\text{Required } A_s = \frac{T}{f_s} = \frac{M/jd}{f_s}$$

$$\text{Required } A_s = \frac{12{,}000 \times 5.20}{20{,}000 \times 7.58} = 0.41 \text{ sq in. per one-ft strip}$$

$$\text{Required } \Sigma o = \frac{V}{ujd} = \frac{6{,}930}{200 \times 7.58} = 4.57 \text{ in. per one-ft strip}$$

A strip projecting from critical section 2–2 is shown in Fig. 9–32(d). For a one-ft width of strip at this section,

$$M = 0.85 \times \frac{5.44 \times (1.0)^2}{2} = 2.31 \text{ ft-kips}$$

$$V = 0.85 \times 5.44 \times 1.0 = 4.62 \text{ kips}$$

$$\text{Required } A_s = \frac{12,000 \times 2.31}{20,000 \times 7.15} = 0.194 \text{ sq in.}$$

$$\text{Required } \Sigma o = \frac{4,620}{200 \times 7.15} = 3.2 \text{ in.}$$

The reinforcement in the long direction (perpendicular to section 1–1) can be provided by

> No. 4 bars at 4-in. centers ($A_s = 0.60$; $\Sigma o = 4.7$), or by
> No. 5 bars at 5-in. centers ($A_s = 0.74$; $\Sigma o = 4.7$), or by
> No. 6 bars at 6-in. centers ($A_s = 0.88$; $\Sigma o = 4.7$)

The smaller the bar size, the cheaper the footing steel will be. The labor cost for placing the steel will rise, of course, as the number of bars increases. Tentatively, assume that the No. 5 bars will be used. Seven bars will be needed.

The short reinforcement (perpendicular to section 2–2) must be selected in a slightly different manner. Section 1204(g) of the ACI Code gives a manner of distribution for the total amount of reinforcement in the short direction. In order to use that distribution, the total amount of short steel is computed. The length of section 2–2 is 4 ft, so that

$$A_s = 4 \times 0.194 = 0.78 \text{ sq in.}$$

$$\Sigma o = 4 \times 3.2 = 12.8 \text{ in.}$$

Of this total amount, the central portion of section 2–2, a portion 3 ft long, must contain the following fraction of the total:

$$\frac{2}{S + 1} = \frac{2}{\frac{4}{3} + 1} = \frac{6}{7}$$

The steel in the central 3-ft length of section 2–2 must have

$$A_s = \frac{6}{7} \times 0.78 = 0.67 \text{ sq in.}$$

$$\Sigma o = \frac{6}{7} \times 12.8 = 11.0 \text{ in.}$$

The steel for the central 3-ft portion could be provided by six No. 5 bars, equally spaced at about 6-in. centers. The outer portions must contain the balance which is $\frac{1}{7}$ of the total reinforcement for the section. In this case, each outer strip would be required to have

$$A_s = \frac{1}{14} \times 0.78 = 0.06 \text{ sq in.}$$

$$\Sigma o = \frac{1}{14} \times 12.8 = 0.91 \text{ in.}$$

One more No. 5 bar in each outer strip will provide the necessary steel. The outer strips are each 6 in. wide, so that a uniform distribution of the eight No. 5 bars is practical and fills the requirements of Section 1204(g). While the final distribution is uniform in this case, an unequal distribution would very likely occur if the ratio S were larger.

The final design for the footing is shown in Fig. 9–32(f). Notice that the vertical bars of the column are extended downward into the footing. This is done so as to transfer the load of those bars, through bond, into the footing. Their extension is enough to provide bonding area to develop the full allowable load for the bars. (See Section 1206 of the ACI Code.) The allowable load for each of the No. 6 vertical bars is $16,000 \times 0.44 = 7,040$ lb. The allowable bond stress is 250 psi. The length of imbedment required is therefore

$$\frac{7,040}{250 \times 2.4} = 11.7 \text{ in.}$$

That much imbedment in the footing would bring the end of the vertical bar nearly to the soil, so the bars are bent into a horizontal position as shown. The total length of imbedment per bar must be 11.7 in. or more, the length of the horizontal portion being included.

Two $\frac{3}{4}$-in. anchor bolts are shown. Holes for these bolts are provided in the column base plate. The length of the anchor bolts is determined by their bond requirements. The allowable load on the threaded section of the bolt is

$$20,000 \times 0.302 = 6,040 \text{ lb}$$

The bolts are made from plain bars, not deformed, so the allowable bond stress is only $0.045f_c$, which is 113 psi. The length of imbedment required is

$$\frac{6,040}{113 \times 2.4} = 22.3 \text{ in.}$$

A hook is required for undeformed bars, regardless of the length computed. A 24-in. imbedment is shown.

PROBLEMS

9-1. A beam section is shown by Fig. 9–33. The 28-day strength of the concrete is 3,500 psi. Using intermediate-grade steel and the ACI Specification:

a) What steel area, A_s, is required for balanced design?

b) What is the allowable bending moment with balanced design?

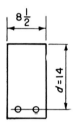

FIG. 9–33.

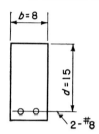

FIG. 9–34.

9-2. The beam of Fig. 9–34 consists of 3,000-lb concrete and rail steel. Compute the flexural stresses, f_c and f_s, caused by a bending moment of 29 ft-kips.

9-3. A small existing building purchased by your company has a floor slab of unknown capacity. You are requested to compute the allowable live load per square foot for this slab. The records show the slab to be 6 in. thick, reinforced with 1/2-in. round bars at 5-in. centers. The steel is near the bottom with 3/4 in. of cover. The slab is a one-way slab, acting as a simple beam. The clear space between the supporting walls is 12 ft; the slab has a 6-in. length of bearing on each wall. Concrete with a strength of 3,000 psi at 28 days was specified.

9-4. Design a reinforced concrete beam section to resist a bending moment of 41 ft-kips. Use f_c' of 3,000 psi, and intermediate-grade steel. Specify the bar sizes to be used and check for cover and spacing.

9-5. Your plant has a concrete flume for carrying cooling water to an outdoor settling tank. To improve access to various parts of the plant, it is decided to cover the flume. Access to the flume must be provided, however, so a removable cover is desirable. Corrosion would make steel covers an unwise choice. Reinforced concrete covers, as shown in Fig. 9–35, in

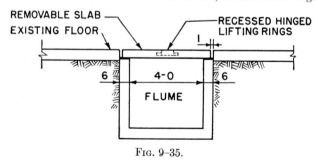

FIG. 9–35.

sections about six feet long could be removed by a crane when necessary. Design a cover using intermediate-grade steel and 3,000-lb concrete. Assume a floor live load of 200 lb per sq ft.

9-6. Compute the allowable shear V for the section of Fig. 9–34 and Problem 9–2:

a) As limited by diagonal tension
b) As limited by bond

9-7. Using the known dead load and the allowable live load you have computed, what is the diagonal tensile stress for the slab investigated in Problem 9–3? What is the bond stress? If either the diagonal tensile or the bond stress exceeds the allowable value, to what should the live load per square foot be limited?

9-8. A beam with stirrups is shown by Fig. 9–36. The concrete has a strength of 3,000 psi at 28 days, and the steel is of intermediate grade. What spacing of stirrups is required:

a) Where the shear V is 30 kips?
b) Where V is 21 kips? (Note ACI Code, Sect. 806.)

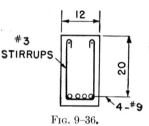

Fig. 9–36.

9-9. A straightening and bending machine for occasional use is needed in your plant. Little space is available and the purchase price of a ready-made machine cannot be justified. You are considering the solution shown in Fig. 9–37. The "backbone" of the equipment is a concrete beam, to be

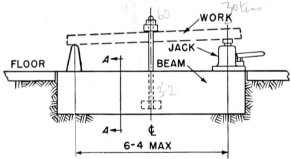

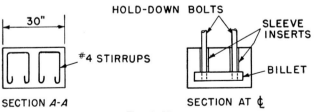

Fig. 9–37.

imbedded with its top flush with the floor. Large hold-down bolts are inserted in threaded holes in a steel billet which is cast in the bottom of the beam. The work to be bent is held down by these bolts, supported on one end by a movable block, and raised at the other by a hydraulic jack. A 30-ton jack, now owned by the company, will be used.

Design the concrete beam. Use f'_c of 3,000 psi, and intermediate-grade steel. Choose the effective depth, the over-all depth, the main steel (size and number), and the stirrup spacing. Use as shallow a section as is practical without resort to double reinforcing.

9–10. A trench for two flight conveyors is shown by Fig. 9–38(a). Heat and disagreeable fumes from the material carried by the conveyors have been found harmful to the workers on the floor above. It is decided to

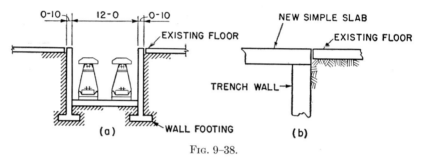

Fig. 9–38.

cover the trench and to ventilate it by exhaust fans at one end. The fumes will damage structural steel, so a cover of concrete is planned. As one possibility, a simple slab could be constructed as shown in Fig. 9–38(b). The walls of the trench would be cut down to place the new slab flush with the existing floor. Design the slab, using f'_c of 3,000 psi, intermediate-grade steel, and a live load of 200 lb per sq ft. Show complete details, including shrinkage and temperature steel.

9–11. Your plant, built in 1942, has a concrete floor slab on steel beams as shown by Fig. 9–39. The concrete was specified as 3,000-lb concrete,

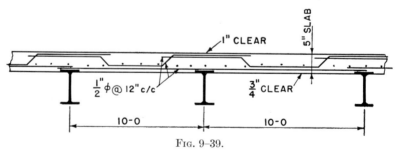

Fig. 9–39.

but the records do not show which type of steel was used. Based on the strength of the floor slab, to what amount should the live load per square foot be limited?

9-12. It is planned to construct a roof over a driveway between two one-story factory buildings. One manner of doing this is to support a concrete slab from steel beams, as in Fig. 9–40, the beams resting on bearing plates in

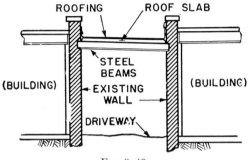

FIG. 9–40.

pockets cut into the existing walls. (It would be necessary to determine whether the wall thickness is sufficient to carry this load. The local building code should be consulted.) Design a roof slab, using beams at 6-ft centers. The live load is to be 30 lb per sq ft. Show complete detail, including shrinkage and temperature steel.

9-13. Compute the allowable bending moment for the beam section of Fig. 9–41. Use intermediate-grade steel and f'_c of 3,500 psi.

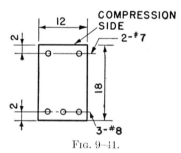

FIG. 9–41.

9-14. At one section of the trench of Problem 9–10 and Fig. 9–38(a), provision must be made for access to the conveyor and for the removal of large

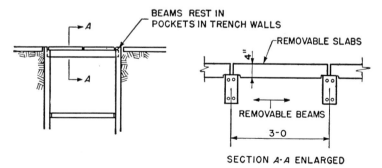

SECTION A-A ENLARGED

FIG. 9–42.

parts. It is deemed advisable to have a removable cover over about 24 ft of the trench. A possible type of removable cover is shown by Fig. 9–42. Precast slab sections measuring 6 ft by 3 ft are supported by precast beams at 3-ft centers. The beams are supported on bearing plates in pockets cut into the trench walls. The slab sections and beams are to be removed by the overhead crane.

Design the beams, using intermediate-grade steel and 3,000-lb concrete. The beams should be reinforced alike top and bottom so that upside-down installation will not be dangerous.

9–15. A floor slab and supporting tee beam are shown by Fig. 9–43. Use intermediate-grade steel and f'_c of 3,000 psi. What is the allowable bending moment if the slab thickness t is 6 in.? What is the allowable shear V:

a) Based on diagonal tension?
b) Based on bond?

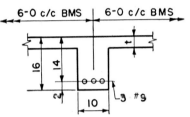

(BEAM SPAN= 20-0)

Fig. 9–43.

9–16. What is the allowable bending moment for the tee beam of Problem 9–15 when the slab thickness t is only 4 in.?

9–17. As an alternate to the simple slab of Problem 9–10 (Fig. 9–38), consider a thinner slab supported on tee beams as shown by Fig. 9–44. Pockets

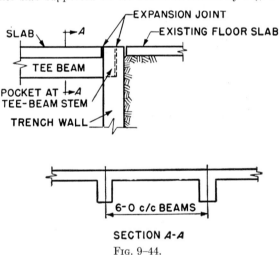

SECTION *A-A*

Fig. 9–44.

must be cut into the wall at each beam; elsewhere, the walls are not changed.

a) Design the slab.
b) Design the tee beams for the support of the slab.

9–18. What is the allowable axial load for a column of the following description? Size 10 in. × 10 in.; length between lateral supports 11 ft 6 in.; reinforced with 4 one-in. round bars; ties are 3/8-in. round spaced at 10-in. centers; intermediate grade steel; and $f'_c = 3{,}000$ psi.

9–19. In Example 9–16 (Fig. 9–28) a column was designed for the support of a new set of bins. An alternate plan is being considered in which two such sets of bins will be placed next to each other. The columns at adjacent corners will be common to both sets and will each receive 80 kips of load from the bins. The upper steel column will be 8 in. × 8 in. Design a tied concrete column for this alternate scheme.

9–20. Based on the strength of the footing itself, what is the allowable total load P per foot for the wall footing of Fig. 9–45? Consider flexure, bond, and diagonal tension. The steel is intermediate grade and f'_c is 2,500 psi. The footing was made in 1941.

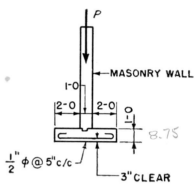

Fig. 9–45.

9–21. Design a square footing to support the column of Problem 9–19. The record prints of the building design show that an allowable bearing pressure of 5,000 lb per sq ft was used. Use $f'_c = 3{,}000$ psi, and intermediate grade steel.

9–22. When the excavations are being made for the footing of Problem 9–21, you discover that the edge of an existing footing for a building column is only 1 ft 11 in. from the center of one of the new bin-support columns, as shown in Fig. 9–46. This is insufficient space to permit installation of

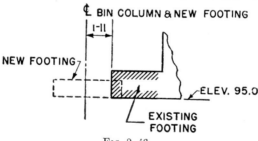

Fig. 9–46.

the square footing you originally designed. Redesign for this new and unpredicted condition. Allow a space of about two inches between the new footing and the old.

CHAPTER 10

DESIGN IN TIMBER

10–1. Structure of Wood. The basic structural unit in wood is the wood cell, an elongated hollow cell having walls of cellulose. Many such cells are cemented to each other by a material called lignin. The physical properties of the wood depend on the condition of the cellulose in the cell walls, the dimensions of the cells, and the arrangement of the cells in the wood.

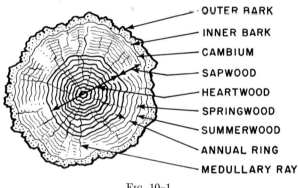

FIG. 10–1.

Fig. 10–1 shows the cross section of a tree. Most of the cells are longitudinal ones, their length being perpendicular to the cross section. Growth occurs through the addition of new cells by the cambium layer. Cells formed in the moist spring months have large interior spaces, those formed in the summer months have smaller spaces. This causes the springwood and the summerwood to differ, and the tree to have "annual rings." Summerwood is more dense; it has more cellulose (less cell space) per unit of cross section.

Some cells are placed in a radial position. Groups of these cells are visible as "medullary rays." Some species have prominent medullary rays; others practically none.

Food materials are transported by the cambium and by parts of the tree close to the bark. The wood near the surface is saturated with these liquid food materials, while that nearer the center no longer carries them. The two types of wood have a different appearance. The outer

406

wood is called "sapwood"; the inner, "heartwood." Sapwood is usually a lighter color than heartwood.

Timber is classified as "softwood" or "hardwood." The choice of these names was unfortunate, as they bear no relationship at all to the hardness of the wood. Softwood is from trees having needle leaves, such as pine, spruce, fir, hemlock, and larch. Hardwood is from trees with broad leaves, such as oak, maple, hickory, ash, or birch.

10–2. Strength Properties. Wood cells are tubular, their length being many times their diameter. They are oriented in nearly parallel directions. Thus, wood is non-isotropic; its strength properties vary with the load direction. This is easily seen by considering one cell. A wood cell is like a tube with a cap at each end. Fig. 10–2 shows such a tube. In (a)

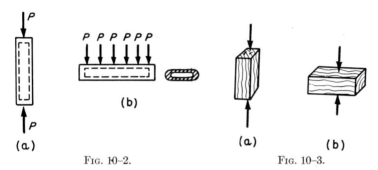

Fig. 10–2.   Fig. 10–3.

the tube has a longitudinal load. The resistance of the tube to such a load is good. In (b) the tube is loaded in the other direction. A load of intensity P which could be endured longitudinally would flatten the tube when applied as in (b). In wood the action is similar, but it involves many such tubes alongside each other.

The strength properties of importance include the following:

1. Compression parallel to the grain, Fig. 10–3(a). In this the average cell is loaded somewhat like the tube of Fig. 10–2(a).
2. Compression perpendicular to the grain, Fig. 10–3(b). The average individual cell is loaded like the tube of Fig. 10–2(b).
3. Shear parallel to the grain.
4. Tension parallel to the grain.
5. Modulus of rupture, the imaginary bending stress given by the flexure formula, $f = Mc/I$, at ultimate moment for a test beam.
6. Modulus of elasticity.

All of the above properties are measured using the test procedures of the American Society for Testing Materials.

10–3. Factors Affecting the Strength of Wood. The strength properties listed above are affected by several variable factors, all of which must be considered in establishing design standards.

The species is the first variable to consider. Some species grow cells with thick walls, others with thin walls. Thus, some species have more load-carrying cellulose per square inch of cross section. Other factors remaining constant, more cellulose per square inch means more strength per square inch.

The arrangement of the cells differs among species. Wood with many medullary rays is "reinforced." The longitudinal cells are thus tied together firmly, and they cannot buckle so easily. The strength properties are usually improved by the presence of medullary rays.

Density is an important factor. Density is defined as the percentage of summerwood (measured on a radial line on the cross section). Dense wood has more cellulose and less cell space per unit area than does non-dense wood.

Wood is strongest in most respects when dry. Water that is absorbed by the cell wall material softens the wall and weakens the wood. Free water in the cell spaces of wood having saturated walls has no further effect, except possibly under impact loading.

The duration of the load has a large effect. In general, the longer the load is in place, the lower will be the strength. The resistance to loads of very short duration, such as impact, is much higher than the resistance to ordinary live loads.

A very important factor is the presence of defects. The types of defect are many, including:

1. Cross grain, in which the grain direction is not parallel to the length of the timber
2. Knots
3. Checks and shakes, which are longitudinal separations in the wood, usually caused by uneven shrinkage during drying
4. Decay

10–4. Allowable Stresses. All of the factors mentioned above are considered when an allowable stress is established. The specifications for timber design usually quote the allowables in a form like that of Table 11 in Appendix B. To use the table one must know the grade of the timber in question.

Lumber is classified first according to its use, as *yard lumber, shop lumber,* or *structural lumber.* Structural lumber is then graded into a number of stress grades. The grading rules consider the number, type, size, and location of the defects. Grading rules are published by the

U.S. Department of Agriculture and by the lumber associations. The grading of structural lumber should be done by a competent inspector.

Allowable stresses are given by the table for various grades of lumber. Those allowables are based on the strengths observed for small clear specimens (no defects), tested according to ASTM standards. The observed strengths are divided by the desired factor of safety to give basic working stresses for clear wood. The basic stresses are further reduced according to the quality of the lumber in question, giving the allowable stresses of Table 11.

The quoted stresses must now be adjusted by the engineer according to the duration of load. The quoted stresses are for "normal load." normal load consists of either full design load for three years, or the continuous application for the life of the structure of 90 per cent of full design load. For certain other load durations, the allowable stresses must be changed as follows:

1. Load duration longer or more intense than normal. Use 90 per cent of the quoted allowable stress.
2. Two months durations, as for snow load. Use 115 per cent of the quoted allowable.
3. Seven days duration. Use 125 per cent of the quoted allowable.
4. Wind or earthquake. Use $133\frac{1}{3}$ per cent of the quoted allowable.
5. Impact. Use 200 per cent of the quoted allowable.

The above increases or decreases are not cumulative. For a combination of loads, the percentage shown for the shortest loading of the combination is used to find the allowable stress for the combined loading.

EXAMPLE 10–1. A beam of Dense No. 1 Structural Southern Pine is subject to the following load types: dead load, normal floor load, and a possible brief overload of one-week total duration. What are the allowable bending stresses for various load conditions?

Dead load plus normal floor load.........allow the quoted stress of 1,600 psi
Dead load alone......................allow 0.90 × 1,600 = 1,440 psi
Dead load plus brief overload of floor......allow 1.25 × 1,600 = 2,000 psi

Each of the allowables above would be compared with the actual stress caused by the combination in question to determine whether the member is satisfactory.

EXAMPLE 10–2. A rafter of Douglas fir (Inland Region, Com. Structural) is subject to uniformly distributed loads as follows: dead load, 700 lb; snow load, 900 lb; and wind load, 500 lb. Which load combination would control the design, and what is the allowable bending stress? Assume that one-half of the snow load could occur with full wind.

The controlling combination is the one requiring the largest section modulus. The required section modulus is proportional to the load and inversely proportional to the allowable flexural stress. The controlling loading, therefore, is the one for which the ratio of load to allowable stress is the largest.

The quoted allowable (Table 11) is 1,450 psi. The computations are tabulated below:

Load Combination	Allowable flexural stress F_b	Load/F_b
Dead load = 700 lb	0.9 × 1,450 = 1,310 psi	0.535
Dead load and snow = 1,600	1.15 × 1,450 = 1,670	0.960
Dead load, ½ snow, and wind = 1,650	1.33 × 1,450 = 1,930	0.855

The combination including dead load and snow will control the design.

10–5. Sizes of Lumber.   Table 12 in Appendix B gives the sizes and section properties of finished lumber. The nominal size is the approximate actual size of the rough-cut lumber. When all four surfaces of the rough-cut lumber are planed smooth, it is called S4S, meaning "surfaced on four sides." This is the most common, but other kinds can be had, such as S2S, or S2S1E (surfaced on two sides and one edge).

When all four surfaces are planed, the piece is reduced to the size shown by Table 12. Nominal dimensions of up to 6 in. are reduced $\frac{3}{8}$ in. by planing; nominal dimensions over 6 in. are reduced $\frac{1}{2}$ in. Thus, a rough-cut 2 × 12 measures 2 in. by 12 in. The finished 2 × 12 measures $1\frac{5}{8}$ in. by $11\frac{1}{2}$ in. It is still called a "2 by 12." In speaking of lumber, the finished size is usually understood unless it is definitely stated otherwise.

10–6. Beams.   Timber beams are subject to three main types of failure—bending, horizontal shear, and bearing at supports or at concentrated loads. The design of a timber beam requires proportioning to prevent these failures. Deflections may sometimes affect the choice of section.

To select a section for bending, the flexure formula, $f = Mc/I$, is used just as for steel beams. (For non-rectangular beams, an additional term called a "form factor" must be included in the equation.[1])

The intensity of shearing stress at any point is given by the equation

$$v = VQ/Ib$$

[1]Forest Products Laboratory, *Wood Handbook* (Washington, D. C.: U. S. Department of Agriculture, 1940).

in which v is the unit shearing stress, either vertical or horizontal; V is the effective shear at the cross section; Q is the static moment of the area of cross section between the extreme fiber and the point in question, taken about the center of gravity of the entire cross section; I is the moment of inertia of the complete cross section; and b is the width of the cross section at the point in question.

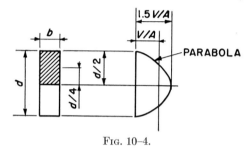

FIG. 10–4.

A rectangular beam is shown by Fig. 10–4. For a point at mid-height, Q is $(bd/2)(d/4) = bd^2/8$, and

$$v = \frac{VQ}{Ib} = \frac{Vbd^2/8}{(bd^3/12)b} = \frac{1.5V}{bd} = 1.5V/A$$

For a rectangular section in bending, the maximum unit shear is 1.5 times the average shear V/A, A being the total area of the cross section.

Horizontal shearing stress may cause failure near the end of a beam. Such a failure is shown by Fig. 10–5. Horizontal shear failure may be described as the sliding of the top and bottom parts with respect to each other, such as the sliding of one page against the next when a book is bent.

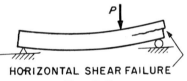

HORIZONTAL SHEAR FAILURE

FIG. 10–5.

Tests by the Forest Products Laboratory show that loads near a support need not be considered when designing to prevent horizontal shear failure. The reason is that the portions of beam above and below a horizontal check near the support each carry a large portion of the shear. For loads near the support, almost all the shear is resisted by the two portions acting as separate members; little of the shear is resisted at the plane of the neutral axis. The tests show that the end reaction can be much larger than indicated by the term V in the shear equation. Thus, certain loads are neglected when computing the effective shear V. Two methods of doing this were developed by the Forest Products Laboratory. The simpler method is more often used. Sometimes, however, it may give over-conservative results. When this happens, the more accurate second method may be used. The two methods of computing the shear V are:

First method:

1. Ignore loads within a distance d (depth of beam) from the center of each support.
2. If moving concentrated loads occur, place the largest one at distance $3d$ (but not more than one-fourth the span) from the support. Apply the other loads at their usual spacing from the maximum one.
3. With the loads so located, compute V at the support in the usual manner.

Second Method.

1. For a concentrated load, use end shear

$$V = \frac{10P(L - x)(x/d)^2}{9L[2 + (x/d)^2]}$$

in which d = depth of beam (in.)
L = span (in.)
P = concentrated load
x = distance from reaction to load

The above equation is used for each concentrated load present, the loads being located as for the first method.

2. For uniform load, use end shear

$$V = \frac{wL}{2}\left(1 - \frac{2d}{L}\right)$$

(This is identical with the treatment of uniform load under the first method.)

The span L for simple beams is the clear distance between supports plus one-half the required bearing length at each end. Where a beam is continuous over a support, L is taken to the center of that support.

Bearing stress is computed as if uniform over the actual bearing area. The computed bearing stress is limited to the allowable for compression perpendicular to the grain (Table 11), adjusted for load duration as required. However, if the bearing length is less than 6 in. and centered not closer than 3 in. to the end of the timber, the allowable bearing stress may be multiplied by the factor

$$\frac{L + 3/8}{L}$$

EXAMPLE 10–3. An existing floor is supported as shown by Fig. 10–6. The area is normally used as a shop office, but during remodeling of the adjacent area it is to be used for storage. The time required is about one month. What is the allowable load per square foot, based on the strength of the joists? Assume that you have checked the grading rules and have classified the joists as common structural Douglas fir. The flooring weighs about 8.5 lb per sq ft.

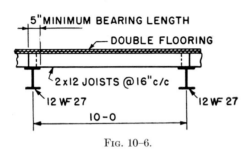

FIG. 10–6.

One should remember that so-called temporary conditions have a remarkable facility for becoming long-term or permanent. The first step would be to make certain that "about one month" would not become "a few months." Assuming that one month is a reasonably certain duration, the solution would proceed as shown.

The capacity will be computed for bending, shear, and end bearing. The allowable stresses are 1.15 times the quoted values, as follows:

For bending, $1.15 \times 1,450 = 1,667$ psi
For shear, $1.15 \times 95 = 109$ psi
For compression perpendicular to grain, $1.15 \times 380 = 437$ psi

The span L in bending and shear computations is the clear space plus one-half the required bearing length at each end. The required bearing length is not known; assume it to be 3 in. Thus,

$$L = 120 - 6.5 + 3 = 116.5 \text{ in.} = 9.71 \text{ ft}$$

Allowable $M = F_b S = 1,667 \times 35.82 = 59,600$ in.-lb $= 4,970$ ft-lb

The allowable load per foot of joist, as limited by bending, is

$$8M/L^2 = 8 \times 4,970/(9.71)^2 = 422 \text{ lb}$$

The capacity in shear is checked next. The effective shear V is computed using the method recommended by the Forest Products Laboratory. Loads closer than 11.5 in. to the center of bearing at each end are neglected. The loads to be considered are shown by Fig. 10–7. The effective shear is the reaction to those loads.

$$V = \frac{7.83w}{2} = 3.92w$$

$$v = 1.5V/A = 1.5 \times 3.92w/18.69 = 0.315w$$

Allowable $v = 109$ psi

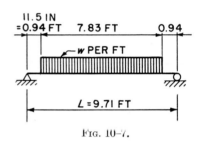

FIG. 10–7.

The allowable load per foot of joist, as limited by shear is

$$w = 109/0.315 = 346 \text{ lb}$$

Finally the capacity in bearing is computed. The length of bearing is shown by Fig. 10–6 as 5 in. minimum. The bearing area for each joist is $1.625 \times 5 = 8.12$ sq in. The bearing center is only $2\frac{1}{2}$ in. from the end of the joist, so the increase factor for short bearings may not be used. The allowable bearing stress is 437 psi. The allowable reaction is

$$R = 437 \times 8.12 = 3,550 \text{ lb}$$

This is the reaction to loads on the 10-ft length of joist between steel beams. The allowable load, as limited by bearing, is

$$w = R/5 = 710 \text{ lb per ft}$$

The smallest allowable load is that based on shear, or 346 lb per ft of joist. Each joist supports a 16-in. width of floor. The dead load supported by one foot of joist is

$$\left(\frac{16}{12} \times 8.5\right) + 5.18 \doteq 17 \text{ lb}$$

The live-load capacity per ft of joist is $346 - 17 = 329$ lb. The allowable live load, based on the joist strength, is $329 \times \frac{12}{16} = 247$ lb per sq ft.

EXAMPLE 10–4. Consider again the temporary wooden bridge of Example 5–7 (Chapter 5) and Fig. 5–14. The bridge is made necessary by a crane breakdown and is to carry wheeled bins of partially completed parts. Design the timber beams. Utility Structural Norway Pine is available at a local lumber yard.

The design is shown in computation-sheet form by Fig. 10–8. A 4×6 is selected for bending. This section is then checked for shear and for end bearing and is found satisfactory. The correction factor

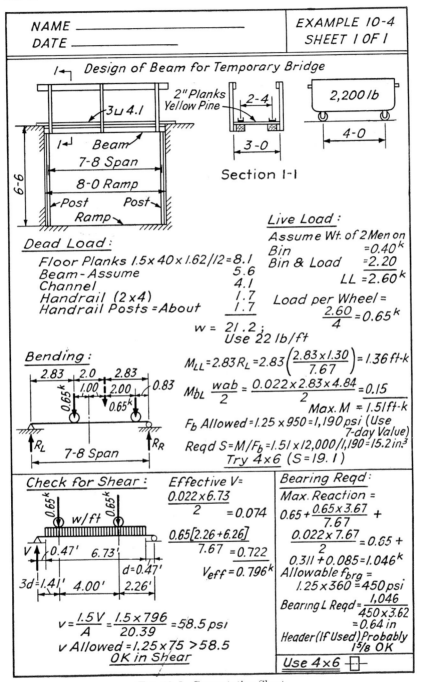

FIG. 10-8. Computation Sheet.

for seven-day load duration is used in determining the allowable stresses.

In solving for the bearing length required, the loads are located to cause the maximum end reaction. The center of the bearing is closer than 3 in. to the end of the timber, so the correction factor for short bearing lengths is not used.

10–7. Lateral Support for Timber Beams.   Lateral buckling or twisting may cause failure of a timber beam, just as it may for a steel beam. To prevent such failure two courses are available. First, the load can be limited so as to provide a factor of safety with respect to buckling failure. Second, the beam can be provided with lateral support, or be made in such proportions that failure is initiated by rupture rather than by buckling. The latter method is more commonly used. It is accomplished by observing certain rules for lateral support, as follows:

1. Where the ratio of depth to width is 2 or less, no lateral support is required.
2. Where the ratio is 3, the ends should be held vertical.
3. Where the ratio is 4, the piece should be held in line by frequent support, as would be provided by bolts joining the vertical laminations of a built-up beam. See Fig. 10–9.

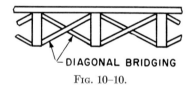

DIAGONAL BRIDGING

Fig. 10–9.   Fig. 10–10.

4. Where the ratio is 5, one edge should be held in line. This could be done by flooring nailed to the joists.
5. Where the ratio is 6, diagonal bridging should be used. See Fig. 10–10. Sets of bridging should be placed at intervals of 8 ft or less. Bridging serves also to transfer load, so that joists receiving concentrated load are assisted by the adjacent joists.
6. Where the ratio is 7, both edges should be held in line. For joists, bridging may be used instead, with the interval between bridging equal to 6 times the joist depth.

In all of the above rules, the nominal dimensions, not actual, should be used. Beams which are not covered by these rules can be designed using the first-mentioned method.[2]

10–8. Notched Beams.   Fig. 10–11(a) shows a common type of end detail. The shearing strength of the beam is reduced by the effect of a

[2]Forest Products Laboratory, *Wood Handbook* (Washington, D. C.: U. S. Department of Agriculture, 1940).

smaller area of cross section at the notch, and it is still further reduced by stress concentrations and irregularities at the change of section. This second effect is less in a notch like that of Fig. 10–11(b) in which

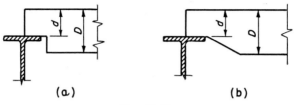

(a)   (b)

Fig. 10–11.

the section change is gradual. However, both types are usually computed in the same manner.

The unit shear for an unnotched beam is

$$v = 1.5V/A$$

Where the area is reduced to a smaller area a at the notch, that effect is reflected by using the smaller area in the equation. The unit shear stress thus computed is then multiplied by the ratio of full depth to reduced depth, covering the effect of concentrations of stress at the abrupt change of section. Thus, the computed shear stress becomes

$$v = \frac{1.5V}{a}\left(\frac{D}{d}\right)$$

In designing a notched beam, the shear stress given by the above computation is limited to the allowable value.

A problem which may meet the attention of the non-civil engineer is that of notches near the center of the span. Revisions to buildings often involve notches to accommodate new conduits, pipes, etc. That these notches affect the strength is recognized, but too often ignored. Older structures may become literally perforated with such holes and notches.

Fig. 10–12 shows such a notch. The bending strength should be computed using the reduced depth at the notch.

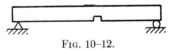

Fig. 10–12.

If the notch is at a section having appreciable shear as well as bending moment, the shear strength and bending strength should both be checked.

10–9. Deep Beams. The factor of safety for timber in bending is set with regard to the modulus of rupture. The modulus of rupture is slightly less for deep beams than for shallow ones. The modulus for small clear specimens of 2-in. depth is used as a base. The ratio of the modulus for larger beams to that for the 2-in. size is called the "depth factor." The depth factor for 12-in. beams is $\frac{9}{10}$. This factor of $\frac{9}{10}$ is included in the quoted allowable bending stresses of Table 11.

If the quoted stresses are used for very deep beams, the safety factor is reduced. To maintain the desired factor of safety, the allowable bending stress must be reduced for deep beams. The depth factor is given for rectangular sections as

$$F = 1 - 0.07(\sqrt{d/2} - 1)$$

in which d is the depth in inches. For a depth of 2 in., F is unity. The quoted allowable includes a depth factor of $\frac{9}{10}$. Thus, to obtain the allowable bending stress for a deeper beam, the quoted allowable should be multiplied by $10F/9$.

That depth beyond which a reduction of allowable should be considered is open to question. For a depth of 19 in. the reduction of allowable stress is about 5 per cent; for 24 in. it is 8 per cent; and for 30 in., 11.4 per cent. In building work it is common to consider stresses within 5 per cent of the allowable stress as acceptable. It would be consistent with that practice to ignore the reduction of allowable bending stress for beams up to 19 in. deep.

10–10. Timber Columns. Timber columns are classified in two ways: according to their construction, and according to their action.

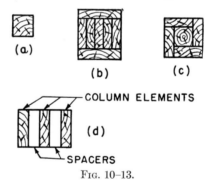

Fig. 10–13.

The three types of construction are shown by Fig. 10–13. The solid column of (a) is a single piece of timber. It is commonly used as a post or building column, or as a compression member in the older type of timber truss.

The laminated columns of (b) and (c) are made of thinner pieces in contact and connected together with spikes or bolts.

The spaced column of (d) consists of thinner elements separated by spacer blocks at the ends and at intervals along the member. This type is used for compression members in modern timber trusses.

For each of the three types a further classification is made according to the probable mode of failure, as follows:

1. Short columns, in which the ratio L/d (laterally unsupported length/least external dimension) does not exceed 11. In these columns, the initial failure does not involve buckling.
2. Intermediate columns, in which buckling is involved, but the action is not that of the "Euler" column. L/d is between 11 and K. The term K is the ratio L/d beyond which the column strength can be predicted by the Euler equation. Its value is given by

$$K = \frac{\pi}{2}\sqrt{\frac{E}{5c}} = 0.702\sqrt{E/c}$$

in which E is the modulus of elasticity and c is the allowable compressive stress given by Table 11.

3. Long columns, in which L/d exceeds K.

10–11. Design of Solid Columns. In short solid columns, the stress c is the allowable unit stress. Designing consists of choosing a section large enough so that the computed stress P/A does not exceed c.

For intermediate columns the allowable P/A is less than c, the reduction being a function of the slenderness. The allowable average unit stress is

$$P/A = c\left[1 - \frac{1}{3}\left(\frac{L}{Kd}\right)^4\right]$$

For long columns the Euler equation is used in the following form:

$$\text{Allowable } P/A = \frac{0.329E}{(L/d)^2}$$

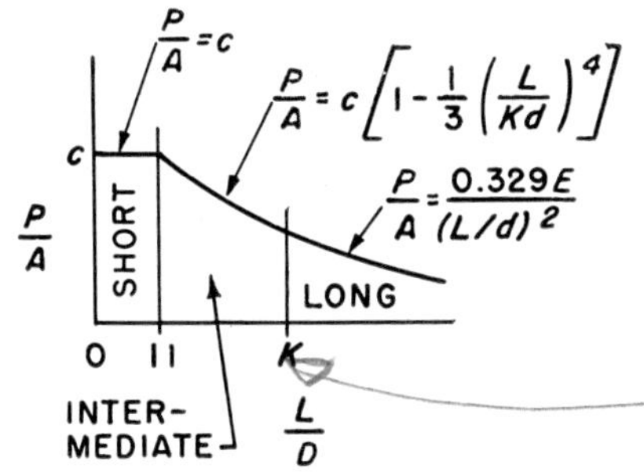

Fig. 10–14.

Fig. 10–14 shows the variation of the allowable P/A with the ratio L/d. This is similar to the curve for steel columns, except that the three ranges are recognized and treated separately in timber design.

Courtesy of Timber Engineering Co.

OILFIELD STRUCTURE OF TIMBER, USING MODERN TIMBER CONNECTORS.

10–12. Design of Laminated Columns. Laminated columns are designed as similar solid columns, but with reduced allowable stresses. Reduction factors have been obtained experimentally for the two arrangements shown by Fig. 10–13(b) and (c). The reduction factors are as follows:

L/d	Per cent of Solid-Column Strength	L/d	Per cent of Solid-Column Strength
6	82	18	65
10	77	22	74
14	71	26	82

The planks should be not wider than five times their thickness. Spikes should be spaced longitudinally at not over six times the plank thickness. In the type shown by Fig. 10–13(b), the spikes must be long enough to extend through two planks and well into the third.

Laminated columns may be made using short pieces butted end to end. The joints should be well staggered along the length of the column. For intermediate and long columns, the above percentages are used with columns of either full-length or short pieces. For short columns, however, the butt-jointed short pieces become embedded into each other, and failure occurs at 75 to 80 per cent of the ultimate P/A for full-length pieces.

EXAMPLE 10–5. Consider again the temporary crossover bridge of Example 5–7 and Example 10–4 (See Fig. 10–8). Select a post for the end supports.

The column load is the maximum reaction of 1.046 kips. The quoted allowable stress c is 650 psi. The height from the ramp to the floor is 78 in. Use for L the distance from the ramp to the center of the beam.

$$L = 78 - 1.62 - 5.62/2 = 73.6 \text{ in.}$$

L/d is not known until a tentative size is considered. The section must be selected by trial. L/d must not exceed 50, so d must be not less than $73.6/50 = 1.47$ in. The minimum practical size would be 2 in. nominal or $1\frac{5}{8}$ in. actual.

Try a 2×4. For this section, L/d is $73.6/1.62 = 45.4$. The modulus of elasticity E is 1,200,000 psi. (Load-duration factors do not apply to E.)

$$\text{Allowable } P/A = \frac{0.329 \times 1,200,000}{(45.4)^2} = 192 \text{ psi}$$

$$\text{Actual } P/A = 1,046/5.89 = 178 \text{ psi}$$

The actual P/A does not exceed the allowable, so a 2×4 post would be satisfactory for strength. For convenience of detail, however, a 4×4 might be used.

EXAMPLE 10–6. A timber building has 6×6 interior columns, 12.0 ft long, of Dense No. 1 Structural Southern Pine. A change is proposed in the layout of equipment on the second floor. This will raise the load on one column to 45 kips. Could that column be removed, reinforced as shown in Fig. 10–15, and replaced, to carry the increased load, which will be practically permanent?

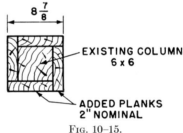

FIG. 10–15.

Allowable stress $c = 0.9 \times 1{,}150 = 1{,}035$ psi

$$L/d = 144/8.87 = 16.2$$

$$K = 0.702 \sqrt{E/c} = 0.702 \sqrt{1{,}600{,}000/1{,}035} = 27.6$$

L/d exceeds 11 but is less than K, so the column is an intermediate column.

For a solid column of the same size, the allowable average unit stress is

$$P/A = 1{,}035\left[1 - \frac{1}{3}\left(\frac{16.2}{27.6}\right)^4 \right] = 995 \text{ psi}$$

The allowable for the laminated column is given by the data of Art. 10–12. Interpolating for L/d of 16.2 gives about 68 per cent. The capacity of the reinforced column is 68 per cent of that for the same size of solid column.

$$\text{Allowable } P = 0.68 \times 0.995(8.875)^2 = 53.3 \text{ kips}$$

The reinforced column would be satisfactory. Bearing plates at the end must be large enough to engage the added column material.

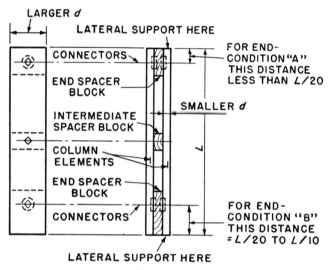

FIG. 10–16.

10–13. Design of Spaced Columns. Design specifications for spaced columns cover those assembled using timber connectors. (See Fig. 10–26.) Such a column is shown in Fig. 10–16. Its elements are separated at the ends and center by spacer blocks. The end blocks are joined to the elements using timber connectors.

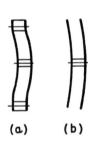

(a)   (b)

FIG. 10–17.

The purpose of end blocks is to fix or partially fix the ends of the elements, so that buckling at failure is as shown in Fig. 10–17(a). Without end blocks, the elements buckle as in (b). Longer end blocks provide better "fixity" of the ends. Two conditions of fixity are shown by Fig. 10–16. The effect of end fixity is covered by a multiplying factor for E in the equation for K and in the Euler equation. The factors are 2.5 for end condition (a) and 3 for end condition (b). Thus for condition (a),

$$K_{(a)} = 0.702 \sqrt{2.5E/c}$$

The column strength is computed as the sum of the strengths of the elements. The column is classed as short when L/d for an individual element is not over 11. When L/d for an element is between 11 and $K_{(a)}$ or $K_{(b)}$, depending on the type of end fixity, the column is considered intermediate. Similarly, it is a long column when L/d for the element exceeds $K_{(a)}$ or $K_{(b)}$. The strength of the individual element is computed using the same equations as for solid columns, but with $K_{(a)}$ or $K_{(b)}$ replacing the term K, and with E multiplied by the fixity factor.

Buckling may be possible in the other plane parallel to the longer face of the elements. This is particularly true when several elements are used. The column capacity as controlled by this type of buckling should be computed. Fixity factors are ignored and the elements analyzed as solid columns, using the larger d and using for L the distance between supports which prevent movement parallel to the larger dimension d. (See Fig. 10-16.)

When the column has buckled as in Fig. 10-17(a), a large shear tends to slide the element along the surface of the spacer block. Connectors joining the element to the block must resist this shear. The amount of the shear depends on the slenderness of the element and on the type of wood. The table below gives shear constants for this purpose. The design shear per plane is equal to the constant multiplied by the cross-sectional area of one element. The connectors in each plane must be selected to resist this shearing force. (The design of connectors is covered later in this chapter.)

L/d for Element	Group A	Group B	Group C
0 to 11	0	0	0
15	38	33	27
20	86	73	61
25	134	114	94
30	181	155	128
35	229	195	162
40	277	236	195
45	325	277	229
50	372	318	263
55	420	358	296
60 to 80	468	399	330

(See Art. 10-20 for species in groups A, B, and C.)

Many detailed requirements exist for proportioning and locating end spacer blocks. These are given by the National Design Specification.

EXAMPLE 10-7. A spaced column is shown by Fig. 10-18. The timber is common structural Douglas fir. Compute the allowable axial load for normal conditions. For what shear should the connectors of each plane be designed?

The 8-in. distance of the connector from the end is more than $L/20$,

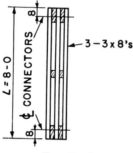

Fig. 10–18.

so end condition (b) and a fixity factor of 3 are used. For one element L/d is $96/2.62 = 36.6$. The ratio K is

$$K_{(b)} = 0.702 \sqrt{3E/c} = 0.702 \sqrt{3 \times 1,500,000/1,250} = 42.1$$

L/d is more than 11 but less than $K_{(b)}$. The column is an intermediate column. The allowable stress

$$P/A = c\left[1 - \frac{1}{3}\left(\frac{L}{K_{(b)}d}\right)^4\right] = 1,250\left[1 - \frac{1}{3}\left(\frac{36.6}{42.1}\right)^4\right] = 1,010 \text{ psi}$$

The allowable P/A based on buckling in the other plane will now be checked.

$$L/d = 96/7.5 = 12.8$$

$$K = 0.702 \sqrt{1,500,000/1,250} = 24.2 \quad \text{(Intermediate)}$$

$$\text{Allowable } P/A = 1,250\left[1 - \frac{1}{3}\left(\frac{12.8}{24.2}\right)^4\right] = 1,220 \text{ psi}$$

The lower allowable is that controlled by buckling of the elements in the direction of the smaller d. The allowable load for the complete column (three elements) is thus

$$P = 3 \times 19.69 \times 1,010 = 59,700 \text{ lb}$$

The timber is listed under Connector Group A. The table in Art. 10–13 gives the end spacer block constant as 244 lb (interpolated). The connectors in each plane of each end must resist a longitudinal shear of 244 times the area of one element, or $244 \times 19.69 = 4,800$ lb.

10–14. Members with Combined Axial Load and Bending. Two methods are given for the design of these members. The first is the easier to use. It is identical with that specified by the AISC Specification for use with steel members. The member is considered satisfactory when

$$\frac{f_a}{F_a} + \frac{f_b}{F_b} \leqq 1.0$$

in which f_a is the computed stress P/A due to axial load

f_b is the computed flexural stress Mc/I

F_a and F_b are the allowable unit stresses for axial load alone and for bending alone, respectively

This method may be used with all three types of column. For spaced columns, however, it is limited to cases in which the bending is parallel to the larger d of the element.

When greater accuracy is desired, the second method[3] of design is used. In this method, various combinations of bending and axial load are treated separately. The equations are more elaborate and include more of the effective variables. Ordinarily, however, the simpler method shown above is sufficient.

10–15. Round Members. The modulus of rupture for a beam of round cross section is taken as 1.18 times that for a square section having the same area. For a round section $M = 1.18fI/c$. For a square section, $M = fI/c$. The two expressions for moment are equal when the area of the square is equal to that of the circle. Thus, the bending strength of a round section is equal to that of a square section having the same cross-sectional area.

Similarly, the strength of a round solid column, or of a round solid column with bending, is equal to that of a square member having the same area of cross section.

Round members are often tapered. Examples are telephone poles, or timber piles. For bending, the member is treated as one of varying section. The stress at a particular section is computed using the properties of a square section having the same area as the round section in question.

For tapered columns a compromise value of d is used in the column formulas. The value used is $d_{min} + \frac{1}{3}(d_{max} - d_{min})$, but not more than $1.5d_{min}$. If the column is round, a similar square column is analyzed, having an area equal to that of the round column at the compromise value of d.

10–16. Fastenings. There are hundreds of types of fastener for timber. The more common and useful types covered here are nails, spikes, bolts, and modern timber connectors.

[3]*National Design Specification for Stress-Grade Lumber and Its Fastenings* (Washington, D. C.: National Lumber Manufacturers Association, 1952).

The analysis of fastenings is influenced by the same variables as that of rivets in steel structures, and by other factors that are peculiar to wood. The effect of bending of the fastener is of prime importance, however. This bending causes wide variations of bearing pressure between the fastener and the wood. It makes a mathematical solution for stress distribution impractical, perhaps even next to impossible. Accordingly, the design information is mostly tabular information based on extensive research by the Forest Products Laboratory.

10–17. Nails and Spikes. Nails are made in many types, with variations of shank, head, and point shape. In most types, several lengths are available. The "common" wire nail is the one most used for structural purposes. The size of a common nail is quoted in "pennyweight." Common nail sizes range from sixpenny (6d) to sixtypenny (60d). The dimensions of common nails are shown by Table 13 of Appendix B.

Common wire spikes are similar to nails but have larger diameters for corresponding lengths. Spikes are made in lengths from 3 to 12 in.

The strength of nails or spikes is affected by several factors, including the diameter, length of penetration, direction of loading, specific gravity of the wood, moisture content of the wood, duration of loading, and direction of the nail relative to the grain.

Some terms must now be explained. A nail driven into "side grain" is shown by Fig. 10–19(a). The nail is roughly perpendicular to the

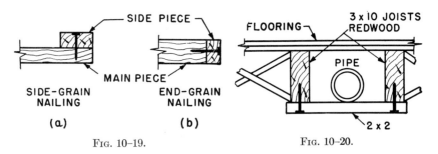

FIG. 10–19.

FIG. 10–20.

grain direction. In Fig. 10–19(b) the nailing is "end-grain," the nail being roughly parallel to the grain of the main piece. In each case the piece near the head is called the "side piece"; the piece receiving the point, the "main piece."

Nails can be loaded laterally, in a direction tending to shear the nail; or parallel to the nail, tending to withdraw it.

The allowable lateral load for a nail is

$$P = KD^{3/2}$$

in which K is a constant depending on the specific gravity of the wood, and D is the diameter of the nail in inches. The factor K is shown by Table 14.

The equation above is for a standard penetration of the point into the main piece, equal to not less than $\frac{2}{3}$ of the nail length for softwoods or $\frac{1}{2}$ the nail length for hardwoods. With less than standard penetration, the allowable load P is obtained by interpolation. Assume that P is zero for no penetration and that P is proportional to the penetration. The smallest penetration permitted in the main piece is $\frac{1}{2}$ the nail length for softwood, or $\frac{2}{3}$ for hardwood. For penetration greater than standard, no increase of load is allowed.

Where the main piece and side piece are of different densities, the lighter one controls. Thus, the smaller value of K is used. For nails in end grain, use only two-thirds of the allowable lateral load for side grain. Where the side piece is metal instead of wood, allow a 25 per cent increase of load. If the wood is unseasoned and will be loaded while wet or unseasoned, the safe load for side nailing is three-fourths of that given by the equation. To all of the above is added a correction for load duration, the equation being for normal loading conditions.

The allowable load in a withdrawal direction from side grain is

$$p = 1{,}380G^{2.5}D$$

in which p is the allowable load per inch of penetration in the main piece, G is the specific gravity of the main piece (See Table 15), and D is the nail diameter in inches. This load may be used either for seasoned wood, or for unseasoned wood which will remain wet. For unseasoned wood which will dry after nailing, only $\frac{1}{4}$ of the load given by the equation may be used. Corrections for load duration should be used.

The allowable withdrawal load from end grain is zero.

EXAMPLE 10–8. The floor joists of an existing building show in Fig. 10–20. It is planned to locate a pipe as shown. The bridging will be removed from one space, and the pipe supported on 2×2 slats. What size nail is needed if the load per slat is 90 lb?

The load is permanent, so the corresponding normal load is $90/0.9 = 100$ lb, or 50 lb per nail. K for redwood is 1,350 and G is 0.42. The selection must proceed by trial.

Try a 12d nail.

$$p = 1{,}380(0.42)^{2.5} \times 0.148 = 23.3 \text{ lb per in.}$$

$$\text{Penetration in main piece} = 3.25 - 1.63 = 1.62 \text{ in.}$$

$$\text{Allowable } P = 1.62 \times 23.3 = 37.8 \text{ lb} \quad \text{Unsatisfactory}$$

Try a 20d nail.

$$p = 23.3\left(\frac{0.192}{0.148}\right) = 30.2 \text{ lb per in.}$$

Penetration in main piece $= 4.00 - 1.63 = 2.37$ in.

Allowable $P = 2.37 \times 30.2 = 71.5$ lb   Satisfactory

Further calculations would show the twentypenny nail to be the smallest satisfactory size.

EXAMPLE 10–9. The floor framing around a stairway opening is shown in Fig. 10–21. The left ends of the short joists are supported by a header,

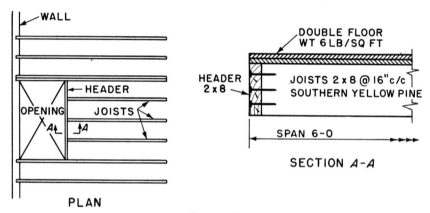

FIG. 10–21.

as shown in section A–A. How many nails must be used, and of what size? The floor is for office purposes.

The end reaction of one joist is computed first. The recommended live load (Appendix B) is 80 lb per sq ft. The end reaction is:

Live Load, $3 \times 80 \times 16/12 = 320$ lb

Flooring, $3 \times 6 \times 16/12 \quad = \quad 24$

Joist, $3 \times 3.38 \qquad\qquad = \quad 10$

Reaction $= 354$ lb (Normal conditions)

The joist is the main piece. Penetration in the joist (softwood) must be at least one-half of the nail length. Thus, nails shorter than $2\,(1\frac{5}{8}) = 3\frac{1}{4}$ in. long need not be considered.

The allowable load for a 16d nail, in side grain and with full standard penetration, is

$$P = KD^{3/2} = 1,650(0.0652) = 107 \text{ lb per nail}$$

Courtesy of Timber Engineering Co.

OILFIELD STRUCTURES OF TIMBER, USING MODERN TIMBER CONNECTORS.

(The value is given in Table 13, so that actual use of the equation can be omitted.)

Standard penetration $= \frac{2}{3} \times 3.50 = 2.33$ in.

Actual penetration $= 3.50 - 1.63 = 1.87$ in.

Allowable load per 16d nail in side grain $= 107\left(\dfrac{1.87}{2.33}\right) = 86$ lb

Allowable per 16d nail in end grain $= \frac{2}{3} \times 86 = 57$ lb

Number of 16d nails required $= \dfrac{354}{57} = 7$

The seven nails would be quite crowded. The computations are repeated for a larger size.

Try 20d.

Standard penetration $= \frac{2}{3} \times 4 = 2.66$ in.

Actual penetration $= 4.00 - 1.63 = 2.37$ in.

Allowable per 20d nail in end grain $= \left(\dfrac{2}{3}\right)\left(\dfrac{2.37}{2.66}\right)(139) = 82$ lb

Number of 20d nails required $= \dfrac{354}{82} = 5$

Try 30d.

Standard penetration $= \frac{2}{3} \times 4.50 = 3.00$ in.

Actual penetration $= 4.50 - 1.63 = 2.87$ in.

Allowable per 30d nail in end grain $= \left(\frac{2}{3}\right)\left(\frac{2.87}{3.00}\right)(155) = 99$ lb

Number of 30d nails required $= \dfrac{354}{99} = 4$

Either of the last two solutions would be satisfactory.

10–18. Bolted Connections. Factors affecting the strength of bolted connections are the bearing strength of the wood, the ratio of main-member thickness to bolt diameter, the direction and duration of loading, and the condition of the wood.

Table 16 of Appendix B is used for the design of bolted joints. The table is based on extensive tests at the Forest Products Laboratory. The allowable loads shown are for double-shear connections in which the side pieces are at least one-half as thick as the main pieces. This con-

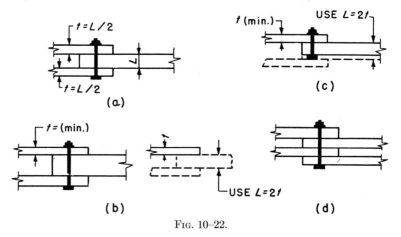

Fig. 10–22.

dition is shown by Fig. 10–22(a). For other joint details, adjustments are made, as follows:

1. When either side piece is less than one-half as thick as the main piece, use the tabulated strength for a joint whose main-member thickness L is twice the thickness of the thinner actual side piece. Thus, for Fig. 10–22(b), use $L = 2t$.
2. For the single-shear joint of Fig. 10–22(c), use one-half the load tabulated for a double-shear joint whose L is twice the thickness of the thinner actual member.

3. For a joint having four or more members, as in Fig. 10–22(d) the allowable load for each shear plane is computed separately, and is one-half the tabulated value for a double-shear joint whose main-member thickness L is equal to the thickness of the thinner actual piece adjacent to the plane in question.

Adjustments for load duration are made as necessary.

The values of Table 16 are for seasoned wood, used dry. Use $\frac{3}{4}$ of the tabulated allowables for timber which is exposed to the weather. If the timber will remain wet, use only $\frac{2}{3}$ of the tabulated values. If green

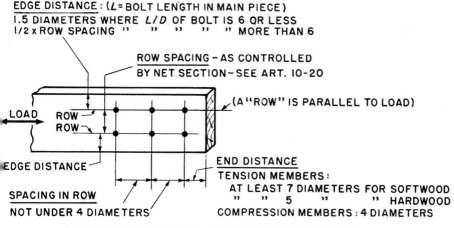

EDGE DISTANCE: ($L=$ BOLT LENGTH IN MAIN PIECE)
1.5 DIAMETERS WHERE L/D OF BOLT IS 6 OR LESS
1/2 x ROW SPACING ''   ''   ''   ''   '' MORE THAN 6

ROW SPACING – AS CONTROLLED
BY NET SECTION – SEE ART. 10-20

(A "ROW" IS PARALLEL TO LOAD)

LOAD   ROW
       ROW

EDGE DISTANCE

END DISTANCE
TENSION MEMBERS:
   AT LEAST 7 DIAMETERS FOR SOFTWOOD
   ''   '' 5   ''   '' HARDWOOD
COMPRESSION MEMBERS: 4 DIAMETERS

SPACING IN ROW
NOT UNDER 4 DIAMETERS

(a) BOLT PLACEMENT – LOAD PARALLEL TO GRAIN

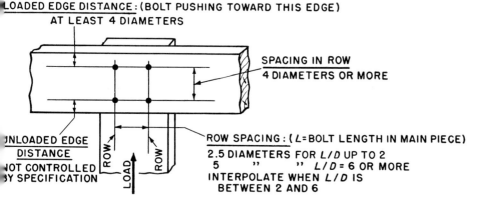

LOADED EDGE DISTANCE: (BOLT PUSHING TOWARD THIS EDGE)
   AT LEAST 4 DIAMETERS

SPACING IN ROW
4 DIAMETERS OR MORE

UNLOADED EDGE
   DISTANCE
NOT CONTROLLED
BY SPECIFICATION

ROW SPACING: ($L=$ BOLT LENGTH IN MAIN PIECE)
2.5 DIAMETERS FOR L/D UP TO 2
5   ''   '' $L/D=6$ OR MORE
INTERPOLATE WHEN L/D IS
BETWEEN 2 AND 6

ROW
ROW
LOAD

(b) BOLT PLACEMENT – LOAD PERPENDICULAR TO GRAIN

Fig. 10–23.

timber is used in locations where it will become dried, use only $\frac{4}{10}$ of the tabulated allowables.

When the side pieces are metal plates, a 25 per cent increase of load is permitted for loading parallel to the grain. No increase is allowed for loads perpendicular to the grain.

The table shows allowable loads parallel to and perpendicular to the grain. Bolted connections, of bracing for example, are often loaded at some other angle. The Hankinson formula gives the allowable in this case as

$$N = \frac{PQ}{P \sin^2 \theta + Q \cos^2 \theta}$$

in which P and Q are the allowable loads parallel to and perpendicular to the grain, respectively, and θ is the angle between the load and grain directions.

The arrangement of the bolts is controlled by a set of rules for spacing and edge distance[4]. The most important of these are shown pictorially on the joint drawings of Fig. 10–23.

EXAMPLE 10–10. What is the allowable reaction for the beam of Fig. 10–24? Check both joint strength and horizontal shear. The member is exposed to the weather and has permanent load.

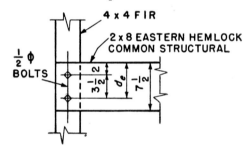

FIG. 10–24.

The joint is a single-shear connection. The load in the joist is perpendicular to the grain. Twice the thickness of the thinner piece is $3\frac{1}{4}$ in. The tabulated allowable for a double-shear joint with a $3\frac{1}{4}$-in. main member is interpolated as

$$460 + \tfrac{2}{5}(90) = 496 \text{ lb}$$

The allowable load per bolt in single shear, corrected for exposure and for load duration, is

[4]*National Design Specifications for Stress-Grade Lumber and Its Fastenings* (Washington, D. C.: National Lumber Manufacturers Association, 1952), Section 601.

$$0.50 \times 496 \times 0.75 \times 0.90 = 167 \text{ lb}$$

The allowable reaction for two bolts is 334 lb.

The horizontal shear strength of the joist is reduced by a connection of this type. The shear stress is computed as V/bd_e, where d_e is the distance from the top to the center of the lower bolt. The stress should be limited to the allowable for horizontal shear, or $0.90 \times 60 = 54$ psi.

$$\text{Allowable } V = vbd_e = 54 \times 1.62 \times 5.5 = 481 \text{ lb}$$

The bolt strength controls, and the allowable reaction is 334 lb.

EXAMPLE 10–11. What is the allowable load P in the brace of Fig. 10–25, based on the bolted connection? The brace has short-time loads

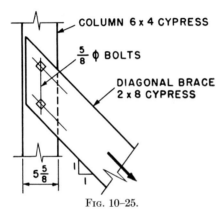

COLUMN 6 x 4 CYPRESS

$\frac{5}{8} \phi$ BOLTS

DIAGONAL BRACE
2 x 8 CYPRESS

$5\frac{5}{8}$

FIG. 10–25.

such as wind or earthquake only. The structure is exposed to the weather and may remain wet for long periods.

Twice the thickness of the thinner piece is $3\frac{1}{4}$ in. For a double-shear joint with a $3\frac{1}{4}$-in. main member, the tabulated allowable loads for one $\frac{5}{8}$-in. bolt are (interpolated):

$$P = 1,952 \text{ lb parallel to the grain}$$

$$Q = 1,020 \text{ lb perpendicular to the grain}$$

The allowable load N at 45 degrees to the grain is computed using the Hankinson formula.

$$N = \frac{1,952 \times 1,020}{1,952 \sin^2 45 + 1,020 \cos^2 45} = 1,340 \text{ lb}$$

For single-shear, N is one-half as much, or 670 lb per bolt. Correction factors of $1\frac{1}{3}$ for load duration, and $\frac{2}{3}$ for exposure are now applied. The allowable brace load, based on the two bolts is

$$2 \times 670 \times \tfrac{4}{3} \times \tfrac{2}{3} = 1,190 \text{ lb}$$

10–19. Modern Timber Connectors.   A few of the many varieties of modern timber connector are shown by Fig. 10–26. In general, they consist of rings or plates which are imbedded in each of the members to be connected. More than 60 types have been used in Europe. Since the

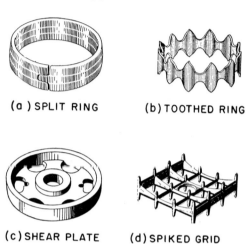

(a) SPLIT RING   (b) TOOTHED RING

(c) SHEAR PLATE   (d) SPIKED GRID

Courtesy of the Timber Engineering Co.

FIG. 10–26.

1920's, modern connectors have become popular in the United States, many patented varieties being made.

The object of timber connectors is to provide stronger joints that are inexpensive and practical. It is possible to develop the axial-load capacity of a member with timber connectors. Usually it is impractical or too expensive to do so with nails or bolts alone.

The split-ring of Fig. 10–26(a) is installed in pre-cut grooves in the two pieces to be connected. A light bolt is used to hold the pieces in contact. An assembled joint is shown in cross section by Fig. 10–27. The split ring is the modern connector most used.

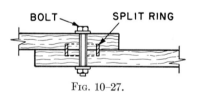

BOLT   SPLIT RING

FIG. 10–27.

The toothed ring of Fig. 10–26(b) is installed by clamping between the parts to be connected. A special high-strength bolt with a ball-bearing washer squeezes the members together, forcing the ring into the wood on each side. The special bolt is then removed and replaced by an ordinary bolt which prevents the members from coming apart.

Fig. 10–26(c) shows a shear plate. These are useful in structures which are to be taken apart and re-assembled frequently. Shear plates are set into pre-cut grooves in the timbers to be joined. Bolts carry the load from the shear plate of one timber to the shear plate of the other. A shear plate may be used also to connect timber to metal.

Fig. 10–26(d) shows a spiked grid. These are embedded in the timbers by pressure. A flat type is used to connect flat timbers together. A single-curve grid is available for connecting a flat piece to a round piece. Spiked grids are used mostly for timber trestles, wharves, and docks.

10–20. Split Rings. The action of a split-ring joint is shown by Fig. 10–28. Bearing pressure between the ring and the wood is indicated

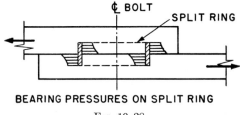

BEARING PRESSURES ON SPLIT RING

Fig. 10–28.

by shading. The ring is like a long key. It acts in shear to transfer bearing pressure from one piece to the other.

The allowable load for a split-ring connection depends on the physical properties of the wood. These are considered by arranging the commonly used species in three groups, as follows:

CONNECTOR LOAD GROUPING OF SPECIES STRUCTURALLY GRADED

Group A	Group B	Group C
Douglas fir (dense)	Douglas fir (coast region)	Cypress, southern and tidewater red
Oak, red and white	Larch, western	Hemlock, West Coast
Pine, southern (dense)	Pine, southern	Pine, Norway
		Redwood

(Split rings can be used with other species. The charts shown here, however, are for use with the above species. The Timber Engineering Company will provide information regarding other species.)

Other factors affecting the joint capacity are the thickness of the members and the angle of the load to the grain. (See Fig. 10–29.) Both factors are included in the charts of allowable load shown by Fig. 10–30. The use of the charts will be shown by examples.

FIG. 10–29.

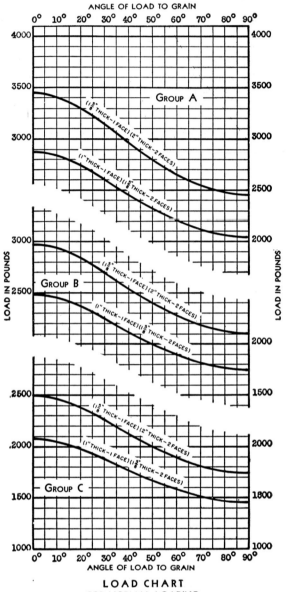

2½″ SPLIT RING DATA

Split Ring—Dimensions	
Inside Diameter at center when closed......................	2½″
Inside diameter at center when installed....................	2.54″
Thickness of ring at center.......	0.163″
Thickness of ring at edge........	0.123″
Depth...........................	¾″
Weight, per 100 rings, lbs........	28
Lumber, Minimum dimensions allowed	
Width........................	3⅝″
Thickness, rings in one face.....	1″
Thickness, rings opposite in both faces.........................	1⅝″
Bolt, diameter...................	½″
Bolt hole, diameter.............	9/16″
Projected Area for portion of one ring within a member, square inches.........................	1.10
Washers, minimum	
Round, Cast or Malleable Iron, diameter....................	2⅝″
Square Plate	
Length of Side...............	2″
Thickness.................	⅛″
(For trussed rafters and similar light construction standard wrought washers may be used.)	

LOAD CHART
FOR NORMAL LOADING
ONE 2½″ SPLIT RING AND BOLT IN SINGLE SHEAR

Courtesy of the Timber Engineering Co.

Fig. 10–30.

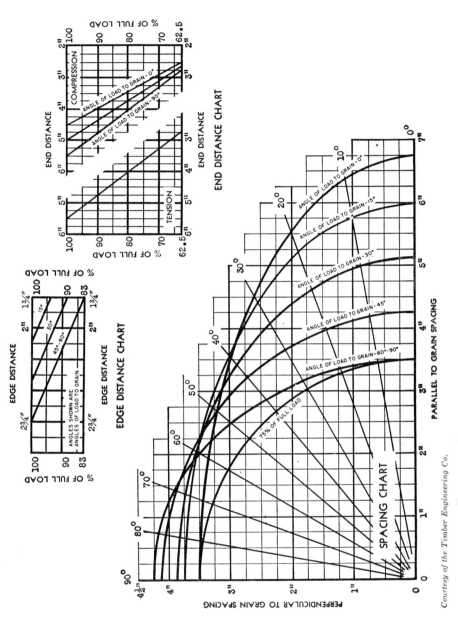

Courtesy of the Timber Engineering Co.

FIG. 10-31. Spacing, End Distance, and Edge Distance for 2½-in. Split Rings.

Courtesy of Timber Engineering Co.

OILFIELD STRUCTURES OF TIMBER, USING MODERN TIMBER CONNECTORS.

The allowable load shown by the chart is adjusted as required for load duration. For wood unseasoned when fabricated but seasoned when loaded, the allowable is reduced 20 per cent. For wood unseasoned or wet when loaded, it is reduced 33 per cent.

The capacity of a split-ring connection is affected also by the spacing, edge distance, and end distance of the rings. Charts governing these dimensions are shown in Fig. 10–31. The spacing chart has five parabolic curves giving the spacing required for full load at the particular angle of load to grain shown on the curve. Interpolate between the curves for

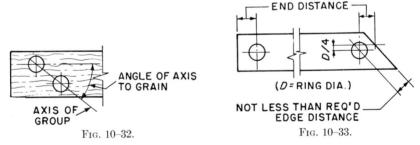

FIG. 10–32.   FIG. 10–33.

intermediate angles of load to grain. The line joining two connectors is called the "axis." (See Fig. 10–32.) When the axis is parallel to or perpendicular to the grain, the spacing is read on one of the base lines at the end of a parabolic line. For an axis at some intermediate angle to the grain, the spacing is given by the length of a radiating line from the origin to the intersection with the proper parabola. The distance along the radial line is the center-to-center spacing. Components of the spacing are read on the horizontal and vertical base lines of the chart.

A quarter circle is labeled "75% of Full Load." The required spacing at this load is constant for all angles of load to grain. For loads less than 75 per cent of full load, the spacing given by the quarter circle is used as a minimum. For loads between 75 and 100 per cent of full load, the required spacing is found by interpolating on the proper radial line between the curves for 75 per cent and for full-load spacing.

The definition of "end distance" is shown by Fig. 10–33. The left detail is for a square cut; the right detail shows the timber cut at an angle. End-distance requirements are set so as to avoid a "shearout" failure of the wood (see Chapter 8) and so as to avoid splitting. The chart for end distance is in two sections, one for tension members and one for compression.

Two types of edge distance are shown by Fig. 10–34. Edge distance

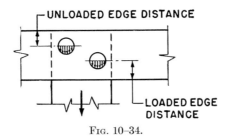

FIG. 10–34.

is measured perpendicular to the edge of the member. The required loaded-edge distances are given by a third chart on Fig. 10–31. The absolute minimum allowable edge distance is shown at the extreme right edge of the chart. That value is used also as the required unloaded edge distance.

Certain connectors may have their allowable loads reduced because of spacing, end distance, or edge distance. In that case, the lowest allowable computed for one connector is used as the allowable for all the connectors in the joint.

The common sizes of split ring are $2\frac{1}{2}$ in. and 4 in. Data for 4-in. split rings are shown by Figs. 10–35 and 10–36.

Similar charts are published for other types of connector, including shear plates and toothed rings. Load tables are available for spiked grids.[5]

EXAMPLE 10–12. Two 3 × 10 beams supporting new equipment are to be connected to existing 8 × 8 columns in your plant as shown

[5] *TECO Design Manual for Teco Timber Connector Construction* (Washington, D. C.: Timber Engineering Co.).

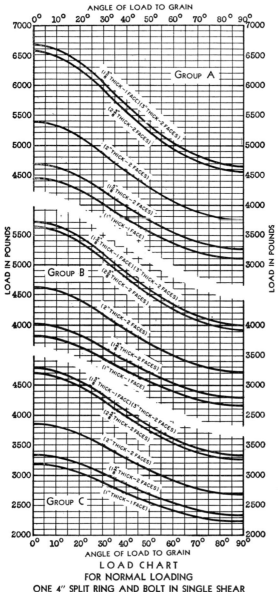

4" SPLIT RING DATA

Split Ring—Dimensions	
Inside Diameter at center when closed................	4"
Inside diameter at center when installed.............	4.06"
Thickness of ring at center...	0.193"
Thickness of ring at edge...	0.133"
Depth.......................	1"
Weight, per 100 rings, lbs.......	70
Lumber, Minimum dimensions allowed	
Width.......................	5½"
Thickness, rings in one face......	1"
Thickness, rings opposite in both faces......................	1⅝"
Bolt, diameter	¾"
Bolt hole, diameter.............	13/16"
Projected Area for portion of one ring within a member, square inches.......................	2.25
Washers, minimum	
Round, Cast or Malleable Iron, diameter....................	3"
Square Plate	
Length of Side...............	3"
Thickness..................	3/16"
(For trussed rafters and similar light construction standard wrought washers may be used.)	

LOAD CHART
FOR NORMAL LOADING
ONE 4" SPLIT RING AND BOLT IN SINGLE SHEAR

Courtesy of the Timber Engineering Co.

Fig. 10–35.

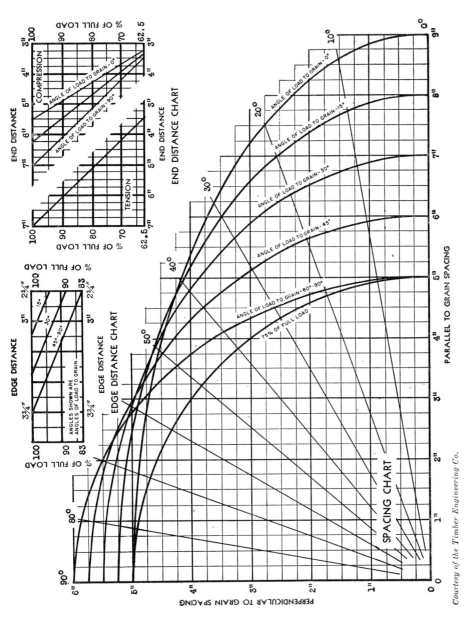

Fig. 10-36. Spacing, End Distance, and Edge Distance for 4-in. Split Rings.

Courtesy of the Timber Engineering Co.

in Fig. 10–37. Two $2\frac{1}{2}$-in. split rings are to be used at each end of each 3×10. What is the maximum allowable reaction for normal loading? How should the rings be spaced?

The column wood is of group C. The load on the ring is vertical, parallel to the grain of the column. The column has rings in each face and is over 2 in. thick, so the upper curve for group C is used (Fig. 10–30). The allowable load between ring and column is the ordinate of that curve over 0°, or 2,500 lb.

The beam wood is group C and the load is perpendicular to the grain of the beam. The wood is over $1\frac{5}{8}$ in. thick and has rings in one face

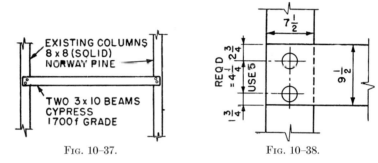

EXISTING COLUMNS
8 x 8 (SOLID)
NORWAY PINE

TWO 3 x 10 BEAMS
CYPRESS
1700 f GRADE

Fig. 10–37.   Fig. 10–38.

only, so the upper curve for group C is used. The ordinate of this line over 90° is 1,740 lb.

The value in the beam is lower and controls. A reaction of $2 \times 1,740 = 3,480$ lb will be allowed if two rings can be properly spaced and if the horizontal shear stress is not excessive.

Refer now to Fig. 10–31. The spacing for the beam is given by the parabola marked "Angle of grain to load-60°–90°." If the rings are placed in a vertical line, the axis is at 90° to the grain, and the required spacing is read at the intersection of the 90° radial line and the parabola. The required spacing is $4\frac{1}{4}$ in. This is shown in Fig. 10–38. A $1\frac{3}{4}$-in. edge distance is required for the unloaded (lower) edge. For full load, the edge distance for the upper edge must be $2\frac{3}{4}$ in. or more.

Now add the above spacing and edge distances. Their sum is $8\frac{3}{4}$ in., but the depth available is $9\frac{1}{2}$ in. A vertical axis is satisfactory, and the spacing is increased to 5 in. so as to use the available space.

The reaction is now computed as limited by shear. The shearing stress must not exceed the value in Table 11, and is given by the equation $v = V/bh_e$. The term h_e is the distance from the top of the beam to the bottom of the slot for the lower connector, or

$$9.50 - 1.75 + 2.50/2 = 9.0 \text{ in.}$$

The allowable unit shear is 145 psi, and

Allowable $V = 145 \times 2\frac{5}{8} \times 9.0 = 3,430$ lb

This is less than the allowable for two rings. Thus, the allowable reaction for one 3×10 is 3,430 lb. The final detail is shown by Fig. 10–38.

EXAMPLE 10–13. A 2×6 diagonal brace joins a 4×8 vertical column as shown at the upper right of Fig. 10–39. Design the connection using $2\frac{1}{2}$-in. split rings. The timbers are both of group C. The loading shown is due to wind.

The solution involves choosing the number of rings and their location in the joint. It is shown in computation-sheet form by Fig. 10–39.

The load capacity per ring is found using Fig. 10–30. The load is due to wind, so an increase of one-third is allowed. Two rings are used, each carrying 85 per cent of its full allowable load.

The spacing required is found using Fig. 10–31. The spacing for rings fully loaded is found first. That for the diagonal is found using the parabola marked "Angle of Load to Grain-0°." For the column the load and the axis are both at 45° to the grain. The spacing is given by the intersection of the parabola marked "45°" and the radial line for 45° (interpolated). The length of the radial line from the origin to the intersection point is the required spacing. The components of that length are read at the edges of the chart. A comparison shows that the spacing required for the diagonal is larger than that for the vertical; and it, therefore, controls.

The value obtained above is for a fully loaded connector. Those in this example have only 85 per cent of full load. The required spacing for 75 per cent load is found next. Finally, by interpolation, the spacing for 85 per cent full load is determined as 4.80 in. minimum.

In the final detail at the bottom of the sheet, the computed requirements for edge distance, end distance, and spacing, are either met or slightly exceeded.

10–21. Tension Members. Discussion of tension members was left until now since their design is dependent on joint design. For all tension members, the tensile stress on the gross area of cross section should be limited to that given by Table 11. In addition, conditions at the minimum or critical cross section must be considered.

For bolted members, the net area is computed deducting for all holes on the cross section. Full deduction is made for staggered holes near the section. The net area must be, for softwoods, at least 80 per cent of the total bearing area of all the bolts in the end connection. For hardwoods the percentage required is 50.[6]

[6]Forest Products Laboratory, *Wood Handbook* (Washington, D. C.: U. S. Dept. of Agriculture, 1940).

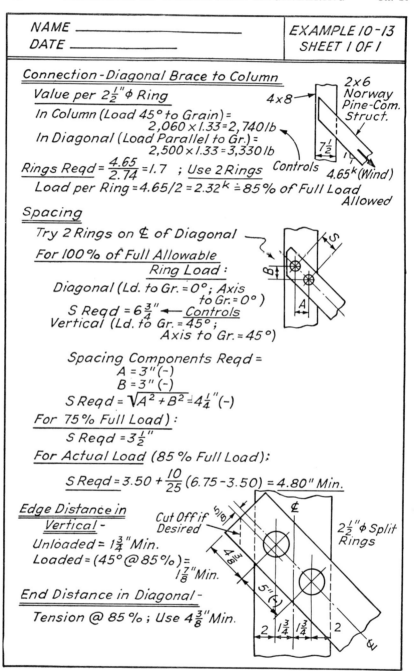

NAME _____	EXAMPLE 10-13
DATE _____	SHEET 1 OF 1

Connection - Diagonal Brace to Column

Value per $2\frac{1}{2}$"ϕ Ring

In Column (Load 45° to Grain) =
$$2,060 \times 1.33 = 2,740\,lb$$

In Diagonal (Load Parallel to Gr.) =
$$2,500 \times 1.33 = 3,330\,lb$$

Rings Reqd = $\frac{4.65}{2.74}$ = 1.7 ; <u>Use 2 Rings</u> Controls 4.65^k (Wind)

Load per Ring = 4.65/2 = 2.32^k ≐ 85% of Full Load Allowed

2x6 Norway Pine-Com. Struct.

4x8

$7\frac{1}{2}$

Spacing

Try 2 Rings on ℄ of Diagonal

<u>For 100% of Full Allowable Ring Load :</u>

Diagonal (Ld. to Gr. = 0°; Axis to Gr. = 0°)
$$S\ Reqd = 6\frac{3}{4}" \leftarrow \underline{Controls}$$
Vertical (Ld. to Gr. = 45°; Axis to Gr. = 45°)

Spacing Components Reqd =
$$A = 3"(-)$$
$$B = 3"(-)$$
$$S\ Reqd = \sqrt{A^2 + B^2} \doteq 4\frac{1}{4}"(-)$$

<u>For 75% Full Load) :</u>
$$S\ Reqd = 3\frac{1}{2}"$$

<u>For Actual Load (85% Full Load):</u>
$$S\ Reqd = 3.50 + \frac{10}{25}(6.75 - 3.50) = 4.80"\ Min.$$

<u>Edge Distance in Vertical -</u>

Cut Off if Desired

Unloaded = $1\frac{3}{4}$" Min.

Loaded = (45° @ 85%) = $1\frac{7}{8}$" Min.

<u>End Distance in Diagonal -</u>

Tension @ 85% ; Use $4\frac{3}{8}$" Min.

$2\frac{1}{2}$"ϕ Split Rings

$2 \quad 1\frac{3}{4} \quad 1\frac{3}{4} \quad 2$

FIG. 10–39. Computation Sheet.

For members with ring-type connectors, the net area is the gross area minus the projected area of the rings and bolts on the cross section. The area to be subtracted is shaded in Fig. 10–40. The bolts used are $\frac{1}{2}$ in. for $2\frac{1}{2}$-in. split rings, and $\frac{3}{4}$ in. for 4-in. split rings.

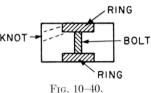

In fabrication care is taken to install rings where the wood is free from defects. When a knot approaching the maximum size allowed for the particular grade of lumber occurs closer to the critical section than one-half ring diameter, further re-

Fig. 10–40.

duction is made in computing the net area. Portions of the knot not obscured by the ring and bolt must be deducted. Such a portion of knot is shown dotted in Fig. 10–40.

The wood of the remaining net section is of high quality. The stress allowed for the net area is based on the basic stress for clear wood, with no reductions of allowable stress because of defects. The recommended allowable values of P/A_{net} are given by the tabulation below.

Load Duration	Thickness of Member	Allowable P/A_{net}		
		Group A Wood	Group B Wood	Group C Wood
Normal	4″ or less	2,350	2,000	1,650
	Over 4″	1,850	1,600	1,300
Snow	4″ or less	2,700	2,300	1,900
	Over 4″	2,150	1,850	1,500
Wind or Earthquake	4″ or less	3,100	2,650	2,200
	Over 4″	2,500	2,150	1,750
Permanent	4″ or less	2,100	1,800	1,500
	Over 4″	1,700	1,450	1,200

EXAMPLE 10–14. Check the diagonal member of Example 10–13 and Fig. 10–39, for suitability as a tension member.

Allowable stress on gross area $= 1,100 \times 1.33 = 1,465$ psi (Table 11)

Actual stress on gross area $= 4,650/9.14 = 510$ psi   Satisfactory

Net area $= 9.14 - 1.10 - (\frac{1}{2} \times 1.25) = 7.42$ sq in.

Allowable $P/A_n = 2,200$ psi

Computed $P/A_n = 4,650/7.42 = 627$ psi   Satisfactory

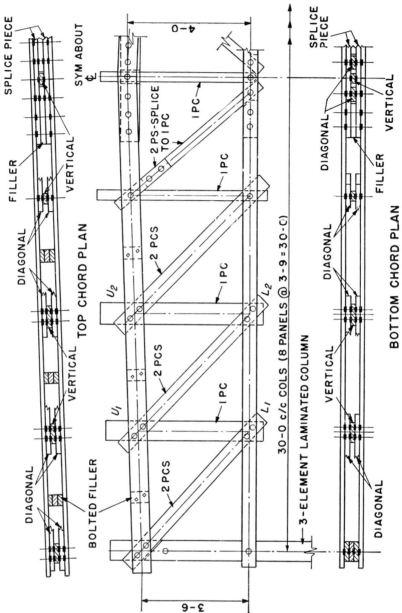

Fig. 10–41. Timber Roof Truss Using $2\frac{1}{2}$-In. Split-Ring Connectors.

10–22. Trusses. Early timber trusses were heavy, with massive solid chords and compressive web members, and usually with steel rods for tensile web members. With the introduction of modern timber connectors it became possible to build lighter and more economical trusses of many types. Consequently, timber trusses are in common use for bridges, industrial and commercial buildings, and even residences.

A typical timber truss is shown by Fig. 10–41. The top chord is designed as a spaced column, its two elements being held apart by the inserted web members. Intermediate spacers are bolted between the elements at the center of each panel. For convenience of detail, the bottom chord also has two elements. The web members are alternately two-element and one-element. The members are connected at panel points by split rings. The top- and bottom-chord plans show the position of the rings.

The design of a truss is merely the design of a compatible group of tension members, compression members, and connections. In timber trusses the connections must be considered in detail early in the design procedure, since spacing and edge-distance requirements may control the size of certain members. For example, the verticals U_1L_1 and U_2L_2 in Fig. 10–41 could be as small as 2 × 4, if axial load alone controlled; but 2 × 8's must be used to provide space for two rings in each plane of the joints.

As a general procedure for designing a timber truss, the following is suggested:

1. Determine the bar stresses for dead load and for the predicted types of live load.
2. Decide upon a species and stress grade of timber. This decision will be affected by locality and the local supply of timber.
3. Design the members, probably starting with the top chord.
4. Design the joints, usually starting with the ones having the greatest loads.

Actually, it will not be possible to keep a clear-cut separation of steps 3 and 4. The initial choices of members may be revised as the joints are designed. A designer with foresight looks ahead to joint problems as he selects the members. Finally, a suitable combination of members and connections is determined.

The non-civil may seldom be involved with the complete design of a timber roof truss. He may be required to plan some special-purpose truss, however. It is even more likely that he may at some time be required to analyze truss-type connections. Since the connections are a critical part of the truss design, and perhaps the only difficult part, the example which follows will show in detail the analysis of a truss

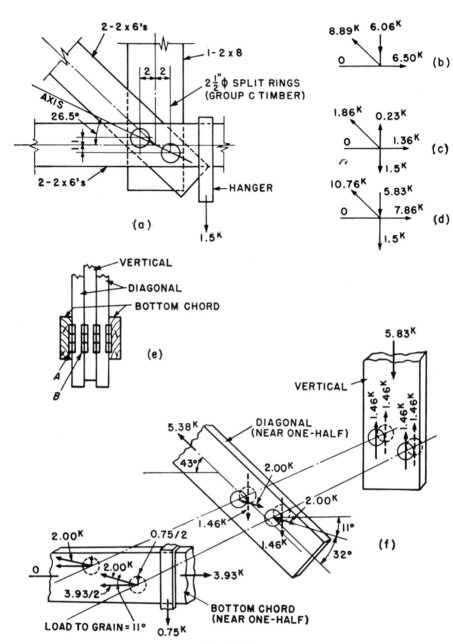

Fig. 10–42.

joint. The complete truss analysis consists of many such joint computations, plus checks on the allowable loads for the members.

EXAMPLE 10–15. A conveyor is to be hung from the bottom chord of the timber trusses in your plant. The trusses are like that of Fig. 10–41. Hangers will be placed over the chord adjacent to joint L_1, which is shown in detail by Fig. 10–42(a). As a part of your check on the ability of the truss to withstand the new load, check the strength of this joint. You have found, by the methods of Chapter 5, that the maximum load from the conveyor is 1.5 kips, and that this load will be active much of the time.

The bar stresses for dead load and snow were found on record prints of the design drawings. These are shown by Fig. 10–42(b). You have computed the stresses due to the conveyor as shown in (c). The total stresses are shown in (d).

A cross section of the joint shows in Fig. 10–42(e). Two rings are present in each contact surface. Each pair of rings serves a particular purpose in transferring stress from member to member. When a clear picture of that purpose is obtained, the analysis of the joint is easy.

The purpose of each set of rings shows in the "exploded" view of Fig. 10–42(f). The analysis is started with the vertical. Its load is resisted equally by four rings, each pushing upward with a force of $5.83/4 = 1.46$ kips.

Next the outer members (bottom chord) are considered. The two rings in the inner face of one element hold it in equilibrium against a force of $7.86/2 = 3.93$ kips toward the right, and against one-half the conveyor load, or 0.75 kip downward. The rings resist with forces of 2.00 kips each, inclined at 11°, as shown.

Finally, the loads of the rings on the diagonal are considered. The rings on the outer face (set A) transfer load from the chord to the diagonal. The load applied by these rings to the diagonal is equal and opposite to that which they apply to the chord, or 2.00 kips per ring, inclined at 11°, down toward the right. The rings in the far face transfer load from the vertical to the diagonal. These rings push downward with 1.46 kips each. As a check, the resultant of all the ring loads on the diagonal is computed, and is found to be 5.38 kips. This is the same as the axial load in the diagonal. Note however, that the rings in the diagonal are not equally loaded. Nor can the ring loads be easily computed except by considering the diagonal last. As a general rule, the center and outside members should be considered first, the intermediate ones last.

The allowable loads for each location are now computed using the charts of Figs. 10–30 and 10–31.

Ring Location	Angle of Load to Grain	Use Curve	Value Shown	Allowable = 1.15 × Value Shown
Chord to Diag.				
in chord	11°	C—upper	2,450 lb	2,820 lb
in diagonal	32°	C—lower	1,860	2,140
Vert. to Diag.				
in vertical	0°	C—lower	2,080	2,390
in diagonal	47°	C—lower	1,700	1,950

The above would be allowed if the required full load spacing and edge distance were present. The check is completed by computing the required spacing and edge distance for each set of rings. The axis of the ring group is inclined at 26.5° to the horizontal.

Ring Location	Angle of Load to Grain	Angle of Axis to Grain	Per cent of Full Load	Spacing (in.) Reqd.	Spacing (in.) Provided	Loaded E.D. (in.) Reqd.	Loaded E.D. (in.) Provided
Chord to Diag.							
in chord	11°	26.5°	71.0%	3.50	4.47	1.75	1.81
in diagonal	32°	16.5°	93.5	3.98*	4.47	2.12	2.17
Vert. to Diag.							
in vertical	0°	63.5°	61.0	3.50	4.47	1.75	1.75
in diagonal	47°	16.5°	75.0	3.50	4.47	1.75	2.17

In computing the spacing marked with an asterisk, above, it was necessary to obtain the required spacing components for 100 per cent full load, solve for the resultant spacing, and then interpolate between that value for 100 per cent load, and 3.50 in. for 75 per cent load. The spacings and edge distances provided are equal to or larger than those required. The joint is satisfactory for the increased loads.

PROBLEMS

10–1. What is the allowable flexural stress for prime structural hemlock under: (a) permanent load; (b) full load for six months with about 85 per cent of full load continuously; (c) wind; and (d) impact?

10–2. A wood member is subject to the following bending moments in foot-pounds: dead load, 1,000; normal live load, 1,100; wind, 800; and impact, 800. What load combination will control the design of the member?

10–3. Your company has moved to a new location. It is desired to post an allowable live load for a part of the building having 2 × 10 joists on 14-in. centers. The clear span is 11 ft 0 in., with 4 in. of bearing on cross beams at each end. The double flooring is about $1\frac{5}{8}$ in. thick. You have inspected the joists and rate them as No. 2 Southern Pine. What is the allowable normal live load per square foot?

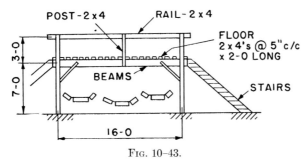

FIG. 10–43.

10–4. A walkway over a series of belt conveyors is to be built as shown in Fig. 10–43. Select the beams. Use a live load of 50 lb per sq ft. Common structural Douglas fir is available.

10–5. Several machines weighing 5,000 lb each are to be skidded across a dock to another part of your plant. You have on hand several 4 × 6 timbers

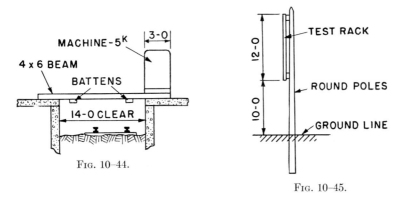

FIG. 10–44.

FIG. 10–45.

of 1075-grade red oak. How many timbers should be used as a minimum? Fig. 10–44 shows the crossing.

10–6. What is the allowable concentrated load for a 10 × 20 beam of white oak, 1300f grade, with bearings 6 in. long and 18 ft center-to-center:

    a) Based on bending?
    b) Based on shear?
    c) Based on bearing?

10–7. A large exposure-test rack is shown by Fig. 10–45. The support is by round poles of utility structural hemlock, about 6 in. in diameter at the ground line. At what maximum spacing can the poles be placed, based on resistance to wind only?

10–8. Select a solid square column of No. 1 southern pine, having a laterally unsupported length L of 3 ft, and an axial load P of 11 kips.

10–9. Same as Problem 10–8, but for length L of 9 ft.

10–10. Same as Problem 10–8, but for length L of 14 ft.

10–11. A wood column in your plant has been damaged by trucks and must be replaced. The column is 8×8, of 1,000f Douglas fir, and 10 ft 0 in. long. The local supplier cannot provide 8×8 timber. He can provide common structural Douglas fir in the following sizes: 6×6, 2×6, 2×8, 2×10, and 3×10. Design a built-up replacement column.

10–12. What is the allowable axial load for a spaced column 10 ft 0 in. long, consisting of two 3×8 planks of Dense No. 1 Structural southern pine, with the connectors of the end spacer blocks placed 9 in. from the end? (Check for buckling with respect to each axis.)

10–13. What nail sizes may be used to join a 2×4 spruce side piece to a 4×4 main piece? What is the allowable lateral load per nail for each size? What is the allowable withdrawal load?

10–14. A scaffold is to be made from unseasoned yellow poplar, nailed together. What is the capacity per 16d nail when the side piece is 2 in. thick?

10–15. A 4×6 crossarm is connected to an outdoor telephone pole by a $\frac{3}{4}$-in. bolt. The pole and crossarm are Norway pine. The pole is 7 in. thick at the connection. What is the allowable shear on the connection?

10–16. A monorail is to be hung from wood roof beams of your plant. Hangers of $\frac{1}{2}$-in. plate will be bolted to the beams as shown in Fig. 10–46. The load

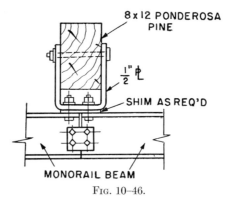

Fig. 10–46.

on one hanger is 1,300 lb. Design the connection using $\frac{5}{8}$-in. bolts. Show the proper spacing and edge distances on a detail of the hanger.

10–17. Design a bolted connection to join the beams selected in Problem 10–4 to 4×4 columns of white pine. Check the beam for horizontal shear.

10–18. A tension splice is shown by Fig. 10–47. What is the allowable load P for normal loading? Check completely.

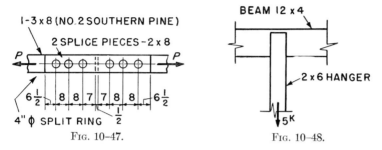

FIG. 10–47.

FIG. 10–48.

10–19. Design a split-ring connection for the hanger and beam of Fig. 10–48. The hanger is cypress and the beam southern pine.

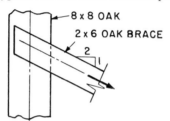

FIG. 10–49.

10–20. Wind loads on a tank cause 4 kips of tension in the 2×6 diagonal brace member shown by Fig. 10–49. Design a split-ring connection using $2\frac{1}{2}$-in. rings, and show the detail of the joint.

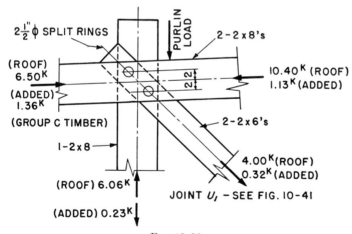

FIG. 10–50.

10–21. Check joint U_1 of the truss of Fig. 10–41. The joint detail and increased loads are shown by Fig. 10–50.

APPENDIX A

PROPERTIES AND DIMENSIONS OF ROLLED STEEL SECTIONS

Courtesy of the American Institute of Steel Construction. The tables reproduced here give only partial lists of the standard sections. For a more nearly complete list see *Steel Construction*, by the American Institute of Steel Construction.

ROLLED STEEL SHAPES

W⁻ SHAPES

PROPERTIES FOR DESIGNING

Nominal Size	Weight per Foot	Area	Depth	Flange Width	Flange Thickness	Web Thickness	AXIS X-X I	AXIS X-X S	AXIS X-X r	AXIS Y-Y I	AXIS Y-Y S	AXIS Y-Y r
In.	Lb.	In.²	In.	In.	In.	In.	In.⁴	In.³	In	In.⁴	In.³	in.
36 x 16½	300	88.17	36.72	16.655	1.680	.945	20290.2	1105.1	15.17	1225.2	147.1	3.73
	280	82.32	36.50	16.595	1.570	.885	18819.3	1031.2	15.12	1127.5	135.9	3.70
	260	76.56	36.24	16.555	1.440	.845	17233.8	951.1	15.00	1020.6	123.3	3.65
	245	72.03	36.06	16.512	1.350	.802	16092.2	892.5	14.95	944.7	114.4	3.62
	230	67.73	35.88	16.475	1.260	.765	14988.4	835.5	14.88	870.9	105.7	3.59
36 x 12	194	57.11	36.48	12.117	1.260	.770	12103.4	663.6	14.56	355.4	58.7	2.49
	182	53.54	36.32	12.072	1.180	.725	11281.5	621.2	14.52	327.7	54.3	2.47
	170	49.98	36.16	12.027	1.100	.680	10470.0	579.1	14.47	300.6	50.0	2.45
	160	47.09	36.00	12.000	1.020	.653	9738.8	541.0	14.38	275.4	45.9	2.42
	150	44.16	35.84	11.972	.940	.625	9012.1	502.9	14.29	250.4	41.8	2.38
33 x 11½	152	44.71	33.50	11.565	1.055	.635	8147.6	486.4	13.50	256.1	44.3	2.39
	141	41.51	33.31	11.535	.960	.605	7442.2	446.8	13.39	229.7	39.8	2.35
	130	38.26	33.10	11.510	.855	.580	6699.0	404.8	13.23	201.4	35.0	2.29
30 x 10½	132	38.83	30.30	10.551	1.000	.615	5753.1	379.7	12.17	185.0	35.1	2.18
	124	36.45	30.16	10.521	.930	.585	5347.1	354.6	12.11	169.7	32.3	2.16
	116	34.13	30.00	10.500	.850	.564	4919.1	327.9	12.00	153.2	29.2	2.12
	108	31.77	29.82	10.484	.760	.548	4461.0	299.2	11.85	135.1	25.8	2.06
27 x 14	177	52.10	27.31	14.090	1.190	.725	6728.6	492.8	11.36	518.9	73.7	3.16
	160	47.04	27.08	14.023	1.075	.658	6018.6	444.5	11.31	458.0	65.3	3.12
	145	42.68	26.88	13.965	.975	.600	5414.3	402.9	11.26	406.9	58.3	3.09
27 x 10	114	33.53	27.28	10.070	.932	.570	4080.5	299.2	11.03	149.6	29.7	2.11
	102	30.01	27.07	10.018	.827	.518	3604.1	266.3	10.96	129.5	25.9	2.08
	94	27.65	26.91	9.990	.747	.490	3266.7	242.8	10.87	115.1	23.0	2.04
24 x 12	120	35.29	24.31	12.088	.930	.556	3635.3	299.1	10.15	254.0	42.0	2.68
	110	32.36	24.16	12.042	.855	.510	3315.0	274.4	10.12	229.1	38.0	2.66
	100	29.43	24.00	12.000	.775	.468	2987.3	248.9	10.08	203.5	33.9	2.63
24 x 9	94	27.63	24.29	9.061	.872	.516	2683.0	220.9	9.85	102.2	22.6	1.92
	84	24.71	24.09	9.015	.772	.470	2364.3	196.3	9.78	88.3	19.6	1.89
	76	22.37	23.91	8.985	.682	.440	2096.4	175.4	9.68	76.5	17.0	1.85
21 x 9	96	28.21	21.14	9.038	.935	.575	2088.9	197.6	8.60	109.3	24.2	1.97
	82	24.10	20.86	8.962	.795	.499	1752.4	168.0	8.53	89.6	20.0	1.93

REGULAR SERIES

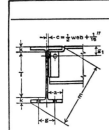

WF SHAPES

DIMENSIONS FOR DETAILING

Nominal Size	Weight per Foot	Depth	Flange Width	Flange Thickness	Web Thickness	Web Half Thickness	a	T	k	m	g_1	c	Usual Gage g
In.	Lb.	In.	In.	In.	In.	In.	In.	In.	In.	In.	In.	In.	In.
$36 \times 16\frac{1}{2}$	300	$36\frac{3}{4}$	$16\frac{5}{8}$	$1\frac{11}{16}$	$\frac{15}{16}$	$\frac{1}{2}$	$7\frac{7}{8}$	$31\frac{1}{8}$	$2\frac{13}{16}$	$40\frac{3}{8}$	4	$\frac{9}{16}$	$5\frac{1}{2}$
	280	$36\frac{1}{2}$	$16\frac{5}{8}$	$1\frac{9}{16}$	$\frac{7}{8}$	$\frac{7}{16}$	$7\frac{7}{8}$	$31\frac{1}{8}$	$2\frac{11}{16}$	$40\frac{1}{4}$	4	$\frac{1}{2}$	$5\frac{1}{2}$
	260	$36\frac{1}{4}$	$16\frac{1}{2}$	$1\frac{7}{16}$	$\frac{7}{8}$	$\frac{7}{16}$	$7\frac{7}{8}$	$31\frac{1}{8}$	$2\frac{9}{16}$	$39\frac{7}{8}$	$3\frac{3}{4}$	$\frac{1}{2}$	$5\frac{1}{2}$
	245	36	$16\frac{1}{2}$	$1\frac{3}{8}$	$\frac{13}{16}$	$\frac{3}{8}$	$7\frac{7}{8}$	$31\frac{1}{8}$	$2\frac{7}{16}$	$39\frac{3}{4}$	$3\frac{3}{4}$	$\frac{7}{16}$	$5\frac{1}{2}$
	230	$35\frac{7}{8}$	$16\frac{1}{2}$	$1\frac{1}{4}$	$\frac{3}{4}$	$\frac{3}{8}$	$7\frac{7}{8}$	$31\frac{1}{8}$	$2\frac{3}{8}$	$39\frac{1}{2}$	$3\frac{1}{2}$	$\frac{7}{16}$	$5\frac{1}{2}$
36×12	194	$36\frac{1}{2}$	$12\frac{1}{8}$	$1\frac{1}{4}$	$\frac{13}{16}$	$\frac{3}{8}$	$5\frac{5}{8}$	$32\frac{1}{4}$	$2\frac{1}{8}$	$38\frac{1}{8}$	$3\frac{1}{4}$	$\frac{7}{16}$	$5\frac{1}{2}$
	182	$36\frac{3}{8}$	$12\frac{1}{8}$	$1\frac{3}{16}$	$\frac{3}{4}$	$\frac{3}{8}$	$5\frac{5}{8}$	$32\frac{1}{4}$	$2\frac{1}{16}$	$38\frac{3}{8}$	$3\frac{1}{4}$	$\frac{7}{16}$	$5\frac{1}{2}$
	170	$36\frac{1}{8}$	12	$1\frac{1}{8}$	$\frac{11}{16}$	$\frac{3}{8}$	$5\frac{5}{8}$	$32\frac{1}{4}$	$1\frac{15}{16}$	$38\frac{1}{8}$	$3\frac{1}{4}$	$\frac{7}{16}$	$5\frac{1}{2}$
	160	36	12	1	$\frac{11}{16}$	$\frac{5}{16}$	$5\frac{5}{8}$	$32\frac{1}{4}$	$1\frac{7}{8}$	38	3	$\frac{3}{8}$	$5\frac{1}{2}$
	150	$35\frac{7}{8}$	12	$\frac{15}{16}$	$\frac{5}{8}$	$\frac{5}{16}$	$5\frac{5}{8}$	$32\frac{1}{4}$	$1\frac{13}{16}$	$37\frac{7}{8}$	3	$\frac{3}{8}$	$5\frac{1}{2}$
$33 \times 11\frac{1}{2}$	152	$33\frac{1}{2}$	$11\frac{5}{8}$	$1\frac{1}{16}$	$\frac{5}{8}$	$\frac{5}{16}$	$5\frac{1}{2}$	$29\frac{3}{4}$	$1\frac{7}{8}$	$35\frac{1}{2}$	3	$\frac{3}{8}$	$5\frac{1}{2}$
	141	$33\frac{1}{4}$	$11\frac{1}{2}$	$\frac{15}{16}$	$\frac{5}{8}$	$\frac{5}{16}$	$5\frac{1}{2}$	$29\frac{3}{4}$	$1\frac{3}{4}$	$35\frac{1}{4}$	3	$\frac{3}{8}$	$5\frac{1}{2}$
	130	$33\frac{1}{8}$	$11\frac{1}{2}$	$\frac{7}{8}$	$\frac{9}{16}$	$\frac{5}{16}$	$5\frac{1}{2}$	$29\frac{3}{4}$	$1\frac{11}{16}$	$35\frac{1}{8}$	3	$\frac{3}{8}$	$5\frac{1}{2}$
$30 \times 10\frac{1}{2}$	132	$30\frac{1}{4}$	$10\frac{1}{2}$	1	$\frac{5}{8}$	$\frac{5}{16}$	5	$26\frac{7}{8}$	$1\frac{11}{16}$	$32\frac{1}{8}$	3	$\frac{3}{8}$	$5\frac{1}{2}$
	124	$30\frac{1}{8}$	$10\frac{1}{2}$	$\frac{15}{16}$	$\frac{5}{8}$	$\frac{5}{16}$	5	$26\frac{7}{8}$	$1\frac{5}{8}$	$31\frac{7}{8}$	3	$\frac{3}{8}$	$5\frac{1}{2}$
	116	30	$10\frac{1}{2}$	$\frac{7}{8}$	$\frac{9}{16}$	$\frac{5}{16}$	5	$26\frac{7}{8}$	$1\frac{9}{16}$	$31\frac{3}{4}$	$2\frac{3}{4}$	$\frac{3}{8}$	$5\frac{1}{2}$
	108	$29\frac{7}{8}$	$10\frac{1}{2}$	$\frac{3}{4}$	$\frac{9}{16}$	$\frac{5}{16}$	5	$26\frac{7}{8}$	$1\frac{1}{2}$	$31\frac{5}{8}$	$2\frac{3}{4}$	$\frac{3}{8}$	$5\frac{1}{2}$
27×14	177	$27\frac{1}{4}$	$14\frac{1}{8}$	$1\frac{3}{16}$	$\frac{3}{4}$	$\frac{3}{8}$	$6\frac{3}{4}$	23	$2\frac{1}{8}$	$30\frac{3}{4}$	$3\frac{1}{4}$	$\frac{7}{16}$	$5\frac{1}{2}$
	160	$27\frac{1}{8}$	14	$1\frac{1}{16}$	$\frac{11}{16}$	$\frac{5}{16}$	$6\frac{3}{4}$	23	$2\frac{1}{16}$	$30\frac{1}{2}$	$3\frac{1}{4}$	$\frac{3}{8}$	$5\frac{1}{2}$
	145	$26\frac{7}{8}$	14	1	$\frac{5}{8}$	$\frac{5}{16}$	$6\frac{3}{4}$	23	$1\frac{15}{16}$	$30\frac{3}{8}$	$3\frac{1}{4}$	$\frac{3}{8}$	$5\frac{1}{2}$
27×10	114	$27\frac{1}{4}$	$10\frac{1}{2}$	$\frac{15}{16}$	$\frac{9}{16}$	$\frac{5}{16}$	$4\frac{3}{4}$	24	$1\frac{5}{8}$	$29\frac{1}{2}$	$2\frac{3}{4}$	$\frac{3}{8}$	$5\frac{1}{2}$
	102	$27\frac{1}{8}$	10	$\frac{13}{16}$	$\frac{1}{2}$	$\frac{1}{4}$	$4\frac{3}{4}$	24	$1\frac{9}{16}$	$28\frac{7}{8}$	$2\frac{3}{4}$	$\frac{5}{16}$	$5\frac{1}{2}$
	94	$26\frac{7}{8}$	10	$\frac{3}{4}$	$\frac{1}{2}$	$\frac{1}{4}$	$4\frac{3}{4}$	24	$1\frac{7}{16}$	$28\frac{3}{4}$	$2\frac{3}{4}$	$\frac{5}{16}$	$5\frac{1}{2}$
24×12	120	$24\frac{1}{4}$	$12\frac{1}{8}$	$\frac{15}{16}$	$\frac{9}{16}$	$\frac{5}{16}$	$5\frac{3}{4}$	$20\frac{7}{8}$	$1\frac{11}{16}$	$27\frac{1}{8}$	3	$\frac{3}{8}$	$5\frac{1}{2}$
	110	$24\frac{1}{8}$	12	$\frac{7}{8}$	$\frac{1}{2}$	$\frac{1}{4}$	$5\frac{3}{4}$	$20\frac{7}{8}$	$1\frac{5}{8}$	27	$2\frac{3}{4}$	$\frac{5}{16}$	$5\frac{1}{2}$
	100	24	12	$\frac{3}{4}$	$\frac{1}{2}$	$\frac{1}{4}$	$5\frac{3}{4}$	$20\frac{7}{8}$	$1\frac{9}{16}$	$26\frac{7}{8}$	$2\frac{3}{4}$	$\frac{5}{16}$	$5\frac{1}{2}$
24×9	94	$24\frac{1}{4}$	9	$\frac{7}{8}$	$\frac{1}{2}$	$\frac{1}{4}$	$4\frac{1}{4}$	$21\frac{3}{8}$	$1\frac{7}{16}$	$25\frac{7}{8}$	$2\frac{3}{4}$	$\frac{5}{16}$	$5\frac{1}{2}$
	84	$24\frac{1}{8}$	9	$\frac{3}{4}$	$\frac{1}{2}$	$\frac{1}{4}$	$4\frac{1}{4}$	$21\frac{3}{8}$	$1\frac{3}{8}$	$25\frac{3}{4}$	$2\frac{3}{4}$	$\frac{5}{16}$	$5\frac{1}{2}$
	76	$23\frac{7}{8}$	9	$\frac{11}{16}$	$\frac{7}{16}$	$\frac{1}{4}$	$4\frac{1}{4}$	$21\frac{3}{8}$	$1\frac{1}{4}$	$25\frac{5}{8}$	$2\frac{1}{2}$	$\frac{5}{16}$	$5\frac{1}{2}$
21×9	96	$21\frac{1}{8}$	9	$\frac{15}{16}$	$\frac{9}{16}$	$\frac{5}{16}$	$4\frac{1}{4}$	18	$1\frac{9}{16}$	23	$2\frac{3}{4}$	$\frac{3}{8}$	$5\frac{1}{2}$
	82	$20\frac{7}{8}$	9	$\frac{13}{16}$	$\frac{1}{2}$	$\frac{1}{4}$	$4\frac{1}{4}$	18	$1\frac{7}{16}$	$22\frac{3}{4}$	$2\frac{3}{4}$	$\frac{5}{16}$	$5\frac{1}{2}$

ROLLED STEEL SHAPES

WF SHAPES
PROPERTIES FOR DESIGNING

Nominal Size	Weight per Foot	Area	Depth	Flange Width	Flange Thickness	Web Thickness	AXIS X-X I	S	r	AXIS Y-Y I	S	r
In.	Lb.	In.²	In.	In.	In.	In.	In.⁴	In.³	In.	In.⁴	In.³	In.
21 x 8¼	73	21.46	21.24	8.295	.740	.455	1000.3	150.7	8.64	66.2	16.0	1.76
	69	20.02	21.13	8.270	.685	.430	1478.3	139.9	8.59	60.4	14.6	1.74
	62	18.23	20.99	8.240	.615	.400	1326.8	126.4	8.53	53.1	12.9	1.71
18 x 8¾	70	20.56	18.00	8.750	.751	.438	1153.9	128.2	7.49	78.5	17.9	1.95
	64	18.80	17.87	8.715	.686	.403	1045.8	117.0	7.46	70.3	16.1	1.93
18 x 7½	60	17.64	18.25	7.558	.695	.416	984.0	107.8	7.47	47.1	12.5	1.63
	55	16.19	18.12	7.532	.630	.390	889.9	98.2	7.41	42.0	11.1	1.61
	50	14.71	18.00	7.500	.570	.358	800.6	89.0	7.38	37.2	9.9	1.59
16 x 8½	64	18.80	16.00	8.500	.715	.443	833.8	104.2	6.66	68.4	16.1	1.91
	58	17.04	15.86	8.464	.645	.407	746.4	94.1	6.62	60.5	14.3	1.88
16 x 7	50	14.70	16.25	7.073	.628	.380	655.4	80.7	6.68	34.8	9.8	1.54
	45	13.24	16.12	7.039	.563	.346	583.3	72.4	6.64	30.5	8.7	1.52
	40	11.77	16.00	7.000	.503	.307	515.5	64.4	6.62	26.5	7.6	1.50
	36	10.59	15.85	6.992	.428	.299	446.3	56.3	6.49	22.1	6.3	1.45
14 x 12	84	24.71	14.18	12.023	.778	.451	928.4	130.9	6.13	225.5	37.5	3.02
	78	22.94	14.06	12.000	.718	.428	851.2	121.1	6.09	206.9	34.5	3.00
14 x 10	74	21.76	14.19	10.072	.783	.450	796.8	112.3	6.05	133.5	26.5	2.48
	68	20.00	14.06	10.040	.718	.418	724.1	103.0	6.02	121.2	24.1	2.46
	61	17.94	13.91	10.000	.643	.378	641.5	92.2	5.98	107.3	21.5	2.45
14 x 8	53	15.59	13.94	8.062	.658	.370	542.1	77.8	5.90	57.5	14.3	1.92
	48	14.11	13.81	8.031	.593	.339	484.9	70.2	5.86	51.3	12.8	1.91
	43	12.65	13.68	8.000	.528	.308	429.0	62.7	5.82	45.1	11.3	1.89
14 x 6¾	38	11.17	14.12	6.776	.513	.313	385.3	54.6	5.87	24.6	7.3	1.49
	34	10.00	14.00	6.750	.453	.287	339.2	48.5	5.83	21.3	6.3	1.46
	30	8.81	13.86	6.733	.383	.270	289.6	41.8	5.73	17.5	5.2	1.41
12 x 12	92	27.06	12.62	12.155	.856	.545	788.9	125.0	5.40	256.4	42.2	3.08
	85	24.98	12.50	12.105	.796	.495	723.3	115.7	5.38	235.5	38.9	3.07
	79	23.22	12.38	12.080	.736	.470	663.0	107.1	5.34	216.4	35.8	3.05
	72	21.16	12.25	12.040	.671	.430	597.4	97.5	5.31	195.3	32.4	3.04
	65	19.11	12.12	12.000	.606	.390	533.4	88.0	5.28	174.6	29.1	3.02
12 x 10	58	17.06	12.19	10.014	.641	.359	476.1	78.1	5.28	107.4	21.4	2.51
	53	15.59	12.06	10.000	.576	.345	426.2	70.7	5.23	96.1	19.2	2.48
12 x 8	50	14.71	12.19	8.077	.641	.371	394.5	64.7	5.18	56.4	14.0	1.96
	45	13.24	12.06	8.042	.576	.336	350.8	58.2	5.15	50.0	12.4	1.94
	40	11.77	11.94	8.000	.516	.294	310.1	51.9	5.13	44.1	11.0	1.94

REGULAR SERIES

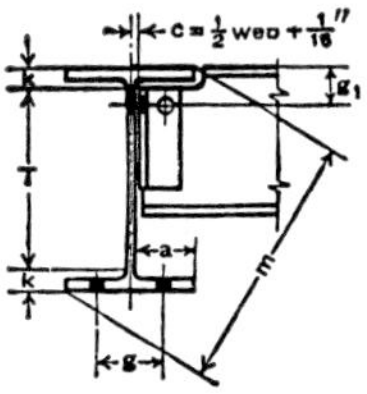

WF SHAPES

DIMENSIONS FOR DETAILING

Nominal Size	Weight per Foot	Depth	Flange Width	Flange Thickness	Web Thickness	Web Half Thickness	Distance a	Distance T	Distance k	Distance m	Distance g1	Distance c	Usual Gage g
In.	Lb.	In.	In.	In.	In.	In.	In.	In.	In.	In.	In.	In.	In.
21 x 8 1/4	73	21 1/4	8 1/4	3/4	1/2	1/4	4	18 5/8	1 5/16	22 7/8	2 1/2	5/16	5 1/2
	68	21 1/8	8 1/4	11/16	7/16	1/4	4	18 5/8	1 1/4	22 3/4	2 1/2	5/16	5 1/2
	62	21	8 1/4	5/8	3/8	3/16	4	18 5/8	1 3/16	22 5/8	2 1/2	1/4	5 1/2
18 x 8 3/4	70	18	8 3/4	3/4	7/16	1/4	4 1/8	15 3/8	1 5/16	20	2 3/4	5/16	5 1/2
	64	17 7/8	8 3/4	11/16	7/16	3/16	4 1/8	15 3/8	1 1/4	20	2 1/2	1/4	5 1/2
18 x 7 1/2	60	18 1/4	7 1/2	11/16	7/16	3/16	3 5/8	15 7/8	1 3/16	19 7/8	2 1/2	1/4	3 1/2
	55	18 1/8	7 1/2	5/8	3/8	3/16	3 5/8	15 7/8	1 1/8	19 5/8	2 1/2	1/4	3 1/2
	50	18	7 1/2	9/16	3/8	3/16	3 5/8	15 7/8	1 1/16	19 1/2	2 1/4	1/4	3 1/2
16 x 8 1/2	64	16	8 1/2	11/16	7/16	1/4	4	13 3/8	1 5/16	18 1/8	2 1/2	5/16	5 1/2
	58	15 7/8	8 1/2	5/8	7/16	1/4	4	13 3/8	1 1/4	18	2 1/2	5/16	5 1/2
16 x 7	50	16 1/4	7 1/8	5/8	3/8	3/16	3 3/8	14	1 1/8	17 3/4	2 1/2	1/4	3 1/2
	45	16 1/8	7	9/16	3/8	3/16	3 3/8	14	1 1/16	17 5/8	2 1/4	1/4	3 1/2
	40	16	7	1/2	5/16	3/16	3 3/8	14	1	17 1/2	2 1/4	1/4	3 1/2
	36	15 7/8	7	7/16	5/16	3/16	3 3/8	14	15/16	17 3/8	2 1/4	1/4	3 1/2
14 x 12	84	14 1/8	12	3/4	7/16	1/4	5 3/4	11 3/8	1 3/8	18 5/8	2 3/4	5/16	5 1/2
	78	14	12	11/16	7/16	1/4	5 3/4	11 3/8	1 5/16	18 1/2	2 1/2	5/16	5 1/2
14 x 10	74	14 1/4	10 1/8	13/16	7/16	1/4	4 3/4	11 3/8	1 3/8	17 1/2	2 3/4	5/16	5 1/2
	68	14	10	11/16	7/16	1/4	4 3/4	11 3/8	1 5/16	17 1/4	2 1/2	5/16	5 1/2
	61	13 7/8	10	5/8	3/8	3/16	4 3/4	11 3/8	1 1/4	17 1/8	2 1/2	1/4	5 1/2
14 x 8	53	14	8	11/16	3/8	3/16	3 7/8	11 3/8	1 1/4	16 1/8	2 1/2	1/4	5 1/2
	48	13 3/4	8	9/16	3/8	3/16	3 7/8	11 3/8	1 3/16	16	2 1/2	1/4	5 1/2
	43	13 5/8	8	1/2	5/16	3/16	3 7/8	11 3/8	1 1/8	15 7/8	2 1/2	1/4	5 1/2
14 x 6 3/4	38	14 1/8	6 3/4	1/2	5/16	3/16	3 1/4	12 1/8	1	15 3/4	2 1/4	1/4	3 1/2
	34	14	6 3/4	7/16	5/16	3/16	3 1/4	12 1/8	15/16	15 5/8	2 1/4	1/4	3 1/2
	30	13 7/8	6 3/4	3/8	5/16	1/8	3 1/4	12 1/8	7/8	15 1/2	2 1/4	3/16	3 1/2
12 x 12	92	12 5/8	12 1/8	7/8	9/16	5/16	5 3/4	9 3/4	1 7/16	17 1/2	2 3/4	3/8	5 1/2
	85	12 1/2	12 1/8	13/16	1/2	1/4	5 3/4	9 3/4	1 3/8	17 1/2	2 3/4	5/16	5 1/2
	79	12 3/8	12 1/8	3/4	1/2	1/4	5 3/4	9 3/4	1 5/16	17 3/8	2 3/4	5/16	5 1/2
	72	12 1/4	12	11/16	7/16	1/4	5 3/4	9 3/4	1 1/4	17 1/4	2 1/2	5/16	5 1/2
	65	12 1/8	12	5/8	3/8	3/16	5 3/4	9 3/4	1 3/16	17 1/8	2 1/2	1/4	5 1/2
12 x 10	58	12 1/4	10	5/8	3/8	3/16	4 7/8	9 3/4	1 1/4	15 7/8	2 1/2	1/4	5 1/2
	53	12	10	9/16	3/8	3/16	4 7/8	9 3/4	1 3/16	15 5/8	2 1/2	1/4	5 1/2
12 x 8	50	12 1/4	8 1/8	5/8	3/8	3/16	3 7/8	9 3/4	1 1/4	14 5/8	2 1/2	1/4	5 1/2
	45	12	8	9/16	3/8	3/16	3 7/8	9 3/4	1 3/16	14 1/2	2 1/2	1/4	5 1/2
	40	12	8	1/2	5/16	3/16	3 7/8	9 3/4	1 1/8	14 3/8	2 1/2	1/4	5 1/2

ROLLED STEEL SHAPES

WF SHAPES
PROPERTIES FOR DESIGNING

Nominal Size	Weight per Foot	Area	Depth	Flange		Web Thickness	AXIS X-X			AXIS Y-Y		
				Width	Thickness		I	S	r	I	S	r
In.	Lb.	In.²	In.	In.	In.	In.	In.⁴	In.³	In.	In.⁴	In.³	In.
12 x 6½	36	10.59	12.24	6.565	.540	.305	280.8	45.9	5.15	23.7	7.2	1.50
	31	9.12	12.09	6.525	.465	.265	238.4	39.4	5.11	19.8	6.1	1.47
	27	7.97	11.95	6.500	.400	.240	204.1	34.1	5.06	16.6	5.1	1.44
10 x 10	72	21.18	10.50	10.170	.808	.510	420.7	80.1	4.46	141.8	27.9	2.59
	66	19.41	10.38	10.117	.748	.457	382.5	73.7	4.44	129.2	25.5	2.58
	60	17.66	10.25	10.075	.683	.415	343.7	67.1	4.41	116.5	23.1	2.57
	54	15.88	10.12	10.028	.618	.368	305.7	60.4	4.39	103.9	20.7	2.56
	49	14.40	10.00	10.000	.558	.340	272.9	54.6	4.35	93.0	18.6	2.54
10 x 8	33	9.71	9.75	7.964	.433	.292	170.9	35.0	4.20	36.5	9.2	1.94
10 x 5¾	29	8.53	10.22	5.799	.500	.289	157.3	30.8	4.29	15.2	5.2	1.34
	25	7.35	10.08	5.762	.430	.252	133.2	26.4	4.26	12.7	4.4	1.31
	21	6.19	9.90	5.750	.340	.240	106.3	21.5	4.14	9.7	3.4	1.25
8 x 8	40	11.76	8.25	8.077	.558	.365	146.3	35.5	3.53	49.0	12.1	2.04
	35	10.30	8.12	8.027	.493	.315	126.5	31.1	3.50	42.5	10.6	2.03
	31	9.12	8.00	8.000	.433	.288	109.7	27.4	3.47	37.0	9.2	2.01
8 x 6½	28	8.23	8.06	6.540	.463	.285	97.8	24.3	3.45	21.6	6.6	1.62
	24	7.06	7.93	6.500	.398	.245	82.5	20.8	3.42	18.2	5.6	1.61
8 x 5¼	20	5.88	8.14	5.268	.378	.248	69.2	17.0	3.43	8.5	3.2	1.20
	17	5.00	8.00	5.250	.308	.230	56.4	14.1	3.36	6.7	2.6	1.16

REGULAR SERIES

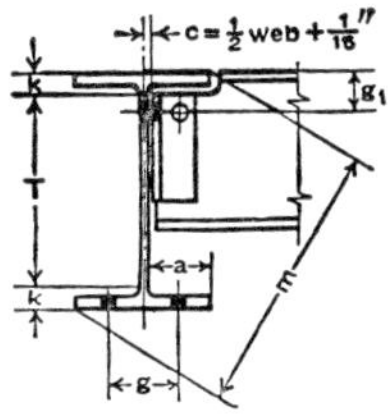

WF SHAPES

DIMENSIONS FOR DETAILING

Nominal Size	Weight per Foot	Depth	Flange		Web		Distance						Usual Gage
			Width	Thickness	Thickness	Half Thickness	a	T	k	m	g_1	c	g
In.	Lb.	In.	In.	In.	In.	In.	In.	In.	In.	In.	In.	In.	In.
12 x 6½	36	12¼	6⅝	9/16	5/16	3/16	3⅛	10⅜	15/16	14	2¼	¼	3½
	31	12⅛	6½	7/16	¼	⅛	3⅛	10⅜	⅞	13¾	2¼	3/16	3½
	27	12	6½	⅜	¼	⅛	3⅛	10⅜	13/16	13⅝	2¼	3/16	3½
10 x 10	72	10½	10⅛	13/16	½	¼	4⅞	7⅞	1 5/16	14⅝	2¾	5/16	5½
	66	10⅜	10⅛	¾	7/16	¼	4⅞	7⅞	1¼	14½	2½	5/16	5½
	60	10¼	10⅛	11/16	7/16	¼	4⅞	7⅞	1 3/16	14⅜	2½	5/16	5½
	54	10⅛	10	⅝	⅜	3/16	4⅞	7⅞	1⅛	14¼	2½	¼	5½
	49	10	10	9/16	⅜	3/16	4⅞	7⅞	1 1/16	14⅛	2½	¼	5½
10 x 8	33	9¾	8	7/16	5/16	3/16	3⅞	7⅞	15/16	12⅝	2¼	¼	5½
10 x 5¾	29	10¼	5¾	½	5/16	3/16	2¾	8½	⅞	11¾	2¼	¼	2¾
	25	10⅛	5¾	7/16	¼	⅛	2¾	8½	13/16	11⅝	2¼	3/16	2¾
	21	9⅞	5¾	5/16	¼	⅛	2¾	8½	11/16	11½	2	3/16	2¾
8 x 8	40	8¼	8⅛	9/16	⅜	3/16	3⅞	6⅜	15/16	11⅝	2¼	¼	5½
	35	8⅛	8	½	5/16	3/16	3⅞	6⅜	⅞	11½	2¼	¼	5½
	31	8	8	7/16	5/16	3/16	3⅞	6⅜	13/16	11⅜	2¼	¼	5½
8 x 6½	28	8	6½	7/16	5/16	⅛	3⅛	6⅜	13/16	10½	2¼	3/16	3½
	24	7⅞	6½	⅜	¼	⅛	3⅛	6⅜	¾	10¼	2¼	3/16	3½
8 x 5¼	20	8⅛	5¼	⅜	¼	⅛	2½	6¾	11/16	9¾	2¼	3/16	2¾
	17	8	5¼	5/16	¼	⅛	2½	6¾	⅝	9⅝	2¼	3/16	2¾

ROLLED STEEL SHAPES

WF SHAPES
MISCELLANEOUS (B)
COLUMNS AND BEAMS

PROPERTIES FOR DESIGNING

Nominal Size	Weight per Foot	Area	Depth	Flange		Web Thick-ness	AXIS X-X			AXIS Y-Y		
				Width	Thick-ness		I	S	r	I	S	r
In.	Lb.	In.²	In.	In.	In.	In.	In.⁴	In.³	In.	In.⁴	In.³	In.

WF SHAPES AND LIGHT COLUMNS

6 WF	25	7 37	6.37	6.080	.456	.320	53.5	16.8	2.69	17.1	5.6	1.52
6 x 6	20	5.90	6.20	6.018	.367	.258	41.7	13.4	2.66	13.3	4.4	1.50
	15.5	4.62	6.00	6.000	.269	.240	30.3	10.1	2.56	9.69	3.2	1.45
5 WF	18.5	5.45	5.12	5.025	.420	.265	25.4	9.94	2.16	8.89	3.54	1.28
5 x 5	16	4.70	5.00	5.000	.360	.240	21.3	8.53	2.13	7.51	3.00	1.26
4 WF	13	3.82	4.16	4.060	.345	.280	11.3	5.45	1.72	3.76	1.85	.99

LIGHT BEAMS

12 x 4	22	6.47	12.31	4.030	.424	.260	155.7	25.3	4.91	4.55	2.26	.84
	19	5.62	12.16	4.010	.349	.240	130.1	21.4	4.81	3.67	1.83	.81
	16½	4.86	12.00	4.000	.269	.230	105.3	17.5	4.65	2.79	1.39	.76
10 x 4	19	5.61	10.25	4.020	.394	.250	96.2	18.8	4.14	4.19	2.08	.86
	17	4.98	10.12	4.010	.329	.240	81.8	16.2	4.05	3.45	1.72	.83
	15	4.40	10.00	4.000	.269	.230	68.8	13.8	3.95	2.79	1.39	.80
8 x 4	15	4.43	8.12	4.015	.314	.245	48.0	11.8	3.29	3.30	1.65	.86
	13	3.83	8.00	4.000	.254	.230	39.5	9.88	3.21	2.62	1.31	.83
6 x 4	16	4.72	6.25	4.030	.404	.260	31.7	10.1	2.59	4.32	2.14	.96
	12	3.53	6.00	4.000	.279	.230	21.7	7.24	2.48	2.89	1.44	.90

JOISTS

12 x 4	14	4.14	11.91	3.970	.224	.200	88.2	14.8	4.61	2.25	1.13	.74
10 x 4	11½	3.39	9.87	3.950	.204	.180	51.9	10.5	3.92	2.01	1.02	.77
8 x 4	10	2.95	7.90	3.940	.204	.170	30.8	7.79	3.23	1.99	1.01	.82
6 x 4	8½	2.50	5.83	3.940	.194	.170	14.8	5.07	2.43	1.89	.96	.87

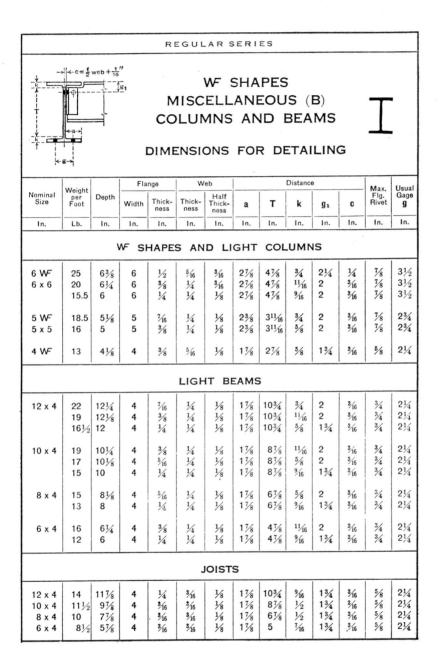

			Flange		Web		Distance					Max. Flg. Rivet	Usual Gage g
Nominal Size	Weight per Foot	Depth	Width	Thickness	Thickness	Half Thickness	a	T	k	g_1	c		
In.	Lb.	In.	In.	In.	In.	In.	In.	In.	In.	In.	In.	In.	In.

REGULAR SERIES

WF SHAPES MISCELLANEOUS (B) COLUMNS AND BEAMS

DIMENSIONS FOR DETAILING

$c = \frac{1}{2}\,web + \frac{1}{16}''$

Nominal Size	Weight per Foot	Depth	Width	Thickness	Thickness	Half Thickness	a	T	k	g_1	c	Max. Flg. Rivet	Usual Gage g
WF SHAPES AND LIGHT COLUMNS													
6 WF	25	6⅜	6	½	5/16	3/16	2⅞	4⅞	¾	2¼	¼	⅞	3½
6 x 6	20	6¼	6	⅜	¼	3/16	2⅞	4⅞	11/16	2	3/16	⅞	3½
	15.5	6	6	¼	¼	⅛	2⅞	4⅞	9/16	2	3/16	⅞	3½
5 WF	18.5	5⅛	5	7/16	¼	⅛	2⅜	3¹¹/16	¾	2	3/16	⅞	2¾
5 x 5	16	5	5	⅜	¼	⅛	2⅜	3¹¹/16	⅝	2	3/16	⅞	2¾
4 WF	13	4⅛	4	⅜	5/16	⅛	1⅞	2⅞	⅝	1¾	3/16	⅝	2¼
LIGHT BEAMS													
12 x 4	22	12¼	4	7/16	¼	⅛	1⅞	10¾	¾	2	3/16	¾	2¼
	19	12⅛	4	⅜	¼	⅛	1⅞	10¾	11/16	2	3/16	¾	2¼
	16½	12	4	¼	¼	⅛	1⅞	10¾	⅝	1¾	3/16	¾	2¼
10 x 4	19	10¼	4	⅜	¼	⅛	1⅞	8⅞	11/16	2	3/16	¾	2¼
	17	10⅛	4	5/16	¼	⅛	1⅞	8⅞	⅝	2	3/16	¾	2¼
	15	10	4	¼	¼	⅛	1⅞	8⅞	9/16	1¾	3/16	¾	2¼
8 x 4	15	8⅛	4	5/16	¼	⅛	1⅞	6⅞	⅝	2	3/16	¾	2¼
	13	8	4	¼	¼	⅛	1⅞	6⅞	9/16	1¾	3/16	¾	2¼
6 x 4	16	6¼	4	⅜	¼	⅛	1⅞	4⅞	11/16	2	3/16	¾	2¼
	12	6	4	¼	¼	⅛	1⅞	4⅞	9/16	1¾	3/16	¾	2¼
JOISTS													
12 x 4	14	11⅞	4	¼	3/16	⅛	1⅞	10¾	9/16	1¾	3/16	⅝	2¼
10 x 4	11½	9⅞	4	3/16	3/16	⅛	1⅞	8⅞	½	1¾	3/16	⅝	2¼
8 x 4	10	7⅞	4	3/16	3/16	⅛	1⅞	6⅞	½	1¾	3/16	⅝	2¼
6 x 4	8½	5⅞	4	3/16	3/16	⅛	1⅞	5	7/16	1¾	3/16	⅝	2¼

ROLLED STEEL SHAPES

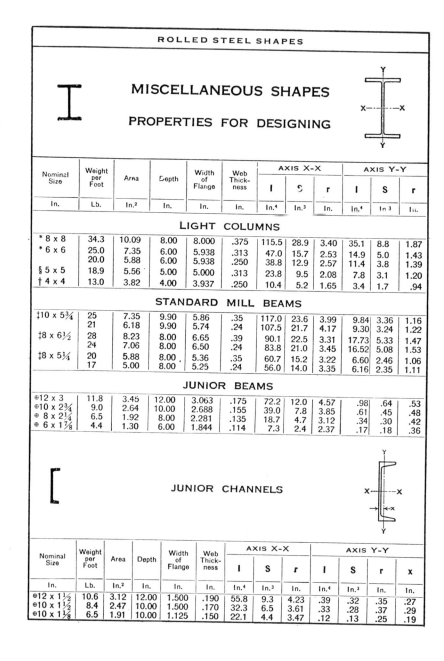

MISCELLANEOUS SHAPES

PROPERTIES FOR DESIGNING

Nominal Size	Weight per Foot	Area	Depth	Width of Flange	Web Thick-ness	AXIS X-X			AXIS Y-Y		
						I	S	r	I	S	r
In.	Lb.	In.²	In.	In.	In.	In.⁴	In.³	In.	In.⁴	In.³	In.
LIGHT COLUMNS											
* 8 x 8	34.3	10.09	8.00	8.000	.375	115.5	28.9	3.40	35.1	8.8	1.87
* 6 x 6	25.0	7.35	6.00	5.938	.313	47.0	15.7	2.53	14.9	5.0	1.43
	20.0	5.88	6.00	5.938	.250	38.8	12.9	2.57	11.4	3.8	1.39
§ 5 x 5	18.9	5.56	5.00	5.000	.313	23.8	9.5	2.08	7.8	3.1	1.20
† 4 x 4	13.0	3.82	4.00	3.937	.250	10.4	5.2	1.65	3.4	1.7	.94
STANDARD MILL BEAMS											
‡10 x 5¾	25	7.35	9.90	5.86	.35	117.0	23.6	3.99	9.84	3.36	1.16
	21	6.18	9.90	5.74	.24	107.5	21.7	4.17	9.30	3.24	1.22
‡8 x 6½	28	8.23	8.00	6.65	.39	90.1	22.5	3.31	17.73	5.33	1.47
	24	7.06	8.00	6.50	.24	83.8	21.0	3.45	16.52	5.08	1.53
‡8 x 5¼	20	5.88	8.00	5.36	.35	60.7	15.2	3.22	6.60	2.46	1.06
	17	5.00	8.00	5.25	.24	56.0	14.0	3.35	6.16	2.35	1.11
JUNIOR BEAMS											
⊕12 x 3	11.8	3.45	12.00	3.063	.175	72.2	12.0	4.57	.98	.64	.53
⊕10 x 2¾	9.0	2.64	10.00	2.688	.155	39.0	7.8	3.85	.61	.45	.48
⊕ 8 x 2¼	6.5	1.92	8.00	2.281	.135	18.7	4.7	3.12	.34	.30	.42
⊕ 6 x 1⅞	4.4	1.30	6.00	1.844	.114	7.3	2.4	2.37	.17	.18	.36

JUNIOR CHANNELS

Nominal Size	Weight per Foot	Area	Depth	Width of Flange	Web Thick-ness	AXIS X-X			AXIS Y-Y			
						I	S	r	I	S	r	x
In.	Lb.	In.²	In.	In.	In.	In.⁴	In.³	In.	In.⁴	In.³	In.	In.
⊕12 x 1½	10.6	3.12	12.00	1.500	.190	55.8	9.3	4.23	.39	.32	.35	.27
⊕10 x 1½	8.4	2.47	10.00	1.500	.170	32.3	6.5	3.61	.33	.28	.37	.29
⊕10 x 1⅛	6.5	1.91	10.00	1.125	.150	22.1	4.4	3.47	.12	.13	.25	.19

REGULAR SERIES

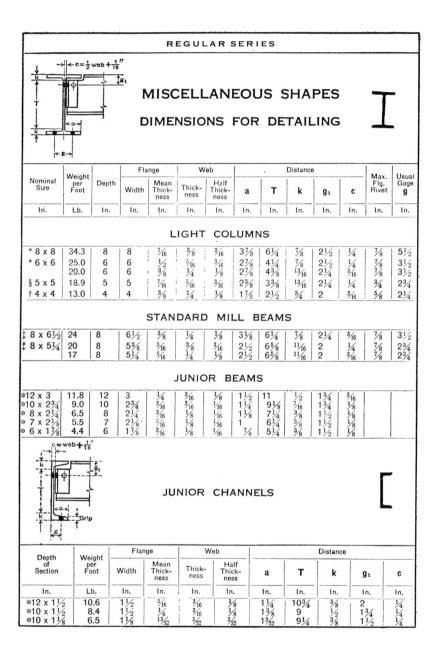

$c = \frac{1}{2} web + \frac{1}{16}''$

MISCELLANEOUS SHAPES
DIMENSIONS FOR DETAILING

$c = web + \frac{1}{16}''$

Nominal Size	Weight per Foot	Depth	Flange Width	Flange Mean Thickness	Web Thickness	Web Half Thickness	a	T	k	g₁	c	Max. Flg. Rivet	Usual Gage g
In.	Lb.	In.	In.	In.	In.	In.	In.	In.	In.	In.	In.	In.	In.

LIGHT COLUMNS

Nominal Size	Weight per Foot	Depth	Width	Mean Thick	Thick	Half Thick	a	T	k	g₁	c	Max Flg Rivet	Usual Gage g
* 8 x 8	34.3	8	8	$\frac{7}{16}$	$\frac{3}{8}$	$\frac{3}{16}$	$3\frac{7}{8}$	$6\frac{1}{4}$	$\frac{7}{8}$	$2\frac{1}{2}$	$\frac{1}{4}$	$\frac{7}{8}$	$5\frac{1}{2}$
* 6 x 6	25.0	6	6	$\frac{1}{2}$	$\frac{5}{16}$	$\frac{3}{16}$	$2\frac{7}{8}$	$4\frac{1}{4}$	$\frac{7}{8}$	$2\frac{1}{2}$	$\frac{1}{4}$	$\frac{7}{8}$	$3\frac{1}{2}$
	20.0	6	6	$\frac{3}{8}$	$\frac{1}{4}$	$\frac{1}{8}$	$2\frac{7}{8}$	$4\frac{3}{8}$	$\frac{13}{16}$	$2\frac{1}{4}$	$\frac{3}{16}$	$\frac{7}{8}$	$3\frac{1}{2}$
§ 5 x 5	18.9	5	5	$\frac{7}{16}$	$\frac{5}{16}$	$\frac{3}{16}$	$2\frac{3}{8}$	$3\frac{3}{8}$	$\frac{13}{16}$	$2\frac{1}{4}$	$\frac{1}{4}$	$\frac{3}{4}$	$2\frac{3}{4}$
† 4 x 4	13.0	4	4	$\frac{3}{8}$	$\frac{1}{4}$	$\frac{1}{8}$	$1\frac{7}{8}$	$2\frac{1}{2}$	$\frac{3}{4}$	2	$\frac{3}{16}$	$\frac{5}{8}$	$2\frac{1}{4}$

STANDARD MILL BEAMS

Nominal Size	Weight per Foot	Depth	Width	Mean Thick	Thick	Half Thick	a	T	k	g₁	c	Max Flg Rivet	Usual Gage g
‡ 8 x 6½	24	8	$6\frac{1}{2}$	$\frac{3}{8}$	$\frac{1}{4}$	$\frac{1}{8}$	$3\frac{1}{8}$	$6\frac{1}{4}$	$\frac{7}{8}$	$2\frac{1}{4}$	$\frac{3}{16}$	$\frac{7}{8}$	$3\frac{1}{2}$
‡ 8 x 5¼	20	8	$5\frac{3}{8}$	$\frac{5}{16}$	$\frac{3}{8}$	$\frac{3}{16}$	$2\frac{1}{2}$	$6\frac{5}{8}$	$\frac{11}{16}$	2	$\frac{1}{4}$	$\frac{7}{8}$	$2\frac{3}{4}$
	17	8	$5\frac{1}{4}$	$\frac{5}{16}$	$\frac{1}{4}$	$\frac{1}{8}$	$2\frac{1}{2}$	$6\frac{5}{8}$	$\frac{11}{16}$	2	$\frac{3}{16}$	$\frac{7}{8}$	$2\frac{3}{4}$

JUNIOR BEAMS

Nominal Size	Weight per Foot	Depth	Width	Mean Thick	Thick	Half Thick	a	T	k	g₁	c		
⊕12 x 3	11.8	12	3	$\frac{1}{4}$	$\frac{3}{16}$	$\frac{1}{8}$	$1\frac{1}{2}$	11	$\frac{1}{2}$	$1\frac{3}{4}$	$\frac{3}{16}$		
⊕10 x 2¾	9.0	10	$2\frac{3}{4}$	$\frac{3}{16}$	$\frac{3}{16}$	$\frac{1}{16}$	$1\frac{1}{4}$	$9\frac{1}{2}$	$\frac{7}{16}$	$1\frac{3}{4}$	$\frac{1}{8}$		
⊕ 8 x 2¼	6.5	8	$2\frac{1}{4}$	$\frac{3}{16}$	$\frac{1}{8}$	$\frac{1}{16}$	$1\frac{1}{8}$	$7\frac{1}{4}$	$\frac{3}{8}$	$1\frac{1}{2}$	$\frac{1}{8}$		
⊕ 7 x 2⅛	5.5	7	$2\frac{1}{8}$	$\frac{3}{16}$	$\frac{1}{8}$	$\frac{1}{16}$	1	$6\frac{1}{4}$	$\frac{3}{8}$	$1\frac{1}{2}$	$\frac{1}{8}$		
⊕ 6 x 1⅞	4.4	6	$1\frac{7}{8}$	$\frac{3}{16}$	$\frac{1}{8}$	$\frac{1}{16}$	$\frac{7}{8}$	$5\frac{1}{4}$	$\frac{3}{8}$	$1\frac{1}{2}$	$\frac{1}{8}$		

JUNIOR CHANNELS

Depth of Section	Weight per Foot	Flange Width	Flange Mean Thickness	Web Thickness	Web Half Thickness	a	T	k	g₁	c
In.	Lb.	In.	In.	In.	In.	In.	In.	In.	In.	In.
⊕12 x 1½	10.6	$1\frac{1}{2}$	$\frac{5}{16}$	$\frac{3}{16}$	$\frac{1}{8}$	$1\frac{1}{4}$	$10\frac{3}{4}$	$\frac{5}{8}$	2	$\frac{1}{4}$
⊕10 x 1½	8.4	$1\frac{1}{2}$	$\frac{1}{4}$	$\frac{3}{16}$	$\frac{1}{8}$	$1\frac{3}{8}$	9	$\frac{1}{2}$	$1\frac{3}{4}$	$\frac{1}{4}$
⊕10 x 1⅛	6.5	$1\frac{1}{8}$	$\frac{13}{32}$	$\frac{5}{32}$	$\frac{3}{32}$	$1\frac{3}{32}$	$9\frac{1}{4}$	$\frac{3}{8}$	$1\frac{1}{2}$	$\frac{1}{4}$

ROLLED STEEL SHAPES

AMERICAN STANDARD BEAMS

PROPERTIES FOR DESIGNING

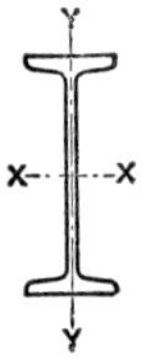

Nominal Size	Weight per Foot	Area	Depth	Flange		Web Thick-ness	AXIS X-X			AXIS Y-Y		
				Width	Thick-ness		I	S	r	I	S	r
In.	Lb.	In.²	In.	In	In.	In.	In.⁴	In.³	In.	In.⁴	In.³	In.
24 x 7⅞	120.0	35.13	24.00	8.048	1.102	.798	3010.8	250.9	9.26	84.9	21.1	1.56
	105.9	30.98	24.00	7.875	1.102	.625	2811.5	234.3	9.53	78.9	20.0	1.60
24 x 7	100.0	29.25	24.00	7.247	.871	.747	2371.8	197.6	9.05	48.4	13.4	1.29
	90.0	26.30	24.00	7.124	.871	.624	2230.1	185.8	9.21	45.5	12.8	1.32
	79.9	23.33	24.00	7.000	.871	.500	2087.2	173.9	9.46	42.9	12.2	1.36
20 x 7	95.0	27.74	20.00	7.200	.916	.800	1599.7	160.0	7.59	50.5	14.0	1.35
	85.0	24.80	20.00	7.053	.916	.653	1501.7	150.2	7.78	47.0	13.3	1.38
20 x 6¼	75.0	21.90	20.00	6.391	.789	.641	1263.5	126.3	7.60	30.1	9.4	1.17
	65.4	19.08	20.00	6.250	.789	.500	1169.5	116.9	7.83	27.9	8.9	1.21
18 x 6	70.0	20.46	18.00	6.251	.691	.711	917.5	101.9	6.70	24.5	7.8	1.09
	54.7	15.94	18.00	6.000	.691	.460	795.5	88.4	7.07	21.2	7.1	1.15
15 x 5½	50.0	14.59	15.00	5.640	.622	.550	481.1	64.2	5.74	16.0	5.7	1.05
	42.9	12.49	15.00	5.500	.622	.410	441.8	58.9	5.95	14.6	5.3	1.08
12 x 5¼	50.0	14.57	12.00	5.477	.659	.687	301.6	50.3	4.55	16.0	5.8	1.05
	40.8	11.84	12.00	5.250	.659	.460	268.9	44.8	4.77	13.8	5.3	1.08
12 x 5	35.0	10.20	12.00	5.078	.544	.428	227.0	37.8	4.72	10.0	3.9	.99
	31.8	9.26	12.00	5.000	.544	.350	215.8	36.0	4.83	9.5	3.8	1.01
10 x 4⅝	35.0	10.22	10.00	4.944	.491	.594	145.8	29.2	3.78	8.5	3.4	.91
	25.4	7.38	10.00	4.660	.491	.310	122.1	24.4	4.07	6.9	3.0	.97
8 x 4	23.0	6.71	8.00	4.171	.425	.441	64.2	16.0	3.09	4.4	2.1	.81
	18.4	5.34	8.00	4.000	.425	.270	56.9	14.2	3.26	3.8	1.9	.84
7 x 3⅝	20.0	5.83	7.00	3.860	.392	.450	41.9	12.0	2.68	3.1	1.6	.74
	15.3	4.43	7.00	3.660	.392	.250	36.2	10.4	2.86	2.7	1.5	.78
6 x 3⅜	17.25	5.02	6.00	3.565	.359	.465	26.0	8.7	2.28	2.3	1.3	.68
	12.5	3.61	6.00	3.330	.359	.230	21.8	7.3	2.46	1.8	1.1	.72
5 x 3	14.75	4.29	5.00	3.284	.326	.494	15.0	6.0	1.87	1.7	1.0	.63
	10.0	2.87	5.00	3.000	.326	.210	12.1	4.8	2.05	1.2	.82	.65
4 x 2⅝	9.5	2.76	4.00	2.796	.293	.326	6.7	3.3	1.56	.91	.65	.58
	7.7	2.21	4.00	2.660	.293	.190	6.0	3.0	1.64	.77	.58	.59
3 x 2⅜	7.5	2.17	3.00	2.509	.260	.349	2.9	1.9	1.15	.59	.47	.52
	5.7	1.64	3.00	2.330	.260	.170	2.5	1.7	1.23	.46	.40	.53

REGULAR SERIES

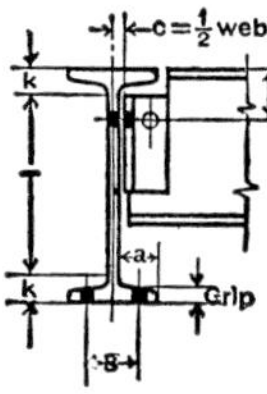

AMERICAN STANDARD BEAMS

DIMENSIONS FOR DETAILING

Depth of Section	Weight per Foot	Flange Width	Flange Mean Thickness	Web Thickness	Web Half Thickness	Distance a	Distance T	Distance k	Distance g_1	Distance c	Grip	Max. Flange Rivet	Usual Gage g
In.	Lb.	In.	In.	In.	In.	In.	In.	In.	In.	In.	In.	In.	In.
24	120.0	8	1⅛	13/16	7/16	3⅝	20⅛	1 15/16	3¼	½	1⅛	1	4
	105.9	7⅞	1⅛	⅝	5/16	3⅝	20⅛	1 15/16	3¼	⅜	1⅛	1	4
24	100.0	7¼	⅞	¾	⅜	3¼	20¾	1⅝	3	7/16	⅞	1	4
	90.0	7⅛	⅞	⅝	5/16	3¼	20¾	1⅝	3	⅜	⅞	1	4
	79.9	7	⅞	½	¼	3¼	20¾	1⅝	3	5/16	⅞	1	4
20	95.0	7¼	15/16	13/16	7/16	3¼	16½	1¾	3¼	½	15/16	1	4
	85.0	7	15/16	11/16	5/16	3¼	16½	1¾	3¼	⅜	⅞	1	4
20	75.0	6⅜	13/16	⅝	5/16	2⅞	16⅞	1 9/16	3	⅜	13/16	⅞	3½
	65.4	6¼	13/16	½	¼	2⅞	16⅞	1 9/16	3	5/16	¾	⅞	3½
18	70.0	6¼	11/16	¾	⅜	2¾	15¼	1⅜	2¾	7/16	11/16	⅞	3½
	54.7	6	11/16	½	¼	2¾	15¼	1⅜	2¾	5/16	11/16	⅞	3½
15	50.0	5⅝	⅝	9/16	5/16	2½	12½	1¼	2¾	⅜	9/16	¾	3½
	42.9	5½	⅝	7/16	¼	2½	12½	1¼	2¾	5/16	9/16	¾	3½
12	50.0	5½	11/16	11/16	⅜	2⅜	9⅜	1 5/16	2¾	7/16	11/16	¾	3
	40.8	5¼	11/16	½	¼	2⅜	9⅜	1 5/16	2¾	5/16	⅝	¾	3
12	35.0	5⅛	9/16	7/16	¼	2⅜	9¾	1⅛	2½	5/16	½	¾	3
	31.8	5	9/16	⅜	3/16	2⅜	9¾	1⅛	2½	¼	½	¾	3
10	35.0	5	½	⅝	5/16	2⅛	8	1	2½	⅜	½	¾	2¾
	25.4	4⅝	½	5/16	3/16	2⅛	8	1	2½	¼	½	¾	2¾
8	23.0	4⅛	7/16	7/16	¼	1⅞	6¼	⅞	2¼	5/16	7/16	¾	2¼
	18.4	4	7/16	5/16	⅛	1⅞	6¼	⅞	2¼	3/16	7/16	¾	2¼
7	20.0	3⅞	⅜	7/16	¼	1¾	5⅜	13/16	2	5/16	⅜	⅝	2¼
	15.3	3⅝	⅜	¼	⅛	1¾	5⅜	13/16	2	3/16	⅜	⅝	2¼
6	17.25	3⅝	⅜	½	¼	1½	4½	¾	2	5/16	⅜	⅝	2
	12.5	3⅜	⅜	¼	⅛	1½	4½	¾	2	3/16	5/16		
5	14.75	3¼	5/16	½	¼	1⅜	3⅝	11/16	2	5/16	5/16	½	1¾
	10.0	3	5/16	¼	⅛	1⅜	3⅝	11/16	2	3/16	5/16	½	1¾
4	9.5	2¾	5/16	5/16	3/16	1¼	2¾	⅝	2	¼	5/16	½	1½
	7.7	2⅝	5/16	3/16	⅛	1¼	2¾	⅝	2	3/16	5/16		
3	7.5	2½	¼	⅜	3/16	1⅛	1⅞	9/16		¼	¼	⅜	1½
	5.7	2⅜	¼	3/16	⅛	1⅛	1⅞	9/16		3/16	¼	⅜	1½

ROLLED STEEL SHAPES

AMERICAN STANDARD CHANNELS

PROPERTIES FOR DESIGNING

Nominal Size	Weight per Foot	Area	Depth	Flange Width	Flange Average Thickness	Web Thickness	AXIS X-X I	AXIS X-X S	AXIS X-X r	AXIS Y-Y I	AXIS Y-Y S	AXIS Y-Y r	x
In.	Lb.	In.²	In.	In.	In.	In.	In.⁴	In.³	In.	In.⁴	In.³	in.	in.
*18 x 4	58.0	16.98	18.00	4.200	.625	.700	670.7	74.5	6.29	18.5	5.6	1.04	.88
	51.9	15.18	18.00	4.100	.625	.600	622.1	69.1	6.40	17.1	5.3	1.06	.87
	45.8	13.38	18.00	4.000	.625	.500	573.5	63.7	6.55	15.8	5.1	1.09	.89
	42.7	12.48	18.00	3.950	.625	.450	549.2	61.0	6.64	15.0	4.9	1.10	.90
15 x 3⅜	50.0	14.64	15.00	3.716	.650	.716	401.4	53.6	5.24	11.2	3.8	.87	.80
	40.0	11.70	15.00	3.520	.650	.520	346.3	46.2	5.44	9.3	3.4	.89	.78
	33.9	9.90	15.00	3.400	.650	.400	312.6	41.7	5.62	8.2	3.2	.91	.79
12 x 3	30.0	8.79	12.00	3.170	.501	.510	161.2	26.9	4.28	5.2	2.1	.77	.68
	25.0	7.32	12.00	3.047	.501	.387	143.5	23.9	4.43	4.5	1.9	.79	.68
	20.7	6.03	12.00	2.940	.501	.280	128.1	21.4	4.61	3.9	1.7	.81	.70
10 x 2⅝	30.0	8.80	10.00	3.033	.436	.673	103.0	20.6	3.42	4.0	1.7	.67	.65
	25.0	7.33	10.00	2.886	.436	.526	90.7	18.1	3.52	3.4	1.5	.68	.62
	20.0	5.86	10.00	2.739	.436	.379	78.5	15.7	3.66	2.8	1.3	.70	.61
	15.3	4.47	10.00	2.600	.436	.240	66.9	13.4	3.87	2.3	1.2	.72	.64
9 x 2½	20.0	5.86	9.00	2.648	.413	.448	60.6	13.5	3.22	2.4	1.2	.65	.59
	15.0	4.39	9.00	2.485	.413	.285	50.7	11.3	3.40	1.9	1.0	.67	.59
	13.4	3.89	9.00	2.430	.413	.230	47.3	10.5	3.49	1.8	.97	.67	.61
8 x 2¼	18.75	5.49	8.00	2.527	.390	.487	43.7	10.9	2.82	2.0	1.0	.60	.57
	13.75	4.02	8.00	2.343	.390	.303	35.8	9.0	2.99	1.5	.86	.62	.56
	11.5	3.36	8.00	2.260	.390	.220	32.3	8.1	3.10	1.3	.79	.63	.58
7 x 2⅛	14.75	4.32	7.00	2.299	.366	.419	27.1	7.7	2.51	1.4	.79	.57	.53
	12.25	3.58	7.00	2.194	.366	.314	24.1	6.9	2.59	1.2	.71	.58	.53
	9.8	2.85	7.00	2.090	.366	.210	21.1	6.0	2.72	.98	.63	.59	.55
6 x 2	13.0	3.81	6.00	2.157	.343	.437	17.3	5.8	2.13	1.1	.65	.53	.52
	10.5	3.07	6.00	2.034	.343	.314	15.1	5.0	2.22	.87	.57	.53	.50
	8.2	2.39	6.00	1.920	.343	.200	13.0	4.3	2.34	.70	.50	.54	.52
5 x 1¾	9.0	2.63	5.00	1.885	.320	.325	8.8	3.5	1.83	.64	.45	.49	.48
	6.7	1.95	5.00	1.750	.320	.190	7.4	3.0	1.95	.48	.38	.50	.49
4 x 1⅝	7.25	2.12	4.00	1.720	.296	.320	4.5	2.3	1.47	.44	.35	.46	.46
	5.4	1.56	4.00	1.580	.296	.180	3.8	1.9	1.56	.32	.29	.45	.46
3 x 1½	6.0	1.75	3.00	1.596	.273	.356	2.1	1.4	1.08	.31	.27	.42	.46
	5.0	1.46	3.00	1.498	.273	.258	1.8	1.2	1.12	.25	.24	.41	.44
	4.1	1.19	3.00	1.410	.273	.170	1.6	1.1	1.17	.20	.21	.41	.44

$f = \frac{M}{S}$

REGULAR SERIES

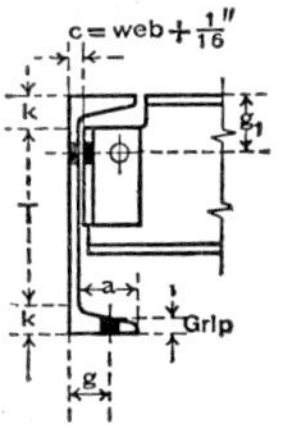

AMERICAN STANDARD CHANNELS

DIMENSIONS FOR DETAILING

Depth of Section	Weight per Foot	Flange		Web		Distance					Grip	Max. Flange Rivet	Usual Gage
		Width	Mean Thickness	Thickness	Half Thickness	a	T	k	g_1	c			g
In.	Lb.	In.	In.	In.	In.	In.	In.	In.	In.	In.	In.	In.	In.
*18	58.0	4 1/4	5/8	11/16	3/8	3 1/2	15 3/8	1 5/16	2 3/4	3/4	5/8	1	2 1/2
	51.9	4 1/8	5/8	5/8	5/16	3 1/2	15 3/8	1 5/16	2 3/4	11/16	5/8	1	2 1/2
	45.8	4	5/8	1/2	1/4	3 1/2	15 3/8	1 5/16	2 3/4	9/16	5/8	1	2 1/2
	42.7	4	5/8	7/16	1/4	3 1/2	15 3/8	1 5/16	2 3/4	1/2	5/8	1	2 1/2
15	50.0	3 3/4	5/8	3/4	3/8	3	12 3/8	1 5/16	2 3/4	13/16	5/8	1	2 1/4
	40.0	3 1/2	5/8	9/16	1/4	3	12 3/8	1 5/16	2 3/4	5/8	5/8	1	2
	33.9	3 3/8	5/8	7/16	3/16	3	12 3/8	1 5/16	2 3/4	1/2	5/8	1	2
12	30.0	3 1/8	1/2	1/2	1/4	2 5/8	9 7/8	1 1/16	2 1/2	9/16	1/2	7/8	1 3/4
	25.0	3	1/2	3/8	3/16	2 5/8	9 7/8	1 1/16	2 1/2	7/16	1/2	7/8	1 3/4
	20.7	3	1/2	5/16	1/8	2 5/8	9 7/8	1 1/16	2 1/2	3/8	1/2	7/8	1 3/4
10	30.0	3	7/16	11/16	3/8	2 3/8	8 1/8	15/16	2 1/2	3/4	7/16	3/4	1 3/4
	25.0	2 7/8	7/16	9/16	1/4	2 3/8	8 1/8	15/16	2 1/2	5/8	7/16	3/4	1 3/4
	20.0	2 3/4	7/16	3/8	3/16	2 3/8	8 1/8	15/16	2 1/2	7/16	7/16	3/4	1 1/2
	15.3	2 5/8	7/16	1/4	1/8	2 3/8	8 1/8	15/16	2 1/2	5/16	7/16	3/4	1 1/2
9	20.0	2 5/8	7/16	7/16	1/4	2 1/4	7 1/4	7/8	2 1/2	1/2	7/16	3/4	1 1/2
	15.0	2 1/2	7/16	5/16	3/16	2 1/4	7 1/4	7/8	2 1/2	3/8	7/16	3/4	1 3/8
	13.4	2 3/8	7/16	1/4	1/8	2 1/4	7 1/4	7/8	2 1/2	5/16	3/8	3/4	1 3/8
8	18.75	2 1/2	3/8	1/2	1/4	2	6 3/8	13/16	2 1/4	9/16	3/8	3/4	1 1/2
	13.75	2 3/8	3/8	5/16	3/16	2	6 3/8	13/16	2 1/4	3/8	3/8	3/4	1 3/8
	11.5	2 1/4	3/8	1/4	1/8	2	6 3/8	13/16	2 1/4	5/16	3/8	3/4	1 3/8
7	14.75	2 1/4	3/8	7/16	1/4	1 7/8	5 3/8	13/16	2	1/2	3/8	5/8	1 1/4
	12.25	2 1/4	3/8	5/16	3/16	1 7/8	5 3/8	13/16	2	3/8	3/8	5/8	1 1/4
	9.8	2 1/8	3/8	1/4	1/8	1 7/8	5 3/8	13/16	2	5/16	3/8	5/8	1 1/4
6	13.0	2 1/8	3/8	7/16	1/4	1 3/4	4 1/2	3/4	2	1/2	5/16	5/8	1 3/8
	10.5	2	3/8	5/16	3/16	1 3/4	4 1/2	3/4	2	3/8	3/8	5/8	1 1/8
	8.2	1 7/8	3/8	3/16	1/8	1 3/4	4 1/2	3/4	2	1/4	5/16	5/8	1 1/8
5	9.0	1 7/8	5/16	5/16	3/16	1 1/2	3 5/8	11/16	2	3/8	5/16	1/2	1 1/8
	6.7	1 3/4	5/16	3/16	1/8	1 1/2	3 5/8	11/16	2	1/4	5/16	1/2	1 1/8
4	7.25	1 3/4	5/16	5/16	3/16	1 3/8	2 3/4	5/8	2	3/8	5/16	1/2	1
	5.4	1 5/8	3/16	5/16	1/8	1 3/8	2 3/4	5/8	2	1/4	1/4	1/2	1
3	6.0	1 5/8	1/4	3/8	3/16	1 1/4	1 3/4	5/8		7/16	5/16	1/2	7/8
	5.0	1 1/2	1/4	1/4	1/8	1 1/4	1 3/4	5/8		5/16	1/4	1/2	7/8
	4.1	1 3/8	1/4	3/16	1/8	1 1/4	1 3/4	5/8		1/4	1/4		

ROLLED STEEL SHAPES

ANGLES
EQUAL LEGS
PROPERTIES FOR DESIGNING

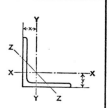

Size	Thickness	Weight per Foot	Area	AXIS X-X AND AXIS Y-Y				AXIS Z-Z
				I	S	r	x or y	r
In.	In	Lb.	In.²	In.⁴	In.³	In.	In.	In.
8 x 8	1⅛	56.9	16.73	98.0	17.5	2.42	2.41	1.56
	1	51.0	15.00	89.0	15.8	2.44	2.37	1.56
	⅞	45.0	13.23	79.6	14.0	2.45	2.32	1.57
	¾	38.9	11.44	69.7	12.2	2.47	2.28	1.57
	⅝	32.7	9.61	59.4	10.3	2.49	2.23	1.58
	⁹⁄₁₆	29.6	8.68	54.1	9.3	2.50	2.21	1.58
	½	26.4	7.75	48.6	8.4	2.50	2.19	1.59
6 x 6	1	37.4	11.00	35.5	8.6	1.80	1.86	1.17
	⅞	33.1	9.73	31.9	7.6	1.81	1.82	1.17
	¾	28.7	8.44	28.2	6.7	1.83	1.78	1.17
	⅝	24.2	7.11	24.2	5.7	1.84	1.73	1.18
	⁹⁄₁₆	21.9	6.43	22.1	5.1	1.85	1.71	1.18
	½	19.6	5.75	19.9	4.6	1.86	1.68	1.18
	⁷⁄₁₆	17.2	5.06	17.7	4.1	1.87	1.66	1.19
	⅜	14.9	4.36	15.4	3.5	1.88	1.64	1.19
	⁵⁄₁₆	12.5	3.66	13.0	3.0	1.89	1.61	1.19
5 x 5	⅞	27.2	7.98	17.8	5.2	1.49	1.57	.97
	¾	23.6	6.94	15.7	4.5	1.51	1.52	.97
	⅝	20.0	5.86	13.6	3.9	1.52	1.48	.98
	½	16.2	4.75	11.3	3.2	1.54	1.43	.98
	⁷⁄₁₆	14.3	4.18	10.0	2.8	1.55	1.41	.98
	⅜	12.3	3.61	8.7	2.4	1.56	1.39	.99
	⁵⁄₁₆	10.3	3.03	7.4	2.0	1.57	1.37	.99
4 x 4	¾	18.5	5.44	7.7	2.8	1.19	1.27	.78
	⅝	15.7	4.61	6.7	2.4	1.20	1.23	.78
	½	12.8	3.75	5.6	2.0	1.22	1.18	.78
	⁷⁄₁₆	11.3	3.31	5.0	1.8	1.23	1.16	.78
	⅜	9.8	2.86	4.4	1.5	1.23	1.14	.79
	⁵⁄₁₆	8.2	2.40	3.7	1.3	1.24	1.12	.79
	¼	6.6	1.94	3.0	1.1	1.25	1.09	.80

REGULAR SERIES

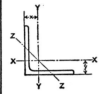

ANGLES
EQUAL LEGS
PROPERTIES FOR DESIGNING

Size	Thickness	Weight per Foot	Area	AXIS X-X AND AXIS Y-Y				AXIS Z-Z
				I	S	r	x or y	r
In.	In.	Lb.	In.²	In.⁴	In.³	In.	In.	In.
3½ x 3½	½	11.1	3.25	3.6	1.5	1.06	1.06	.68
	7⁄16	9.8	2.87	3.3	1.3	1.07	1.04	.68
	3⁄8	8.5	2.48	2.9	1.2	1.07	1.01	.69
	5⁄16	7.2	2.09	2.5	.98	1.08	.99	.69
	¼	5.8	1.69	2.0	.79	1.09	.97	.69
3 x 3	½	9.4	2.75	2.2	1.1	.90	.93	.58
	7⁄16	8.3	2.43	2.0	.95	.91	.91	.58
	3⁄8	7.2	2.11	1.8	.83	.91	.89	.58
	5⁄16	6.1	1.78	1.5	.71	.92	.87	.59
	¼	4.9	1.44	1.2	.58	.93	.84	.59
	3⁄16	3.71	1.09	.96	.44	.94	.82	.59
2½ x 2½	½	7.7	2.25	1.2	.72	.74	.81	.49
	3⁄8	5.9	1.73	.98	.57	.75	.76	.49
	5⁄16	5.0	1.47	.85	.48	.76	.74	.49
	¼	4.1	1.19	.70	.39	.77	.72	.49
	3⁄16	3.07	.90	.55	.30	.78	.69	.49
2 x 2	3⁄8	4.7	1.36	.48	.35	.59	.64	.39
	5⁄16	3.92	1.15	.42	.30	.60	.61	.39
	¼	3.19	.94	.35	.25	.61	.59	.39
	3⁄16	2.44	.71	.27	.19	.62	.57	.39
	1⁄8	1.65	.48	.19	.13	.63	.55	.40
1¾ x 1¾	¼	2.77	.81	.23	.19	.53	.53	.34
	3⁄16	2.12	.62	.18	.14	.54	.51	.34
	1⁄8	1.44	.42	.13	.10	.55	.48	.35
1½ x 1½	¼	2.34	.69	.14	.13	.45	.47	.29
	3⁄16	1.80	.53	.11	.10	.46	.44	.29
	1⁄8	1.23	.36	.08	.07	.47	.42	.30
1¼ x 1¼	¼	1.92	.56	.08	.09	.37	.40	.24
	3⁄16	1.48	.43	.06	.07	.38	.38	.24
	1⁄8	1.01	.30	.04	.05	.38	.36	.25
1 x 1	¼	1.49	.44	.04	.06	.29	.34	.20
	3⁄16	1.16	.34	.03	.04	.30	.32	.19
	1⁄8	.80	.23	.02	.03	.30	.30	.20

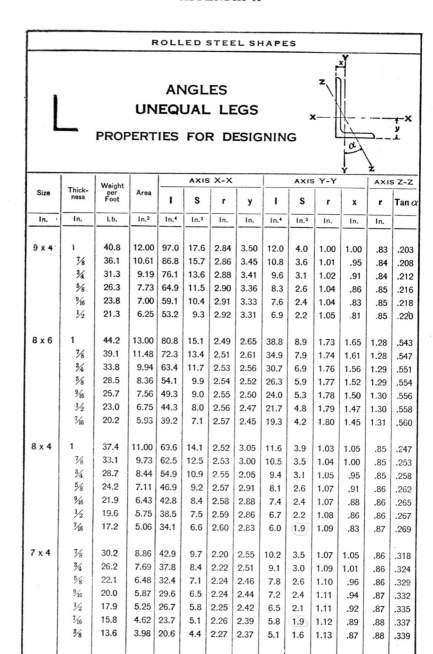

ROLLED STEEL SHAPES

ANGLES
UNEQUAL LEGS
PROPERTIES FOR DESIGNING

Size	Thickness	Weight per Foot	Area	AXIS X-X				AXIS Y-Y				AXIS Z-Z	
				I	S	r	y	I	S	r	x	r	Tan α
In.	In.	Lb.	In.²	In.⁴	In.³	In.	In.	In.⁴	In.³	In.	In.	In.	
9 x 4	1	40.8	12.00	97.0	17.6	2.84	3.50	12.0	4.0	1.00	1.00	.83	.203
	⅞	36.1	10.61	86.8	15.7	2.86	3.45	10.8	3.6	1.01	.95	.84	.208
	¾	31.3	9.19	76.1	13.6	2.88	3.41	9.6	3.1	1.02	.91	.84	.212
	⅝	26.3	7.73	64.9	11.5	2.90	3.36	8.3	2.6	1.04	.86	.85	.216
	⁹⁄₁₆	23.8	7.00	59.1	10.4	2.91	3.33	7.6	2.4	1.04	.83	.85	.218
	½	21.3	6.25	53.2	9.3	2.92	3.31	6.9	2.2	1.05	.81	.85	.220
8 x 6	1	44.2	13.00	80.8	15.1	2.49	2.65	38.8	8.9	1.73	1.65	1.28	.543
	⅞	39.1	11.48	72.3	13.4	2.51	2.61	34.9	7.9	1.74	1.61	1.28	.547
	¾	33.8	9.94	63.4	11.7	2.53	2.56	30.7	6.9	1.76	1.56	1.29	.551
	⅝	28.5	8.36	54.1	9.9	2.54	2.52	26.3	5.9	1.77	1.52	1.29	.554
	⁹⁄₁₆	25.7	7.56	49.3	9.0	2.55	2.50	24.0	5.3	1.78	1.50	1.30	.556
	½	23.0	6.75	44.3	8.0	2.56	2.47	21.7	4.8	1.79	1.47	1.30	.558
	⁷⁄₁₆	20.2	5.93	39.2	7.1	2.57	2.45	19.3	4.2	1.80	1.45	1.31	.560
8 x 4	1	37.4	11.00	69.6	14.1	2.52	3.05	11.6	3.9	1.03	1.05	.85	.247
	⅞	33.1	9.73	62.5	12.5	2.53	3.00	10.5	3.5	1.04	1.00	.85	.253
	¾	28.7	8.44	54.9	10.9	2.55	2.95	9.4	3.1	1.05	.95	.85	.258
	⅝	24.2	7.11	46.9	9.2	2.57	2.91	8.1	2.6	1.07	.91	.86	.262
	⁹⁄₁₆	21.9	6.43	42.8	8.4	2.58	2.88	7.4	2.4	1.07	.88	.86	.265
	½	19.6	5.75	38.5	7.5	2.59	2.86	6.7	2.2	1.08	.86	.86	.267
	⁷⁄₁₆	17.2	5.06	34.1	6.6	2.60	2.83	6.0	1.9	1.09	.83	.87	.269
7 x 4	⅞	30.2	8.86	42.9	9.7	2.20	2.55	10.2	3.5	1.07	1.05	.86	.318
	¾	26.2	7.69	37.8	8.4	2.22	2.51	9.1	3.0	1.09	1.01	.86	.324
	⅝	22.1	6.48	32.4	7.1	2.24	2.46	7.8	2.6	1.10	.96	.86	.329
	⁹⁄₁₆	20.0	5.87	29.6	6.5	2.24	2.44	7.2	2.4	1.11	.94	.87	.332
	½	17.9	5.25	26.7	5.8	2.25	2.42	6.5	2.1	1.11	.92	.87	.335
	⁷⁄₁₆	15.8	4.62	23.7	5.1	2.26	2.39	5.8	1.9	1.12	.89	.88	.337
	⅜	13.6	3.98	20.6	4.4	2.27	2.37	5.1	1.6	1.13	.87	.88	.339

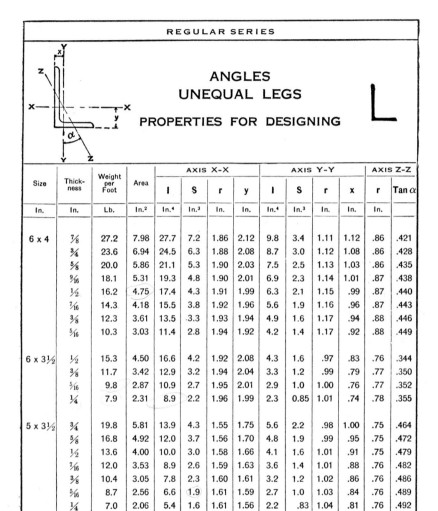

				AXIS X-X				AXIS Y-Y				AXIS Z-Z	
Size	Thick-ness	Weight per Foot	Area	I	S	r	y	I	S	r	x	r	Tan α
In.	In.	Lb.	In.²	In.⁴	In.³	In.	In.	In.⁴	In.³	In.	In.	In.	
6 x 4	⅞	27.2	7.98	27.7	7.2	1.86	2.12	9.8	3.4	1.11	1.12	.86	.421
	¾	23.6	6.94	24.5	6.3	1.88	2.08	8.7	3.0	1.12	1.08	.86	.428
	⅝	20.0	5.86	21.1	5.3	1.90	2.03	7.5	2.5	1.13	1.03	.86	.435
	⁹⁄₁₆	18.1	5.31	19.3	4.8	1.90	2.01	6.9	2.3	1.14	1.01	.87	.438
	½	16.2	4.75	17.4	4.3	1.91	1.99	6.3	2.1	1.15	.99	.87	.440
	⁷⁄₁₆	14.3	4.18	15.5	3.8	1.92	1.96	5.6	1.9	1.16	.96	.87	.443
	⅜	12.3	3.61	13.5	3.3	1.93	1.94	4.9	1.6	1.17	.94	.88	.446
	⁵⁄₁₆	10.3	3.03	11.4	2.8	1.94	1.92	4.2	1.4	1.17	.92	.88	.449
6 x 3½	½	15.3	4.50	16.6	4.2	1.92	2.08	4.3	1.6	.97	.83	.76	.344
	⅜	11.7	3.42	12.9	3.2	1.94	2.04	3.3	1.2	.99	.79	.77	.350
	⁵⁄₁₆	9.8	2.87	10.9	2.7	1.95	2.01	2.9	1.0	1.00	.76	.77	.352
	¼	7.9	2.31	8.9	2.2	1.96	1.99	2.3	0.85	1.01	.74	.78	.355
5 x 3½	¾	19.8	5.81	13.9	4.3	1.55	1.75	5.6	2.2	.98	1.00	.75	.464
	⅝	16.8	4.92	12.0	3.7	1.56	1.70	4.8	1.9	.99	.95	.75	.472
	½	13.6	4.00	10.0	3.0	1.58	1.66	4.1	1.6	1.01	.91	.75	.479
	⁷⁄₁₆	12.0	3.53	8.9	2.6	1.59	1.63	3.6	1.4	1.01	.88	.76	.482
	⅜	10.4	3.05	7.8	2.3	1.60	1.61	3.2	1.2	1.02	.86	.76	.486
	⁵⁄₁₆	8.7	2.56	6.6	1.9	1.61	1.59	2.7	1.0	1.03	.84	.76	.489
	¼	7.0	2.06	5.4	1.6	1.61	1.56	2.2	.83	1.04	.81	.76	.492
5 x 3	½	12.8	3.75	9.5	2.9	1.59	1.75	2.6	1.1	.83	.75	.65	.357
	⁷⁄₁₆	11.3	3.31	8.4	2.6	1.60	1.73	2.3	1.0	.84	.73	.65	.361
	⅜	9.8	2.86	7.4	2.2	1.61	1.70	2.0	.89	.84	.70	.65	.364
	⁵⁄₁₆	8.2	2.40	6.3	1.9	1.61	1.68	1.8	.75	.85	.68	.66	.368
	¼	6.6	1.94	5.1	1.5	1.62	1.66	1.4	.61	.86	.66	.66	.371

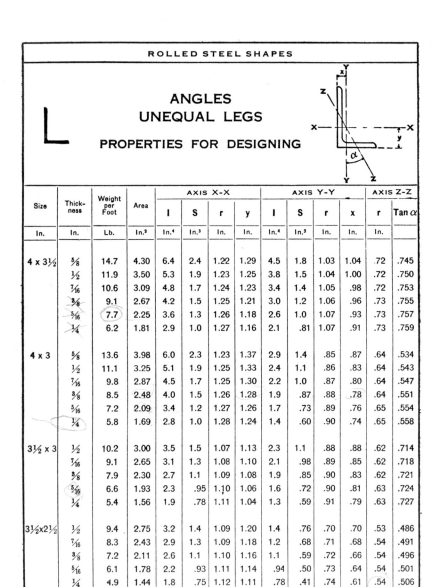

				AXIS X-X				AXIS Y-Y				AXIS Z-Z	
Size	Thick-ness	Weight per Foot	Area	I	S	r	y	I	S	r	x	r	Tan α
In.	In.	Lb.	In.²	In.⁴	In.³	In.	In.	In.⁴	In.³	In.	In.	In.	
4 x 3½	⅝	14.7	4.30	6.4	2.4	1.22	1.29	4.5	1.8	1.03	1.04	.72	.745
	½	11.9	3.50	5.3	1.9	1.23	1.25	3.8	1.5	1.04	1.00	.72	.750
	⁷⁄₁₆	10.6	3.09	4.8	1.7	1.24	1.23	3.4	1.4	1.05	.98	.72	.753
	⅜	9.1	2.67	4.2	1.5	1.25	1.21	3.0	1.2	1.06	.96	.73	.755
	⁵⁄₁₆	7.7	2.25	3.6	1.3	1.26	1.18	2.6	1.0	1.07	.93	.73	.757
	¼	6.2	1.81	2.9	1.0	1.27	1.16	2.1	.81	1.07	.91	.73	.759
4 x 3	⅝	13.6	3.98	6.0	2.3	1.23	1.37	2.9	1.4	.85	.87	.64	.534
	½	11.1	3.25	5.1	1.9	1.25	1.33	2.4	1.1	.86	.83	.64	.543
	⁷⁄₁₆	9.8	2.87	4.5	1.7	1.25	1.30	2.2	1.0	.87	.80	.64	.547
	⅜	8.5	2.48	4.0	1.5	1.26	1.28	1.9	.87	.88	.78	.64	.551
	⁵⁄₁₆	7.2	2.09	3.4	1.2	1.27	1.26	1.7	.73	.89	.76	.65	.554
	¼	5.8	1.69	2.8	1.0	1.28	1.24	1.4	.60	.90	.74	.65	.558
3½ x 3	½	10.2	3.00	3.5	1.5	1.07	1.13	2.3	1.1	.88	.88	.62	.714
	⁷⁄₁₆	9.1	2.65	3.1	1.3	1.08	1.10	2.1	.98	.89	.85	.62	.718
	⅜	7.9	2.30	2.7	1.1	1.09	1.08	1.9	.85	.90	.83	.62	.721
	⁵⁄₁₆	6.6	1.93	2.3	.95	1.10	1.06	1.6	.72	.90	.81	.63	.724
	¼	5.4	1.56	1.9	.78	1.11	1.04	1.3	.59	.91	.79	.63	.727
3½x2½	½	9.4	2.75	3.2	1.4	1.09	1.20	1.4	.76	.70	.70	.53	.486
	⁷⁄₁₆	8.3	2.43	2.9	1.3	1.09	1.18	1.2	.68	.71	.68	.54	.491
	⅜	7.2	2.11	2.6	1.1	1.10	1.16	1.1	.59	.72	.66	.54	.496
	⁵⁄₁₆	6.1	1.78	2.2	.93	1.11	1.14	.94	.50	.73	.64	.54	.501
	¼	4.9	1.44	1.8	.75	1.12	1.11	.78	.41	.74	.61	.54	.506

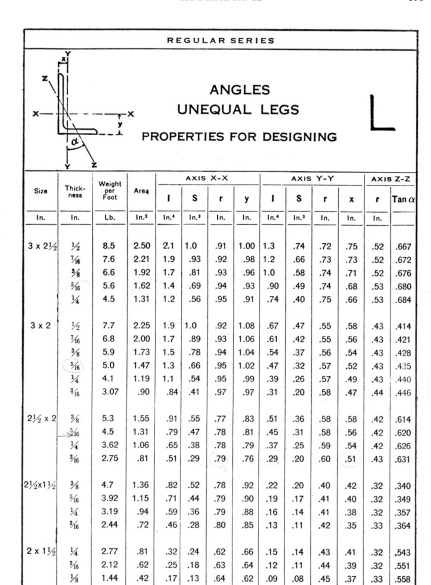

REGULAR SERIES

ANGLES

UNEQUAL LEGS

PROPERTIES FOR DESIGNING

Size	Thick-ness	Weight per Foot	Area	AXIS X-X				AXIS Y-Y				AXIS Z-Z	
				I	S	r	y	I	S	r	x	r	Tan α
In.	In.	Lb.	In.²	In.⁴	In.³	In.	In.	In.⁴	In.³	In.	In.	In.	
3 x 2½	½	8.5	2.50	2.1	1.0	.91	1.00	1.3	.74	.72	.75	.52	.667
	⁷⁄₁₆	7.6	2.21	1.9	.93	.92	.98	1.2	.66	.73	.73	.52	.672
	⅜	6.6	1.92	1.7	.81	.93	.96	1.0	.58	.74	.71	.52	.676
	⁵⁄₁₆	5.6	1.62	1.4	.69	.94	.93	.90	.49	.74	.68	.53	.680
	¼	4.5	1.31	1.2	.56	.95	.91	.74	.40	.75	.66	.53	.684
3 x 2	½	7.7	2.25	1.9	1.0	.92	1.08	.67	.47	.55	.58	.43	.414
	⁷⁄₁₆	6.8	2.00	1.7	.89	.93	1.06	.61	.42	.55	.56	.43	.421
	⅜	5.9	1.73	1.5	.78	.94	1.04	.54	.37	.56	.54	.43	.428
	⁵⁄₁₆	5.0	1.47	1.3	.66	.95	1.02	.47	.32	.57	.52	.43	.435
	¼	4.1	1.19	1.1	.54	.95	.99	.39	.26	.57	.49	.43	.440
	³⁄₁₆	3.07	.90	.84	.41	.97	.97	.31	.20	.58	.47	.44	.446
2½ x 2	⅜	5.3	1.55	.91	.55	.77	.83	.51	.36	.58	.58	.42	.614
	⁵⁄₁₆	4.5	1.31	.79	.47	.78	.81	.45	.31	.58	.56	.42	.620
	¼	3.62	1.06	.65	.38	.78	.79	.37	.25	.59	.54	.42	.626
	³⁄₁₆	2.75	.81	.51	.29	.79	.76	.29	.20	.60	.51	.43	.631
2½x1½	⅜	4.7	1.36	.82	.52	.78	.92	.22	.20	.40	.42	.32	.340
	⁵⁄₁₆	3.92	1.15	.71	.44	.79	.90	.19	.17	.41	.40	.32	.349
	¼	3.19	.94	.59	.36	.79	.88	.16	.14	.41	.38	.32	.357
	³⁄₁₆	2.44	.72	.46	.28	.80	.85	.13	.11	.42	.35	.33	.364
2 x 1½	¼	2.77	.81	.32	.24	.62	.66	.15	.14	.43	.41	.32	.543
	³⁄₁₆	2.12	.62	.25	.18	.63	.64	.12	.11	.44	.39	.32	.551
	⅛	1.44	.42	.17	.13	.64	.62	.09	.08	.45	.37	.33	.558
1¾x1¼	¼	2.34	.69	.20	.18	.54	.60	.09	.10	.35	.35	.27	.486
	³⁄₁₆	1.80	.53	.16	.14	.55	.58	.07	.08	.36	.33	.27	.496
	⅛	1.23	.36	.11	.09	.56	.56	.05	.05	.37	.31	.27	.506

APPENDIX B

TABLES

TABLE 1

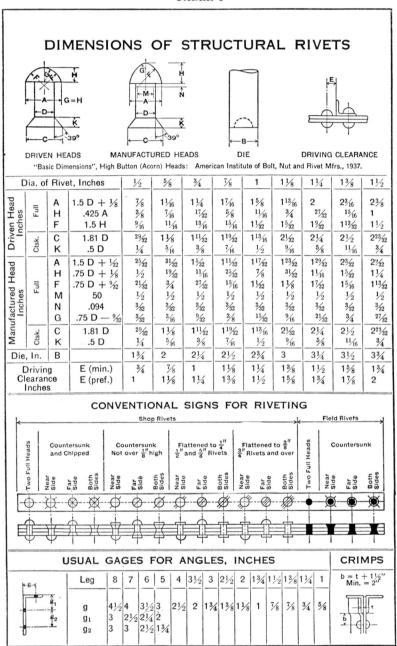

DIMENSIONS OF STRUCTURAL RIVETS

DRIVEN HEADS	MANUFACTURED HEADS	DIE	DRIVING CLEARANCE

"Basic Dimensions", High Button (Acorn) Heads: American Institute of Bolt, Nut and Rivet Mfrs., 1937.

Dia. of Rivet, Inches				$\frac{1}{2}$	$\frac{5}{8}$	$\frac{3}{4}$	$\frac{7}{8}$	1	$1\frac{1}{8}$	$1\frac{1}{4}$	$1\frac{3}{8}$	$1\frac{1}{2}$
Driven Head Inches	Full	A	1.5 D + $\frac{1}{8}$	$\frac{7}{8}$	$1\frac{1}{16}$	$1\frac{1}{4}$	$1\frac{7}{16}$	$1\frac{5}{8}$	$1\frac{13}{16}$	2	$2\frac{3}{16}$	$2\frac{3}{8}$
		H	.425 A	$\frac{3}{8}$	$\frac{7}{16}$	$\frac{17}{32}$	$\frac{5}{8}$	$\frac{11}{16}$	$\frac{25}{32}$	$\frac{3}{4}$	$\frac{27}{32}$	$\frac{15}{16}$	1
		F	1.5 H	$\frac{9}{16}$	$\frac{11}{16}$	$\frac{13}{16}$	$\frac{15}{16}$	$1\frac{1}{32}$	$1\frac{5}{32}$	$1\frac{9}{32}$	$1\frac{13}{32}$	$1\frac{1}{2}$
	Ctsk.	C	1.81 D	$\frac{29}{32}$	$1\frac{1}{8}$	$1\frac{11}{32}$	$1\frac{19}{32}$	$1\frac{13}{16}$	$2\frac{1}{32}$	$2\frac{1}{4}$	$2\frac{1}{2}$	$2\frac{23}{32}$
		K	.5 D	$\frac{1}{4}$	$\frac{5}{16}$	$\frac{3}{8}$	$\frac{7}{16}$	$\frac{1}{2}$	$\frac{9}{16}$	$\frac{5}{8}$	$\frac{11}{16}$	$\frac{3}{4}$
Manufactured Head Inches	Full	A	1.5 D + $\frac{1}{32}$	$\frac{25}{32}$	$\frac{31}{32}$	$1\frac{5}{32}$	$1\frac{11}{32}$	$1\frac{17}{32}$	$1\frac{23}{32}$	$1\frac{29}{32}$	$2\frac{3}{32}$	$2\frac{9}{32}$
		H	.75 D + $\frac{1}{8}$	$\frac{1}{2}$	$\frac{19}{32}$	$\frac{11}{16}$	$\frac{25}{32}$	$\frac{7}{8}$	$\frac{31}{32}$	$1\frac{1}{16}$	$1\frac{5}{32}$	$1\frac{1}{4}$
		F	.75 D + $\frac{9}{32}$	$\frac{21}{32}$	$\frac{3}{4}$	$\frac{27}{32}$	$\frac{15}{16}$	$1\frac{1}{32}$	$1\frac{1}{8}$	$1\frac{7}{32}$	$1\frac{5}{16}$	$1\frac{13}{32}$
		M	50	$\frac{1}{2}$	$\frac{1}{2}$	$\frac{1}{2}$	$\frac{1}{2}$	$\frac{1}{2}$	$\frac{1}{2}$	$\frac{1}{2}$	$\frac{1}{2}$	$\frac{1}{2}$
		N	.094	$\frac{3}{32}$	$\frac{3}{32}$	$\frac{3}{32}$	$\frac{3}{32}$	$\frac{3}{32}$	$\frac{3}{32}$	$\frac{3}{32}$	$\frac{3}{32}$	$\frac{3}{32}$
		G	.75 D − $\frac{9}{32}$	$\frac{3}{32}$	$\frac{3}{16}$	$\frac{9}{32}$	$\frac{3}{8}$	$\frac{15}{32}$	$\frac{9}{16}$	$\frac{21}{32}$	$\frac{3}{4}$	$\frac{27}{32}$
	Ctsk.	C	1.81 D	$\frac{29}{32}$	$1\frac{1}{8}$	$1\frac{11}{32}$	$1\frac{19}{32}$	$1\frac{13}{16}$	$2\frac{1}{32}$	$2\frac{1}{4}$	$2\frac{1}{2}$	$2\frac{23}{32}$
		K	.5 D	$\frac{1}{4}$	$\frac{5}{16}$	$\frac{3}{8}$	$\frac{7}{16}$	$\frac{1}{2}$	$\frac{9}{16}$	$\frac{5}{8}$	$\frac{11}{16}$	$\frac{3}{4}$
Die, In.		B		$1\frac{3}{4}$	2	$2\frac{1}{4}$	$2\frac{1}{2}$	$2\frac{3}{4}$	3	$3\frac{1}{4}$	$3\frac{1}{2}$	$3\frac{3}{4}$
Driving Clearance Inches		E (min.)		$\frac{3}{4}$	$\frac{7}{8}$	1	$1\frac{1}{8}$	$1\frac{1}{4}$	$1\frac{3}{8}$	$1\frac{1}{2}$	$1\frac{5}{8}$	$1\frac{3}{4}$
		E (pref.)		1	$1\frac{1}{8}$	$1\frac{1}{4}$	$1\frac{3}{8}$	$1\frac{1}{2}$	$1\frac{5}{8}$	$1\frac{3}{4}$	$1\frac{7}{8}$	2

CONVENTIONAL SIGNS FOR RIVETING

Shop Rivets	Field Rivets

Two Full Heads	Countersunk and Chipped			Countersunk Not over $\frac{1}{8}''$ high			Flattened to $\frac{1}{4}''$ $\frac{1}{2}''$ and $\frac{5}{8}''$ Rivets			Flattened to $\frac{3}{8}''$ $\frac{3}{4}''$ Rivets and over			Two Full Heads	Countersunk		
	Near Side	Far Side	Both Sides	Near Side	Far Side	Both Sides	Near Side	Far Side	Both Sides	Near Side	Far Side	Both Sides		Near Side	Far Side	Both Sides

USUAL GAGES FOR ANGLES, INCHES | CRIMPS

Leg	8	7	6	5	4	$3\frac{1}{2}$	3	$2\frac{1}{2}$	2	$1\frac{3}{4}$	$1\frac{1}{2}$	$1\frac{3}{8}$	$1\frac{1}{4}$	1
g	$4\frac{1}{2}$	4	$3\frac{1}{2}$	3		$2\frac{1}{2}$	2	$1\frac{3}{4}$	$1\frac{3}{8}$	$1\frac{1}{8}$	1	$\frac{7}{8}$	$\frac{7}{8}$	$\frac{3}{4}$	$\frac{5}{8}$
g_1	3		$2\frac{1}{2}$	$2\frac{1}{4}$	2										
g_2	3		3		$2\frac{1}{2}$	$1\frac{3}{4}$									

CRIMPS: $b = t + 1\frac{1}{2}''$ Min. = $2''$

Courtesy of American Institute of Steel Construction.

TABLE 2

POWER DRIVEN RIVETS
(SHOP AND FIELD)
AND
TURNED BOLTS IN REAMED HOLES

ALLOWABLE LOADS IN KIPS

Shear .... 15,000 lbs. per square inch
Bearing: S. S. .... 32,000 " " " "
" D. S. .... 40,000 " " " "

Rivet Dia.		½		⅝		¾		⅞		1		1⅛		1¼	
Area		.1963		.3068		.4418		.6013		.7854		.9940		1.2272	
Single Shear		2.95		4.60		6.63		9.02		11.78		14.91		18.41	
Double Shear		5.89		9.20		13.25		18.04		23.56		29.82		36.82	
Thickness of Plate		Bearing		Bearing		Bearing		Bearing		Bearing		Bearing		Bearing	
		32.0	40.0	32.0	40.0	32.0	40.0	32.0	40.0	32.0	40.0	32.0	40.0	32.0	40.0
.125	⅛	2.00	2.50	2.50	3.12	3.00	3.75								
.140		2.24	2.80	2.80	3.50	3.36	4.20	3.92	4.90						
.160		2.56	3.20	3.20	4.00	3.84	4.80	4.48	5.60						
.180		2.88	3.60	3.60	4.50	4.32	5.40	5.04	6.30						
.1875	3/16	3.00	3.75	3.75	4.69	4.50	5.62	5.25	6.56						
.200		....	4.00	4.00	5.00	4.80	6.00	5.60	7.00	6.40	8.00				
.220		....	4.40	4.40	5.50	5.28	6.60	6.16	7.70	7.04	8.80				
.240		....	4.80	4.80	6.00	5.76	7.20	6.72	8.40	7.68	9.60				
.250	¼	....	5.00	....	6.25	6.00	7.50	7.00	8.75	8.00	10.0				
.260		....	5.20	....	6.50	6.24	7.80	7.28	9.10	8.32	10.4	9.36	11.7		
.280		....	5.60	....	7.00	6.72	8.40	7.84	9.80	8.96	11.2	10.1	12.6		
.300		....	6.00	....	7.50	....	9.00	8.40	10.5	9.60	12.0	10.8	13.5		
.3125	5/16	....	....	....	7.81	....	9.38	8.75	10.9	10.0	12.5	11.3	14.1		
.320		....	....	....	8.00	....	9.60	8.96	11.2	10.2	12.8	11.5	14.4	12.8	16.0
.340		....	....	....	8.50	....	10.2	....	11.9	10.9	13.6	12.2	15.3	13.6	17.0
.360		....	....	....	9.00	....	10.8	....	12.6	11.5	14.4	13.0	16.2	14.4	18.0
.375	⅜	....	....	....	9.38	....	11.3	....	13.1	12.0	15.0	13.5	16.9	15.0	18.8
.380		....	....	....	....	....	11.4	....	13.3	....	15.2	13.7	17.1	15.2	19.0
.400		....	....	....	....	....	12.0	....	14.0	....	16.0	14.4	18.0	16.0	20.0
.420		....	....	....	....	....	12.6	....	14.7	....	16.8	15.1	18.9	16.8	21.0
.4375	7/16	....	....	....	....	....	13.1	....	15.3	....	17.5	....	19.7	17.5	21.9
.440		....	....	....	....	....	....	....	15.4	....	17.6	....	19.8	17.6	22.0
.460		....	....	....	....	....	....	....	16.1	....	18.4	....	20.7	18.4	23.0
.480		....	....	....	....	....	....	....	16.8	....	19.2	....	21.6	....	24.0
.500	½	....	....	....	....	....	....	....	17.5	....	20.0	....	22.5	....	25.0
.520		....	....	....	....	....	....	....	18.2	....	20.8	....	23.4	....	26.0
.540		....	....	....	....	....	....	....	....	....	21.6	....	24.3	....	27.0
.560		....	....	....	....	....	....	....	....	....	22.4	....	25.2	....	28.0
.5625	9/16	....	....	....	....	....	....	....	....	....	22.5	....	25.3	....	28.1
.580		....	....	....	....	....	....	....	....	....	23.2	....	26.1	....	29.0
.600		....	....	....	....	....	....	....	....	....	24.0	....	27.0	....	30.0
.620		....	....	....	....	....	....	....	....	....	....	....	27.9	....	31.0
.625	⅝	....	....	....	....	....	....	....	....	....	....	....	28.1	....	31.3
.6875	11/16	....	....	....	....	....	....	....	....	....	....	....	30.9	....	34.4
.750	¾	....	....	....	....	....	....	....	....	....	....	....	....	....	37.5

Courtesy of American Institute of Steel Construction.

TABLE 3

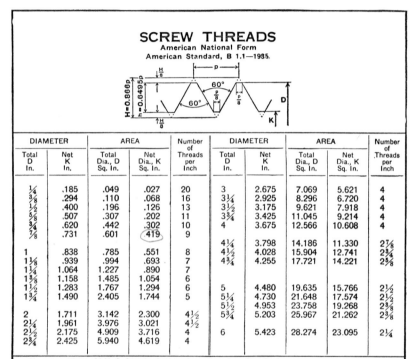

SCREW THREADS
American National Form
American Standard, B 1.1—1935.

DIAMETER		AREA		Number of Threads per Inch	DIAMETER		AREA		Number of Threads per Inch
Total D In.	Net K In.	Total Dia., D Sq. In.	Net Dia., K Sq. In.		Total D In.	Net K In.	Total Dia., D Sq. In.	Net Dia., K Sq. In.	
¼	.185	.049	.027	20	3	2.675	7.069	5.621	4
⅜	.294	.110	.068	16	3¼	2.925	8.296	6.720	4
½	.400	.196	.126	13	3½	3.175	9.621	7.918	4
⅝	.507	.307	.202	11	3¾	3.425	11.045	9.214	4
¾	.620	.442	.302	10	4	3.675	12.566	10.608	4
⅞	.731	.601	.419	9					
					4¼	3.798	14.186	11.330	2⅞
1	.838	.785	.551	8	4½	4.028	15.904	12.741	2¾
1⅛	.939	.994	.693	7	4¾	4.255	17.721	14.221	2⅝
1¼	1.064	1.227	.890	7					
1⅜	1.158	1.485	1.054	6					
1½	1.283	1.767	1.294	6	5	4.480	19.635	15.766	2½
1¾	1.490	2.405	1.744	5	5¼	4.730	21.648	17.574	2½
					5½	4.953	23.758	19.268	2⅜
2	1.711	3.142	2.300	4½	5¾	5.203	25.967	21.262	2⅜
2¼	1.961	3.976	3.021	4½					
2½	2.175	4.909	3.716	4	6	5.423	28.274	23.095	2¼
2¾	2.425	5.940	4.619	4					

Sizes over 4″ are old U. S. Standard; there is no American Standard.
Dimensions are maximum; specify "Free Fit—Class 2." For Bolts from 2½″ to 6″ diameter it is always necessary to bill the number of threads per inch.

Courtesy of American Institute of Steel Construction.

TABLE 4

WEIGHTS OF BUILDING MATERIALS

Materials	Weight Lb. per Sq. Ft.	Materials	Weight Lb. per Sq. Ft.
CEILINGS		**PARTITIONS**	
Gypsum ceiling block, 2″ thick, un-plastered	10	Channel studs, metal lath, cement plaster, solid, 2″ thick	20
Plaster board, unplastered	3	Studs, 2″ x 4″, wood or metal lath, ¾″ plaster both sides	18
Plaster, ¾″, and wood lath	8	Studs, 2″ x 4″ plaster board, ½″ plaster both sides	18
Plaster, ¾″, and metal lath	8	Plaster, ½″, on gypsum block or clay tile (one side)	4
Plaster, on tile or concrete	5	Hollow clay tile, 2″	13
Suspended, metal lath and plaster	10	Hollow clay tile, 3″	16
		Hollow clay tile, 4″	18
		Hollow clay tile, 5″	20
FLOORS		Hollow clay tile, 6″	25
		Hollow clay tile, 8″	30
Hardwood flooring, ⅞″ thick	4	Hollow clay tile, 10″	35
Sheathing, white, red and Oregon pine, spruce or hemlock, ⅞″ thick	2½	Hollow gypsum block, 3″	10
Sheathing, yellow pine, 1″ thick	4	Hollow gypsum block, 4″	13
Wood block, creosoted, 3″ thick	15	Hollow gypsum block, 5″	15½
Cement finish, per inch thick	12	Hollow gypsum block, 6″	16½
Cinder concrete, per inch thick	9	Solid gypsum block, 2″	9½
Cinder concrete fill, per inch thick	5	Solid gypsum block, 3″	13
Terrazzo, Tile, Mastic, Linoleum, per inch thick, including base	12	Steel partitions	4
Gypsum slab, per inch thick	5	**WALLS**	
		Brick, 9″ thick	84
		Brick, 13″ thick	121
		Brick, 18″ thick	168
ROOFS		Brick, 22″ thick	205
		Brick, 26″ thick	243
Corrugated metal	Page 143	Wall tile, 6″ thick	30
Roofing felt, 3 ply and gravel	5½	Wall tile, 8″ thick	33
Roofing felt, 5 ply and gravel	6½	Wall tile, 10″ thick	40
Roofing felt, 3 ply and slag	4½	Wall tile, 12″ thick	45
Roofing felt, 5 ply and slag	5½	Brick 4″, tile backing 4″	60
3-ply ready roofing	1	Brick 4″, tile backing 8″	75
Shingles, wood	2	Brick 9″, tile backing 4″	100
Tile or slate	5-20	Brick 9″, tile backing 8″	115
		Limestone 4″, brick 9″	140
		Limestone 4″, brick 13″	175
		Limestone 4″, tile 8″	90
		Limestone 4″, tile 12″	100
		Corrugated metal siding	Page 143
		Windows, glass, frame and sash	8

Courtesy of American Institute of Steel Construction.

TABLE 5

RECOMMENDED LIVE LOADS
FOR
STORAGE WAREHOUSES
United States Department of Commerce, National Bureau of Standards

Material	Weight per Cubic Foot of Space Lb.	Height of Pile Feet	Weight per Square Foot of Floor Lb.	Recommended Live Load Lb. per Sq. Foot
BUILDING MATERIALS				
Asbestos	50	6	300	
Bricks, Building	45	6	270	
Bricks, Fire Clay	75	6	450	
Cement, Natural	59	6	354	300
Cement, Portland	72 to 105	6	432 to 630	to
Gypsum	50	6	300	400
Lime and Plaster	53	5	265	
Tiles	50	6	300	
Woods, bulk	45	6	270	
DRUGS, PAINTS, OIL, ETC.				
Alum, Pearl, in barrels	33	6	198	
Bleaching Powder, in hogsheads	31	3½	102	
Blue Vitriol, in barrels	45	5	226	
Glycerine, in cases	52	6	312	
Linseed Oil, in barrels	36	6	216	
Linseed Oil, in iron drums	45	4	180	
Logwood Extract, in boxes	70	5	350	
Rosin, in barrels	48	6	288	
Shellac, Gum	38	6	228	200
Soaps	50	6	300	to
Soda Ash, in hogsheads	62	2¾	167	300
Soda, Caustic, in iron drums	88	3⅜	294	
Soda, Silicate, in barrels	53	6	318	
Sulphuric Acid	60	1⅝	100	
Toilet Articles	35	6	210	
Varnishes	55	6	330	
White Lead Paste, in cans	174	3½	610	
White Lead, dry	86	4¾	408	
Red Lead and Litharge, dry	132	3¾	495	
DRY GOODS, COTTON, WOOL, ETC.				
Burlap, in bales	43	6	258	
Carpets and Rugs	30	6	180	
Coir Yarn, in bales	33	8	264	
Cotton, in bales, American	30	8	240	
Cotton, in bales, Foreign	40	8	320	
Cotton Bleached Goods, in cases	28	8	224	
Cotton Flannel, in cases	12	8	96	
Cotton Sheeting, in cases	23	8	184	
Cotton Yarn, in cases	25	8	200	
Excelsior, compressed	19	8	152	200
Hemp, Italian, compressed	22	8	176	to
Hemp, Manila, compressed	30	8	240	250
Jute, compressed	41	8	328	
Linen Damask, in cases	50	5	250	
Linen Goods, in cases	30	8	240	
Linen Towels, in cases	40	6	240	
Silk and Silk Goods	45	8	360	
Sisal, compressed	21	8	168	
Tow, compressed	29	8	232	
Wool, in bales, compressed	48			
Wool, in bales, not compressed	13	8	104	
Wool, Worsteds, in cases	27	8	216	

Courtesy of American Institute of Steel Construction.

TABLE 5 *Continued*

RECOMMENDED LIVE LOADS
FOR
STORAGE WAREHOUSES

United States Department of Commerce, National Bureau of Standards

Material	Weight per Cubic Foot of Space Lb.	Height of Pile Feet	Weight per Square Foot of Floor Lb. •	Recommended Live Load Lb. per Sq. Ft.
GROCERIES, WINES, LIQUORS, ETC.				
Beans, in bags	40	8	320	
Beverages	40	8	320	
Canned Goods, in cases	58	6	348	
Cereals	45	8	360	
Cocoa	35	8	280	
Coffee, Roasted, in bags	33	8	264	
Coffee, Green, in bags	39	8	312	
Dates, in cases	55	6	330	
Figs, in cases	74	5	370	
Flour, in barrels	40	5	200	250
Fruits, Fresh	35	8	280	to
Meat and Meat Products	45	6	270	300
Milk, Condensed	50	6	300	
Molasses, in barrels	48	5	240	
Rice, in bags	58	6	348	
Sal Soda, in barrels	46	5	230	
Salt, in bags	70	5	350	
Soap Powder, in cases	38	8	304	
Starch, in barrels	25	6	150	
Sugar, in barrels	43	5	215	
Sugar, in cases	51	6	306	
Tea, in chests	25	8	200	
Wines and Liquors, in barrels	38	6	228	
HARDWARE, ETC				
Automobile Parts	40	8	320	
Chain	100	6	600	
Cutlery	45	8	360	
Door Checks	45	6	270	
Electrical Goods and Machinery	40	8	320	
Hinges	64	6	384	
Locks, in cases, packed	31	6	186	
Machinery, Light	20	8	160	
Plumbing, Fixtures	30	8	240	300
Plumbing, Supplies	55	6	330	to
Sash Fasteners	48	6	288	400
Screws	101	6	606	
Shafting Steel	125			
Sheet Tin, in boxes	278	2	556	
Tools, Small, Metal	75	6	450	
Wire Cables, on reels			425	
Wire, Insulated Copper, in coils	63	5	315	
Wire, Galvanized Iron, in coils	74	4½	333	
Wire, Magnet, on spools	75	6	450	
MISCELLANEOUS				
Automobile Tires	30	6	180	
Automobiles, uncrated	8		64	
Books (solidly packed)	65	6	390	
Furniture	20			
Glass and Chinaware, in crates	40	8	320	
Hides and Leather, in bales	20	8	160	
Hides, Buffalo, in bundles	37	8	296	
Leather and Leather Goods	40	8	320	
Paper, Newspaper, and Strawboards	35	6	210	
Paper, Writing and Calendared	60	6	360	
Rope, in coils	32	6	192	
Rubber, Crude	50	8	400	
Tobacco, bales	35	8	280	

Courtesy of American Institute of Steel Construction.

TABLE 6

MINIMUM DESIGN LOADS
IN BUILDINGS AND OTHER STRUCTURES

UNIFORMLY DISTRIBUTED FLOOR LOADS

The live loads assumed for purposes of design shall be the greatest loads that probably will be produced by the intended occupancies or uses, provided that the live loads to be considered as uniformly distributed shall be not less than the values given in the following table.

Occupancy or Use	Live Load Lb. per Sq. Ft.	Occupancy or Use	Live Load Lb. per Sq. Ft.
Apartment houses:		Hotels:	
Private apartments	40	Guest rooms	40
Public stairways	100	Corridors serving public rooms	100
Assembly halls:		Public rooms	100
Fixed seats	60	Loft buildings	125
Movable seats	100		
Corridors, upper floors	100	Manufacturing, light	125
Corridors:		Office buildings	
First floor	100	Offices	80
Other floors, same as occupancy served except as indicated		Lobbies	100
		Schools:	
Courtrooms	80	Classrooms	40
Dance halls	100	Corridors	100
Dining rooms, public	100	Stores	125
Dwellings	40		
Hospitals and asylums:		Theatres:	
Operating rooms	60	Aisles, corridors, and lobbies	100
Private rooms	40	Orchestra floor	60
Wards	40	Balconies	60
Public space	80	Stage floor	150

Courtesy of American Institute of Steel Construction.

Note: These are suggested loads only. The local codes should also be consulted.

TABLE 7

PROPERTIES OF CONCRETE REINFORCING BARS

(Older standard type. See the 1947 ACI Building Code, or see Art. 9–4 of this textbook for allowable bond stresses for use with these bars.)

Size and Shape	Area (sq in.)	Perimeter (in.)
$\frac{1}{4}$ in. round	0.05	0.8
$\frac{3}{8}$ in. "	0.11	1.2
$\frac{1}{2}$ in. "	0.20	1.6
$\frac{1}{2}$ in. square	0.25	2.0
$\frac{5}{8}$ in. round	0.31	2.0
$\frac{3}{4}$ in. "	0.44	2.4
$\frac{7}{8}$ in. "	0.60	2.8
1 in. "	0.79	3.1
1 in. square	1.00	4.0
$1\frac{1}{8}$ in. "	1.27	4.5
$1\frac{1}{4}$ in. "	1.56	5.0

TABLE 8

PROPERTIES OF CONCRETE REINFORCING BARS

Size Number	Area (sq in.)	Perimeter (in.)
2	0.05	0.8
3	0.11	1.2
4	0.20	1.6
5	0.31	2.0
6	0.44	2.4
7	0.60	2.7
8	0.79	3.1
9	1.00	3.5
10	1.27	4.0
11	1.56	4.4

Note: For computing coverage, bar spacings, etc., the bar diameter may be taken as $\frac{1}{8}$ in. $\times$ the bar size number.

TABLE 9

AREAS AND PERIMETERS OF CONCRETE REINFORCING BARS IN ONE-FOOT WIDTHS OF SLAB

Top number gives area A_s in square inches per foot width of slab. Bottom number gives perimeter Σo in inches per foot width of slab. Interpolate for $\frac{1}{4}$-in. increments of spacing.

Spacing	Bar Size Number									
	2	3	4	5	6	7	8	9	10	11
2	0.29 / 4.6	0.66 / 7.1	1.20 / 9.4	1.86 / 11.8	2.64 / 14.2					
2½	0.24 / 3.8	0.53 / 5.7	0.96 / 7.5	1.49 / 9.4	2.11 / 11.3	2.88 / 13.2	3.79 / 15.1			
3	0.20 / 3.1	0.44 / 4.7	0.80 / 6.3	1.24 / 7.8	1.76 / 9.4	2.40 / 11.0	3.16 / 12.6			
3½	0.17 / 2.7	0.38 / 4.0	0.69 / 5.4	1.06 / 6.7	1.51 / 8.1	2.06 / 9.4	2.71 / 10.8	3.42 / 12.2		
4	0.15 / 2.4	0.33 / 3.5	0.60 / 4.7	0.93 / 5.9	1.32 / 7.1	1.80 / 8.3	2.37 / 9.4	3.00 / 10.6	3.81 / 12.0	4.68 / 13.3
4½	0.13 / 2.1	0.29 / 3.1	0.53 / 4.2	0.83 / 5.2	1.17 / 6.3	1.60 / 7.3	2.11 / 8.4	2.67 / 9.4	3.39 / 10.7	4.16 / 11.8
5	0.12 / 1.9	0.26 / 2.8	0.48 / 3.8	0.74 / 4.7	1.06 / 5.7	1.44 / 6.6	1.90 / 7.5	2.40 / 8.5	3.05 / 9.6	3.74 / 10.6
5½	0.11 / 1.7	0.24 / 2.6	0.44 / 3.4	0.68 / 4.3	0.96 / 5.1	1.31 / 6.0	1.72 / 6.9	2.18 / 7.8	2.77 / 8.7	3.40 / 9.7
6	0.10 / 1.6	0.22 / 2.4	0.40 / 3.1	0.62 / 3.9	0.88 / 4.7	1.20 / 5.5	1.58 / 6.3	2.00 / 7.1	2.54 / 8.0	3.12 / 8.8
6½	0.09 / 1.5	0.20 / 2.2	0.37 / 2.9	0.57 / 3.6	0.81 / 4.4	1.11 / 5.1	1.46 / 5.8	1.85 / 6.5	2.35 / 7.4	2.88 / 8.2
7	0.09 / 1.4	0.19 / 2.0	0.34 / 2.7	0.53 / 3.4	0.75 / 4.0	1.03 / 4.7	1.35 / 5.4	1.71 / 6.1	2.18 / 6.8	2.67 / 7.6
7½	0.08 / 1.3	0.18 / 1.9	0.32 / 2.5	0.50 / 3.1	0.70 / 3.8	0.96 / 4.4	1.26 / 5.0	1.60 / 5.7	2.03 / 6.4	2.50 / 7.1
8	0.08 / 1.2	0.17 / 1.8	0.30 / 2.4	0.47 / 2.9	0.66 / 3.5	0.90 / 4.1	1.19 / 4.7	1.50 / 5.3	1.91 / 6.0	2.34 / 6.6
8½	0.07 / 1.1	0.16 / 1.7	0.28 / 2.2	0.44 / 2.8	0.62 / 3.3	0.85 / 3.9	1.12 / 4.4	1.41 / 5.0	1.79 / 5.6	2.20 / 6.3
9	0.07 / 1.1	0.15 / 1.6	0.27 / 2.1	0.41 / 2.6	0.59 / 3.1	0.80 / 3.7	1.05 / 4.2	1.33 / 4.7	1.69 / 5.3	2.08 / 5.9
9½	0.06 / 1.0	0.14 / 1.5	0.25 / 2.0	0.39 / 2.5	0.56 / 3.0	0.76 / 3.5	1.00 / 4.00	1.26 / 4.5	1.60 / 5.0	1.97 / 5.6
10	0.06 / 1.0	0.13 / 1.4	0.24 / 1.9	0.37 / 2.4	0.53 / 2.8	0.72 / 3.3	0.95 / 3.8	1.20 / 4.2	1.52 / 4.8	1.87 / 5.3
10½	0.06 / 0.9	0.13 / 1.3	0.23 / 1.8	0.35 / 2.2	0.50 / 2.7	0.69 / 3.1	0.90 / 3.6	1.14 / 4.0	1.45 / 4.6	1.78 / 5.0
11	0.05 / 0.9	0.12 / 1.3	0.22 / 1.7	0.34 / 2.2	0.48 / 2.6	0.65 / 3.0	0.86 / 3.4	1.09 / 3.9	1.39 / 4.4	1.70 / 4.8
11½	0.05 / 0.8	0.11 / 1.2	0.21 / 1.6	0.32 / 2.0	0.46 / 2.5	0.63 / 2.9	0.82 / 3.3	1.04 / 3.7	1.33 / 4.2	1.63 / 4.6
12	0.05 / 0.8	0.11 / 1.2	0.20 / 1.6	0.31 / 2.0	0.44 / 2.4	0.60 / 2.7	0.79 / 3.1	1.00 / 3.5	1.27 / 4.0	1.56 / 4.4

TABLE 10

ALLOWABLE SOIL BEARING PRESSURES

(Note: This list is acceptable in many areas, but local codes should be consulted.)

Material	Allowable Bearing Value (tons/sq ft)
Laminated rocks such as slate and schist, in sound condition (some cracks allowed)	35
Shale in sound condition (some cracks allowed)	10
Hardpan	10
Gravel, sand-gravel mixtures, compact	5
Gravel, sand-gravel mixtures, loose; sand, coarse, compact	4
Sand, coarse, loose; sand, fine, compact	3
Sand, fine, loose	1
Hard clay	6
Medium clay	4
Soft clay	1

TABLE 11

ALLOWABLE UNIT STRESSES FOR NORMAL LOADING CONDITIONS

Species and Grade	Allowable Unit Stresses in Pounds per Square Inch				
	Extreme fiber in bending "f", and tension parallel to grain "t"	Horizontal Shear "H"	Compression perpendicular to grain "c⊥"	Compression parallel to grain "c"	Modulus of Elasticity "E"
PINE, SOUTHERN					
Dense Sel. Structural . . .	2400	120	455	1750	
Sel. Structural Longleaf . .	2400	120	455	1750	
Dense Structural	2000	120	455	1400	
Prime Structural Longleaf .	2000	120	455	1400	
Dense Structural SE&S . .	1800	120	455	1300	
Structural SE&S Longleaf .	1800	120	455	1300	
Merch. Structural Longleaf	1800	120	455	1300	1,600,000
Dense No. 1 Structural . .	1600	120	455	1150	
No. 1 Structural Longleaf .	1600	120	455	1150	
No. 1 Dense	1700	150	455	1400	
No. 1 Longleaf	1700	150	455	1400	
No. 1	1450	125	390	1200	
No. 1 Longleaf 1400 f. . .	1400	140	455	1400	
No. 1 Dense 1400 f.	1400	140	455	1400	
No. 2 Dense	1250	100	455	1025	
No. 2 Longleaf	1250	100	455	1025	
No. 1 1200 f.	1200	120	390	1200	
No. 2	1100	85	390	875	
DOUGLAS FIR, COAST REGION					
Dense Sel. Structural . . .	2150	145	455	1550	
Sel. Structural	1900	120	415	1450	
1700 f.—Dense No. 1 . . .	1700	145	455	1325	
1450 f.—No. 1	1450	120	390	1200	
1100 f.—No. 2	1100	110	390	1075	1,600,000
Dense Sel. Structural . . .	–	–	455	1550	
Sel. Structural	–	–	415	1450	
Dense No. 1	–	–	455	1400	
No. 1	–	–	390	1200	
DOUGLAS FIR, INLAND REGION					
Sel. Structural	2150	145	455	1750	1,600,000
Structural	1900	100	400	1400	1,500,000
Com. Structural	1450	95	380	1250	1,500,000
Sel. Structural	–	–	455	1750	1,600,000
Structural	–	–	400	1400	1,500,000
Com. Structural	–	–	380	1250	1,500,000
CYPRESS, SOUTHERN AND TIDEWATER RED					
1700 f Grade	1700	145		1425	
1300 f Grade	1300	120	360	1125	1,200,000
1450 c Grade	–	–		1450	
1200 c Grade	–	–		1200	
HEMLOCK, EASTERN					
Sel. Structural	1300	85		850	
Prime Structural	1200	60		775	
Com. Structural	1100	60	360	650	1,100,000
Utility Structural	950	60		600	
Sel. Structural	–	–		850	

Courtesy of the Southern Pine Association.

TABLE 11 *Continued*

ALLOWABLE UNIT STRESSES FOR NORMAL LOADING CONDITIONS					
	Allowable Unit Stresses in Pounds per Square Inch				
Species and Grade	Extreme fiber in bending "f", and tension parallel to grain "t"	Horizontal Shear "H"	Compression perpendicular to grain "$c_\perp$"	Compression parallel to grain "c"	Modulus of Elasticity "E"
OAK, RED AND WHITE					
2150 f Grade	2150	145		1550	
1900 f Grade	1900	145		1375	
1700 f Grade	1700	145		1200	
1450 f Grade	1450	120	600	1050	1,500,000
1300 f Grade	1300	120		950	
1325 c Grade	—	—		1325	
1200 c Grade	—	—		1200	
1075 c Grade	—	—		1075	
PINE, NORWAY					
Prime Structural	1200	75		900	
Com. Structural	1100	75	360	775	1,200,000
Utility Structural	950	75		650	
REDWOOD					
Dense Structural	1700	110		1450	
Heart Structural	1300	95	320	1100	1,200,000
Dense Structural	—	—		1450	
Heart Structural	—	—		1100	
SPRUCE, EASTERN					
1450 f Structural Grade . .	1450	110		1050	
1300 f Structural Grade . .	1300	95	300	975	1,200,000
1200 f Structural Grade . .	1200	95		900	

Courtesy of the Southern Pine Association.

TABLE 12

Properties of S 4 S Lumber

Nominal Size	Actual Size S 4 S	Area of Section	Weight per Foot	Moment of Inertia $bd^3/12$	Section Modulus $bd^2/6$
		Inches²	Lb	Inches⁴	Inches³
2 x 4	1⅝x 3⅝	5.89	1.63	6.45	3.56
4 x 4	3⅝x 3⅝	13.14	3.64	14.39	7.94
2 x 6	1⅝x 5⅝	9.14	2.53	24.10	8.57
2½x 6	2⅛x 5⅝	11.95	3.32	31.52	11.21
3 x 6	2⅝x 5⅝	14.77	4.10	38.93	13.84
4 x 6	3⅝x 5⅝	20.39	5.65	53.76	19.12
6 x 6	5⅝x 5⅝	31.64	8.76	83.43	29.66
2 x 8	1⅝x 7½	12.19	3.38	57.13	15.23
2½x 8	2⅛x 7½	15.94	4.43	74.71	19.92
3 x 8	2⅝x 7½	19.69	5.47	92.29	24.61
4 x 8	3⅝x 7½	27.19	7.55	127.44	33.98
6 x 8	5⅝x 7½	42.19	11.72	197.75	52.73
8 x 8	7½x 7½	56.25	15.58	263.67	70.31
2 x10	1⅝x 9½	15.44	4.28	116.10	24.44
2½x10	2⅛x 9½	20.19	5.61	151.83	31.96
3 x10	2⅝x 9½	24.94	6.93	187.55	39.48
4 x10	3⅝x 9½	34.44	9.57	259.00	54.53
6 x10	5⅝x 9½	53.44	14.84	401.89	84.61
8 x10	7½x 9½	71.25	19.74	535.86	112.81
10 x10	9½x 9½	90.25	25.00	678.75	142.89
2 x12	1⅝x11½	18.69	5.18	205.95	35.82
2½x12	2⅛x11½	24.44	6.79	269.32	46.84
3 x12	2⅝x11½	30.19	8.39	332.69	57.86
4 x12	3⅝x11½	41.69	11.58	459.43	79.90
6 x12	5⅝x11½	64.69	17.96	713.07	123.98
8 x12	7½x11½	86.25	23.89	950.55	165.31
10 x12	9½x11½	109.25	30.26	1204.03	209.39
12 x12	11½x11½	132.25	36.63	1457.51	253.48
2 x14	1⅝x13½	21.94	6.09	333.18	49.36
2½x14	2⅛x13½	28.69	7.97	435.69	64.55
3 x14	2⅝x13½	35.44	9.84	538.21	79.73
4 x14	3⅝x13½	48.94	13.59	743.24	110.11
6 x14	5⅝x13½	75.94	21.09	1153.30	170.86
8 x14	7½x13½	101.25	28.05	1537.73	227.81
10 x14	9½x13½	128.25	35.53	1947.80	288.56
12 x14	11½x13½	155.25	43.00	2357.86	349.31
14 x14	13½x13½	182.25	50.48	2767.92	410.06
2 x16	1⅝x15½	25.19	7.00	504.27	65.07
2½x16	2⅛x15½	32.94	9.15	659.44	85.09
3 x16	2⅝x15½	40.69	11.30	814.60	105.11
4 x16	3⅝x15½	56.19	15.61	1124.92	145.15
6 x16	5⅝x15½	87.19	24.22	1745.60	225.23
8 x16	7½x15½	116.25	32.20	2327.42	300.31
10 x16	9½x15½	147.25	40.79	2948.07	380.39
12 x16	11½x15½	178.25	49.37	3568.71	460.48
14 x16	13½x15½	209.25	57.96	4189.36	540.56
16 x16	15½x15½	240.25	66.55	4810.00	620.65
2 x18	1⅝x17½	28.44	7.90	725.75	82.94
2½x18	2⅛x17½	37.19	10.33	949.06	108.46
3 x18	2⅝x17½	45.94	12.76	1172.36	133.98
4 x18	3⅝x17½	63.44	17.62	1618.98	185.03
6 x18	5⅝x17½	98.44	27.34	2512.20	287.11
8 x18	7½x17½	131.25	36.36	3349.61	382.81
10 x18	9½x17½	166.25	46.05	4242.84	484.89
12 x18	11½x17½	201.25	55.75	5136.07	586.98

Courtesy of the Southern Pine Association.

TABLE 13

				LATERAL RESISTANCE—NAILS				
Pennyw't "d"	Length (In.)	Dia. (In.)	$D^{3/2}$	Safe Lateral Resistance in Pounds per nail for Common Wire Nails in Side Grain for Various Values of K (see Species Table 14) based on formula $P = KD^{3/2}$.*				
				$K = 1080$	$K = 1350$	$K = 1500$	$K = 1650$	$K = 2040$
6	2	0.113	0.0380	41	51	57	63	78
8	2½	0.131	0.0474	51	64	71	78	97
10	3	0.148	0.0570	62	77	86	94	116
12	3¼	0.148	0.0570	62	77	86	94	116
16	3½	0.162	0.0652	70	88	98	107	133
20	4	0.192	0.0841	91	114	126	139	172
30	4½	0.207	0.0942	102	127	141	155	192
40	5	0.225	0.1068	115	144	160	176	218
50	5½	0.244	0.1205	130	163	181	199	246
60	6	0.263	0.1349	146	182	202	223	275

*Depth of penetration into wood to be not less than 2/3 nail length for softwoods and ½ nail length for hardwoods.

Courtesy of the Southern Pine Association.

TABLE 14

VALUES OF K IN THE FORMULA $P = KD^{3/2}$ FOR COMMON WIRE NAILS IN LATERAL RESISTANCE	
Species	K
Aspen and largetooth aspen............................... Basswood... Butternut... Cedar, northern and southern white....................... Chestnut... Cottonwood, black and eastern............................ Fir, balsam and commercial white......................... Hemlock, eastern.. Pine, lodgepole, ponderosa, sugar, northern white, and western white... Poplar, yellow... Spruce, Engelmann, red, Sitka, and white..................	1,080
Cedar, Alaska, incense, Port Orford, and western red........ Cedar, eastern red.. Cypress, southern... Douglas fir (Rocky Mountain region)...................... Hemlock, west coast....................................... Pine, Norway.. Redwood.. Tamarack...	1,350
Alder, red... Ash, black... Birch, paper... Elm, American and slippery................................ Gum, black, red, and tupelo............................... Hackberry... Magnolia, cucumber....................................... Magnolia, evergreen....................................... Maple, bigleaf... Maple (soft), red and silver................................ Sugarberry... Sycamore..	1,500
Douglas fir (coast region)................................. Larch, western.. Pine, southern yellow......................................	1,650
Ash, commercial white.................................... Ash, Oregon... Beech... Birch, sweet and yellow.................................... Cherry, black.. Elm, rock... Hickory, true and pecan................................... Locust, honey and black................................... Maple (hard), black and sugar............................. Oak, commercial red and white............................ Walnut, black...	2,040
P = Allowable load per nail in pounds. D = Diameter of nail in inches.	

Courtesy of the Southern Pine Association.

TABLE 15

SPECIFIC GRAVITY (G) AND $G^{2.5}$ FOR VARIOUS SPECIES OF WOOD

(Based on oven-dry weight and volume)

Species	G	$G^{2.5}$
Ash, black	0.53	0.205
Ash, white	0.64	0.327
Birch, yellow	0.66	0.354
Cedar, northern white	0.32	0.058
Cedar, Port Orford	0.44	0.128
Cedar, western red	0.34	0.067
Cottonwood, eastern	0.43	0.122
Cypress, southern	0.48	0.160
Douglas fir	0.51	0.186
Fir, commercial white	0.42	0.114
Gum, black	0.55	0.225
Gum, red	0.53	0.205
Gum, tupelo	0.52	0.196
Hemlock, eastern	0.43	0.122
Hemlock, west coast	0.44	0.128
Hickory	0.80	0.572
Larch, western	0.59	0.267
Maple, hard (sugar)	0.68	0.381
Maple, soft (silver)	0.51	0.186
Oak, commercial red	0.66	0.354
Oak, commercial white	0.71	0.425
Pine, lodgepole	0.43	0.122
Pine, northern white	0.37	0.084
Pine, ponderosa	0.42	0.114
Pine, southern	0.59	0.267
Pine, sugar	0.38	0.089
Redwood	0.42	0.114
Spruce, Sitka	0.42	0.114

TABLE 16

Allowable load in pounds on one bolt loaded at both ends (double shear)*
(Normal Loading Conditions)

Length of bolt in main member	Diameter of bolt		Projected area of bolt	Cypress, tidewater red; Douglas fir, (coast and inland); larch, western; pine, southern longleaf and shortleaf; redwood; tamarack		Cedar, western red; cedar, Alaska, Port Orford; Douglas fir, (Rocky Mountain); hemlock, west coast; pine, Norway		Cedar, northern and southern white; fir, balsam, commercial white; hemlock, eastern; pine, white, ponderosa; spruce, red, Sitka, white, Engelmann		Ash, commercial white; beech; birch, sweet and yellow; elm, rock; hickory, true and pecan; maple, hard; oak, commercial red and white		Maple, soft; elm, soft; gum, black, red, tupelo; sycamore		Ash, black, brown; aspen and large toothed aspen; basswood; birch, paper; chestnut; cottonwood, eastern and western; yellow poplar	
				Parallel to grain	Perpendicular to grain	Parallel to grain	Perpendicular to grain	Parallel to grain	Perpendicular to grain	Parallel to grain	Perpendicular to grain	Parallel to grain	Perpendicular to grain	Parallel to grain	Perpendicular to grain
l	d	l/d	$A=l\times d$	P	Q	P	Q	P	Q	P	Q	P	Q	P	Q
Inches	*Inches*		*Sq. in.*												
1⅝	½	3.3	0.8125	1,000	460	780	320	620	240	1,140	660	940	410	720	290
	⅝	2.6	1.0156	1,260	500	970	370	780	280	1,460	740	1,180	470	900	320
	¾	2.2	1.2188	1,520	560	1,180	410	940	310	1,750	830	1,400	520	1,080	360
	⅞	1.9	1.4219	1,780	620	1,370	460	1,090	340	2,050	910	1,630	560	1,260	400
	1	1.6	1.625	2,030	680	1,560	490	1,250	370	2,340	1,000	1,870	620	1,440	430
2	½	4.0	1.00	1,150	550	940	410	770	300	1,330	800	1,130	500	890	350
	⅝	3.2	1.25	1,540	620	1,200	460	960	340	1,780	910	1,440	580	1,100	400
	¾	2.7	1.50	1,860	700	1,440	490	1,150	380	2,150	1,020	1,730	640	1,330	440
	⅞	2.3	1.75	2,180	770	1,680	560	1,340	420	2,520	1,120	2,020	700	1,560	490
	1	2.0	2.00	2,500	840	1,920	610	1,540	460	2,880	1,220	2,300	770	1,780	530
2⅝	½	5.3	1.3125	1,250	720	1,070	530	940	400	1,440	1,060	1,270	660	1,080	470
	⅝	4.2	1.6406	1,850	830	1,510	600	1,250	440	2,140	1,200	1,820	740	1,440	530
	¾	3.5	1.9688	2,380	910	1,870	670	1,510	500	2,740	1,330	2,260	830	1,750	590
	⅞	3.0	2.2969	2,830	1,010	2,210	730	1,760	550	3,280	1,460	2,640	910	2,040	650
	1	2.6	2.625	3,260	1,100	2,520	800	2,020	600	3,770	1,600	3,020	1,000	2,330	700
3	½	6.0	1.50	1,260	830	1,090	600	980	460	1,450	1,160	1,310	760	1,140	530
	⅝	4.8	1.875	1,940	940	1,630	680	1,390	520	2,230	1,370	1,960	850	1,610	600
	¾	4.0	2.25	2,590	1,070	2,100	770	1,720	580	3,000	1,520	2,520	950	1,990	670
	⅞	3.4	2.625	3,190	1,150	2,510	840	2,020	620	3,670	1,680	3,010	1,040	2,330	730
	1	3.0	3.00	3,710	1,260	2,880	910	2,300	680	4,270	1,820	3,460	1,140	2,660	800
3⅝	½	7.3	1.8125	1,260	960	1,090	720	980	550	1,450	1,220	1,310	860	1,140	640
	⅝	5.8	2.2656	1,970	1,140	1,700	830	1,540	620	2,270	1,610	2,040	1,030	1,780	720
	¾	4.8	2.7188	2,810	1,260	2,360	940	2,020	700	3,240	1,840	2,830	1,150	2,330	800
	⅞	4.1	3.1719	3,620	1,390	2,950	1,010	2,420	760	4,180	2,030	3,540	1,270	2,800	890
	1	3.6	3.625	4,340	1,520	3,440	1,100	2,780	830	5,020	2,210	4,140	1,380	3,220	960
4	½	8.0	2.00	1,260	970	1,090	770	980	600	1,450	1,210	1,310	890	1,140	710
	⅝	6.4	2.50	1,970	1,250	1,700	910	1,540	680	2,270	1,700	2,050	1,140	1,790	790
	¾	5.3	3.00	2,830	1,390	2,440	1,020	2,150	770	3,260	2,020	2,920	1,270	2,480	890
	⅞	4.6	3.50	3,730	1,540	3,120	1,120	2,620	840	4,310	2,230	3,740	1,390	3,020	980
	1	4.0	4.00	4,620	1,680	3,740	1,220	3,060	910	5,330	2,440	4,490	1,520	3,530	1,070
4½	½	9.0	2.25	1,260	960	1,090	780	980	650	1,450	1,180	1,310	880	1,140	760
	⅝	7.2	2.8125	1,970	1,360	1,700	1,030	1,540	770	2,270	1,730	2,050	1,240	1,790	900
	¾	6.0	3.375	2,830	1,570	2,460	1,140	2,220	850	3,260	2,210	2,940	1,430	2,570	1,000
	⅞	5.1	3.9375	3,850	1,730	3,290	1,260	2,870	950	4,450	2,520	3,950	1,570	3,310	1,100
	1	4.5	4.50	4,870	1,880	4,060	1,370	3,380	1,030	5,630	2,750	4,860	1,720	3,910	1,200
	1⅛	4.0	5.0625	5,840	2,050	4,730	1,490	3,860	1,120	6,740	2,990	5,630	1,870	4,480	1,310

*—Three (3) member joint. Common bolts. Yield point 45,000 lbs. per sq. in. For high strength bolts, higher loads may be used. (See Technical Bulletin 332 "The Bearing Strength of Wood Under Bolts.")—U S Forest Products Laboratory.)

Courtesy of the Southern Pine Association.

APPENDIX C

AMERICAN WELDING SOCIETY

STANDARD WELDING SYMBOLS

Reproduced courtesy of the American Welding Society

SUMMARY OF STANDARD
AMERICAN WELD

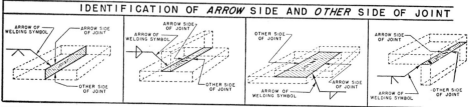

IDENTIFICATION OF *ARROW* SIDE AND *OTHER* SIDE OF JOINT

BASIC WELDING SYM

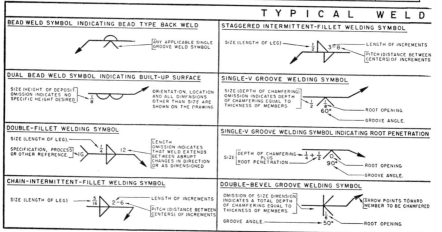

TYPICAL WELD

SUPPLEMENTARY SYMBOLS USED

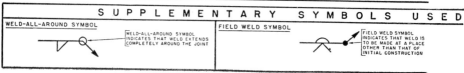

ING SOCIETY

WELDING SYMBOLS

AND *ARROW*-SIDE AND *OTHER*-SIDE *MEMBER* OF JOINT

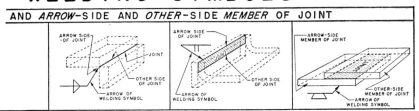

B O L S

LOCATION OF ELEMENTS OF A WELDING SYMBOL

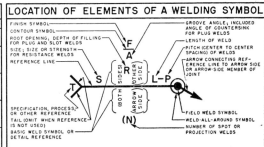

RESISTANCE WELDING SYMBOLS

PROJECTION	SPOT	SEAM	FLASH OR UPSET
	NOT USED	NOT USED	NOT USED
	NOT USED	NOT USED	NOT USED
NOT USED	NOT USED	NOT USED	NOT USED
NOT USED			

I N G   S Y M B O L S

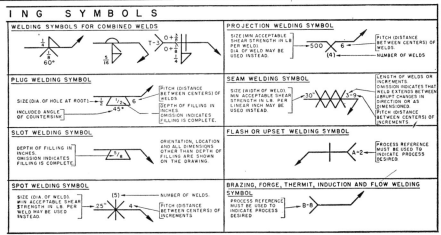

WELDING SYMBOLS FOR COMBINED WELDS

PROJECTION WELDING SYMBOL

PLUG WELDING SYMBOL

SEAM WELDING SYMBOL

SLOT WELDING SYMBOL

FLASH OR UPSET WELDING SYMBOL

SPOT WELDING SYMBOL

BRAZING, FORGE, THERMIT, INDUCTION AND FLOW WELDING SYMBOL

W I T H   W E L D I N G   S Y M B O L S

FLUSH-CONTOUR SYMBOL

CONVEX-CONTOUR SYMBOL

INDEX